Project Maths

Text & Tests 2

Junior Certificate Higher Level Maths

Strands 1–5

O. D. Morris · Paul Cooke · Paul Behan

 The Celtic Press

Acknowledgements
I would like to express my deep gratitude to Aidan Raleigh for his invaluable advice at
all stages of the production of this book.

First published in 2012 by
The Celtic Press
Ground Floor – Block B
Liffey Valley Office Campus
Dublin 22

This reprint: September 2015

ISBN: 978-0-7144-2010-3

Design: Identikit Design
Layout and artwork: Tech-Set Limited, Gateshead

Contents

Preface

Text & Tests 2 – Junior Certificate Higher Level was compiled and written as a two-year course in mathematics for students starting second-year in second-level schools. It follows on from **Text & Tests 1 – Common Introductory Course** which students will have used in first-year. It contains **all five strands** of the **Project Maths Syllabus** for Junior Cycle. The book reflects the overall approach to the teaching of mathematics as envisaged in *Project Maths*. It encourages not only the development of the students' mathematical knowledge and skills but also the understanding needed for continuing their learning of mathematics.

The greater emphasis on the understanding of maths is achieved through the use of well-structured questions and diagrams which lead the student to appreciate the connection and relationship between algebra and graphs. The large selection of real-life problems and graphs will help students appreciate that maths are part of their everyday lives.

The book contains a wide variety of problems from the basic to the advanced, to cater for a range of student abilities and interests. Every effort has been made to contexualise problems so that students can see everyday uses and practical applications of the mathematics they are studying.

The motivating and stimulating full-colour design, together with the large number of well-constructed diagrams, should help the student's understanding of the topic being studied. At the beginning of each chapter, there is a list of **Key Words** that students are expected to know and understand when the chapter is completed. Each chapter concludes with a blue-coloured **Test Yourself** section which provides comprehensive consolidation and revision.

A large selection of digital resources as well as the e-Book will be available online to teachers using this book.

O.D. Morris
Paul Cooke
Paul Behan
March 2012

Algebra 1

Key words

| expression | term | variable | coefficient | constant | like terms |

expression   **term**   **variable**   **coefficient**   **constant**   **like terms**
brackets   **index**   **indices**   **linear equations**   **number line**
natural number   **integer**   **rational numbers**   **real numbers**
inequalities $(> \geqslant < \leqslant)$

Section 1.1 Simplifying expressions

$2x^2 + 3x - 4$ is called an **expression**.

It consists of 3 **terms**.

The terms are separated by a plus $(+)$ or a minus $(-)$ sign.

The letter x is called a **variable**.

A **coefficient** is a number before a variable.

In $2x^2$, the coefficient is 2; in $3x$, the coefficient is 3.

The term -4 is known as a **constant**; it does not change.

In the expression $2x^2 + 5x - 2 + 3x + 4x^2$,

   $2x^2$ and $4x^2$ are called **like terms**;
   $5x$ and $3x$ are also like terms.

The expression $2x^2 + 5x - 2 + 3x + 4x^2$ may be simplified by combining the like terms
as follows:

$$2x^2 + 5x - 2 + 3x + 4x^2$$
$$= 2x^2 + 4x^2 + 5x + 3x - 2$$
$$= 6x^2 + 8x - 2$$

> Like terms only may be
> added or subtracted.

Example 1

Simplify   (i) $4a + 6b + 6 - 2a + b - 3$ (ii) $2x^2 - 3x - 7 - x^2 - 5x + 3$

(i) $4a + 6b + 6 - 2a + b - 3$
   $= 4a - 2a + 6b + b + 6 - 3$
   $= 2a + 7b + 3$

(ii) $2x^2 - 3x - 7 - x^2 - 5x + 3$
   $= 2x^2 - x^2 - 3x - 5x - 7 + 3$
   $= x^2 - 8x - 4$

Exercise 1.1

Simplify each of the following by adding like terms:

1. $3x + 4x - 2x$

2. $7a + 3 + 4a + 6$

3. $5x + y - 2x + 4y$

4. $5a + 2b - 2a - 4b$

5. $12a + b + 3a + 5b$

6. $3x + 2y + 3 + 4x + 3y + 1$

7. $5x - 4 + 2x + 8$

8. $7x - 4 - 3x + 7$

9. $6a + b + 3 + 2a + 2b - 1$

10. $3x + 4 + 2x - 6 + x + 3$

11. $3a - b + 4a + 5b - 2a$

12. $2ab + 4 + 3ab - 2$

13. $2p + 3q - r + p - 4q + 2r$

14. $5k + 3 - 4k + 6 + k - 4$

15. $2ab + c + 5ab - 4c$

16. $3xy + 2z + xy + 9z$

17. $6ab + 2cd - ab + 3cd$

18. $6x - xy + 5x - 7xy$

19. $x^2 - 3x + 4 - 2x^2 + 5x - 3$

20. $3x^2 - 3x + x^2 - 8x + 7$

21. $3a^2 - 2a - 6a + 4a^2 - 3$

22. $y^2 - 8y - 3y^2 + 2y - 3$

23. $3x^2 - 2 + 5x - 4 - 7x + 1$

24. $5a^2 + 2a - 3a^2 + 4 - 3a + 2$

25. $3x^2 - 2x + 4xy + 8$ is an expression.
   - (i) How many terms are there in the expression?
   - (ii) What is the coefficient of xy in the expression?
   - (iii) How many variables are there in the expression?
   - (iv) What is the constant in the expression?

26. Work out and simplify an expression for the perimeter of each of these.

(i)

(ii)

(iii)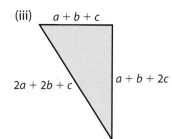

27. Work out an expression for each length marked **?**.

(i)

(ii)

(iii)

(iv)

Section 1.2 Removing brackets

To write $3x \times 4y$ as a single term, we multiply the coefficients 3 and 4 and then multiply the variables x and y.

Thus, $3x \times 4y = 3 \times 4 \times x \times y = 12xy$.

Similarly, (i) $3a \times 6b = 18ab$ (ii) $-3p \times 4q = -12pq$

In your study of algebra so far, you will have learned how to remove brackets as follows:

$a(b + c) = ab + ac$ Here each term inside the bracket is multiplied by a.

Similarly,
(i) $5(2x + 6) = 10x + 30$
(ii) $-4(5a - 2) = -20a + 8$
(iii) $-(6x - 4) = -6x + 4$
(iv) $-(-9a + 6) = 9a - 6$

> If there is a minus outside the brackets, the sign of each term inside the brackets is changed when the brackets are removed.

Multiplication involving indices

As 5×5 can be written as 5^2, similarly $x \times x$ is written as x^2.

Also, $a \times a \times a = a^3$

and $a^2 \times a^2 = a \times a \times a \times a = a^4$
$a^2 \times a^3 = a \times a \times a \times a \times a = a^5$
$3x(2x^2 - x + 4) = 6x^3 - 3x^2 + 12x$

> When multiplying powers of the same number, add the indices.

Multiplying two expressions

Here is a reminder of how to multiply two expressions, each containing two terms:

$$(2x + 3)(3x - 5) = 2x(3x - 5) + 3(3x - 5)$$
$$= 6x^2 - 10x + 9x - 15$$
$$= 6x^2 - x - 15$$

Example 1

Remove the brackets and simplify each of these:

(i) $(2x - 3)(3x - 4)$ (ii) $(2x - 4)(x^2 - 3x + 5)$

(i) $(2x - 3)(3x - 4) = 2x(3x - 4) - 3(3x - 4)$
$$= 6x^2 - 8x - 9x + 12$$
$$= 6x^2 - 17x + 12$$

(ii) $(2x - 4)(x^2 - 3x + 5) = 2x(x^2 - 3x + 5) - 4(x^2 - 3x + 5)$
$$= 2x^3 - 6x^2 + 10x - 4x^2 + 12x - 20$$
$$= 2x^3 - 6x^2 - 4x^2 + 10x + 12x - 20$$
$$= 2x^3 - 10x^2 + 22x - 20$$

Here is a diagram to show that $(a + b)(c + d) = ac + ad + bc + bd$.

The area of the given rectangle is

$(a + b)(c + d)$

The rectangle is divided into 4 smaller rectangles and the area of each rectangle is shown.

This diagram illustrates that $(a + b)(c + d) = ac + ad + bc + bd$.

	a	b
c	ac	bc
d	ad	bd

Exercise 1.2

1. Express each of the following as a single term:

(i) $3 \times 4a$ (ii) $3a \times 5a$ (iii) $2a \times b$ (iv) $3x \times 4y$

(v) $-2a \times 3a$ (vi) $2ab \times 4b$ (vii) $2a^2b \times ab$ (viii) $4 \times a \times 6 \times a^2$

Remove the brackets and simplify each of these:

2. $3(2x - 1) + 5(x + 2)$

3. $2(x - 4) + 3(2x + 5)$

4. $5(3x - 2) - 2(x - 1)$

5. $3(3x + 2) - 4(2x + 1)$

6. $6(2x - 3) + 2(3x - 1)$

7. $5(x - 2) - (2x + 4)$

8. $3(2a - 7) - 5(a - 4)$

9. $2(3a - 4) - (5a - 3)$

10. $2(x^2 - 3x + 1) + 2(x^2 + x - 4)$

11. $5(x^2 - x - 4) - 2(2x^2 - 3x + 2)$

Find the product of each of these:

12. $(2x + 4)(x + 3)$

13. $(3x + 2)(2x + 4)$

14. $(3x + 1)(2x - 4)$

15. $(5x - 2)(2x + 3)$

16. $(2x - 3)(x - 5)$

17. $(5x + 1)(3x - 3)$

18. $(3x + 1)(x^2 + 2x + 1)$

19. $(2x + 4)(2x^2 - x - 3)$

20. $(5x - 2)(x^2 - x + 4)$

21. $(3x - 2)(2x^2 - 3x + 7)$

22. $(4x - 1)(x^2 - 4x + 6)$

23. $(4x - 3)(2x^2 - 3x + 2)$

24. $(3a - 4)(2a^2 - 3a + 2)$

25. $(2y - 7)(y^2 + 3y + 1)$

26. Find an expression for the area of each of these shapes.
Simplify each expression fully.

(i)

(ii)

(iii)
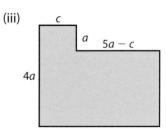

27. Find the missing expressions in these statements.

    (i) $d(\boxed{}) = d^2 + 5d$ (ii) $2n(\boxed{}) = 2n^2 - 8n$

    (iii) $3p(\boxed{}) = 15p - 3p^2$ (iv) $5k(\boxed{}) = 20k + 5k^2$

28. Find the missing term in each statement.

    (i) $5p \times \boxed{} = 10pq$ (ii) $\boxed{} \times 7n = 21mn$ (iii) $3a^2 \times \boxed{} = 9a^2b$

    (iv) $\boxed{} \times 2y^2 = 10x^2y^2$ (v) $3cd^2 \times \boxed{} = 15c^3d^2$ (vi) $\boxed{} \times 7vw^3 = 28v^3w^4$

Section 1.3 Evaluating expressions

When $x = 3$, the value of $2x + 5$ is $2(3) + 5 = 6 + 5 = 11$

When $x = 2$, the value of $3x^2 - 6x$ is $3(2)^2 - 6(2) = 3(4) - 12 = 12 - 12 = 0$

Example 1

If $a = 2, b = 3$ and $c = -4$, find the value of

    (i) $a + b$ (ii) $2a - b$ (iii) $3a^2 - 2c$ (iv) $2c^2 - 4ab$

    (i) $a + b = 2 + 3 = 5$ (ii) $2a - b = 2(2) - 3$

                                                     $= 4 - 3 = 1$

    (iii) $3a^2 - 2c = 3(2)^2 - 2(-4)$ (iv) $2c^2 - 4ab = 2(-4)^2 - 4(2)(3)$

                       $= 3(4) + 8$ $= 2(16) - 4(6)$

                       $= 12 + 8 = 20$ $= 32 - 24 = 8$

Remember

When evaluating an expression,

    (i)   multiply and divide before you add or subtract

   (ii)   any number multiplied by zero is zero, e.g. $6 \times 0 = 0$

Example 2

If $x = 3$ and $y = -2$, find the value of $3x^2 - 4xy - 2y^2$.

$3x^2 - 4xy - 2y^2 = 3(3)^2 - 4(3)(-2) - 2(-2)^2$

                    $= 3(9) - 4(-6) - 2(4)$ ... square before you multiply

                    $= 27 + 24 - 8$

                    $= 51 - 8$

                    $= 43$

Exercise 1.3

1. If $x = 4$, find the value of each of these:

   (i) $3x$ (ii) $2x + 6$ (iii) $7 - x$ (iv) $x^2 + 3$ (v) $3x^2 - 2x - 7$

2. If $a = 3$ and $b = -2$, find the value of each of these:

   (i) $2a + b$ (ii) $a^2 + ab$ (iii) $2a^2 + b^2$ (iv) $3ab + 2b^2$

3. If $a = 1, b = 2$ and $c = 3$, find the value of:

   (i) $2a + b$ (ii) $3ab - c$ (iii) $4abc + 3c$

   (iv) $3bc - 4ab$ (v) $3abc - 2ac$ (vi) $5bc - 2ab$

   (vii) $\dfrac{3a + 6b}{c}$ (viii) $\dfrac{4b - 2a}{c}$ (ix) $\dfrac{6c - ab}{4b}$

4. If $x = 1\frac{1}{2}$ and $y = \frac{1}{2}$, find the value of:

   (i) $4x + 2y$ (ii) $3x + y$ (iii) $2x - 4y$ (iv) $8xy$

5. If $a = 4$ and $b = 3$, find the value of:

   (i) $a^2 + b$ (ii) $b^2 - 2a$ (iii) $3a^2 - 2b^2$ (iv) $a^2b - 2ab$

6. If $x = 2$, find the value of $2x^2 - 3x + 5$.

7. If $a = 5, b = 2$ and $c = 8$, evaluate each of these:

   (i) $a - bc$ (ii) $2a^2 - bc$ (iii) $a(b - c)^2$

8. Calculate the value of each of the following expressions when $p = 2, q = 3$ and $r = 6$:

   (i) $r(p + q)$ (ii) $rp + q$ (iii) $\dfrac{r}{pq}$ (iv) $\dfrac{q + r}{p}$ (v) $5r^2$

9. If $x = 2, y = -3$ and $z = 1$, evaluate

   (i) $x^2 - 3xy + 2z$ (ii) $2y^2 - 3xy$ (iii) $z^2 - 3x^2y + 4y$

10. The area of a triangle is given by the formula $A = \dfrac{bh}{2}$.

    Work out the areas of triangles where

    (i) $b = 25\,\text{cm}, h = 10\,\text{cm}$
    (ii) $b = 16\,\text{cm}, h = 12\,\text{cm}$

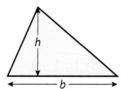

11. The area, A square units, of a trapezium
    is given by the formula $A = \frac{1}{2}(a + b)h$.
    (a, b and h are shown on the diagram.)
    Use the formula to calculate the areas
    of trapeziums for which

    (i) $a = 9\,\text{cm}, b = 16\,\text{cm}, h = 10\,\text{cm}$
    (ii) $a = 14\,\text{cm}, b = 30\,\text{cm}, h = 11\,\text{cm}$

12. When $m = -1, n = -2$ and $p = 8$, there are four matching pairs here. Can you find them?

13. Evaluate $\dfrac{3}{x+3} + \dfrac{4}{2x+6}$, when $x = \frac{1}{3}$.

Section 1.4 Solving linear equations

The three scales below will help you recall the steps involved in solving an equation. We need to solve the equation $3x + 2 = 14$.

| Take 2 from both sides | Divide both sides by 3 | $x = 4$ is the solution |

The scales above illustrate that solving an equation requires us to change the equation into a simpler one. This is done by adding, subtracting, multiplying or dividing both sides of the equation by the **same number**.

Example 1

Solve the equation $3x - 5 = 16$

$$3x - 5 = 16$$
$$3x - 5 + \mathbf{5} = 16 + \mathbf{5} \quad \text{... add 5 to both sides}$$
$$3x = 21$$
$$x = 7 \quad \text{... divide both sides by 3}$$

Example 2

Solve the equation $3(2x - 6) = 2(2x + 1)$

$$3(2x - 6) = 2(2x + 1)$$
$$6x - 18 = 4x + 2 \quad \text{... remove the brackets}$$
$$6x - \mathbf{4x} - 18 = 4x + 2 - \mathbf{4x} \quad \text{... take } 4x \text{ from each side}$$
$$2x - 18 = 2$$
$$2x - 18 + \mathbf{18} = 2 + \mathbf{18} \quad \text{... add 18 to each side}$$
$$2x = 20$$
$$x = 10 \quad \text{... divide each side by 2}$$

Exercise 1.4

1. Write down the missing numbers to make these equations true:

   (i) $\square + 8 = 15$ (ii) $12 - \square = 8$ (iii) $\square \times 3 = 30$

   (iv) $\square \times 6 + 2 = 26$ (v) $27 \div \square + 1 = 10$ (vi) $7 + 5 + \dfrac{\square}{2} = 15$

2. Solve each of these equations:

   (i) $2x = 8$ (ii) $3x = 27$ (iii) $5x = 35$ (iv) $6x = 42$ (v) $9x = 63$

Solve each of these equations:

3. $4x + 2 = 14$	**4.** $2x - 9 = 3$	**5.** $2x - 7 = 5$
6. $3 + 2x = 11$	**7.** $6 + 3x = 9$	**8.** $2 + 7x = 30$
9. $6x - 2 = 4x + 10$	**10.** $7x - 9 = 3x + 11$	**11.** $9x - 15 = 3x + 3$
12. $x + 7 = 2x - 1$	**13.** $2x + 6 = 4x - 6$	**14.** $3x + 1 = 5x - 13$
15. $5x - 2 = 40 - x$	**16.** $3x + 7 = 32 - 2x$	**17.** $6 + 2x = 33 - x$

Remove the brackets and solve the following equations:

18. $3(2x + 1) = 2x + 11$	**19.** $2(2x + 5) = 5x + 5$
20. $4(2x - 3) = 2(3x - 5)$	**21.** $4(3x + 6) = 3(5x - 2)$
22. $5(2x - 4) + 1 = 3(2x - 1)$	**23.** $6(2x + 1) + 4 = 5(3x - 1)$
24. $5(x - 2) - 3x = 3(x - 5)$	**25.** $5(2x + 3) = 4(2x + 1) + 15$
26. $5(x + 3) - 25 = 6(2 - x)$	**27.** $10(x + 4) - 1 = 3(2x + 5)$
28. $4(x - 2) - 9 = 3 - (x + 5)$	**29.** $3(x - 1) = 18 - 5(x + 1)$
30. $3(5x + 7) + 2(3x - 5) = 5(2x + 11)$	**31.** $5(3x - 2) = 3(2x + 1) + 2x + 1$

32. Work out what x stands for in each of these.

   (i)   (ii)

33. Find the values of x and f in these figures.
The perimeter is given in each case.

 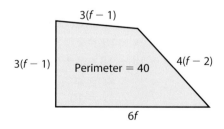

Section 1.5 Solving problems using linear equations

The ability to change a problem expressed in words into a mathematical equation and then solve it is very important in mathematics.

The following examples will show how equations can be formed from word problems.

Example 1

When five times a certain number is reduced by 4, the result is the same as adding 7 to four times the number.
Find the number.

Let x be the required number.

Equation:
$$5x - 4 = 4x + 7$$
$$5x - 4 - 4x = 4x + 7 - 4x \quad \text{... take } 4x \text{ from each side}$$
$$x - 4 = 7$$
$$x - 4 + 4 = 7 + 4 \quad \text{... add 4 to each side}$$
$$x = 11$$

The required number is 11.

Example 2

(i) Find an expression, in terms of x, for the perimeter of this rectangle.
Give your answer in its simplest form.

(ii) The perimeter of the rectangle is 44 cm.
Write down an equation and solve it to find the value of x.

(i) Perimeter $= (2x + 1) + x + (2x + 1) + x$
$\qquad\qquad = (6x + 2)$ cm

(ii) Perimeter $= 44 \implies x + 2 = 44$
$$6x + 2 - 2 = 44 - 2$$
$$6x = 42$$
$$x = 7$$

Exercise 1.5

1. If I multiply a number by 4 and then add 3, the result is the same as adding 8 to three times the number.
   Form an equation in x and solve it to find the number.

2. I think of a number, multiply it by 8 and then subtract 2.
   I get the same result as when I multiply this number by 2 and add 10. What is this number?

3. One number is 5 greater than another number.
   If the smaller number is added to twice the larger number, the answer is 28.
   Find the two numbers.

4. Ann is 3 years older than Helen.
   If twice the sum of their ages is 50 years, how old is Ann?

5. (i) Find an expression for the perimeter of this triangle.
   (ii) What value of x gives a perimeter of 55?

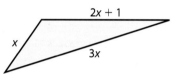

6. If we subtract 4 from a number and then multiply the result by 5, the answer is 15.
   Find the number.

7. I think of a number, increase it by 4 and double the answer.
   The result is 20 more than the number. Find this number.

8. Use your knowledge of angles to form an equation and solve it to find the value of a.

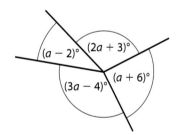

9. A triangle and rectangle are shown below:

   Find the value of x which
   (i) gives a triangle with a perimeter of 63
   (ii) gives a triangle and rectangle with equal perimeters
   (iii) makes the rectangle into a square.

10. Here is a fraction: $\dfrac{x}{\Box}$.

The denominator of the fraction is 5 more than the numerator.
If 1 is added to the numerator and 2 is subtracted from the denominator, the fraction will become $\frac{4}{5}$. Find the fraction.

11. The number in each brick is found by adding the two numbers above it.
Find the missing expressions in each of the diagrams below.
Write equations to find the value of x in each case.

(i)

18	x	23

$\Box$	$\Box$

57

(ii)

12. In an arithmagon, the number in a square is
the sum of the numbers in the two circles
either side of it.

(i) Explain why the number in circle **B**
is $20 - x$.

(ii) What is the number in circle **C** in
terms of x?

(iii) Form an equation across the base of the triangle and solve it to find the value
of x.

13. Find an expression in x for the area of the
shaded portion of this figure.

If the area of this shaded portion is 38 cm²,
find the value of x.

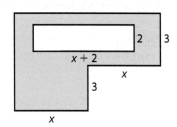

14. Ruth is x years old. Write, in terms of x,
(i) her age 6 years ago
(ii) her age in 12 years time.

In 12 years time, Ruth will be three times as old as she was 6 years ago.
Find Ruth's age now.

15. 166 people live in an apartment block and of these, x are women.
There are 8 fewer men than women and there are 30 more children than women.
How many women live in the block?

16. In a race between two cities, one person travels by air, another by sea and the third by train.

The sea voyage takes 120 minutes longer than the train journey, and the air route takes 80 minutes less than the train journey.

If the total travelling time is 10 hours and 40 minutes, use algebra to find the time taken by each of the race participants.

Section 1.6 Plotting numbers on the number line

In your study of numbers so far, you will have dealt with **natural numbers** and **integers**. These numbers are described again below and illustrated on the number line.

1. Natural numbers are the counting numbers starting at 1.
They are denoted by the capital letter **N**.

$N = 1, 2, 3, 4, 5, \ldots$

The arrow indicates that the dots continue indefinitely.

2. Integers are whole numbers which may be positive or negative.
They are denoted by the capital letter **Z**.
The integers are illustrated here on the number line.

$Z = \ldots, -3, -2, -1, 0, 1, 2, 3, \ldots$

3. Real numbers describe all the numbers on the number line.
These numbers include natural numbers, integers, fractions, decimals and numbers such as $\sqrt{5}, \sqrt{7}, \pi, \ldots$

Since every number on the number line is a real number, we say that real numbers 'fill' the number line. For this reason, real numbers are represented on the number line by a heavy or 'bold' line as shown below.
The capital letter **R** is used to denote the set of real numbers.

Inequalities

The speed limit for cars driving in a city is generally 60 km/hr.
This could be written as speed $\leqslant 60$ or $S \leqslant 60$.
This means that S could be 60, 58, 56, 40, $\ldots$
The statement $S \leqslant 60$ is an example of an **inequality**.

$x + 3 = 7$ is an example of an **equation** since one side is *equal* to the other.
However, $x + 3 > 7$ is an example of an **inequality** since one side is **not equal** to the other side.

Here are the four inequality signs we will use.

$>$	$<$	$\geqslant$	$\leqslant$
is greater than	is less than	is greater than or equal to	is less than or equal to

We will now use these inequality signs to show how different numbers can be shown on the number line.

1. Natural numbers

The inequality $x \geqslant 4, x \in N$ means that x may be any whole number greater than or equal to 4, i.e., 4, 5, 6, 7, ...
These are represented on the number line below:

2. Integers

The inequality $x > -2, x \in Z$ represents all the integers greater than -2, i.e., $-1, 0, 1, 2, 3, ...$
These are represented on the number line below:

3. Real numbers

The inequality $x \geqslant 3, x \in R$ is the set of all real numbers greater than or equal to 3.
The inequality $x \geqslant 3$ is represented on the number line as follows:

The 'bold' line indicates that all the points on the line are included and the closed circle at 3 shows that the number 3 is **included**.

The inequality $x > -2, x \in R$ is shown below.
The 'empty' circle at -2 is used to show that -2 is not included.

Combined inequalities

It is clear that $7 > 4$ but $4 < 7$.
This illustrates that when the two parts of an inequality are interchanged, the inequality sign must also be changed.

Thus, (i) if $8 > 3$, then $3 < 8$ (ii) if $x \geqslant 5$, then $5 \leqslant x$

Here are two inequalities: $x \geqslant 2, x \in R$

$x < 5, x \in R$

If we combine these inequalities, then x lies between 2 and 5.
2 is included but 5 is not.
We can write this as $2 \leqslant x$ and $x < 5$ or as the combined inequality **$2 \leqslant x < 5$**.

Exercise 1.6

1. State whether each of the following is true or false:
   (i) $3 \in N$ (ii) $4 \in Z$ (iii) $-5 \in N$ (iv) $2.5 \in R$
   (v) $-3\frac{1}{2} \in N$ (vi) $0.5 \in N$ (vii) $2\frac{3}{8} \in R$ (viii) $\sqrt{17} \in R$

2. Insert $>$ or $<$ in each of the boxes below:
   (i) $6 \ \square \ 4$ (ii) $-5 \ \square \ 2$ (iii) $6 \ \square \ -2$ (iv) $-4 \ \square \ 3$

3. Write a mathematical sentence for each of these:
   (i) x is less than 4
   (ii) 2 is greater than -3
   (iii) the speed limit (S) is 40 km/hr
   (iv) b is less than or equal to -5
   (v) the minimum age (A) is 18
   (vi) the maximum age (A) is 60.

4. If $x \in N$, state the values x may have in each of the following inequalities:
   (i) $x < 4$ (ii) $x \leqslant 5$ (iii) $x < 6\frac{1}{2}$
   (iv) $x > 2$ and $x < 7$ (v) $x \geqslant 1$ and $x \leqslant 4$ (vi) $x \geqslant 2$ and $x < 8$

5. If $x \in Z$, state the values x may have in each of the following inequalities:
   (i) $x \geqslant -2$ and $x \leqslant 1$ (ii) $x \geqslant 0$ and $x \leqslant 4$ (iii) $x \geqslant -3$ and $x \leqslant 0$
   (iv) $x \geqslant -4$ and $x < 1$ (v) $x > -5$ and $x < 2$ (vi) $x > -2\frac{1}{2}$ and $x < 3\frac{1}{4}$

6. Graph each of the following inequalities on the number line:
   (i) $x \geqslant 3, x \in N$ (ii) $x \leqslant 4, x \in N$ (iii) $x > 3, x \in N$
   (iv) $x \leqslant 2, x \in Z$ (v) $x \geqslant -3, x \in Z$ (vi) $x > -2, x \in Z$

7. Choose one of $x = 3, x \leqslant 3, x < 3, x > 3$ or $x \geqslant 3$ to describe each graph below:
   (i)   (ii)
   (iii)   (iv)

8. Write the inequality represented by each of these number lines:
   (i)   (ii)
   (iii)
   (iv)
   (v)
   (vi)

14

9. Graph each of the following on the number line:

    (i) $x \geqslant 1, x \in R$ (ii) $x \geqslant -3, x \in R$ (iii) $x \leqslant 4, x \in R$

    (iv) $x > 3, x \in R$ (v) $x < -1, x \in R$ (vi) $x < 4, x \in R$

10. Write down the values x may have in each of the following combined inequalities:

    (i) $3 \leqslant x \leqslant 6, x \in N$ (ii) $-3 < x < 4, x \in N$

    (iii) $-2 \leqslant x \leqslant 5, x \in Z$ (iv) $-3 < x < 4, x \in Z$

11. Write an inequality for each of the following diagrams:

    (i)   1   2   3   4   5   (ii)   −1   0   1   2

    (iii)   −3 −2 −1   0   1   (iv)   −3   0   3   6   9

    (v)   −4 −2   0   2   4   (vi)   −5   0   5   10   15   20

12. Which of the numbers in the given panel are in the set of values given by $0 < x \leqslant 5, x \in R$?

    −3 $\sqrt{9}$

    0   −4.5

    $\sqrt{20}$ 6

13. m is a multiple of 4.

    Find all the values of m so that $10 \leqslant m \leqslant 24$.

14. Which of the numbers below satisfy the inequality $x^2 < 100$?

         9   15   10   −4   −11   0   10.5

15. Write each of the following sentences as a mathematical statement. Let n stand for the number in each case.

    (i)   I have at least 6 shirts in my wardrobe.

    (ii)   The temperature in a fridge must be 5°C or less.

    (iii) Hand baggage must not exceed 10 kg.

    (iv) Gillian has more than 5 DVDs.

    (v)   There are at least 20 pupils in my class but definitely not more than 30.

    (vi) I think of a number n, multiply it by 5 and then subtract 12. The result is greater than −7.

Section 1.7 Solving inequalities

Here are scales that show $10 > 8$.

$10 > 8$

Would the scales stay as they are if

  ❯ the same amount is added to both sides

  ❯ the same amount is subtracted from both sides

  ❯ the mass on each side is doubled

  ❯ the mass on each side is halved ?

The answer to each question is 'yes'.

The answers to the four questions above illustrate two very important results for inequalities:

Rules for inequalities

1. An inequality remains true when the same number is added to or subtracted from both sides.

2. An inequality remains true when both sides are multiplied or divided by the same **positive** number.

Here are some numerical examples:

We know that the inequality   **6 > 4**
Add 4 to both sides: $10 > 8$ ... true
Subtract 7 from both sides: $3 > 1$ ... true
Multiply both sides by 3: $18 > 12$ ... true
Divide both sides by 2: $3 > 2$ ... true

Multiplication by a negative number

Consider again the inequality $6 > 4$.
Multiply both sides by -2: $-12 > -8$ ... false ... as $-12 < -8$.

This illustrates that the inequality sign must be changed or reversed when both sides of an inequality are multiplied or divided by the same **negative** number.

(i) $2 < 5$, but $2 \times (-2) > 5 \times (-2)$
    i.e. $-4 > -10$

(ii) $8 > 6$, but $\dfrac{8}{-2} < \dfrac{6}{-2}$
     i.e. $-4 < -3$

> If an inequality is multiplied or divided by the same negative number, the inequality sign must be reversed.

Example 1

Solve the inequality $5x - 3 \geqslant 12, x \in N$ and graph the solution on the number line.

$$5x - 3 \geqslant 12$$
$$5x \geqslant 12 + 3 \quad \text{...add 3 to both sides}$$
$$5x \geqslant 15$$
$$x \geqslant 3 \quad \text{...divide both sides by 5}$$

The solution is graphed on the number line below.

Example 2

Solve the inequality $4 - 3x > -5, x \in Z$ and graph the solution on the number line.

$$4 - 3x > -5$$
$$-3x > -5 - 4 \quad \text{...take 4 from each side}$$
$$-3x > -9$$
$$3x < 9 \quad \text{...multiply both sides by } -1 \text{ and reverse the inequality sign}$$
$$x < 3 \quad \text{...divide both sides by 3}$$
$$\therefore \quad x = 2, 1, 0, -1, ...$$

The solution is graphed on the number line below.

Combined inequalities

As stated in the previous section, the inequality $2 < x \leq 7, x \in N$ consists of the two inequalities,

(i) $2 < x$ and (ii) $x \leq 7$
i.e. $x > 2$ and $x \leq 7$
$\therefore \quad x = 3, 4, 5, 6, 7,$ as $x \in N$

Similarly, $-4 \leq x - 3 < 2$ consists of these inequalities:

(i) $-4 \leq x - 3$ and (ii) $x - 3 < 2$.

Example 3

Solve the inequality $-5 < 1 - 3x \leq 10, x \in R$ and illustrate the solution on the number line.

The inequality $-5 < 1 - 3x \leq 10$ is a combination of the two inequalities,
(i) $-5 < 1 - 3x$ and (ii) $1 - 3x \leq 10$

We solve each inequality separately:
(i) $-5 < 1 - 3x$ (ii) $1 - 3x \leq 10$
$\qquad 3x < 1 + 5$ $-3x \leq 10 - 1$
$\qquad 3x < 6$ $-3x \leq 9$
$\qquad x < 2$ $3x \geq -9$
                               $x \geq -3$

$\therefore x < 2$ and $x \geq -3$

Exercise 1.7

1. Which of the following inequalities are equivalent to $a \geqslant 10$?

    Ⓐ $a - 5 \geqslant 5$ **Ⓑ** $2a \geqslant 20$ **Ⓒ** $a + 5 \geqslant 5$ **Ⓓ** $\frac{1}{2}a \geqslant 5$ **Ⓔ** $a + \frac{1}{2} \geqslant 10\frac{1}{2}$

2. Which of the following inequalities are equivalent to $m < 3$?

    Ⓐ $m + 2 < 5$ **Ⓑ** $2m < 4$ **Ⓒ** $3 > m$ **Ⓓ** $8 > m + 5$ **Ⓔ** $6 > 2m$

Solve the following inequalities and graph the solution on the number line in each case:

3. $x - 1 \leqslant 4, x \in N$
4. $3x - 2 \leqslant 10, x \in N$
5. $4x - 5 \leqslant 11, x \in N$
6. $3x + 5 \leqslant 14, x \in N$
7. $2x + 5 \leqslant 1, x \in Z$
8. $3x - 5 \leqslant 7, x \in Z$
9. $3x - 1 < -10, x \in Z$
10. $5x - 2 \leqslant 8, x \in Z$
11. $3x - 5 \leqslant 7, x \in R$
12. $2x + 2 \leqslant 8, x \in R$
13. $5x + 7 < 17, x \in R$
14. $3 - x \leqslant 4, x \in R$
15. $5 - 2x \geqslant -7, x \in R$
16. $1 - 5x > -14, x \in R$
17. $-2 < x \leqslant 5, x \in Z$
18. $0 \leqslant x < 4, x \in R$
19. $-5 \leqslant 3x + 1 < 7, x \in R$
20. $-9 < 2x + 1 \leqslant 7, x \in Z$
21. $-3 \leqslant 2x + 3 < 5, x \in Z$
22. $-5 \leqslant 1 - 3x < 10, x \in R$
23. $2 \leqslant 4x + 4 < 7, x \in R$
24. $-5 < 4x + 3 \leqslant 11, x \in R$
25. $4 \leqslant 5x - 6 \leqslant 29, x \in N$
26. $-7 \leqslant 3x - 1 < 14, x \in R$

27. Find the solution set of $0 \leqslant 2x - 11 < x$, where x is a prime number.

28. If $A = \{x \mid 2x - 4 \leqslant 6\}$ and $B = \{x \mid 4 - 2x < 0\}$ where $x \in N$ in each set, list the elements of $A \cap B$.

29. If $a > b$, which *one* of the following is not true for all $a, b \in R$?

    (i) $2a > 2b$ (ii) $-a < -b$ (iii) $a - 3 < b - 3$ (iv) $\dfrac{a}{5} > \dfrac{b}{5}$

30. List all the integers, x, for which $x^2 < 24$.

31. A new toll-road is built and c represents the number of cars entering the city per hour.

    (i) Write an inequality for c, if the number of cars is known to be between 350 and 500 during peak hour.
    (ii) Show the inequality on a number line.
    (iii) Write a new inequality for c, if the number of cars is known to be between 120 and 200 inclusive during the middle of the day.
    (iv) Show the inequality for c on a number line.
    (v) Write a new inequality for c, if the traffic flow at night is thought to be about one-tenth of the traffic during the middle of the day.

Test yourself 1

1. (a) (i) Remove the brackets and simplify this expression:

$2x(3x - 4) - 3(1 - 3x)$

(ii) Solve the equation $2(x + 2) - 3(x - 3) = x + 7$

(b) Solve the inequality $4 \leqslant 5x - 6 \leqslant 14, x \in R$, and illustrate your solution on the number line.

(c) Write an expression for the perimeter of the given rectangle.
If the perimeter of the rectangle is 36 cm, find the value of x.

2. (a) (i) Which of the expressions in the boxes has the highest value when $x = 5$?
(ii) Which of the expressions has the lowest value when $x = 5$?

(b) The side [AB] of this triangle is x cm long. [BC] is 3 cm longer than [AB], and [CA] is 1 cm shorter.

(i) Write down an expression for the length of [BC].
(ii) Write down an expression for the length of [CA].
(iii) Write down and simplify an expression for the perimeter of triangle ABC.
(iv) The perimeter of the triangle is 44 cm.
Form an equation in x and solve it to find the lengths of the three side.

3. (a) (i) By forming an equation, work out what x stands for.
(ii) What is the length of the plank?

(b) Show on the number line the range of values of x for which

$-3 \leqslant 2x - 1 \leqslant 7, x \in R.$

(c) The given figure consists of a square and a rectangle.

(i) If the perimeter of the figure is p cm, express p in terms of x, y and z.
(ii) If $x = 2y, y = 2z$ and $p = 55$, find the value of x.

4. (a) Solve the equation $5(x - 2) + 11 = 6x - 10$.

(b) (i) Expand and simplify $(3x - 2)(2x^2 + x + 3)$.

(ii) Evaluate $\dfrac{ab}{a - b}$ when $a = \frac{1}{2}$ and $b = \frac{1}{3}$.

(c) One number is 4 greater than another number. When three times the smaller number is added to twice the larger one, the result is 43. Find the numbers.

5. (a) Find the perimeter of each triangle below when $x = 3$.

(i)

(ii)

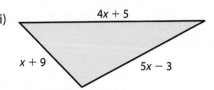

(b) (i) Find an expression for the perimeter of the yellow triangle.
(ii) What value of x gives a yellow triangle with a perimeter of 143?

(c) (i) Find an expression for the perimeter of the green triangle.
(ii) What value of x gives a green triangle with a perimeter of 50?
(iii) What value of x gives both triangles the same perimeter?

6. (a) Form an equation for the given triangle and solve it.
The perimeter is 48 cm and equal sides are marked.

(b)

(i) When $t = 3$, three of the above expressions have a value of -4. Find these expressions.
(ii) When $t = -2$, three of the above expressions have the same value. Find these expressions.

(c) The given rectangle consists of a shaded part and an unshaded part. The shaded part is $3x$ by $2x$.

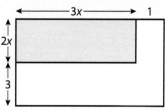

(i) Find, in terms of x, the area of the whole rectangle.
(ii) Find, in terms of x, the area of the unshaded part.
(iii) If the area of the unshaded part is 58 sq. units, find the value of x.

Factors

Section 2.1 Factorising with common factors

Since $9 \times 5 = 45$, we say that 9 and 5 are **factors** of 45.
15 and 3 are also factors of 45.

The factors of 24 are 1, 2, 3, 4, 6, ⑫, 24.
The factors of 36 are 1, 2, 3, 4, 6, 9, ⑫, 18, 36.

The highest common factor is 12.

Here are two algebraic terms: $6xy$ and $12x$.
The highest common factor of the numbers is 6.
The highest common factor of the variables is x.
So the highest common factor of the two terms is $6 \times x$, i.e. $6x$.

Similarly, the highest common factors of

(i) $3a$ and $6a^2 = 3a$

(ii) $6x^2 - 12xy = 6x$

(iii) $5a^2b - 15ab = 5ab$

(iv) $4x^2 + 16xy^2 = 4x$

Take the expression $5x + 10$.

$5x + 10 = 5(x + 2)$

5 and $(x + 2)$ are called the **factors** of $5x + 10$.

To factorise an algebraic expression:

> Find the highest common factor and write it outside the brackets.
> Divide each term by this factor and write the results inside the brackets.
> Check your result by expanding the brackets.

Here are some expressions that have been factorised:

(i) $x^2 + 7x = x(x + 7)$

(ii) $3x^2 - 9x = 3x(x - 3)$

(iii) $3xy - 12x = 3x(y - 4)$

(iv) $12x^2y^2 - 6xy = 6xy(2xy - 1)$

Exercise 2.1

1. Write down the highest common factor of each of these:

    (i) 9 and 12   (ii) 12 and 18   (iii) 14 and 21   (iv) 21 and 35

2. Write down the highest common factor of each of these:

    (i) $4x$ and $12x$ (ii) $3n$ and $9n$ (iii) $10x$ and $15x$

    (iv) $3a^2$ and $6a$ (v) $3xy$ and $12x^2$ (vi) $2a^2b$ and $6ab$

3. Copy and complete each of these:

    (i) $7x + 14y = 7($ $)$ (ii) $16a + 24b = 8($ $)$

    (iii) $ab + bc = b($ $)$ (iv) $3a^2 + 6a = 3a($ $)$

    (v) $5x^2 - 15xy = 5x($ $)$ (vi) $12xy - 18yz = 6y($ $)$

    (vii) $15x^3 + 10x^2y = 5x^2($ $)$ (viii) $6a^2b - 8ab^2 + 4ab = 2ab($ $)$

Factorise each of the following:

    4. $6x + 18y$ **5.** $3ab + 3bc$ **6.** $6ax - 12ay$

    7. $6a^2 - 12a$ **8.** $7x^2 - 28x$ **9.** $15x^2 + 25xy$

    10. $3x^2 - 6x^2y$ **11.** $3ab^2 - 6ab$ **12.** $3p^2 - 6pq$

    13. $2x^2y - 6x^2z$ **14.** $6y^2z + 10y^2$ **15.** $10p^2q + 5pq^2$

    16. $2a^3 - 4a^2 + 8a$ **17.** $4x^2 - 6xy + 8xz$ **18.** $5xy^2 - 20x^2y$

    19. $4x^2y^2 - 8xy$ **20.** $5x^3 - 10x^2 + 15x$ **21.** $2a^2b - 4ab^2 + 12abc$

22.

E	H	P	S	O	A	I	L	G	R	T	U	N
5	$2a$	$3a$	$2b$	$7b$	a^2	ab	$3b^2$	$a+b$	$a-5b$	$2a-b$	$ab+1$	$2a+3b$

Fully factorise each expression below as the product of two factors.
Use the code above to find a letter for each factor.
Rearrange each set of letters to spell a bird.

    (i) $3a^2 - 15ab$ $2a^3 - a^2b$ $7ab - 35b^2$

    (ii) $4a^2 - 2ab$ $2a^2b + 2a$ $2ab - 10b^2$

    (iii) $7ab + 7b^2$ $5a - 25b$ $2ab^2 + 2b$

    (iv) $4ab - 2b^2$ $3b^2a + 3b^3$ $a^3 - 5a^2b$ $2a^2b + 3ab^2$

Section 2.2 Factorising by grouping terms ———————

Some four-termed expressions do not have an overall common factor, but can be factorised by pairing the four terms.

For example,

$$\underbrace{ab + ac}_{} + \underbrace{bd + dc}_{}$$

$$= a(b + c) + d(b + c) \qquad \text{... factorising each pair separately}$$

$$= (b + c)(a + d) \qquad \text{... removing common factor } (b + c)$$

Example 1

Find the factors of (i) $2ab + 2ac + 3bx + 3cy$

(ii) $3ax - bx - 3ay + by$

(i) $2ab + 2ac + 3bx + 3cx = 2a(b + c) + 3x(b + c)$

$$= (b + c)(2a + 3x)$$

(ii) $3ax - bx - 3ay + by = x(3a - b) - y(3a - b)$

$$= (3a - b)(x - y)$$

Note: Sometimes it may be necessary to reorder terms before the method shown above can be used.

Example 2

Factorise $6x^2 + 2a - 3ax - 4x$

Regroup: $6x^2 - 3ax + 2a - 4x$

$3x(2x - a) + 2(a - 2x) \qquad \text{...}$

$$= 3x(2x - a) - 2(2x - a)$$

$$= (2x - a)(3x - 2)$$

$\therefore$ $6x^2 + 2a - 3ax - 4x = (2x - a)(3x - 2)$

> Here we had no common factor, so we changed $2(a - 2x)$ to $-2(2x - a)$. $(2x - a)$ is now a common factor.

Note: Be careful when dealing with negative terms.

For example,   (i) $-3ax - 6ay = -3a(x + 2y)$

(ii) $-5x^2 + 10xy = -5x(x - 2y)$

Factorise fully each of the following:

1. $2a(x + y) + 3(x + y)$

2. $3x(2a - b) - 4(2a - b)$

3. $3a(2b - c) - 4(2b - c)$

4. $2x(5y - z) + b(5y - z)$

5. $2a(x - 2y) - (x - 2y)$

6. $a^2 + ab + ac + bc$

7. $x^2 - ax + 3x - 3a$

8. $ab + ac - 5b - 5c$

9. $ab + 5b + 3a + 15$

10. $3x^2 - 3xz + 4xy - 4yz$

11. $2c^2 - 4cd + c - 2d$

12. $2ax - 6ay - 3x + 9y$

13. $2ac - 4ad + bc - 2bd$

14. $3xy - 3xyz + 2z - 2z^2$

15. $8ax + 4ay - 6bx - 3by$

16. $6ax^2 + 9a - 8x^2 - 12$

17. $x(2y - z) - 2y + z$

18. $an - 5a - 5b + bn$

19. $2x^2y - 2xz - 3xy + 3z$

20. $7y^2 - 21by + 2ay - 6ab$

21. $4a^2b - 3b - 6a + 2ab^2$

22. $12a^2 - 8ab + 9ac - 6bc$

23. $10ab - 5ac - 2bd + cd$

24. $4x^2 + 3ay - 2ax - 6xy$

25. $6a^2 + 15xy - 10ay - 9ax$

26. $6xy + 12yz - 8xz - 9y^2$

27. $3abx^2 - 5axy - 3bxy + 5y^2$

28. $6a^2c - 6ab - 4bc + 9a^3$

29. $x^2 - x(2a - b) - 2ab$

30. $6x^2 - 3y(3x - 2a) - 4ax$

Section 2.3 Difference of two squares

Numbers such as 1, 4, 9, 16, 25, ... are called **perfect squares** as they are obtained by multiplying some whole number by itself, e.g., $4 = 2^2, 9 = 3^2, ...$

Similarly, in algebra, $4x^2 = (2x)^2$ and $9y^2 = (3y)^2$.

Expressions such as $10^2 - 4^2, x^2 - y^2$ and $4x^2 - 9$ are known as the **difference of two squares**.

When you multiply $(x + y)(x - y)$, you get $\boldsymbol{x^2 - y^2}$.
Thus, the factors of $x^2 - y^2$ are $(x + y)(x - y)$.

$$x^2 - y^2 = (x + y)(x - y)$$

In words: (first)^2 − (second)^2 = (first + second)(first − second)

Here is an area model of the difference of two squares.

Area of large square $= x^2$

Area of shaded square $= y^2$

Unshaded area $= x^2 - y^2$ ...... ①

    Area of B $= x(x - y)$

    Area of A $= y(x - y)$

Area of B + A $= x(x - y) + y(x - y)$

                  $= (x - y)(x + y)$ ...... ②

Equating ① and ② we get: $\mathbf{x^2 - y^2 = (x - y)(x + y)}$

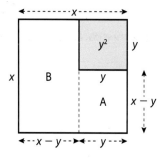

Example 1

Factorise

  (i) $9x^2 - 4$ (ii) $25a^2 - 81b^2$ (iii) $x^2y^2 - 4a^2b^2$

  (i) $9x^2 - 4 = (3x)^2 - (2)^2 = (3x + 2)(3x - 2)$

  (ii) $25a^2 - 81b^2 = (5a)^2 - (9b)^2 = (5a + 9b)(5a - 9b)$

  (iii) $x^2y^2 - 4a^2b^2 = (xy)^2 - (2ab)^2 = (xy + 2ab)(xy - 2ab)$

Example 2

  (i) Factorise $12x^2 - 75y^2$

 (ii) Evaluate $51^2 - 49^2$ without using a calculator.

  (i) Here it is not immediately obvious that $12x^2 - 75y^2$ involves the difference of two squares.

     However, if we take out the common factor 3 we get $3(4x^2 - 25y^2)$,

          $12x^2 - 75y^2 = 3(4x^2 - 25y^2)$

                      $= 3[(2x)^2 - (5y)^2]$

                      $= 3(2x + 5y)(2x - 5y)$

 (ii) $51^2 - 49^2 = (51 + 49)(51 - 49)$ ... using the difference of two squares

                $= (100)(2)$

                $= 200$

Exercise 2.3

Factorise each of the following:

1. $x^2 - y^2$ **2.** $a^2 - b^2$ **3.** $x^2 - 4y^2$

4. $x^2 - 16y^2$ **5.** $4x^2 - y^2$ **6.** $9x^2 - 16y^2$

7. $4a^2 - 25b^2$ **8.** $36x^2 - 49y^2$ **9.** $64x^2 - 9y^2$

10. $16x^2 - 25$ **11.** $25x^2 - 1$ **12.** $36x^2 - 25$

13. $15x^2 - 64y^2$ **14.** $1 - 36x^2$ **15.** $1 - 81y^2$

16. $36 - 121y^2$ **17.** $49a^2 - 4b^2$ **18.** $(xy)^2 - 4$

19. $(ab)^2 - 25$ **20.** $x^2y^2 - 16$ **21.** $a^2b^2 - 49$

22. $(5xy)^2 - 36$ **23.** $16a^2b^2 - 25$ **24.** $9x^2y^2 - 1$

25. $4a^2b^2 - 49c^2d^2$ **26.** $121a^2 - 64b^2c^2$ **27.** $81h^2k^2 - 25p^2q^2$

28. First take out the highest common factor and then factorise each of the following:
     (i) $3x^2 - 27y^2$ (ii) $12x^2 - 3y^2$ (iii) $27x^2 - 3y^2$
     (iv) $45 - 5x^2$ (v) $45k^2 - 20$ (vi) $4a^2x^2 - 36y^2$

29. Challenge: factorise $a^4 - b^4$ as far as possible.

30. Use the difference of two squares to evaluate each of these:
     (i) $96^2 - 4^2$ (ii) $23^2 - 17^2$ (iii) $(7.9)^2 - (2.1)^2$ (iv) $(9.4)^2 - (0.6)^2$

31. Simplify $(3x + b)(6x - 2b) - (2y + b)(4y - 2b)$.
     Now factorise fully the simplified expression.

32. Simplify and hence factorise $(3x - 2y)^2 - y(5y - 12x)$.

Section 2.4 Factorising quadratic expressions

An expression of the form $ax^2 + bx + c$, where a, b and c are numbers is called a **quadratic expression** since the highest power of x is 2.

Since $(x + 5)(x + 2) = x^2 + 7x + 10$, we say that $(x + 5)$ and $(x + 2)$ are the factors of $x^2 + 7x + 10$.

In the product $(x + 5)(x + 2) = x^2 + 7x + 10$,

$\overbrace{}$ outside terms

inside terms

(i) x^2 is obtained from the product $x \times x$

(ii) 10 is the product of 5 and 2, the two number terms

(iii) $7x$ is obtained by adding the product of the outside terms to the product of the inside terms
     i.e. $2x + 5x = 7x$.

> An expression in the form $ax^2 + bx + c$ is generally called a quadratic trinomial as it contains 3 terms.

We factorise a quadratic expression by 'trial and error' to find numbers such that the product of the outside terms added to the product of the inside terms gives the middle term.

Here are the factors of $x^2 + 8x + 15$:

outside terms

$(x + 5)(x + 3)$

inside terms

$3x + 5x = 8x$

$3 \times 5 = 15$

Example 1

Factorise $3x^2 + 10x + 8$.

The factors of $3x^2 + 10x + 8$ will take the form $(3x + ?)(x + ?)$

The factors of 8 are 8×1 or 4×2

Investigate 4 and 2: $(3x + 2)(x + 4)$

Outside + inside terms
$= 12x + 2x$
$= 14x$ ...... incorrect

Try again: $(3x + 4)(x + 2)$

Outside + inside terms
$= 6x + 4x = 10x$
...... correct

The factors of $3x^2 + 10x + 8$ are $(3x + 4)(x + 2)$

Final term positive

If the third term of a quadratic expression is positive and the middle term is negative,
e.g. $x^2 - 8x + 15$, the factors will take the form
  shown on the right.

$(x - ?)(x - ?)$

Example 2

Find the factors of $2x^2 - 11x + 12$.

The factors will take the form $(2x - ?)(x - ?)$

$-8x$

$(2x - 3)(x - 4)$ ... correct factors

$-3x$

$\therefore \quad 2x^2 - 11x + 12 = (2x - 3)(x - 4)$

Factors of 12:

6×2

4×3

12×1

Final term negative

If the final term is negative, the factors will take either
of the forms shown on the right.

$(x + ?)(x - ?)$

or

$(x - ?)(x + ?)$

Example 3

Factorise   (i) $8x^2 + 10x - 3$ (ii) $7x^2 - 19xy - 6y^2$

(i) $8x^2 + 10x - 3 = (4x - 1)(2x + 3)$

$$12x - 2x = 10x \qquad \text{(correct)}$$

∴ $8x^2 + 10x - 3 = (4x - 1)(2x + 3)$

(ii) $7x^2 - 19xy - 6y^2 = (7x + 3y)(x - 2y)$

$$-14xy + 3xy = -11xy \qquad \text{(incorrect)}$$

$(7x + 2y)(x - 3y)$

$$-21xy + 2xy = -19xy \qquad \text{(correct)}$$

∴ $7x^2 - 19xy - 6y^2 = (7x + 2y)(x - 3y)$

Exercise 2.4

Factorise each of the following:

1. $x^2 + 5x + 6$
2. $x^2 + 8x + 12$
3. $x^2 + 9x + 14$
4. $x^2 + 11x + 24$
5. $x^2 + 12x + 20$
6. $x^2 + 12x + 27$
7. $x^2 + 11x + 30$
8. $x^2 + 15x + 44$
9. $x^2 + 20x + 36$
10. $2x^2 + 5x + 2$
11. $2x^2 + 11x + 14$
12. $5x^2 + 21x + 4$
13. $x^2 - 7x + 12$
14. $x^2 - 9x + 18$
15. $x^2 - 9x + 20$
16. $x^2 - 14x + 24$
17. $x^2 - 12x + 27$
18. $x^2 - 13x + 36$
19. $2x^2 - 7x + 3$
20. $3x^2 - 17x + 10$
21. $5x^2 - 17x + 6$
22. $3x^2 - 17x + 20$
23. $5x^2 + 27x - 18$
24. $3x^2 - 14x + 15$
25. $x^2 - 4x - 12$
26. $x^2 - 3x - 10$
27. $x^2 + 7x - 18$
28. $x^2 + 7x - 30$
29. $x^2 - 13x - 30$
30. $x^2 - 18x - 40$
31. $2x^2 - 7x - 15$
32. $3x^2 + 11x - 20$
33. $5x^2 - 12x - 9$
34. $x^2 - 6x - 72$
35. $8x^2 + 10x - 3$
36. $2x^2 - 19x + 9$
37. $12x^2 - 11x - 5$
38. $6x^2 + x - 15$
39. $8x^2 - 14x + 3$
40. $3x^2 + 13x - 10$
41. $9x^2 + 24x + 16$
42. $5x^2 - 31x + 6$
43. $3x^2 - x - 14$
44. $6x^2 - 11x + 3$
45. $12x^2 - 23x + 10$
46. $9x^2 + 25x - 6$
47. $6x^2 + x - 22$
48. $9x^2 - x - 10$
49. $4x^2 - 11x + 6$
50. $10x^2 - 17x - 20$
51. $36x^2 - 7x - 4$
52. $12x^2 - 17x + 6$
53. $15x^2 - 14x - 8$
54. $24x^2 + 2x - 15$

Section 2.5 Using factors to simplify algebraic fractions

The fraction $\frac{10}{15}$ can be simplified by dividing above and below by the common factor 5.

$$\frac{^2\cancel{10}}{_3\cancel{15}} = \frac{2}{3}$$

Similarly, $\frac{x^2 - 4}{x + 2}$ can be simplified by dividing above and below by a common factor.

$$\frac{x^2 - 4}{x + 2} = \frac{\cancel{(x + 2)}^1(x - 2)}{\cancel{(x + 2)}_1} = x - 2$$

Example 1

Simplify (i) $\dfrac{3n - 12}{n - 4}$ (ii) $\dfrac{3x^2 - 5x - 2}{x - 2}$

(i) $\dfrac{3n - 12}{n - 4} = \dfrac{3(n - 4)^1}{(n - 4)_1}$

$= 3$

(ii) $\dfrac{3x^2 - 5x - 2}{x - 2} = \dfrac{(3x + 1)(x - 2)^1}{(x - 2)_1}$

$= 3x + 1$

Exercise 2.5

1. Simplify each of the following:

   (i) $\dfrac{14}{35}$ (ii) $\dfrac{7x}{14}$ (iii) $\dfrac{9x^2}{3x}$ (iv) $\dfrac{8p^2}{2p}$ (v) $\dfrac{9x^2y}{3xy}$

2. Simplify each of the following:

   (i) $\dfrac{4x + 4y}{4}$ (ii) $\dfrac{12(a + b)}{3(a + b)}$ (iii) $\dfrac{3x + 12}{x(x + 4)}$ (iv) $\dfrac{4a - 8b}{3(a - 2b)}$

Simplify each of the following, using factors where necessary:

3. $\dfrac{(x - 1)(x + 3)}{x + 3}$

4. $\dfrac{2(y - 1)(y + 3)}{y - 1}$

5. $\dfrac{x^2 + 8x + 7}{x + 1}$

6. $\dfrac{x - 4}{x^2 - 6x + 8}$

7. $\dfrac{x - 2}{x^2 + 5x - 14}$

8. $\dfrac{3x - 3}{x^2 - 2x + 1}$

9. $\dfrac{2x - 6}{x^2 + x - 12}$

10. $\dfrac{x^2 + x - 30}{x - 5}$

11. $\dfrac{a^2 + 2ab}{3a + 6b}$

12. $\dfrac{x^2 - 9}{x - 3}$

13. $\dfrac{a^2 - 16}{3a - 12}$

14. $\dfrac{n + 9}{n^2 + 18n + 81}$

15. $\dfrac{4x - 8}{x^2 - 4}$

16. $\dfrac{2x^2 + 5x - 3}{2x - 1}$

17. $\dfrac{2x^2 + 11x + 15}{2x + 5}$

18. $\dfrac{ab - ac}{b - c}$

19. $\dfrac{5 - x}{x - 5}$

20. $\dfrac{3a + 9}{a^2 - 1} \div \dfrac{a + 3}{a - 1}$

Test yourself 2

1. (a) (i) Complete the following: $6x^2 - 18xy = 6x($ $)$

        (ii) Factorise $x^2 - 10x + 24$

   (b) Factorise each of these:

        (i) $7a + 7b + xa + xb$ (ii) $25a^2 - 81$

   (c) Factorise and hence simplify $\dfrac{4x^2 - 7x - 2}{4x^2 - 8x}$

2. (a) Factorise each of these:

        (i) $6x^2 - x - 2$ (ii) $6a^2 + 2ab + 3ac + bc$

   (b) Factorise each of these:

        (i) $6a^2x + 3ax^2 - 9ax$ (ii) $3x^2 - 48$

   (c) Factorise fully and simplify $\dfrac{6x^2 - 11x - 10}{4x^2 - 25}$

3. (a) Factorise each of these:

        (i) $8a^2b + 2ab^2$ (ii) $3x^2 - 16x + 21$

   (b) Factorise fully each of these:

        (i) $2x^2 - 8y^2$ (ii) $2xy - xz - 2y + z$

   (c) Simplify $(2x - z)(6x + 3z) - (6a - 3z)(2a + z)$ and factorise fully the simplified expression.

4. (a) Factorise each of the following:

        (i) $15bc - 3c^2$ (ii) $24x^2 + x - 3$

   (b) Factorise fully each of these:

        (i) $8x^2 - 2y^2$ (ii) $ax - 2ay + 2by - bx$

   (c) Factorise fully and simplify $\dfrac{10x^2 - 29x + 10}{4x^2 - 25}$

5. (a) Factorise each of the following:

        (i) $3x^2 + 2x - 8$ (ii) $a^2 + ab - 2a - 2b$

   (b) Factorise fully each of these:

        (i) $5a^2 - 125b^2$ (ii) $2x^3 + 3x^2 - 2xy^2 - 3y^2$

   (c) Factorise and simplify $\dfrac{2x^2 - 15x + 18}{x^3 - 36x}$

chapter 3

Sets

Key words

equal sets   union   intersection   subset   universal set
complement of a set   cardinal number (#)   set difference
commutative property   associative property   distributive property

Section 3.1 Revision of sets terminology

In this section we will revise the sets operations that you will have met in first-year.

1. Equal sets

Two sets are **equal** if they contain exactly the same elements.

If $A = \{2, 4, 6, 8\}$ and $B = \{4, 6, 8, 2\}$, then **$A = B$**.

2. Union of two sets ($A \cup B$)

The **union** of two sets A and B is found by putting together in a new set all the elements of A and B without repeating an element. It is written **$A \cup B$**.

If $A = \{1, 2, 3, 4\}$ and $B = \{3, 4, 5, 6\}$,
then $A \cup B = \{1, 2, 3, 4, 5, 6\}$.

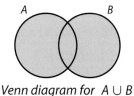

Venn diagram for $A \cup B$

3. Intersection of two sets ($A \cap B$)

The **intersection** of two sets A and B is the set of elements that are in both A and B.

It is written **$A \cap B$**.

In the given Venn diagram, $A \cap B$ is shaded.

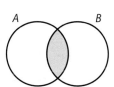

4. Subsets ($B \subset A$)

Set B is a **subset** of set A if all the elements of B are contained in A.

It is written **$B \subset A$**.

If $A = \{1, 2, 3, 4, 5\}$ and $B = \{3, 5\}$, then $B \subset A$.

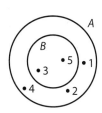

5. The universal set (*U*)

The set from which all other sets being considered are taken is called the **universal set**.

It is denoted by the capital letter **U** and is represented by a rectangle.

6. The complement of a set (*A′*)

The complement of a set *A* is the set of elements in the universal set *U* which are not in *A*.

It is written as **A′** and is illustrated by the shaded area in the given Venn diagram.

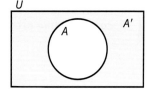

7. The cardinal number of a set (#)

The number of elements in a set is called the **cardinal number** of the set.

The symbol **#** is used to denote the cardinal number.

From the given Venn diagram,

$\#A = 6$ $\#B = 6$

$\#(A \cap B) = 2$ $\#(A \cup B) = 10$.

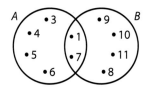

Example 1

In a class of 30 pupils, 17 study German, 16 study Spanish and 5 study both German and Spanish.

Represent this information on a Venn diagram.

Use the Venn diagram to write down the number of pupils who study

  (i) German only   (ii) Spanish only   (iii) neither German nor Spanish.

We use the given information to fill in the Venn diagram.

First place 5 in the set *G* ∩ *S*.

  (i) German only = 17 − 5 = 12

  (ii) Spanish only = 16 − 5 = 11

  (iii) Neither = 30 − 12 − 5 − 11

       = 2

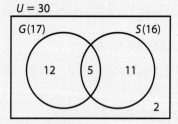

Exercise 3.1

1. From the given Venn diagram, list the elements of each of these sets:

   (i) A (ii) B

   (iii) $A \cap B$ (iv) $A \cup B$

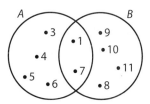

2. Using the Venn diagram on the right, list the elements of the following sets:

   (i) A (ii) $A \cap B$ (iii) A'

   (iv) B' (v) $(A \cup B)'$ (vi) $A' \cap B$

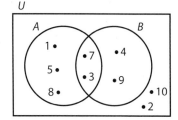

3. In the given Venn diagram, each dot represents an element.

Write down

   (i)   #A (ii)   #B (iii)   #U

   (iv)   #$(A \cup B)$ (v)   #$(A \cap B)$ (vi)   #$(A \cup B)'$

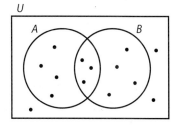

4. Draw a Venn diagram to illustrate this information:

     #$(A) = 15$, #$(B) = 14$ and #$(A \cap B) = 7$

Find   #$(A \cup B)$.

5. Given $U = \{1, 2, 3, \ldots, 12\}$
           $A = \{1, 2, 3, 4, 5, 6\}$
           $B = \{3, 5, 7, 9, 11\}$

Make a copy of the given Venn diagram and fill in the given information.

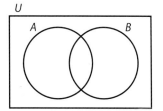

6. Copy the given Venn diagram and fill in the four regions, given that

     #$U = 42$, #$A = 21$, #$B = 18$ and #$(A \cap B) = 6$

Now write down

   (i)   #$(A \cup B)$ (ii)   #B' (iii)   #$(A \cup B)'$

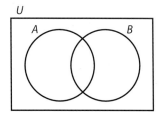

7. Copy this Venn diagram and shade in the region that represents $A' \cap B$.

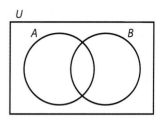

8. In the given Venn diagram,

U is the set of pupils in the class

B is the set of pupils who play basketball

F is the set of pupils who play football.

   (i)   How many pupils play both games?
   (ii) How many pupils are there in the class?
   (iii) How many pupils play football only?
   (iv) How many pupils play neither of the two games?

9. In a class of 32 girls, 16 play hockey and 12 play tennis.
If 10 girls play neither of these games, represent this information on a Venn diagram.
Use the Venn diagram to write down
   (i) the number of girls who play both games
   (ii) the number of girls who play hockey but not tennis.

10. In a survey of 40 households, 22 had a dog and 16 had a cat.
If 8 households had both a cat and a dog, represent this information on a Venn diagram
and write down how many households had neither.

11. All 32 pupils in a class study French (F) or German (G) or both.
24 study French and 18 study German.
If $\#(F \cap G) = x$, write an equation in x and solve it to find its value.

12. Given that $\#(U) = 18$, $\#(A) = 11$ and $\#(B) = 13$, find

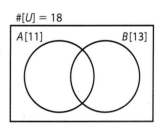

   (i)   the least value of $\#(A \cap B)$
   (ii) the greatest value of $\#(A \cup B)$
   (iii) the greatest value of $\#(A \cap B)$.

13. In the given Venn diagram,

$\#(A) = 24$, $\#(B) = 16$ and $\#(A \cup B)' = 6$.

Use this diagram to find

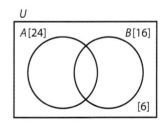

   (i)   the greatest value of $\#(A \cap B)$
   (ii) the greatest value of $\#(U)$
   (iii) the least value of $\#(U)$.

Section 3.2 Set difference

In this section we introduce a new term called **set difference**.

To illustrate set difference, we take two sets A and B, where

$A = \{1, 2, 3, 4, 5, 6\}$ and $B = \{4, 6, 8, 10\}$.

If we remove from set A all the elements which are in set B, we have **A less B**.

A less B is denoted by $A \backslash B$.

∴ $A \backslash B = \{1, 2, 3, 5\}$

Set difference $A \backslash B$ is the set of elements of A which are not in B.

Set difference can be illustrated by Venn diagrams as follows:

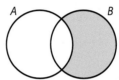

Shaded area is $A \backslash B$ Shaded area is $B \backslash A$

Example 1

If $A = \{a, b, c, d, e, f, g\}$, and $B = \{e, f, g, h, i\}$, find

(i) $A \backslash B$ (ii) $B \backslash A$ (iii) $(A \cup B) \backslash (A \cap B)$

(i) $A \backslash B$ is the set of elements of A which are not in B.
∴ $A \backslash B = \{a, b, c, d\}$

(ii) $B \backslash A = \{h, i\}$

(iii) $A \cup B = \{a, b, c, d, e, f, g, h, i\}$ and $A \cap B = \{e, f, g\}$
∴ $(A \cup B) \backslash (A \cap B) = \{a, b, c, d, h, i\}$

The commutative property

It is obvious that $3 + 4 = 4 + 3$ and that $3 \times 4 = 4 \times 3$.

This illustrates that addition and multiplication are **commutative**.

By this we mean that we can change the order in which two numbers are added (or multiplied) without changing the result.

However, since $6 - 2 \neq 2 - 6$, we can say that subtraction is not commutative.

Again, if $A = \{2, 3, 4, 5\}$ and $B = \{4, 5, 6, 7\}$,
then $A \cup B = B \cup A = \{2, 3, 4, 5, 6, 7\}$.
Also, $A \cap B = B \cap A = \{4, 5\}$.

The union of sets and the intersection of sets are commutative.

Taking the sets A and B above, we have

(i) $A \backslash B = \{2, 3\}$ (ii) $B \backslash A = \{6, 7\}$

This illustrates that $A \backslash B \neq B \backslash A$ and so set difference is not commutative.

Remember   Set difference is not commutative.

Exercise 3.2

1. $A = \{1, 2, 3, 4, 5, 6, 7, 8\}$, $B = \{3, 6, 9, 10\}$ and $C = \{2, 4, 6, 8\}$.
   List the elements of the following sets.
     (i) $A \backslash B$ (ii) $B \backslash C$ (iii) $A \backslash C$ (iv) $C \backslash A$

2. From the given Venn diagram, list the elements of
     (i) $A \backslash B$
     (ii) $B \backslash A$
     (iii) $U \backslash A$
     (iv) $U \backslash (A \cap B)$

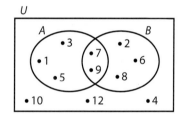

3. Based on the given Venn diagram, say if each of the
   following is true or false:
     (i) $3 \in A \backslash B$ (ii) $7 \in B \backslash A$
     (iii) $\#(B \backslash A) = 3$ (iv) $\#U = 12$
     (v) $\#(A \cap B) = 2$ (vi) $6 \in U \backslash A$
     (vii) $\#(U \backslash A) = 6$ (viii) $\#(U \backslash B) = 8$

4. Given $X = \{2, 4, 6, 8, 10, 12\}$ and $Y = \{3, 6, 9, 12, 15\}$.
   Find   (i) $X \backslash Y$ (ii) $Y \backslash X$
   Is $X \backslash Y = Y \backslash X$? What has your result shown?

5. $U = \{a, b, c, d, e, f, g, h, i\}$, $A = \{d, f, g, e, i\}$, $B = \{b, e, h, i\}$.
   Draw a Venn diagram to illustrate these sets.
   Use the Venn diagram to write down
     (i) $\#(A \backslash B)$ (ii) $\#(U \backslash A)$ (iii) $\#[U \backslash (A \cup B)]$ (iv) $\#[U \backslash (A \cap B)]$

6. Make three copies of the Venn diagram on the
   right and shade in
     (i) $A \backslash B$
     (ii) $U \backslash A$
     (iii) $U \backslash (A \cap B)$

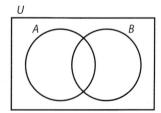

36

7. If $U = \{$All the people who live in Newtown$\}$
   $A = \{$Car owners who live in Newtown$\}$
   $B = \{$Retired people who live in Newtown$\}$,
   describe in words each of the following sets:

   (i) $U \backslash A$ (ii) $U \backslash B$ (iii) $A \backslash B$ (iv) $B \backslash A$ (v) $A \cap B$

Section 3.3 Venn diagrams involving three sets

A Venn diagram for three sets in the universal set U is
shown on the right.

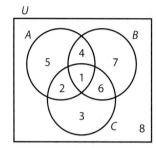

The eight regions shown are described below.

   Region 1 represents $A \cap B \cap C$ Region 2 represents $(A \cap C) \backslash B$
   Region 3 represents $C \backslash (A \cup B)$ Region 4 represents $(A \cap B) \backslash C$
   Region 5 represents $A \backslash (B \cup C)$ Region 6 represents $(B \cap C) \backslash A$
   Region 7 represents $B \backslash (A \cup C)$ Region 8 represents $U \backslash (A \cup B \cup C)$

> ## Example 1
>
> $U = \{1, 2, 3, 4, 5, 6, 7, 8, 9, 10, 11, 12\}$ $A = \{2, 4, 6, 8, 10\}$
> $B = \{3, 4, 5, 6\}$ $C = \{5, 6, 7, 8\}$
>
> Illustrate these sets on a Venn diagram and list the elements of
>   (i) $A \cap B \cap C$ (ii) $B \cap C$ (iii) $(A \cap B) \backslash C$ (iv) $B \backslash (A \cap B \cap C)$.
>
> The Venn diagram is shown on the right.
>
> (i) $A \cap B \cap C = \{6\}$
> (ii) $B \cap C = \{5, 6\}$
> (iii) $A \cap B = \{4, 6\}$
> $\therefore\ (A \cap B) \backslash C = \{4, 6\} \backslash \{5, 6, 7, 8\} = \{4\}$
> (iv) $B \backslash (A \cap B \cap C) = \{3, 4, 5, 6\} \backslash \{6\}$
> $= \{3, 4, 5\}$
>
>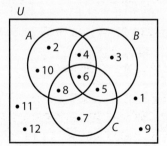

The associative property

Earlier in this chapter it was stated that addition is **commutative**, since $3 + 4 = 4 + 3$
or $a + b = b + a$.

We will now consider any three numbers – a, b and c – and examine what happens under the
operations of addition, subtraction, multiplication and division.

Take the addition of the numbers 3, 4 and 5.

If we combine them using different pairs, it can be seen that

$(3 + 4) + 5 = 3 + (4 + 5)$, since both add up to 12.

Notice that the numbers can be combined using different pairs without changing the result.

| *Definition* | An operation (*) is said to be **associative** if $(a * b) * c = a * (b * c)$. |

Examples   (i) $(2 + 3) + 4 = 2 + (3 + 4)$ illustrates that addition is associative.

(ii) $(12 ÷ 6) ÷ 2 ≠ 12 ÷ (6 ÷ 2)$ illustrates that division is not associative.

Example 2

$A = \{1, 3, 5, 6\}, B = \{2, 3, 5, 7, 8\}$ and $C = \{3, 4, 6, 8\}$ are three sets.

Investigate whether   (i) $(A \cap B) \cap C = A \cap (B \cap C)$

(ii) $(A \backslash B) \backslash C = A \backslash (B \backslash C)$

(i) $A \cap B = \{3, 5\}$

$(A \cap B) \cap C = \{3, 5\} \cap \{3, 4, 6, 8\} = \{3\}$

$(B \cap C) = \{3, 8\}$

$A \cap (B \cap C) = \{1, 3, 5, 6\} \cap \{3, 8\} = \{3\}$

Since $(A \cap B) \cap C = A \cap (B \cap C) = \{3\}$, this illustrates that the intersection of sets is associative.

(ii) $A \backslash B = \{1, 3, 5, 6\} \backslash \{2, 3, 5, 7, 8\} = \{1, 6\}$

$(A \backslash B) \backslash C = \{1, 6\} \backslash \{3, 4, 6, 8\} = \{1\}$

$A \backslash (B \backslash C) = \{1, 3, 5, 6\} \backslash \{2, 5, 7\} = \{1, 3, 6\}$

This shows that $(A \backslash B) \backslash C ≠ A \backslash (B \backslash C)$.

| *Remember* | Union and intersection of sets are associative but set difference is not. |

The distributive property

You will already know that $3 (4 + 5) = (3 \times 4) + (3 \times 5)$

$$= 12 + 15 = 27$$

Also, $3(4 + 5) = 3(9) = 27$

This illustrates **the distributive property** of multiplication over addition.

The following worked example investigates whether union of sets is distributive over intersection and whether intersection is distributive over union.

Example 3

$A = \{3, 4, 5, 6\}$, $B = \{5, 6, 7, 8\}$ and $C = \{2, 4, 6, 8, 10\}$ are three sets.

(i) Investigate if $A \cup (B \cap C) = (A \cup B) \cap (A \cup C)$.

(ii) Investigate if $A \cap (B \cup C) = (A \cap B) \cup (A \cap C)$.

(i) Is $A \cup (B \cap C) = (A \cup B) \cap (A \cup C)$?

$A \cup (B \cap C) = \{3, 4, 5, 6\} \cup \{6, 8\} = \{3, 4, 5, 6, 8\}$

$(A \cup B) \cap (A \cup C) = \{3, 4, 5, 6, 7, 8\} \cap \{2, 3, 4, 5, 6, 8, 10\}$

$\qquad\qquad\qquad\qquad = \{3, 4, 5, 6, 8\}$

$\therefore$ $A \cup (B \cap C) = (A \cup B) \cap (A \cup C) = \{3, 4, 5, 6, 8\}$

(ii) Is $A \cap (B \cup C) = (A \cap B) \cup (A \cap C)$?

$A \cap (B \cup C) = \{3, 4, 5, 6\} \cap \{2, 4, 5, 6, 7, 8, 10\} = \{4, 5, 6\}$

$(A \cap B) \cup (A \cap C) = \{5, 6\} \cup \{4, 6\} = \{4, 5, 6\}$

$\therefore$ $A \cap (B \cup C) = (A \cap B) \cup (A \cap C) = \{4, 5, 6\}$

The example above illustrates two important properties of sets highlighted below.

1. Union of sets is distributive over intersection.

2. Intersection of sets is distributive over union.

Exercise 3.3

1. The given Venn diagram shows three sets A, B and C.
List the elements of these sets:

(i) A

(ii) B

(iii) $A \cap B$

(iv) $A \cap B \cap C$

(v) $A \backslash B$

(vi) $B \backslash (A \cup C)$

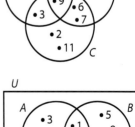

2. The given Venn diagram shows three sets A, B and C
in the universal set U.
List the elements of the following sets:

(i) $A \cap B \cap C$

(ii) $A \cap B$

(iii) $A \backslash (B \cup C)$

(iv) $(A \cap B) \backslash C$

(v) $C \backslash (A \cup B)$

(vi) $(A \cup B \cup C)'$

3. The Venn diagram on the right shows the universal set U and three intersecting sets A, B and C. The number of elements in each region is given in brackets.

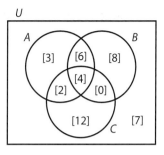

Use the Venn diagram to find

(i) #(A)
(ii) #$[(A \cup B)\backslash C]$
(iii) #$(A \cup B \cup C)'$
(iv) #$[A\backslash(B \cup C)]$
(v) #$[(A \cap C)\backslash B]$.

4. A, B and C are three sets in the universal set U, as shown in the given Venn diagram. Say if each of the following statements is true or false:

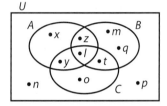

(i) $A\backslash B = \{x, y\}$
(ii) #$B = 5$
(iii) $C\backslash A = \{o, t, l\}$
(iv) #$(A \cup C) = 6$
(v) $B \cap C = \{l, o, t\}$
(vi) #$(A \cup B) = 9$
(vii) $A \cap B \cap C = \{l\}$
(viii) $(A \cap C)\backslash B = \{y, l\}$

5. Draw a Venn diagram showing three intersecting sets A, B and C in the universal set U. Enter the correct cardinal number in each region based on the following information:

#$(A \cap B \cap C) = 2$ #$(A \cap B) = 7$ #$(B \cap C) = 6$ #$(A \cap C) = 8$
#$(A) = 16$ #$(B) = 20$ #$(C) = 19$ #$(U) = 50$.

Use your diagram to find

(i) #$(A \cup B)'$
(ii) #$[A\backslash(B \cup C)]$
(iii) #$[(A \cup B)\backslash C]$.

6. Describe the set indicated by the shaded area in each of the following Venn Diagrams:

(i)   (ii)   (iii)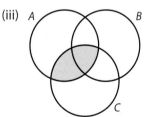

7. Using separate Venn diagrams similar to that shown on the right, shade in the region that represents each of the following sets:

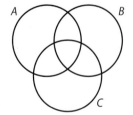

(i) $A \cap B$
(ii) $(A \cap B)\backslash C$
(iii) $A\backslash(B \cup C)$
(iv) $(B \cap C)\backslash A$.

8. State whether each of the following statements is always true for $a, b, c \in R$. If the statement is not true, give an example to show why.

   (i) $a + b = b + a$
   (ii) $(a + b) + c = a + (b + c)$
   (iii) $a \div b = b \div a$
   (iv) $a - b = b - a$
   (v) $(a - b) - c = a - (b - c)$
   (vi) $a \div (b \div c) = (a \div b) \div c$

9. Name the property of real numbers illustrated by each of these examples:

   (i) $6 + 7 = 7 + 6$
   (ii) $(3 \times 4) \times 5 = 3 \times (4 \times 5)$
   (iii) $6 - 4 \neq 4 - 6$
   (iv) $2(4 + 5) = (2 \times 4) + (2 \times 5)$
   (v) $(8 - 4) - 2 \neq 8 - (4 - 2)$
   (vi) $(24 \div 6) \div 2 \neq 24 \div (6 \div 2)$

10. $A = \{0, 2, 4, 6, 8, 10\}$, $B = \{1, 2, 3, 4, 5\}$ and $C = \{3, 4, 5, 6, 7\}$.
    Use these three sets to show that

    $$A \cup (B \cap C) = (A \cup B) \cap (A \cup C).$$

    What property of sets does this statement illustrate?

11. Use the sets in Question **10.** above to show that

    $$(A \backslash B) \backslash C \neq A \backslash (B \backslash C)$$

    What property of sets does this statement illustrate?

12. Which property of sets is illustrated by each of the following?

    (i) $A \cup B = B \cup A$
    (ii) $A \cap (B \cap C) = (A \cap B) \cap C$
    (iii) $(A \cup B) \cup C = A \cup (B \cup C)$
    (iv) $A \cap (B \cup C) = (A \cap B) \cup (A \cap C)$
    (v) $A \cup (B \cap C) = (A \cup B) \cap (A \cup C)$
    (vi) $A \backslash (B \backslash C) \neq (A \backslash B) \backslash C$

Section 3.4 Solving problems using three sets

In this section we will deal with problems that involve the use of three sets.

With this type of problem, it is always advisable to fill in the number of elements in the region that represents the intersection of the three sets.

If the number of elements in this region is not given directly, we let x represent this number.

Example 1

100 students were asked which of the three items – sweets (S), soft drinks (D) or crisps (C) – they had bought during a school outing.

6 students bought all three	31 students bought crisps
41 students bought sweets	23 students bought a soft drink only
14 students bought crisps and a soft drink	15 students bought crisps and sweets
12 students bought sweets and a soft drink	

Illustrate this information on a Venn diagram and write down the number of students who bought
   (i) none of these items
   (ii) sweets only
   (iii) two items only
   (iv) one item only.

We draw three intersecting circles S, D and C to represent sweets, soft drinks and crisps, respectively.

$S \cap D \cap C = 6$
$C \cap D = 14$; so $\#(C \cap D) \backslash S = 14 - 6 = 8$
$C \cap S = 15$; so $\#(C \cap S) \backslash D = 15 - 6 = 9$

We can now complete the Venn diagram from the given information and write down the required answers.

   (i) Number that bought none of these is:
$$100 - (20 + 6 + 6 + 9 + 23 + 8 + 8)$$
$$= 100 - 80 = 20$$

   (ii) Number that bought sweets only = 20
   (iii) Number that bought two items only = $9 + 6 + 8 = 23$
   (iv) Number that bought one item only = $20 + 23 + 8 = 51$

Example 2

There are 86 students taking languages in a school and all take at least one of the languages – French, German and Spanish.

57 take French, 42 take German and 31 take Spanish.

If 25 take French and German, 17 take French and Spanish and 5 take German and Spanish, find how many students take all three languages.

(In this type of problem, where we are asked for the cardinal number of the intersection of the three sets, we denote the number in this region by x. We then express the cardinal numbers of the other regions in terms of x, as shown opposite.)

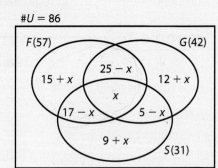

The number of students taking French only is obtained as follows:

$$57 - [25 - x + x + 17 - x]$$
$$= 15 + x$$

Similarly, $(12 + x)$ take German only and $(9 + x)$ take Spanish only.

The sum of the cardinal numbers of all the regions is 86.

∴ $(15 + x) + (25 - x) + x + (17 - x) + (9 + x) + (5 - x) + (12 + x) = 86$

∴ $83 + x = 86$

∴ $x = 3$

Therefore 3 students take all three languages.

Exercise 3.4

1. The Venn diagram on the right shows the results of a survey of a number of adults to find out which of the games golf, tennis or football, if any, they play.

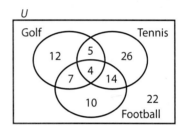

   From the diagram, find the number of people who play

   (i) golf

   (ii) both golf and tennis

   (iii) all three games

   (iv) football only

   (v) none of these games

   (vi) both football and tennis

   (vii) both tennis and football but not golf.

   What was the total number of people surveyed?

2. In a language school, all students attending study one or more of the three languages French, English and German.

   85 students study French, 60 study English and 25 study German.

   If 18 study both French and English, 10 study both French and German, 8 study both English and German and 5 study all three languages, illustrate this information by a Venn diagram and use it to find

   (i) how many students attend the school

   (ii) how many students study one language only

   (iii) how many students study both English and French but not German.

3. At a road checkpoint, 100 cars were examined for defective tyres, brakes and lights.
   It was found that 12 had defective tyres, 9 had defective brakes, 13 had defective lights, 6 had defective lights and brakes, 7 had defective lights and tyres, 6 had defective tyres and brakes, while 4 cars had all three defects.
   Represent this information by a Venn diagram and find
   (i) the number of cars which had defective brakes only
   (ii) the number of cars which had two defects only
   (iii) the number of cars which had defective tyres and brakes but not defective lights
   (iv) the number of cars with no defect.

4. At the end of a touring holiday, 90 US tourists were asked which of the three cities – Dublin, Cork or Galway – they had visited.
   60 had visited Dublin, 18 had visited Cork and 50 had visited Galway.
   30 visited both Dublin and Galway; 10 visited both Dublin and Cork; 6 visited both Cork and Galway.
   If 4 had visited all three cities, find how many tourists
   (i) visited Cork only
   (ii) visited both Dublin and Galway but not Cork
   (iii) visited none of the three cities.

5. 100 people were asked which of the papers – *Times*, *Mail* or *Independent* – they had bought on the previous Sunday.
   The results showed that 32 people had bought the *Times*, 48 had bought the *Independent* and 35 had bought the *Mail*.
   It was found also that 12 people bought both the *Independent* and the *Times*, 11 bought both the *Times* and the *Mail*, 13 bought both the *Independent* and the *Mail*, while 5 people bought all three papers.
   Illustrate this information on a Venn diagram and then answer these questions:
   (i) How many people bought none of these 3 papers?
   (ii) How many people bought the *Times* only?
   (iii) How many people bought the *Independent* and the *Mail* but not the *Times*?
   (iv) How many people bought two papers only?

6. A survey was taken of 54 students, each of whom was studying one or more of the 3 subjects A, B and C.
   6 students studied B and C.
   5 students studied A and C.
   3 times as many students studied A and B as studied all 3 subjects.
   20 students altogether studied B.
   17 students studied C only and 14 students studied A only.
   Using x to represent those students who studied all 3 subjects, illustrate the above information on a Venn diagram.
   Hence find the value of x.

7. In a survey, 100 people were asked which of three magazines – *A*, *B* and *C* – they had read on the previous day.

It was found that 29 people read *A*, 40 people read *B* and 38 people read *C*.

Also, 10 people read *A* and *B* but not *C*

12 people read *B* and *C* but not *A*

7 people read *A* and *C* but not *B*

and 30 people did not read any of the three magazines.

Find (i) the number of people who read all three magazines

(ii) the number of people who read one magazine only.

8. 120 Junior Certificate Students took examinations in Maths, Science and French and all students passed in at least one subject. *M* represents those who passed in Maths, *S* those who passed in Science and *F* those who passed in French.

The following are the results of the examination:

$\#M = 80$, $\#S = 90$, $\#(M \cap S \cap F) = 45$, $\#(M \cap S) = 58$,

$\#(M \cap F) = 55$ and $\#[S \backslash (M \cup F)] = 15$.

(i) How many students passed in Science only?

(ii) How many students passed in Science and French but failed Maths?

(iii) How many students passed in two subjects only?

9. In the Venn diagram on the right, the numbers in the brackets represent the number of elements in each region.

If $\#(U) = 50$ and $\#(B) = 16$, find the value of *x* and the value of *y*.

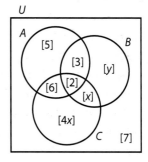

10. A survey was taken of a group of 44 students, each of whom was studying one or more of the three subjects – History, Geography and Art.

28 studied History.   6 students studied History only.

30 students studied Geography.   15 students studied both History and Geography.

22 students studied Art.   3 students studied all three subjects.

(i) Use a Venn diagram to find the number of students who studied History and Geography but not Art.

(ii) How many students studied History and Art but not Geography?

(iii) Find the number of students who studied Geography only.

(**Hint:** Let *x* represent the number of students who studied Geography and Art but not History.)

11. In the Venn Diagram on the right,

        U = {students in a third-level college}
        F = {students who study French}
        G = {students who study Geography}
        H = {students who study History}.

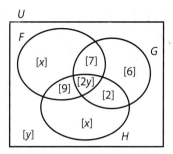

The numbers of students in the various subsets are shown.

For example, 7 students study French and Geography but not History, and y students study none of these subjects.

Given that #(U) = 75 and #(F) = 46, calculate the value of x and the value of y.

Test yourself 3

1. (a) U = {1, 2, 3, ..., 10}, A = {1, 3, 5, 7} and B = {5, 7, 8, 9}.
     List the elements of these sets:

     (i) $A \cap B$ (ii) $(A \cup B)'$.

  (b) Copy this Venn diagram and shade in the region that represents $A' \cap B$.

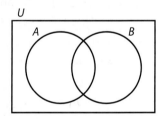

  (c) X and Y are sets in the universal set U.
     If #U = 50, #X = 28, #Y = 34 and #($X \cup Y$) = 43, draw a Venn diagram to illustrate this information.
     Now find   (i) #($X \cap Y$)   (ii) #($X \backslash Y$)   (iii) #($X \cup Y$)'   (iv) #X'

2. (a) Based on the given Venn diagram, write down the elements of these sets:

     (i) A (ii) $A \backslash B$
     (iii) A' (iv) $(A \cup B)'$

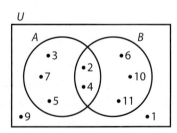

(b) 50 soccer fans were asked which of three soccer matches – A, B and C – they had seen over a given weekend.
5 said they had seen all three matches;
16 had seen both A and B;
15 had seen both B and C;
8 had seen match B only;
a total of 23 had seen match C and a total of 25 had seen match A;
2 people did not see any of the matches.

Draw a Venn diagram to illustrate this information and then answer these questions:
   (i)   How many people had seen match B?
   (ii) How many people had seen both match A and match C but not B?
   (iii) How many people had seen match A only?

3. (a) The given Venn diagram shows the number of elements in each of the sets A, B and C.
Use the Venn diagram to write down
   (i)   #(A ∪ B)
   (ii) #[(A ∪ B)\C]
   (iii) #[(B ∩ C)\A]
   (iv) #[A ∪ B ∪ C]

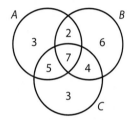

(b) In the given Venn diagram, the number in the brackets represents the number of elements in that region.
If #(P ∪ Q) = 22 and #Q = 3(#P),
find the values of x and y.

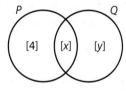

(c) In the given Venn diagram, #X = 30, #Y = 18 and #(X ∪ Y)′ = 8.

   (i)   What is the greatest possible value of #U ?
   (ii) What is the least possible value of #U ?
   (iii) If #U = 44, find #(X ∩ Y).

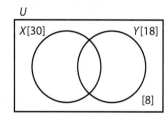

4. (a) A = {1, 2, 3, 6, 8, 10, 12}, B = {3, 4, 5, 6} and C = {3, 5, 8, 10}.
Investigate if A ∩ (B ∪ C) = (A ∩ B) ∪ (A ∩ C).
What property of sets does your investigation prove or disprove?

(b) In a survey, 100 people were asked if they had been on a sun holiday or a skiing holiday the previous year.
60 had been on a sun holiday, 15 had been on a skiing holiday and 30 had been on neither.
Copy the given Venn diagram and insert the appropriate numbers in the brackets.

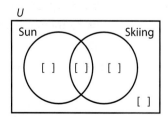

(c)   In the given Venn diagram,

#$U = 80$, #$A = 40$, #$B = 50$,

#$(A \cap B) = x$ and #$(A \cup B)' = y$.

(i)   What is the maximum value of x?
(ii) What is the minimum value of x?
(iii) What is the maximum value of y?
(iv) What is the value of x when $y = 4$?

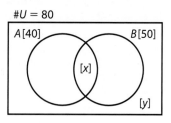

#$U = 80$

$A[40]$ $B[50]$

$[x]$

$[y]$

5. (a)   In the given Venn diagram,

#$(U) = u$, #$(A) = a$, #$(B) = b$,

#$(A \cap B) = c$ and #$(A \cup B)' = d$.

(i)   Express u in terms of a, b, c and d.
(ii) Express d in terms of u, a, b, and c.
(iii) If $c = b$, what can you say about the sets A and B?
(iv) If $b > a$, what is the maximum value of c?

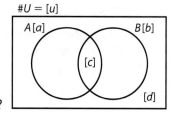

#$U = [u]$

$A[a]$ $B[b]$

$[c]$

$[d]$

(b)   A number of people were asked which of the three papers – The Journal (J), The News (N) and The Tribune (T) – they had bought the previous week.

Some of the results are shown in the Venn diagram on the right.

Copy and complete the Venn diagram given that

(i)   20 people bought The News
(ii) 23 people bought The Journal
(iii) 10 people bought The Journal and The Tribune
(iv) 8 people bought The Tribune only.

Given that there were 40 people in the survey who bought The Tribune or The Journal or both, find the value of x.

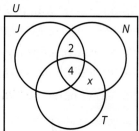

U

J N

2

4

x

T

6. (a)   In the Venn diagram on the right, which **one** of the following statements is true?

(i) $6 \in (A \setminus B)$
(ii) #$A = 2$
(iii) #$(A \cup B) = 2$
(iv) #$(A \cup B)' = 2$

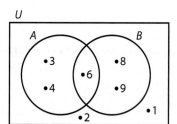

U

A B

•3   •8
   •6
•4   •9

•2   •1

(b)   In the given Venn diagram,

#$U = 50$, #$A = 24$, #$B = b$,

#$(A \cap B) = 8$ and #$(A \cup B)' = g$.

(i)   What is the value of g when $b = 30$?
(ii) What is the maximum value of g?
(iii) What is the minimum value of b?
(iv) What is the maximum value of b?

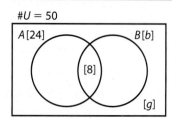

#$U = 50$

$A[24]$ $B[b]$

$[8]$

$[g]$

Applied Arithmetic

Key words

value added tax (VAT)   profit   loss   cost price   selling price

income tax   standard rate   higher rate   standard rate cut-off point

universal social charge (USC)   PRSI   currency exchange

compound interest   principal   rate   final amount   depreciation

Section 4.1 VAT – Profit and loss

When dealing with problems involving percentages, it is very important to be able to convert a percentage to a decimal.

When a percentage is expressed as a decimal, the electronic calculator is particularly useful for finding the required percentage.

Some examples are highlighted below:

> To find 4%, multiply by 0.04.   To find 104%, multiply by 1.04.
> To find $6\frac{1}{2}$%, multiply by 0.065.   To find $106\frac{1}{2}$%, multiply by 1.065.
> To find 12%, multiply by 0.12.   To find 112%, multiply by 1.12.
> To find 87%, multiply by 0.87.   To find 187%, multiply by 1.87.

1. Value-added tax (VAT)

Value-added tax or **VAT** is a government tax which is added to many of the things that we buy. In most shops the marked price of an item includes VAT and so we do not have to calculate it.

Sometimes the prices of more expensive items such as television sets and furniture are given without VAT. In these cases the shopkeeper calculates the VAT amount and adds it to the price of the item.

If an article is priced at €280 plus VAT at 23%, the full price can be worked out as follows:

1% of €280 = €2.80

23% = €2.80 × 23 = €64.40

∴ the full price = €280 + €64.40 = €344.40

 Using a calculator:

100% + 23% = 123%

To find 123%, we multiply by 1.23

Full price = €280 × 1.23 = €344.40

Example 1

The rate of VAT on electrical goods is 23%.

(i) Find the selling price of a washing machine priced at €650 + VAT.

(ii) If the selling price of an *ipad* is €738, find its price before VAT is added on.

(i) 23% of €650 = €650 × 0.23 = €149.50

∴ the selling price of the washing machine = €650 + €149.50

OR   = €799.50

Adding 23% gives 123%.

123% of €650 = €650 × 1.23 = €799.50 ... as above.

(ii) €738 represents 123% of the price before VAT is added.

$$123\% = €738$$

$$1\% = \frac{738}{123}$$

$$100\% = \frac{738}{123} \times \frac{100}{1} = €600$$

> You may also divide by 1.23 to get your answer.

Example 2

A rail fare goes up by 6% to €42.40.
What was the old fare?

The old fare is multiplied by 1.06 to get the new fare.

So the new fare has to be divided by 1.06 to get the old fare.

Old fare = €42.40 ÷ 1.06 = €40.

$? \longrightarrow \boxed{\times\ 1.06} \longrightarrow €42.40$

$€40 \longleftarrow \boxed{\div\ 1.06} \longleftarrow €42.40$

2. Percentage profit and loss

When dealing with percentage profit or loss, we base this percentage on the **cost price** unless otherwise stated.

$$\text{Percentage profit} = \frac{\text{Profit}}{\text{Cost price}} \times \frac{100}{1}\ ;\ \ \text{Percentage loss} = \frac{\text{Loss}}{\text{Cost price}} \times \frac{100}{1}$$

Example 3

By selling a car for €14 400, a dealer would lose 4% on the purchase price.
 (i) What did the dealer pay for the car?
 (ii) Find his percentage profit if he had sold the car for €17 250.

 (i) €14 400 represents 96% of the purchase price.

$$96\% = €14\,400$$
$$1\% = €150$$
$$100\% = €15\,000, \text{ i.e., the purchase price} = €15\,000.$$

 (ii) Profit = €17 250 − €15 000 = €2250

$$\text{Percentage profit} = \frac{2250}{15\,000} \times \frac{100}{1} = 15\%$$

Exercise 4.1

1. Express each of these percentages as decimals:
   (i) 7%   (ii) $3\frac{1}{2}\%$ (iii) 12%   (iv) 15%   (v) $16\frac{1}{2}\%$
   (vi) 104%   (vii) 110%   (viii) 114%   (ix) 125%   (x) $87\frac{1}{2}\%$

2. (i) Increase 120 by 10%   (ii) Increase 150 by 6%
   (iii) Decrease 600 by 5%   (iv) Decrease 820 by $12\frac{1}{2}\%$

3. Train fares are increased by 4%.
   (i) Find the new fare if the old fare was €28.
   (ii) If the new fare is €36.40, find the old fare.

4. The price of a theatre ticket goes up 7% to €26.75.
   What was the price before the increase?

5. The price of a bicycle is €520 plus VAT at 23%.
   Find the price of the bicycle after VAT is added.

6. The price of a television set is €984.
   If this includes VAT at 23%, find the price before VAT is added.

7. An electricity bill amounts to €204.30 after VAT at $13\frac{1}{2}\%$ is added.
   Find the amount of the bill before VAT is added.

8. In a sale, the price of a piece of furniture was reduced by 15%.
   If the sale price was €1360, what was the price before the sale?

9. In a sale, the marked prices are reduced by 30%.
   (i) Calculate the sale price of a jacket if the marked price is €350.
   (ii) Find the marked price of a dress if the sale price is €168.

10. By selling a jacket for €416, a store makes a profit of 30%.
    (i) Find the cost price of the jacket.
    (ii) If the jacket is reduced by 10% in a sale, calculate the percentage profit the store now has on the cost price.

11. By selling a laptop for €1150, a store makes a profit of 25%.
    At what price should the laptop be sold to make a profit of 20%?

12. When an item is sold for €176, the profit is 10% on the cost price. When the selling price is increased to €192, calculate the percentage profit on the cost price.

13. A greengrocer buys 30 boxes of strawberries at €5.25 each and sells 28 of them at a profit of 30%. If the remaining two boxes are unsaleable, find his percentage profit on the deal.

14. The price of a games console is €615 which includes VAT at 23%.

    Store A offers a discount of 24% on the selling price.
    Store B says it will not charge VAT.
    Store C says it will reduce the price before VAT is added by 25% and then charge VAT at 23% on the reduced price.

    In which store is the selling price the cheapest and by how much?

15. *Kelly Og's* Corn Flakes are sold in standard packs of 500 g for €2.40.
    During a promotion, the quantity in a pack is increased by 20%, but the price stays the same.
    Calculate the percentage reduction in the price per kilogram during the promotion.

16. A shop advertised "Everything half price in our sale", but also now advertises that there is "An additional 15% off sale prices".
    To what percentage reduction on the original price is the new offer equivalent?

Section 4.2 Household bills

The questions in this section deal with various household bills such as electricity, gas, phone, postage and insurance.

When dealing with bills that involve meter readings, the number of units used is found as follows:

Number of units used = Present Reading − Previous Reading

Example 1

Calculate the electricity bill from the information given below:

> Standing charge: €18.60
> Present meter reading: 38423 Previous meter reading: 37483
> Cost per unit: 23 cent
> VAT on total bill: 13%

Number of units used = 38423 − 37483 = 940
Cost of electricity used = 940 × 23 cent = 940 × €0.23
$$= €216.20$$
Amount of bill before VAT = €18.60 + €216.20 = €234.80
VAT = €234.80 × 0.13 = €30.52

Total bill = €234.80 + €30.52
$$= €265.32$$

Exercise 4.2

1. A householder's electricity bill is charged in the following way:
   (i)   A standing charge of €26.80
   (ii) 1256 units at 23c per unit
   (iii) VAT at 13% on the total bill.
   Find the total amount of the electricity bill.

2. A supplier charges for electricity supplied in the following way:

   Day rate: 24c per unit   *Night rate:* 10.5c per unit.

   Calculate the electricity bill for each of the following users based on the unit rates given above. VAT at $12\frac{1}{2}$% is added to each bill.

Name	No. of units used at *day rate*	No. of units used at *night rate*	Standing Charge
D. Maher	420	130	€28.90
G. O'Gorman	560	370	€25.60

3. Mrs Heaton received a bill of €130.80 for electricity used in a two-month period.
   The bill included a standing charge of €25.20.
   If each unit of electricity cost 22 cent, find how many units were used.

4. Rachel's gas meter was read on 1 March.
   The reading was [1][7][4][2]
   92 days later the meter was read again.
   The reading was [1][9][5][6]
   Calculate the total gas bill that Rachel will have to pay for the 92 days from 1 March if VAT at 13% is added.

   QAQ GAS SUPPLIES
   CHARGES:
   Standing charge – 28c per day
   Gas used – 84c per unit

53

5. A householder is charged for the gas that he uses in the following way:
   Standing charge €26.30.
   Reducing rate for therms used:

          0–20 therms: €1.40 per therm
          21–40 therms: €1.26 per therm
          over 40 therms: €1.06 per therm.

   Calculate the householder's bill for a period in which he uses 54 therms and VAT at $12\frac{1}{2}\%$ is added.

6. John hired the car for 8 days and drove 850 kilometres.
   (i) How much did the hire of the car cost him?
   (ii) Elaine hired a similar car for 10 days. If her bill for hiring the car amounted to €1610, how many kilometres did she travel?

SPEEDY'S CAR HIRE

€70 per day & 40c per kilometre

7. Alan earns €12.80 per hour for working a basic week of 38 hours.
   Overtime is paid at 'time and a half'.
   The table below shows the hours Alan worked last week.

Day	Monday	Tuesday	Wednesday	Thursday	Friday
Hours	10	8	7	9	12

   (i) How many hours overtime did he work last week?
   (ii) Calculate his total pay for last week.
   (iii) If Alan earned €582.40 in a particular week, how many hours overtime did he work?

8. *Eircom* charges 15c for each metered unit used. If each local call uses 1 unit every 3 minutes (or part thereof) during peak time, calculate the cost of each of these local calls made at peak time:

	Starting time	Finishing time
(i)	9.07 a.m.	9.12 a.m.
(ii)	12.49 p.m.	1.04 p.m.
(iii)	11.54 a.m.	12.16 p.m.

9. The charges for Olivia's 'bill-pay' phone per month are as follows.

Fixed charge:	€15
Call charges:	First 50 minutes free.
	Additional minutes, 18 cent per minute.
Text messages:	First 100 text messages free.
	Additional text messages, 14 cent each.

During June, Olivia used 120 minutes call-time and sent 128 text messages.

   (i) Calculate the charge for all her phone calls.

  (ii) Find the total amount of her bill for the month.

During July, Olivia used 143 minutes call-time and sent x text messages.

 (iii) If her bill amounted to €39.02, find the value of x.

10. When Anna uses her car on a business trip, she is allowed to claim 68 cent per km for the first 80 km and 42 cent per kilometre for the rest of the journey.

   (i) How much can she claim for a 135 km journey?

  (ii) On one occasion she claimed €119.08. How far did she travel?

11. Kate wants a smartphone.

These are the tariffs offered.

If Kate wants to use her phone for at least 120 minutes per month (but always less than 143), which tariff should she choose for the cheapest deal?

Tariff	Cost/month	Call cost/min
1	€15	40c
2	€24	26c
3	€30	15c
4	€40	8c

Section 4.3 Income tax

In this country, wage and salary earners pay income tax on all their incomes at one of two rates.
These rates are called the **Standard Rate** and the **Higher Rate**.
In 2012, the Standard Rate was 20% and the Higher Rate was 41%.
However these rates can change from year to year.

At the beginning of the year, each employed person is given a **tax credit** and a **standard rate cut-off point**. If the standard rate cut-off point is €30 000, this means that the person pays income tax at the standard rate (say 20%) on the first €30 000 of income. Any income above €30 000 is taxed at the higher rate (say 41%). When this income tax has been calculated, it is called the **gross tax**. The person's tax credit is then deducted from the gross tax to give the **tax payable**.

Tax payable = Gross tax − tax credit

Example 1

A printer has a weekly wage of €800. He pays income tax on all his wages at the standard rate of 20%. If he has a tax credit of €48 a week, find how much income tax he pays.

Gross tax = 20% of €800
$\qquad$ = €800 × 0.2 = €160
Tax payable = Gross tax − tax credits
$\qquad$ = €160 − €48
$\qquad$ = €112

∴ he pays €112 income tax each week.

The Higher Rate

The diagram below illustrates the amount of income tax a person with a gross weekly wage of €700 would pay if the standard rate cut-off point is €500 and the tax credit is €80 per week.

Standard Rate (20%)	Higher Rate (40%)
€500 @ 20% = €100	€200 @ 40% = €80

↑
Standard rate cut-off point (€500)

Gross tax = €500 @ 20% + €200 @ 40%
$\qquad$ = €100 $\qquad$ + €80 $\qquad$ = €180
Tax payable = Gross tax − tax credits
$\qquad$ = €180 − €80 = €100

Example 2

A woman's income for the year is €45 000. She has a standard rate cut-off point of €28 000 and a tax credit of €4000. If the standard rate of income tax is 20% and the higher rate is 41%, how much income tax does she pay for the year?

Gross tax = 20% of €28 000 + 41% of the remainder of her salary
$\qquad$ = 20% of €28 000 + 41% of €17 000 … Remainder = €17 000
$\qquad$ = (28 000 × 0.2) + (17 000 × 0.41)
$\qquad$ = 5600 + 6970 = €12 570

Tax payable = Gross tax − tax credit
$\qquad$ = €12 570 − €4000

∴ Tax payable = €8570

Example 3

A man pays €4500 income tax for the year and he has a tax credit of €2400.
If he pays tax at the standard rate of 20% on all his income, calculate his gross
income for the year.

$$\text{Tax payable} = \text{Gross tax} - \text{tax credit}$$

$$\Rightarrow \quad €4500 = \text{Gross tax} - €2400$$

$$\Rightarrow \quad \text{Gross tax} = €4500 + €2400 = €6900$$

Gross tax = 20% of gross income

$$\Rightarrow \quad 20\% \text{ of gross income} = €6900$$

$$1\% \text{ of gross income} = €\frac{6900}{20}$$

$$100\% \text{ of gross income} = €\frac{6900}{20} \times \frac{100}{1}$$

$$\therefore \text{ gross income} = €34\,500$$

Universal Social Charge (USC)

The Universal Social Charge (USC) came into effect on 1st January 2011.
It replaced other levies which were abolished from that date.

The rates of USC per year and per week are given below:

Income thresholds		
Per year	**Rate of USC**	**Per week**
Up to €10 036	2%	Up to €193
From €10 036 to €16 016	4%	From €193 to €308
In excess of €16 016	7%	In excess of €308

PRSI (Pay-Related Social Insurance)

PRSI is another deduction from a person's wage or income.

It is used by the state to pay unemployment benefits and old-age pensions.

The most widely-used rate is 4%.

Example 4

Conor has a weekly wage of €840.
He pays the USC at the usual rates and PRSI at 4%.
He has a tax credit of €65 and pays income tax at the standard rate of 20%.
Calculate his take-home pay after all deductions.

USC: €193 @ 2% + (€308 − €193) @ 4% + (€840 − €308) @ 7%
    = €193 × 0.02 + €115 × 0.04 + €532 × 0.07
    = €45.70

PRSI: €840 @ 4% = €840 × 0.04 = €33.60

Income tax: Amount = Gross tax − tax credit
            = €840 @ 20% − €65
            = €103

Total deductions: = €45.70 + €33.60 + €103
            = €182.30

Take-home pay: = €840 − €182.30
            = €657.70

Exercise 4.3

1. Tom's weekly wage is €800.
His tax credit is €90 a week.
He pays income tax at the rate of 20%.
Copy and complete the table on the right
to find Tom's take-home pay.

Gross pay	€800
Tax @ 20%	......
Tax credit	€90
Tax due	......
Take-home pay	......

2. Helen's gross pay for the year is €34 800.
Her tax credit is €2585.
She pays income tax at the rate of 22%.
Copy and complete the table on the right.

Gross pay	
Tax @ 22%	
Tax credit	
Tax due	
Take-home pay	

3. Leah has a weekly wage of €750.
Her weekly tax credit is €72 and the standard rate of tax is 25%.
How much income tax does she pay each week?

4. Conor has a monthly wage of €3200.
   His monthly tax credit is €280 and the standard rate of tax is 22%.
   Find how much income tax he pays each month.

5. Elaine has a weekly wage of €920.
   Her weekly tax credit is €84 and the standard rate of tax is 24%.
   How much income tax does she pay each week?

6. Jill has an annual salary of €42 000.
   Her annual tax credit is €3600 and the standard rate of tax is 22%.
   How much income tax does she pay for the year?

7. A carpenter has a weekly wage of €1050.
   His weekly tax credit is €78 and the standard rate of income tax is 24%.
   (i) Find how much income tax he pays each week.
   (ii) What is his net pay for the week?

8. Angela has an annual salary of €46 000.
   Her standard rate cut-off point is €28 000 and her tax credit is €3200.
   If the standard rate of income tax is 20% and the higher rate is 42%, find
   (i) the gross income tax for the year
   (ii) the amount of income tax paid for the year.

9. A journalist has a weekly wage of €980.
   His standard rate cut-off point is €620 and his tax credits amount to €44. The standard
   rate of income tax is 20% and the higher rate is 42%.
   Find (i) his gross tax for the week
         (ii) the amount of tax he pays each week.

10. Niamh has an annual salary of €48 000.
    She has a standard rate cut-off point of €34 000 and a tax credit of €4600.
    If the standard rate of income tax is 20% and the higher rate is 42%, find how much
    income tax she pays.

11. The Universal Social Charge (USC) rates are given in the table below:

Per year	Rate of USC	Per week
Up to €10 036	2%	Up to €193
€10 036 to €16 016	4%	€193 to €308
In excess of €16 016	7%	In excess of €308

   (i) Aidan has an annual salary of €57 000.
       Calculate his USC for the year.

(ii) Paula has a weekly wage of €950.
Calculate her USC for the week.

(iii) A salesperson has an annual salary of €63 000.
Calculate her USC for the year.

(iv) A plumber has a weekly wage of €1200.
Calculate his USC for the week.

12. A manager has an annual salary of €43 000. Her tax credits amount to €3500 and she pays income tax on all her income at the standard rate of r%.
If she pays €5960 in income tax for the year, find r.

13. A bus driver has a tax credit of €60 a week and pays income tax on all his wages at the standard rate of 20%.
If he pays €140 in income tax for the week, find his gross weekly wage.

14. Linda has a gross annual salary of €48 000 and her standard rate cut-off point is €31 000. The standard rate of income tax is 20% and the higher rate is 35%.
If she pays €7200 in income tax for the year, calculate her tax credit.

15. Helen paid €4400 in income tax for the year. Her tax credits amounted to €2600 and she paid income tax on all her salary at the standard rate of 20%.
Find her gross salary for the year.

16. A man pays €6520 income tax for the year and he has a tax credit of €3600. He pays income tax on all his income at the standard rate of 22%.
Calculate his gross annual salary.

17. Finian has a weekly wage of €900.
His tax credit is €68 and his standard rate cut-off point is €620.
The standard rate of tax is 20% and the higher rate is 42%.
He pays USC at the rates given in Question **11.** above.
He also pays PRSI at the rate of 4% on all his wage.
  (i) How much income tax does he pay for the week?
  (ii) How much does he pay in USC?
  (iii) Calculate how much he pays in PRSI.
  (iv) What is his net pay for the week?

> Net pay is the same as take-home pay.

18. John White is a factory manager and earns €54 000 a year.
His yearly tax credit is €4300 and his standard rate cut-off point is €36 000.
The standard rate of tax is 20% and the higher rate is 42%.
He pays USC as in Question **11.** above and PRSI on all his salary at the rate of 4%.
  (i) How much income tax does he pay in the year?
  (ii) How much does he pay in USC?

(iii) How much in PRSI does he pay?

(iv) Calculate his take-home pay for the year.

(v) Express his take-home pay as a percentage of his gross salary.
Give your answer to the nearest whole number.

19. Emma is paid €10.40 per hour for a 35 hour working week.
For each hour over 35 hours, she is paid $1\frac{1}{2}$ times the normal hourly rate.
Her tax credit for the week is €68 and the standard rate of tax is 26%.
She pays USC as in Question **11.** above and PRSI at the rate of 5%.

If in a particular week she worked 45 hours, find

(i) her gross wage for the week

(ii) the amount of income tax she paid

(iii) the amount of USC she paid

(iv) the amount of PRSI she paid

(v) her net pay for the week.

20. A woman paid €6600 in income tax for the year.
She had a tax credit of €4600 and her standard rate cut-off point was €28 000.
The standard rate of income tax was 20% and the higher rate was 40%.

(i) Calculate her gross tax for the year.

(ii) How much income tax did she pay at the standard rate?

(iii) How much income tax did she pay at the higher rate?

(iv) How much income did she earn in excess of €28 000?

(v) What was the woman's gross income for the year?

Section 4.4 Currency exchange

If we travel to a country not in the euro currency zone, we generally change our euro to the currency of that country.

If you see €1 = $1.35 displayed in a bank, how do you convert $100 to euro?

If we require euro in our answer, we put euro on the right-hand side of the 'equation'.

If €1 = $1.35, then

$$\$1.35 = €1 \quad \text{... Reverse the order}$$

$$\$1 = €\frac{1}{1.35}$$

> Put the currency required on the right-hand side of the 'equation'.

$$\$100 = €\frac{1}{1.35} \times \frac{100}{1} = €74.07$$

$$\therefore \ \$100 = €74.07$$

Example 1

If €1 = 120 yen, find
(i) how many yen you would get for €1200
(ii) how many euro would you get for 8000 yen.

(i)   €1 = 120 yen

€1200 = (120 × 1200) yen

= 144 000 yen

(ii)   €1 = 120 yen

120 yen = €1

$1 \text{ yen} = €\dfrac{1}{120}$

$8000 \text{ yen} = €\dfrac{1}{120} \times \dfrac{8000}{1}$

$= €66.666$

8000 yen = €66.67

Example 2

A US visitor exchanged $2000 for euro when the exchange rate was €1 = $1.36. A charge was made for this service. If the person received €1444.20, calculate the charge in euro.

We require euro in our answer, so we put euro on the right-hand side of the equation.

$€1 = \$1.36$

$\Rightarrow \quad \$1.36 = €1$

$\$1 = €\dfrac{1}{1.36}$

$\$2000 = €\dfrac{1}{1.36} \times \dfrac{2000}{1}$

$\$2000 = €1470.59$

The person received €1444.20.

⇒ the charge = €1470.59 − €1444.20 = €26.39
The charge is €26.39.

Exercise 4.4

1. If €1 = 1.3 US dollars, find
  (i) how many dollars you would get for €450
  (ii) how many euro you would get for 800 dollars.

2. If €1 = 120 yen, find
  (i) how many yen you would get for €900
  (ii) how many euro you would get for 9000 yen.

3. Given that €1 = £0.80 sterling, find
   (i) how many pounds sterling you would get for €1200
   (ii) how many euro you would get for £600.

4. On a visit to Switzerland, a person bought a leather
   jacket for 560 Swiss francs.

   If €1 = 1.4 Swiss francs, find the cost of the jacket in euro.

560F

5. If €1 = 1.4 Canadian dollars,
   (i) how many Canadian dollars would you get for €3500?
   (ii) how many euro would you get for 5600 Canadian dollars?

6. If €1 = 9.2 Swedish krona, find
   (i) how much in Swedish krona would you get for €750
   (ii) how much in euro you would get for 1500 Swedish krona.

7. A Swiss visitor exchanged 4200 Swiss francs for euro at an exchange bureau.
   The rate of exchange was €1 = 1.4 Swiss francs.
   Find, in euro, what the visitor received if the bureau charged 1% commission.

8. A Thai tourist paid 140 000 Thai baht to a travel agent for a holiday in Ireland.
   The cost to the travel agent of organising the holiday was €2460.
   Calculate, in baht, the profit made by the travel agent if €1 = 40 baht.

9. When the exchange rate was €1 = 9.8 South African Rand, a woman exchanged
   12 000 South African Rand for euro at a bank. The bank charged a fee for this
   transaction. If the woman received €1166.60, find, in euro, the fee charged by the bank.

10. On a trip to Sweden, a tourist exchanged €4500 for Swedish krona when the exchange
    rate was €1 = 8.75 krona. He spent 25 400 krona and then on his return, exchanged
    what he had left back into euro when the exchange rate was now €1 = 8.60 krona.
    How much did he receive in euro?

11. An Australian tourist exchanged A$2500 for euro at an Irish bank.
    The bank charged a percentage commission for the transaction.
    If the exchange rate was €1 = A$1.36 and the tourist received €1801.47, find the
    percentage commission charged by the bank.

12. A dealer bought Swiss francs when the exchange rate was €1 = 1.45 francs.
    If he received 43 400 francs, find how many euro he exchanged.
    Give your answer to the nearest euro.

    He sold the Swiss francs when the exchange rate was €1 = 1.28 francs.
    Find, correct to the nearest euro, how much the dealer lost or gained in the transaction.

Section 4.5 Compound interest

If we invest €100 in a bank for one year at 6% per annum (per year), we will earn €6 interest.

€100 is called the **principal (P).**
6% is the **rate** per annum (*i*).
€106 is called the **final amount (F).**

Final amount is
principal + interest.

Examine the following, where the rate of interest is 5%.

| €100 earns €5 in 1 year | → | €400 earns €20 in 1 year | → | €700 earns €35 in 1 year |

From this we can see that the interest is the principal (P)
multiplied by the rate (*i*). The rate *i* is always expressed
as a **decimal**.

Interest = P × *i*

If €800 is invested for 1 year at 6% per annum, then

 (i) we multiply €800 by 0.06 to get the interest,
     i.e. €800 × 0.06 = €48
 (ii) We multiply €800 by 1.06 to get the final amount,
     i.e. €800 × 1.06 = €848

Compound interest

Jack invested €800 in a credit union at 6% per annum.
His interest for the first year was €800 × 0.06 = €48.
At the end of the first year he had €848 in his account.
For the second year, €848 earned interest at 6%, that is, the interest earned in the first year
was now itself earning further interest in the second year.
This kind of interest is called **compound interest**.

The basic method for calculating compound interest is illustrated in the following example.

Example 1

€1200 is invested for 3 years at 4% per annum compound interest.
What will the investment amount to?

Principal for the first year   = €1200
Interest for the first year   = 4% of €1200
                                  = 1200 × 0.04 = €48
Principal for the second year   = €1200 + €48 = €1248
Interest for the second year   = 4% of €1248
                                  = 1248 × 0.04 = €49.92

64

Principal for the third year   = €1248 + €49.92 = €1297.92
Interest for the third year   = 4% of €1297.92
                                  = 1297.92 × 0.04
                                  = 51.9168 = €51.92

Final amount at end of third year = €1297.92 + €51.92
                                       = €1349.84

Here is another method of finding the final amount in the example above.

If €1200 is invested for 3 years at 4% per annum, the final amount (**F**) can be calculated like this:

$$€1200 \times \underbrace{1.04 \times 1.04 \times 1.04} = €1200 \times (1.04)^3$$

For 3 years, multiply by $(1.04)^3$.

The pattern shown above leads us to a formula for finding the final amount (F) when a sum of money (P) is invested at compound interest, i, for t years.

$$F = P(1 + i)^t$$

F = final amount
P = principal
i = interest rate
t = number of years

Note: The interest rate **i** is always given in decimal form.

If the interest is 4%, then $(1 + i) = 1.04$.

If the interest is $2\frac{1}{2}$%, then $(1 + i) = 1.025$.

If the interest is 12%, then $(1 + i) = 1.12$.

> ### Example 2
>
> Use the compound interest formula to find the compound interest which accrues on €2800 invested for 3 years at 7.5% per annum.
>
> $F = P(1 + i)^t$
> $= 2800(1 + 0.075)^3$
> $= 2800(1.075)^3$
> $F = €3478.43$ ... by calculator
>
> Compound interest = €3478.43 − €2800 = €678.43

Finding the rate and the principal

If €300 is invested for 1 year at 6% per annum, then the interest is €300 × 0.06 = €18.

However, if we are given that €300 earns €18 in one year, how do we find the interest?

We could reason that if €300 earns €18, then €100 would earn €6, that is, a rate of 6%.

Thus the rate is $\dfrac{18}{\overset{}{\underset{3}{300}}} \times \dfrac{\overset{1}{\cancel{100}}}{1} = \dfrac{18}{3} = 6\%$

$\text{Rate} = \dfrac{\text{Interest}}{\text{Principal}} \times \dfrac{100}{1}\,\%$

Example 3

If €650 amounts to €702 in one year, find the rate.

Interest = €702 − €650 = €52

$\text{Rate} = \dfrac{\text{Interest}}{\text{Principal}} \times \dfrac{100}{1} = \dfrac{52}{650} \times \dfrac{100}{1} = 8$

∴ the rate = 8%

Example 4

What sum of money, invested at 4% per annum compound interest, will amount to €3149.62 after 3 years?

$F = P(1 + i)^t$

$3149.62 = P(1.04)^3$

$P(1.04)^3 = 3149.62$ … here we are looking for the principal, P.

$P = \dfrac{3149.62}{(1.04)^3} = \dfrac{3149.62}{1.1249} = €2800$

The amount invested was €2800.

Depreciation

If a car depreciates in value by 20% a year, then its value at the end of the first year will be 80% of its value at the beginning of the year.

To find 80% of a sum of money, multiply by 0.8 as 80% = 0.8.

If a car cost €25 000 and depreciates in value by 15% each year, then its value

  (i) at the end of the first year = €25 000 × 0.85

 (ii) at the end of the second year = €25 000 × 0.85 × 0.85 = €25 000 × (0.85)²

(iii) at the end of the third year = €25 000 × 0.85 × 0.85 × 0.85

$$= €25\,000 \times (0.85)^3$$

....

At the end of 8 years, its value is €25 000 × (0.85)⁸.

Example 5

A machine depreciates in value by 10% per annum.
If the machine is worth €58 320 at the end of 3 years, find its value when new.

Let P be the value of the machine when new.
Value of P at the end of 3 years $= P(0.9)^3$

$100\% - 10\%$
$= 90\% = 0.9$

$\therefore \quad P(0.9)^3 = 58\,320$
$P(0.729) = 58\,320$

$P = \dfrac{58\,320}{0.729} = 80\,000$

The value of the machine when new is €80 000.

Exercise 4.5

Find the compound interest earned on the investments in Questions (**1–10**), without using the compound interest formula.

1. €400 for 2 years at 6%
2. €800 for 2 years at 8%
3. €900 for 2 years at 5%
4. €1000 for 2 years at 9%
5. €700 for 2 years at 4%
6. €850 for 2 years at 10%
7. €800 for 3 years at 5%
8. €1200 for 3 years at 12%
9. €700 for 3 years at 11%
10. €1800 for 3 years at 4%

11. Use the compound interest formula to find the final amount, correct to the nearest cent, of each of the following investments:
    (i)   €600 for 2 years at 5%
    (ii) €1800 for 2 years at 9%
    (iii) €3500 for 3 years at $7\frac{1}{2}$%
    (iv) €7800 for 3 years at $3\frac{1}{2}$%

12. €4600 was invested for 2 years at compound interest.
    If the rate for the first year was 4% and for the second year was 5%, find the total interest for the two years.

13. €1500 was invested for 2 years at compound interest.
    The rate for the first year was 3% and the rate for the second year was 4%.
    Find the final amount at the end of the two years.

14. A company borrowed €12 000 from a bank at 11% per annum compound interest.
    The company repaid €5000 at the end of the first year.
    How much was owed to the bank at the end of the second year?

15. €700 will amount to €756 after one year if invested at 8% per annum.

    (i) By what number is €700 multiplied to get €756?
    (ii) By what number is €756 divided to get €700?

16. A sum of money is invested at 7% per annum.
    If it amounts to €6848 after one year, find the sum invested.

17. €2500 was invested in a building society.
    If it amounted to €2612.50 after one year, calculate the rate of interest.

18. What sum of money invested for 3 years at 8% per annum compound interest would amount to €1007.77?

19. What sum of money invested at 5% per annum compound interest would amount to €10 988.78 in 6 years?

20. €8000 is invested for 3 years at compound interest.
    The rate for the first year is 5% and for the second year is 6%.
    Find the amount of the investment at the end of two years.
    At the end of the third year, the money invested amounted to €9260.16.
    Calculate the rate of interest for the third year.

21. A person borrows €15 000 for two years.
    Interest for the first year is charged at 12% per annum.
    The person repays €6000 at the end of the first year.
    If the amount owed at the end of the second year is €12 042, find the rate of interest for the second year.

22. A sum of money was invested for 2 years.
    The rate of interest for the first year was 4% and for the second year was 5%.
    The amount at the end of the second year was €9282.
    (i) By what number is €9282 divided to get the amount at the end of the first year?
    (ii) By what number is the amount at the end of the first year divided to get the sum invested?
    What is the sum of money invested?

23. A person invested €10 000 in a building society.
    The rate of interest for the first year was $2\frac{1}{2}$%.
    At the end of the first year, the person invested a further €1000.
    The rate of interest for the second year was 2%.
    Calculate the value of the investment at the end of the second year.

    At the end of the second year, a further €2000 was invested.
    At the end of the third year, the total investment amounted to €14 014.
    Calculate the rate of interest for the third year.

24. A machine cost €15 000.

If it depreciated in value by 15% per annum, find its value at the end of two years.

25. Vans depreciate in value by 20% per annum.

(i) If a van is bought for €23 000, find its value at the end of three years.

(ii) If the value of a van is €11 520 after two years, find its value when new.

26. A new car was bought for €24 000. It decreased in value by 20% in the first year.

If its value at the end of the second year was €16 128, by what percentage did its value decrease during the second year?

Test yourself 4

1. (a) In a two-month period, the McCabes used 980 units of electricity.
   Each unit of electricity cost 21c and the standing charge was €21.30.
   Find the total amount of their bill when VAT at $12\frac{1}{2}$% was added on.

   (b) Sylvia has an annual salary of €42 800.
   Her tax credit is €3350 and her standard rate cut-off point is €31 000.
   If the standard rate of income tax is 20% and the higher rate is 42%, calculate how much income tax she pays for the year.

   (c) A man borrowed €8000 from a bank at 12% per annum compound interest.
   He repaid €3000 at the end of the first year.
   How much did he owe the bank at the end of the second year?

2. (a) €4500 was invested for 2 years at compound interest.
   The rate for the first year was 8% and for the second year 6%.
   Find the total interest earned.

   (b) When the exchange rate is €1 = US$1.28, a person changes US$1920 to euro.
   A charge is made for this service.
   What is the percentage charge if the person receives €1462.50?

   (c) During a sale, all items of mens' clothing are reduced by 20% of the marked price.
   (i) If the sale price of an overcoat was €336, what was the marked price?
   (ii) If the store made a profit of 5% on the cost price of the overcoat during the sale, what percentage profit did it make on the marked price before the sale?

3. (a) Lizzy bought 0.8 kg of pears at €1.90 per kilogram and 1.4 kg of apples. The total cost was €4.46.
   What was the price per kilogram of the apples?

   (b) A jar with 8 chocolates in it weighs 160 g.
   The same jar with 20 chocolates in it weighs 304 g.
   How much does the jar weigh on its own?

   (c) A sum of money invested at compound interest amounted to €5342.40 at the end of two years.
   (i) If the interest rate for the second year was 6%, how much was the investment worth at the end of the first year?
   (ii) If the original sum invested was €4800, find the rate for the first year.

4. (a) Mark often travels to Dublin by train.
   An ordinary return ticket costs €34.50.
   A *leap card* costs €70. If he has one, the return ticket is only €23.
   If he buys one of these integrated travel cards, what is the least number of return

trips to Dublin he must make for the total cost to be less than for ordinary tickets?

(b) Joan Buckley has an annual salary of €39 000.

Her tax credits amount to €4750 and her standard rate cut-off point is €31 000. If the standard rate of income tax is 20% and the higher rate is 40%, find how much income tax she pays for the year.

(c) A sum of money was invested for two years at compound interest.

The rate for the first year was 6% and for the second year $5\frac{1}{2}$%.

If the value of the investment at the end of the two years was €6709.80, find the sum invested.

5. (a) Ruth's electricity bill is based on the following details:

Previous meter reading	46523
Present meter reading	48249
Charge per unit	21.5 cent
Standing charge	€21.40
VAT on total bill	$13\frac{1}{2}$%

Work out the total bill, including VAT.

(b) An Australian visitor to Ireland exchanged 2000 dollars for euro when the exchange rate was €1 = 1.6 Australian dollars.

What was the percentage charge for the transaction if she received €1225?

(c) During the first year, a new car depreciates in value by 20% and during the second year, the car depreciates in value by 15% of its value at the beginning of that year. What is the cost of a new car if its value at the end of the second year is €15 640?

6. (a) Jonathan is offered a choice of the following pay deals:

Ⓐ: 6% increase this year followed by a 6% increase next year

Ⓑ: $5\frac{1}{2}$% increase this year followed by a $6\frac{1}{2}$% increase next year

Which offer should Jonathan accept? Explain your answer.

(b) A woman invested €12 000 in a building society at 7% per annum.

At the end of the first year, she withdrew €B. If the value of her investment at the end of the second year was €8923.80, find the value of B.

(c) Cecil has a tax credit of €3600 a year and his standard rate cut-off point is €30 000. The standard rate of income tax is 20% and the higher rate is 35%. If Cecil pays €7650 income tax for the year, find his gross salary.

Statistics 1 – Collecting data

Key words

data   raw data   numerical data   discrete data
continuous data   categorical data   nominal   ordinal
primary data   secondary data   sample   simple random sample
population   questionnaire   bias   representative

Section 5.1 Types of data

In this section, we revisit some of the words and definitions you encountered in your study of data in first-year.

Data is another name for the facts and pieces of information that we collect.
Data that is not in an organised form is called **raw data**.
Data can be divided into two broad categories, namely **categorical data** and **numerical data**.

Categorical data

Data which fits into a group or category is called **categorical data**.
It is generally described using words such as colour, favourite sport or country of birth.

Categorical data such as

> colours of cars

> male or female

> true/false

> favourite books,   is generally called **nominal data**.

Categorical data in which the categories have an obvious order such as first division, second division, third division, etc., is called **ordinal data**.

Here are some more examples of ordinal data:

> type of car (luxury, executive, family, economy, …)

> examination grades (A, B, C, D, …)

> opinion scales (strongly agree, agree, don't know, disagree, strongly disagree).

Numerical data

Data which can be counted or measured is called **numerical data** because the answer is a number.
Numerical data can be either **discrete** or **continuous**.

Discrete data

Data which can take only certain individual values is called **discrete data**.

Here are some examples of **discrete data**:
> The numbers of goals scored by football teams on a Saturday
> The numbers of desks in the classrooms of the school
> The marks achieved in a test.

Continuous data

Continuous data is measured on some scale and can take any value on that scale.

Here are some examples of **continuous data**:
> The heights of students in your class
> The speeds of cars passing a certain point on a road
> The time taken to complete a 100-metre sprint

Here is a summary of data types:

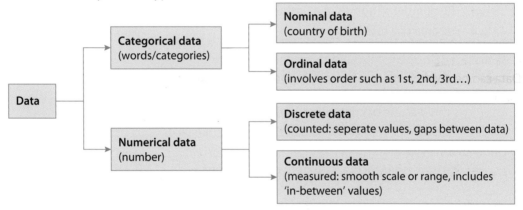

Example 1

For each of the following, write down whether it is numerical or categorical data:
(i)   the number of goals scored in a hockey match
(ii)   the temperature of an oven
(iii) people's hair colours
(iv)   countries where cars were manufactured
(v)   star ratings of the quality of hotels
(vi)   time taken for athletes to run 400 metres.

(i)   numerical   (ii)   numerical   (iii) categorical
(iv)   categorical   (v)   categorical   (vi)   numerical

1. State whether each of the following is numerical or categorical data:
    (i) The number of cars sold by a certain garage last month
    (ii) The favourite soccer teams of pupils in your class
    (iii) The continent of birth of people who came to Ireland in the past year
    (iv) The number of horses in a race
    (v) The time taken by the winning horse to complete the race
    (vi) The blood-types of the teachers in your school
    (vii) The types of trees in a wood
    (viii) The length of time taken to complete a sudoku puzzle.

2. State whether each of the following pieces of numerical data is discrete or continuous:
    (i) The number of animals in the zoo
    (ii) The time taken to run a marathon
    (iii) The score on a dice
    (iv) Patients' body temperatures
    (v) The number of homes in a postal district with internet access
    (vi) The area of a football pitch.

3. (i) Is the breed of this dog categorical or numerical data?
    (ii) The dog weighs 23 kg.
        Is this discrete or continuous data?
    (iii) The dog has 4 legs, is 4 years old and eats 4 *munchies*
        for his lunch.
        State whether each 4 is discrete or continuous.

4. Each of the following is categorical data.
    State whether each is nominal or ordinal.
    (i) The types of animals in a large farm
    (ii) The credit ratings of countries (Triple A, …)
    (iii) The divisions in a football league
    (iv) The countries visited while supporting the Irish soccer team
    (v) The subjects available to study in fifth-year
    (vi) The categories of medals that can be won at the Olympic Games
    (vii) The grades I can get in my Junior Certificate examinations.

5. Eight candidates were interviewed for a job.
    Based on the results of the interview, they were placed in order from 1 to 8.
    Use two words to describe the data contained in each statement.

6. The graphic on the right shows the midday temperatures for each day in July.

  (i)   Are these temperatures discrete or continuous?

  (ii) State whether the graphic contains any categorical data. If it does, is it nominal or ordinal?

  (iii) Are the dates July 1, 2, 3, ... numerical or categorical?
        Explain your conclusion.

July Midday Temperatures

JULY						2011
SUN	MON	TUE	WED	THU	FRI	SAT
	1 17	2 16	3 18	4 18	5 18	6 17
7 19	8 20	9 22	10 22	11 21	12 21	13 22
14 22	15 23	16 24	17 23	18 23	19 23	20 24
21 24	22 23	23 23	24 24	25 25	26 23	27 23
28 25	29 25	30 24	31 25			

7. A Premier League team has 24 first-team players.
Their average age is 26 years.
They were born in Ireland, England, Croatia, Senegal, Italy, France and the Ivory Coast.

Use two words to describe the data contained in each of the three statements above.

Section 5.2 Collecting data

Data is collected for a variety of reasons and from a variety of sources.

> Companies do market reserach to find out what customers like or dislike about their products and to see whether or not they would like new products.

> The government carries out a census of every person in the country every five years. The information gathered is used by other people and organisations for further planning.

Data can be collected by any of these methods:

> Doing a survey by means of a questionnaire and recording what people say

> Carrying out an experiment which may involve the use of technology such as a computer or data logger

> Using sources such as reference books, websites, databases, newspapers and historical records.

Before you collect data, you need to have a clear aim in mind. You then need to decide what sort of data to collect and the most suitable and efficient method of collecting it.

The data you collect can be divided into two broad categories, namely, **primary data** and **secondary data**.

Primary data

Data that is collected by an organisation or individual that is going to use it is called **primary data**.

Secondary data

Data which is already available or has been collected by someone else for a different purpose is called **secondary data**.

Surveys

Primary data is generally collected by means of a **survey**.
The main survey methods are:

> personal interviews in which people are asked questions; this is generally done by means of a **questionnaire**.

> telephone surveys; here the interview is conducted by phone

> **observation**; this involves monitoring behaviour

> **experiments**; these are particularly useful for collecting scientific data; drug companies carry out expeirments to test the benefits and the side-effects of new drugs.

Questionnaires

A **questionnaire** is a set of questions designed to obtain data from individuals.

People who answer questionnaires are called **respondents**.

There are two ways in which the questions can be asked.

> An interviewer asks the questions and fills in the questionnaire

> People are given a questionnaire and asked to fill in the responses themselves.

When you are composing questions for a questionnaire,

> be clear what you want to find out and what data you need

> ask short, concise questions

> start with simple questions to encourage the person who is giving the responses

> provide response boxes where possible: Yes ☐   No ☐

> avoid leading questions such as

> 'Don't you agree that there is too much sport on television?'

or   'Do you think that professional footballers are overpaid?'

> avoid personal questions such as those which involve name, exact age or weight.

Avoiding bias

When you are collecting data, you need to make sure that your survey or experiment is **fair** and avoids **bias**. If bias exists, the data collected might be unrepresentative.

Here are some questions which should be avoided because they suggest a particular answer or they may cause embarrassment or shame.

Have you ever stolen money from your parents?

Yes ☐   No ☐

Few students are likely to answer this question honestly if they have already stolen.

Do you agree that the Minister for Finance should resign because of the poor state of the economy?

Yes ☐   No ☐

This wording of this question suggests that the right answer is 'yes'. It is a leading question and therefore likely to be **biased**.

Frequency tables

If conducting a survey, we often collect a lot of data.
We need to orgainse this data so that it makes sense.
A frequency table is useful for grouping and counting data scores in an efficient way.
The **frequency** of a score is the number of times that score appears in the set of data.

Example 1

Twenty people were surveyed about the number of cars owned in their household.
This is the data collected:

2	2	1	2	0	3	2	1	1	4
1	1	1	2	2	0	3	2	1	2

Use tally marks to construct a frequency table for the data.

For each score in the data set, we draw a tally mark in the tally column. The first score is a 2, so we mark a '|' in the tally column beside 2. We continue until we have made a tally mark for each score.

The completed frequency table is shown on the right.

Always check that the total is equal to the total number of given data.

Score	Tally	Frequency
0				2
1									7
2										8
3				2
4			1
	Total	20

Exercise 5.2

1. State whether each of the following is an example of primary data or secondary data:
   (i) Conor tossed a coin 100 times and recorded the result to investigate if the coin was fair.
   (ii) Brenda counted the number of SUVs that passed the school gate between 9 a.m. and 10 a.m.

(iii) Shane used the internet to check the number of medals Ireland won in boxing in the last four Olympic Games.

(iv) Emer checked the Central Statistics Office website to check the number of people on the Live Register for each of the last twenty four months.

2. A brewery wants to produce a new type of beer.
Suggest how they might use both primary and secondary data to do market research.

3. Niamh wants to find out how often adults go to the cinema.
She uses this question on a questionnaire.

'How many times do you go to the cinema?'

☐   ☐   ☐

Not very often   Sometimes   A lot

(i) Write down **two** things wrong with this question.

(ii) Design a better question for her questionnaire to find out how often adults go to the cinema.
You should include some response boxes.

4. Eamonn is trying to find out what people think of the *FFG Political Party*.
He is trying to decide between these two questions for his questionnaire.
Which question should he use? Explain your answer.

(i) How do you rate the *FFG Party's* economic policies?

Strongly agree ☐   Agree ☐   Don't know ☐   Disagree ☐   Strongly disagree ☐

(ii) Do you agree that the *FFG Party* has the best economic policies?

Yes ☐   No ☐

5. Explain what is wrong with each of the following survey questions.
Suggest a better alternative for each question.

(i) What age are you?

(ii) Would you describe yourself as being well-educated?

(iii) Normal people like animals.
Do you like animals?

(iv) Would you agree that top actors are paid too much?

(v) Have you ever taken illegal drugs?

(vi) Where exactly do you live?

(vii) In view of the huge numbers of road accidents outside this school, do you think the speed limit should be reduced?

6. Aidan wants to find out what students think about the library service at his college.
Part of the questionnaire he has written is shown.

> **Q1.** What is your full name? ....
>
> **Q2.** How many times a week do you go to the library?
>
> ☐ Often ☐ Sometimes ☐ Never

   (i) Why should Q1 not be asked?

   (ii) What is wrong with the choices offered in Q2?

7. This question was included in a questionnaire.

> How old are you?   Young ☐   Middle-aged ☐   Elderly ☐

   (i) What is wrong with the question and responses?

   (ii) Rewrite the question and responses in a better way.

8. Valerie is the manager of a supermarket.
She wants to find out how often people shop at her supermarket.
She will use a questionnaire.

Design a suitable question for Valerie to use on her questionnaire.
You must include some response boxes.

9. Give a reason why questions A and B below should be re-worded before being included in a questionnaire.
Rewrite each one showing exactly how you would present it in a questionnaire.

Question A: Do you live in a working-class or middle-class area?

Question B: The new supermarket seems to be a great success. Do you agree?

10. For each of these questions or statements, what would be the best way to collect the data? Choose from the box.

> **A** questionnaire or data collection sheet
> **B** experiment   **C** other source

   (i) What sport do people in your class watch most often?

   (ii) How often do people go to the theatre? On which days?

   (iii) What percentage of motor vehicle accidents in Ireland occur between 6 p.m. and midnight?

   (iv) Eoin wants to find out if a dice is biased.

11. A mobile phone company wants to carry out a survey.
It wants to find out the distribution of the age and sex of its customers and the frequency with which they use their phones.
The company intends to use a questionnaire.
Write three questions and corresponding responses that will enable the company to efficiently carry out the survey.

12. The results of a quiz (out of 10) for a class of 27 students are as shown:

7	7	8	9	7	5	4	8	9
9	8	10	8	7	5	5	4	1
8	8	9	7	7	4	8	3	1

(i)   Copy and complete the frequency table on the right.

(ii)   What was the highest score in the quiz?

(iii)   How many students scored 4 marks in the quiz?

(iii)   What was the most frequent score?

Score	Tally	Frequency
1	||	2
2		
3		
4		
5		
6		
7		
8		
9		
10		

Section 5.3 Sampling

If you were asked to investigate the claim,

'Rugby players in Ireland are taller than Gaelic football players',

do you measure the heights of all rugby players and all Gaelic football players in the country? This would be an enormous task as there are thousands of players in these categories.

In this study, we use the word **population** to describe **all** the rugby and Gaelic footballers in the country.

When a population is too large for a study, we collect data from some members of the population only. In statistics, this group is called a **sample**. The purpose of a sample is to collect data from some of the population and use it to draw conclusions about the whole population.

Bias

The sample you select for your study is very important. If the sample is not properly selected, the results may be **biased**. If **bias** exists, the results will be distorted and so will not be properly representative of the population as a whole.

The **size** of a sample is also important. If the sample is too small, the results may not be very reliable. If the sample is too large, the data may take a long time to collect and analyse.

Simple random sample

One of the ways to avoid bias in a survey is to take a **simple random sample** (or more commonly called a **random sample**).

In a random sample, every member of the population being considered has an equal chance of being selected. Random samples need to be carefully chosen.

Methods for choosing a **simple random sample** could involve giving each member of the population a number and then selecting the numbers for the sample in one of these ways:

> putting the numbers into a hat and then selecting however many you need for the sample

> using a random number table

> using a random number generator on your calculator or computer.

Electronic calculators are very useful for generating random numbers.

If you want to generate 3-digit numbers, press SHIFT , and then press Ran # .

Now press = and disregard the decimal point.

If the number displayed is 0.107, write 107.

Press = repeatedly to get more random numbers.

Exercise 5.3

1. A school has 820 students and an investigation concerning the school uniform is being conducted.
   40 students from the school are randomly selected to complete the survey on their school uniform. In this situation,
   (i) what is the population size
   (ii) what is the size of the sample?

2. Melanie wants to find out how often people go to the cinema.
   She gives a questionnaire to all the women leaving a cinema.

   Her sample is biased.
   Give **two** possible reasons why.

3. Amy wants to find out how often people play sport.
   She went to a local sports shop and questioned the people she met.
   Explain why this sample is likely to be biased.

4. Dara wants to find out how people get to work each day.
   Which of the following is the most appropriate group to question?
   A: Every fourth person at a bus stop.
   B: A group of people at lunch break.
   C: People arriving late for work.

5. Jennifer wants to investigate if people want longer prison sentences for criminals. Which of the following is the most appropriate group to question?

A: Members of the gardaí.

B: People at a football match.

C: People who have been in prison.

Explain your answer.

6. Amanda wants to choose a sample of 500 adults from the town where she lives. She considers these methods of choosing her sample:

Method 1: Choose people shopping in the town centre on Saturday mornings.

Method 2: Choose names at random from the electoral register.

Method 3: Choose people living in the streets near her house.

Which method is most likely to produce an unbiased sample?
Give a reason for your answer.

7. Comment on any possible bias in the following situations:

(i) Sixth-year students only are interviewed about changes to the school uniform.

(ii) Motorists stopped in peak-hour are interviewed about traffic problems.

(iii) Real estate agents are interviewed about the prices of houses.

(iv) A 'who will you vote for?' survey at an expensive city restaurant.

8. A research company is canvassing peoples' opinions on whether smoking should be banned in all public places.

They canvass people standing outside buildings in the city during office hours. Explain why the data collected is likely to be biased.

9. Use the ⎡Ran #⎤ key on your calculator to choose a sample of 8 pupils from a year-group of 100.

10. Which of the following samples are likely to be representative samples?
For those that are not representative, give a reason why they are not.

(A) Survey task: To test the effectiveness of a new drug for migraines.

Sample: Chosen by giving the drug to all patients, of just one doctor, who suffer from migraines.

(B) Survey task: To survey opinion about fresh bread baked in a local supermarket.

Sample: Chosen by interviewing every 20th shopper at the supermarket checkout on a Saturday

(C) Survey task: To survey the voting intentions of residents of a particular constituency in the coming election.

Sample: A random sample of people at the local train station between 7 a.m. and 9 a.m. are surveyed.

Test yourself 5

1. State whether each of the following sets of data is numerical or categorical:
   (i) Favourite type of apple
   (ii) The number of bicycles in a household
   (iii) The weights of three-year-old children
   (iv) The brands of dog-food on sale in a supermarket
   (v) County of birth.
   (vi) The amount of rainfall in each month of the year.

2. Which of the following are discrete data and which are continuous data?
   (i) The number of matches in a selection of match boxes.
   (ii) Shirt-collar sizes.
   (iii) The lengths of material used to make curtains.
   (iv) The number of vehicles passing through an intersection each hour.
   (v) The stopping distances of cars doing 60 km/hr.

3. State whether each of the following is primary data or secondary data:
   (i) Counting the number of hatchback cars passing the school gate.
   (ii) Looking at records to see how many people passed through Shannon Airport each day in June one year.
   (iii) Examing tourist brochures to find the average weekly snowfall at a skiing resort.
   (iv) Checking *Wikipedia* to see how many gold medals each country won at the London Olympics.

4. The manager of an Aqua Park asks the following two questions on a questionnaire.

   'Do you go to the Aqua Park?'   Sometimes ☐   Often ☐

   'How old are you?'   0 to 10 years ☐   10 to 20 years ☐   over 20 years ☐

   (i) What is wrong with each of these questions?
   (ii) For both questions above, write a better version that the manager can use.

5. (a) Which of the two questions and responses below are the more suitable for inclusion in a questionnaire?
   Give a reason for your selection.
   (i)
   Do you agree that having a lovely, warm, relaxing bath at night helps you go to sleep?
   Yes ☐   No ☐

   (ii)
   Does a warm bath at night help you go to sleep?
   Yes ☐   No ☐   Not sure ☐

(b) A county engineer is carrying out a traffic survey.
He is trying to find out how busy a particular road is.
Each day, he counts the number of cars passing a particular point between 2 p.m. and 3 p.m.
He uses this information to write a report.
State why his sample is likely to be biased.

6. (a) Explain what is wrong with each of the following survey questions and suggest better alternatives.
   (i) How many phones are there in your home?
   (ii) What type of car do you own?
   (iii) What is your email address?

   (b) Tennis players are graded in the following way:

   Class 1,   Class 2,   Class 3,   Class 4,   Class 5.

   Use two words to describe this data.

7. (a) The pupils in a third-year class carried out a survey to find the average amount of time spent in the computer room per person each week.
   The pupils decided to give the questionnaire to one of the following groups.
   Which of these is a good sample?
   Give a reason why each of the others is not a good sample.

   Sample 1   the pupils who used the computer room during one lunch break
   Sample 2   all the pupils in the library during one lunch break
   Sample 3   the first 50 pupils to arrive at school on a particular morning
   Sample 4   every 8th pupil on the school roll

   (b) The management of a theme park have made some changes to the amusements.
   They want to use a questionnaire to find out what people think about the changes.
   The following questions are suggested.
   Write down what is wrong with each of them and design a new question and responses for each that is more suitable.
   (i) What do you think of the new amusements?
       Very good ☐   Good ☐   Satisfactory ☐
   (ii) How much money would you normally expect to pay for each amusement?
       €6–€8 ☐   €8–€10 ☐   More than €10 ☐
   (iii) How often do you visit the park each year?
       Often ☐   Not very often ☐

Perimeter – Area – Volume

Section 6.1 Review of perimeter and area

In your *Common Introductory Course* you found the perimeter and area of squares, rectangles and triangles.

The box below summarises what you learned.

Square	Rectangle	Triangle
Perimeter = 4ℓ	Perimeter = $2(\ell + b)$	Perimeter = length of the three sides
Area = ℓ^2	Area = ℓb	Area = $\frac{1}{2}bh$

Here are three triangles which all have different shapes.

In each triangle, the base (*b*) and perpendicular height (*h*) are shown.

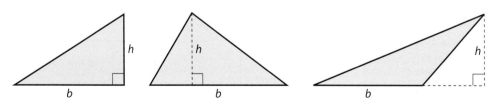

For each triangle, the area $= \frac{1}{2}bh$.

Example 1

Find the area of the shaded region of this figure.

Shaded area = area of rectangle − area of triangle

$$= 20 \times 16 - \tfrac{1}{2} \times 12 \times 9$$
$$= 320 - 54$$
$$= 266 \text{ cm}^2$$

Example 2

The area of the given triangle is 56 cm².
Find the perpendicular height, h.

$$\text{Area} = \tfrac{1}{2} \times 14 \times h$$
$$\therefore \quad \tfrac{1}{2} \times 14 \times h = 56$$
$$7h = 56$$
$$h = 8 \text{ cm}$$

Exercise 6.1

1. Work out the perimeter of each of these rectangles:

(i) 9 cm, 14 cm (ii) 8 cm, 13 cm (iii) 17 cm, 10.5 cm

2. Find the area of each of the rectangles in Question **1.** above.

3. Find the length of the missing side in each of these rectangles:

(i) ? 84 cm² 12 cm (ii) ? 176 cm² 11 cm

(iii) 198 cm² 9 cm ?

4. Work out the perimeter of each of these shapes, where all the angles are right angles:

(i)

(ii)

(iii)

(You have sufficient dimensions to find these perimeters.)

5. Find the length of the side of each square shown below:

(i)

Area = 25 cm²

(ii)

Area = 144 m²

(iii)

Area = 625 cm²

6. Find the area of each of these triangles:

(i)

(ii)

(iii)

7. Work out the areas of these triangles:

(i)

(ii)

(iii)

8. Find the length of the line segment marked *x* in each of these triangles:

(i)

Area = 90 cm²

(ii)

Area = 112 cm²

(iii)

Area = 120 cm²

9. Find the areas of the following shapes which are composed of rectangles and triangles.

(i) 6 cm, 11 cm, 8 cm

(ii) 16 cm, 10 cm, 14 cm

(iii) 12 cm, 15 cm, 20 cm

10. Triangle *B* is double the area of triangle *A*.
The height of both triangles is 6 cm.

    (i) Find the area of triangle *A*.

    (ii) Find the area of triangle *B*.

    (iii) Work out the value of *x*.

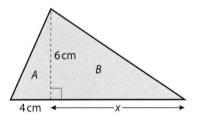

6 cm, *A*, *B*, 4 cm, *x*

11. Find the area of the shaded portion of the
diagram on the right.

Hence find the area of the unshaded part.

3 m, 6 m, 5 m, 7 m

12. Find the area of the shaded figure in the
given diagram.

17 cm, 17 cm, 20 cm, 10 cm, 12 cm, 12 cm

13. Under each figure below, the area is given.
Work out the values of *x*, *y* and *z*.

7 m, 7 m, *x* m

Area = 28 m²

15 cm, *y* cm, 20 cm

Area = 120 cm²

9 m, 8 m, *z* m, 4 m

Area = 60 m²

14. The shape on the right has been drawn on
centimetre dot paper.

Work out the area of this shaded shape.

15. Garry has seven tiles.
Each tile is a square of side 10 cm.

The tiles must be laid edge-to-edge, similar to that shown on the right.

   (i) How can Garry arrange the seven tiles so that the resulting
       shape has the greatest possible perimeter?
   (ii) How can Garry arrange the seven tiles so that the resulting
        shape has the smallest possible perimeter?

Section 6.2 Area of a parallelogram

A parallelogram is a figure in which the opposite
sides are both equal in length and parallel.

By cutting the parallelogram on the left above along the dotted line and then placing the
blue triangle at the other end, a rectangle is formed.

Area of rectangle = 6 cm × 3 cm = 18 cm²

∴   area of parallelogram is also 18 cm², i.e., 6 cm by 3 cm

Area of parallelogram is
   base × perpendicular height.

Area = $b \times h$

Area of this parallelogram

   = base × perpendicular height
   = 12 cm × 8 cm
   = 96 cm²

Exercise 6.2

1. Find the area of each of these parallelograms:

(i)

12 cm

20 cm

(ii)

7 cm

9 cm

(iii)

11 cm

15 cm

2. Work out the area of each of these parallelograms:

(i)

6 cm

10 cm

(ii)

7 cm

7.5 cm

9 cm

(iii)

6 cm

5 cm

7.5 cm

3. Write down the value of *h* in each of these parallelograms:

(i)

h

5 cm

Area = 30 cm²

(ii)

h

9 cm

Area = 63 cm²

(iii)

h

6 cm

Area = 27 cm²

4. Find the area of the parallelogram shown.

Now find the value of *x*.

18 cm

14 cm

x cm

22 cm

5. This design has been drawn on centimetre squared paper.

Calculate:

  (i) the total blue area

  (ii) the total yellow area

  (iii) the ratio of the blue area to the yellow area

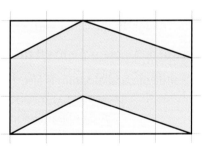

6. Calculate the missing length in each parallelogram:

(i)

7 cm

?

Area = 35 cm²

(ii)

?

12 cm

Area = 78 cm²

(iii)

?

9 cm

Area = 108 cm²

7. Work out the missing length in each parallelogram:

(i)

(ii)

(iii)

8. Work out the area of the given shaded parallelogram.
Hence find the measure of the perpendicular height, *h*.

9. Find the areas of the shaded parts of these figures:

(i)

(ii)

10. Work out the shaded area of the given rectangle
where arrows indicate parallel lines.

Section 6.3 Area and circumference of a circle

The circle on the right was drawn by placing the point of a compass at O.

The point O is called the **centre** of the circle.

The line that traces the circle is called the **circumference**.

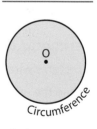

The terms that we will use when dealing with circles are given in the diagrams below:

Length of circumference

> Mark a point on the circumference of a 20 cent coin.
> Place the coin on the ruler with the mark pointing to the scale.
> Roll the coin along the ruler until the mark returns again to the scale.
> Read the length of the circumference from the ruler and you will find that it is a little more than three times the diameter.

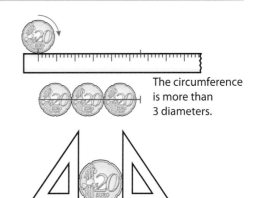

The circumference is more than 3 diameters.

The number by which we multiply the diameter is represented by the greek letter π (pronounced 'pie').

π has no exact decimal or fraction value.

However, when using decimals, we generally use 3.142 as an approximate value.

When using fractions, we use $\frac{22}{7}$ as an approximate value.

> **Approximate values for π**
>
> $\pi = 3.142$ or $\pi = \frac{22}{7}$

Circumference of a circle

> The length of the circumference of a circle is
> $$2\pi r \quad \text{or} \quad \pi d$$
> where $r = $ radius and $d = $ diameter

 The π key on your calculator gives a more exact value than 3.142 or $\frac{22}{7}$. When using your calculator, you should use this key unless told otherwise.

Perimeter of a sector

A sector is part of a circle that is bounded by two radii and an arc.

To find the arc length, ℓ, of a sector, we divide the angle in the sector by 360° to find a fraction.

Then we find this fraction of the circumference.

Length of arc:

$$\ell = \frac{\theta}{360°} \times 2\pi r$$

Example 1

Find the length of the circumference of this circle
using 3.142 as an approximation for π.

Circumference $= 2\pi r$
$$= 2 \times 3.142 \times 12$$
$$= 75.408 \text{ cm}$$
$$= 75.4 \text{ cm, correct to 1 decimal place}$$

12 cm

Example 2

The diagram on the right shows a sector of a circle of radius 21 cm.
Find the length of the perimeter of this figure.
Use $\frac{22}{7}$ as an approximation for π.

The perimeter consists of the arc AB and two radii.
$60° = \frac{1}{6}$ of 360°, so arc AB is $\frac{1}{6}$ of circumference.

Length of arc AB $= \frac{1}{6} \times 2\pi r$
$$= \frac{1}{6} \times \frac{2}{1} \times \frac{22}{7} \times \frac{21}{1}$$
$$= 22 \text{ cm}$$

Total perimeter $= 22 + 21 + 21 = 64 \text{ cm}$

Example 3

The length of the circumference of a circle is 120 cm.
Find the length of the radius of the circle, correct to 1 decimal place.

Circumference $= 2\pi r$
$$\therefore \quad 2\pi r = 120$$
$$r = \frac{120}{2\pi} = \frac{120}{2 \times \pi}$$
$$r = 19.099 \text{ cm} \quad \dots \text{ use } \pi \text{ key on calculator}$$
$$\text{radius} = 19.1 \text{ cm}$$

Calculator tip When using your calculator to find the value of $\dfrac{120}{2 \times \pi}$, enclose the denominator in brackets.

Key in [1] [2] [0] [÷] [(] [2] [×] [π] [)] [=]

The area of a circle

If the 12 sectors of the circle below are cut neatly, they can be formed into a 'rectangle', as shown.

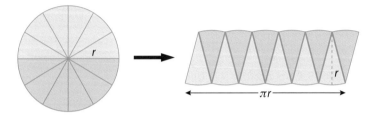

Explain why the length of the rectangle is πr and its height is r.

What is the area of the rectangle?

Explain why the area of the circle is πr^2.

Area of circle $= \pi r^2$ Area of sector $= \dfrac{\theta}{360} \times \pi r^2$

Example 4

(i) Find the area of a circle of radius 14 cm. (Take $\pi = \frac{22}{7}$)

(ii) Find the radius of a circle of area 1386 cm².
Use the π key on your calculator and give your answer correct to the nearest whole number.

(i) Area $= \pi r^2$

$\qquad = \dfrac{22}{7} \times 14^2$

$\qquad = \dfrac{22}{1\cancel{7}} \times \overset{2}{\cancel{14}} \times 14$

$\qquad = 616 \text{ cm}^2$

(ii) $\pi r^2 = 1386$

$\qquad r^2 = \dfrac{1386}{\pi}$

$\qquad r^2 = 441.178$

$\qquad r = \sqrt{441.178} = 21.004$

$\qquad r = 21 \text{ cm}$

Exercise 6.3

1. Name the feature shown, in red, on each circle.

(i)　　　　　　　(ii)　　　　　　　(iii)　　　　　　　(iv)

(v)　　　　　　　(vi)　　　　　　　(vii)　　　　　　　(viii)

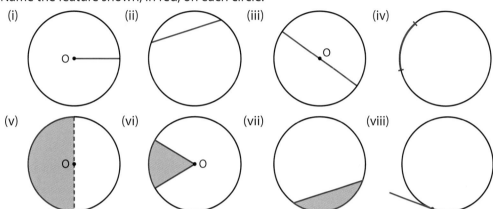

2. Calculate the circumference of each of these circles, using $\pi = 3.14$.

(i)　　　　　　　(ii)　　　　　　　(iii)　　　　　　　(iv)

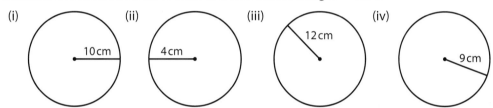

    10 cm　　　　4 cm　　　　12 cm　　　　9 cm

3. Using the approximation $\pi = \frac{22}{7}$, find the circumference of each circle:

(i)　　　　　　　(ii)　　　　　　　(iii)　　　　　　　(iv)

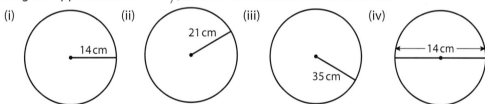

    14 cm　　　21 cm　　　35 cm　　　14 cm

4. Using the approximation $\pi = \frac{22}{7}$, find the area of each circle in Question **3.** above.

5. Use the π key on your calculator to find (a) the area and (b) the perimeter of each of these circles.
Give each answer correct to 1 decimal place.

(i)　　　　　　　(ii)　　　　　　　(iii)　　　　　　　(iv)

    8 cm　　　21 cm　　　11 cm　　　18 cm

6. Using 3.14 as an approximate value for π, calculate the lengths of the circumferences of these circles.

   (i) radius = 13 cm　　　(ii) diameter = 30 cm　　　(iii) radius = 40 cm

7. What fraction of the area of a complete circle is each of these sectors?

(i)   (ii)   (iii)   (iv)

8. Find the length of the arc AB in each of these sectors, taking $\pi = \frac{22}{7}$.

(i)   (ii)   (iii)

9. Using $\pi = \frac{22}{7}$, find the area of each of the sectors in Question **8.** above.

10. Find the perimeters of these shapes, taking $\pi = \frac{22}{7}$.

(i)   (ii)   (iii)

11. Using $\pi = 3.14$, find the area of each of these shapes.

(i)   (ii)   (iii)

Give each answer correct to one place of decimals.

12. A running track is in the shape of a rectangle with semicircular ends, as shown on the right.
Calculate the length of the track. Take $\pi = \frac{22}{7}$.

How many laps would an athlete have to complete in a 10 000 metre race?

13. Taking $\pi = 3.14$, find
   (i) the perimeter
  (ii) the area of the given coloured figure.

Give each answer correct to one decimal place.

14. The area of each circle below is given in terms of π.
Find the length of the radius of each circle.

(i)

Area = 25π cm^2

(ii)

Area = 121π cm^2

(iii)

Area = 169π cm^2

15. The area of a circle is 154 cm^2. Taking $\pi = \frac{22}{7}$, find

(i) the length of the radius

(ii) the length of the circumference.

16. Stephen has a counter device on his bike.
It counts the number of revolutions his wheel has made.
His wheels are 40 cm in diameter.

(i) Stephen cycles to his grandmother's house.
The counter reads 1989.
How far away does his grandmother live?

(ii) How many revolutions does his wheel have to make to travel 1 km?

Give each answer correct to the nearest whole number.

17. Which is the shorter path from A to B

(i) along the 4 semicircles, or

(ii) along the larger semicircle ?

A ⋯⋯⋯⋯⋯⋯⋯⋯⋯ B

├───8 m───┤

18. Taking $\pi = \frac{22}{7}$, find the area of the shaded
portion of the given figure.

7 cm

19. The quadrant shown is cut from a circle of centre O.

(i) Find the area of $\triangle$OAB.

(ii) Find the area of the shaded region,
taking $\pi = \frac{22}{7}$.

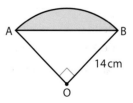

A ◀──────▶ B

14 cm

O

20. To water this rectangular field, a gardener
   uses eleven identical sprinklers, which cover
   the blue areas shown on the diagram.
   The three sprinklers in the middle of the field
   cover circular areas; the four sprinklers on the
   sides cover semi-circular areas; and the four
   sprinklers at the corners cover quadrant areas.

   (i)   What is the radius of each circle?
   (ii) What is the total (blue) area watered by
         the sprinklers?
   (iii) Find, correct to the nearest whole number, the percentage of the lawn that
         is watered.

21. A car with a rectangular rear windscreen (160 cm long
   and 80 cm wide) has one large wiper of length 75 cm.
   The wiper covers the shaded area in the diagram on
   the right. What percentage of the windscreen area
   is **not** cleaned by the wiper?
   Give your answer to the nearest whole number.

22. Alan and Billy raced each other around
   this athletics track. Alan ran along the
   outside perimeter while Billy ran along
   the inside perimeter. After one lap of
   the track, who had run the longer
   distance, and by how much?
   Answer correct to the nearest metre.

Section 6.4 Rectangular solids

The figure on the right is a **rectangular solid** (or **cuboid**).
The space occupied by this solid is called its **volume**.

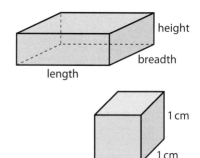

The solid on the right is called a **cube** because its length,
breadth and height are all equal.

Its volume is **1 cm³**, pronounced **one cubic centimetre**.

The figure on the right is made
up of three layers of cubes.
In each layer there are 24 cubes.
In the three layers there are 72 cubes.
From this we can see that the
volume is found by multiplying the
length by the breadth by the height.

Volume = 6 cm × 4 cm × 3 cm = 72 cm³

> Volume of rectangular solid = length × breadth × height

Surface area of rectangular solid

The given solid shows three faces A, B and C.
The three faces that we cannot see are also A, B and C.

Area of A = 5 cm × 4 cm = 20 cm²
Area of B = 3 cm × 4 cm = 12 cm²
Area of C = 5 cm × 3 cm = 15 cm²
∴ Surface area of solid = 2 × 20 cm² + 2 × 12 cm² + 2 × 15 cm²
= 40 cm² + 24 cm² + 30 cm² = 94 cm²

*Surface area
of rectangular
solid*

> The surface area of a rectangular solid of length ℓ, breadth b
> and height h is
>
> $$2\ell b + 2\ell h + 2bh$$

*Volume and
surface area
of a cube*

> Volume = $\ell \times \ell \times \ell = \ell^3$
>
> Surface area = $6\ell^2$

Example 1

Find (i) the volume   (ii) the surface area
of the given rectangular solid.

(i) Volume = $\ell \times b \times h$
= 11 cm × 7 cm × 8 cm = 616 cm³
(ii) Surface area = $2\ell b + 2\ell h + 2bh$
= 2(11 cm × 7 cm) + 2(11 cm × 8 cm) + 2(7 cm × 8 cm)
= 154 cm² + 176 cm² + 112 cm² = 442 cm²

Example 2

The volume of the rectangular box shown is 2156 cm³.
Find the length of the side marked x.

$$\text{Volume} = \text{length} \times \text{breadth} \times \text{height}$$

$$\therefore \quad 2156 \text{ cm}^3 = 22 \text{ cm} \times x \times 7 \text{ cm}$$

$$154x = 2156$$

$$x = \frac{2156}{154} = 14$$

The side marked x is 14 cm.

Nets of solids

If the figure on the left above was folded along the dotted lines, it would form the cube shown on the right.

The figure on the left is called the **net** of the solid.

On the left below is the net of a closed rectangular box.

On the right is the net of an open rectangular box.

A net for a cube was shown above.

Here are two more nets for a cube.

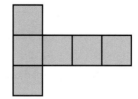

There are 11 possible different nets of a cube.

Example 3

By drawing a net of this closed rectangular box, find its total surface area.

The net for the box is shown below.

Total surface area

$= 60 + 60 + 50 + 50 + 30 + 30$

$= 280 \text{ cm}^2$

Example 4

This is the net of an open box.
If this net is folded along the dotted lines to make a box, find
  (i) the volume of the box
  (ii) the surface area of the outside of the box.

  (i) This is the box that is formed from the net.

  Volume $= 14 \times 8 \times 3$

  $= 336 \text{ cm}^3$

  (ii) Surface area $= 2(14 \times 3) + 2(8 \times 3) + (14 \times 8)$ … no top on box

  $= 84 + 48 + 112 = 244 \text{ cm}^2$

Capacity – the litre

The capacity of a container is the amount of liquid it can hold.
The most commonly-used metric measure of capacity is the **litre**.
A cube with edge of length 10 cm contains 1 litre.

  $\therefore$ $1000 \text{ cm}^3 = 1$ litre

Remember   To convert cubic centimetres (cm³) to litres, divide by 1000.

101

Exercise 6.4

1. Find the volume of each of these rectangular solids:

(i)
2 cm
2 cm
3 cm

(ii)
2 cm
3 cm
5 cm

(iii)
3 cm
3 cm
7 cm

2. Find the surface area of each of the solids in Question **1.** above.

3. Find (a) the volume (b) the surface area of these solid cuboids:

(i)
16 cm
18 cm
8 cm

(ii)
24 cm
20 cm
16 cm

(iii)
3 m
12 m
10 m

4. The diagram shows a rectangular box partly filled with cubes of side 1 cm.
How many more of these cubes are required to fill the box?

4 cm
6 cm
4 cm

5. Five cubes of side 2 cm are joined to make the solid shown.
Which of the following is the surface area of the solid?

(i) 68 cm² (ii) 72 cm² (iii) 20 cm² (iv) 88 cm²

6. Each of the solid shapes below can be broken into two or more rectangular solids.
The dotted lines indicate how the figures may be divided.
Now find the total volume of each of these shapes:

(i)
6 cm
5 cm
5 cm
14 cm
9 cm

(ii)
6 cm
3 cm
2 cm
4 cm
4 cm
8 cm
14 cm

(iii)
10 cm
4 cm
7 cm
9 cm
7 cm
4 cm

7. The framing of a toolshed consists of square, galvanised tubing which costs €12.80 a metre. Find the total cost of the tubing necessary to make the framing of the shed illustrated.

2 m
3 m
4 m

8. The figure on the right shows a stack of cubes of side 3 cm.

    Find   (i) the volume of the stack in cm³
            (ii) the surface area of the stack in cm².

9. The volume of each of the following rectangular solids is given. Find the length of the side marked with a letter.

(i)

3 cm
a   8 cm
Volume = 120 cm³

(ii)

b
6 m   10 m
Volume = 420 m³

(iii)

8 cm
c
14 cm
Volume = 2240 cm³

10. The surface area of this cube is 150 cm².

    Find   (i) the length of the side of the cube
            (ii) the volume of the cube.

11. Hannah is packing packets of soap powder into a box, as shown.

    (i) How many will fit along the 30 cm side?
    (ii) How many packets of soap powder will fit in the box altogether?

30 cm   24 cm   28 cm
4 cm   SOAP POWDER   SOAP POWDER
5 cm   6 cm

12. The volume of a cube is 64 cm³.

    Find   (i) the length of the side of the cube
            (ii) the surface area of the cube.

13. This is the net of a rectangular box.

Find   (i) the surface area of the box

        (ii) the volume of the box.

14. A square sheet of metal has a side of length 30 cm.
Four identical squares of side 4 cm are cut away
from the corners, as shown.
The remaining shape is folded to form a box.

  (i) Is the box an open or closed box?

 (ii) Find the volume of the box.

(iii) Find the outer surface area of the box.

15. The net on the right folds to make a rectangular box.
The rectangle that is shaded blue is the base.

  (i) What is the height of the box?

 (ii) The volume of the box is 84 cm³.
      Find the value of x.

(iii) Find the surface area of the box.

16. This net is folded to make a cube.

  (i) Which vertex will join to N?

 (ii) Which line will join to [CD]?

(iii) Which line will join to [IH]?

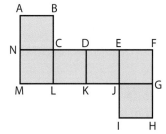

17. The net shown is folded to make a rectangular box.
The pink rectangle will be the base of the box.

  (i) Write down the height of the box.

 (ii) Is the box open or closed?

(iii) Find the volume of the box.

(iv) Work out the surface area of the box.

18. Here are nets of a cube.

A

	1	
2	3	4
	5	
	6	

B

5			
4	1	2	3
6			

C

1			
2	3	4	5
			6

Imagine that each of these nets is folded to make a cube.
For each net, which face would be opposite face 1 when folded?

19. This is the net of a cube of side x cm.
The volume of the cube is numerically equal to the
surface area of the cube.
Write an equation in x and solve it to find the length
of the side of the cube.

x cm

20. If 1 litre $=$ 1000 cm^3, find the capacity of these rectangular containers in litres.

(i)

20 cm
20 cm
15 cm

(ii)

8 cm
10 cm
20 cm

(iii)

30 cm
15 cm
15 cm

21. The rectangular container on the right has a capcity
of 4.8 litres.

(i) Write down the volume of the container in cm^3.
(ii) Find the height h of the container in centimetres.

h
30 cm
20 cm

Section 6.5 Prisms

In the rectangular solid shown, vertical slices parallel
to the front face will all be the same size and shape.
We say that solids like this are solids of **uniform
cross-section**. The cross-section in this case is a triangle.

solid   cross-section

A solid figure with the same cross-section along its length is called a **prism**.

The following solids are all prisms. The cross-sections are shaded.

  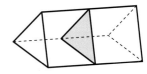

The solid on the right is not a prism because the cross-sections are not uniform.

The figure on the right is a **right prism**.

Its top face is vertically above its base and its sides are rectangles.

Volume of a prism

Volume of a prism = area of cross-section × length
$$= A \times \ell$$

Example 1

Find the area of the triangular cross-section of this prism.
Hence find the volume of the prism.

Area of cross-section $= \frac{1}{2} bh$
$$= \frac{1}{2} \times 8 \times 6 = 24 \text{ cm}^2$$

Volume = Area of cross-section × length
$$= 24 \text{ cm}^2 \times 10 \text{ cm}$$

Volume $= 240 \text{ cm}^3$

$A = \frac{1}{2} bh$

Surface area of a prism

The surface area of a prism is the sum of the areas of its faces.

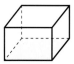

Example 2

Find the total surface area of this triangular
prism by using its net.

A net of the prism is shown.

$A_1 = \frac{1}{2} \times 12 \times 5 = 30 \text{ cm}^2$
$A_2 = 7 \times 5 = 35 \text{ cm}^2$
$A_3 = 12 \times 7 = 84 \text{ cm}^2$
$A_4 = 13 \times 7 = 91 \text{ cm}^2$

Total surface area $= 2 \times A_1 + A_2 + A_3 + A_4$
$= 2 \times 30 + 35 + 84 + 91$
$= 270 \text{ cm}^2$

The net of the given triangular
prism is shown on the right.

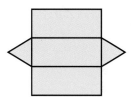

Exercise 6.5

1. The areas of the cross-sections of these prisms are given.
   Find the volume of each prism.

   (i)

   66 cm² 32 cm

   (ii)

   9 cm 124 cm²

   (iii)

   52 cm² 3 cm

2. (i) What is the area of the shaded cross-section
   of this triangular prism?

   (ii) What is the volume of the prism?

   7 cm 9 cm 8 cm

3. The cross-section of this prism is a right-angled triangle. Work out the volume of this prism.

4. Work out the volume of each of these prisms:

(i)

(ii)

(iii)

(iv)

(v)

(vi)

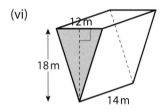

5. (i) How many faces has this prism?

(ii) How many faces are triangular in shape?

(iii) Work out the total surface area of the prism.

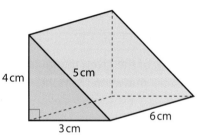

6. Find the total surface area of each of these prisms.

(i)

(ii)

(iii)

7. Find the total surface areas of these prisms:

(i)

(ii)

(iii)

8. Find (a) the volume (b) the surface area of each of these prisms:

(i)

12 m   20 m

5 m   16 m

(ii)

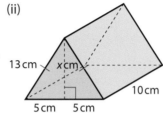

13 m

12 m

9 m

5 m

(iii)

15.5 m

15.5 m   15 m

5 m

9 m

9. In each of the following questions, use Pythagoras' Theorem to calculate the unknown length, x, and then calculate the surface area.

(i)

3 cm x cm

6 cm

4 cm

(ii)

13 cm x cm

10 cm

5 cm   5 cm

Pythagoras' Theorem

a c

b

$$c^2 = a^2 + b^2$$

10. Caroline manufactures tents, as shown on the right.

  (i) Find the surface area of the tent, including the floor.

  (ii) Caroline buys material at €20 per square metre. How much does it cost Caroline for the material to make a tent? Give your answer correct to the nearest €10.

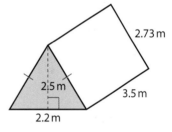

2.73 m

2.5 m

3.5 m

2.2 m

11. This is the net of a triangular prism.

  Find   (i) the volume of the prism

         (ii) the surface area of the prism.

7 cm

5.7 cm

8 cm

7 cm

18 cm

12. This is a triangular prism.
The ends of the prism are equilateral triangles.

  (i) Draw a rectangle 7 cm by 4 cm in the middle of a sheet of paper.

  (ii) Use this rectangle to complete an accurate net for this prism.

4 cm   7 cm

13. Here are four pictures of the same cube.

Which shapes are opposite each other?

14. This is the net of a cube.

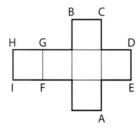

When the net is folded to make a cube, which two other vertices meet at A?

15. This is the net of a 3-D object.

(i) When this net is folded, describe the figure it will make.

(ii) If the volume of the figure is 378 cm³, find the value of x.

Section 6.6 Scale drawing

In everyday life, people such as architects and engineers make scale drawings of buildings and bridges. Builders must then be able to read and understand them so that the structures can be built properly.

> Scale drawings have the same shapes as the objects that they represent but they are of different sizes.

> The scale of a drawing is length of drawing : real length.
  A scale of 1 : 100 means that the real size is 100 times the size of the drawing.

> The scale determines the size of the drawing.
  A 1 : 10 scale drawing would be bigger than a 1 : 100 scale drawing of the same object.

Here is a scale drawing of a clock.

The scale is 1 : 6.

The drawing is 5 cm by 5 cm.

The actual length of the clock is 5 cm × 6
$$= 30 \text{ cm}$$

Accordingly, the actual dimensions of the clock
are 30 cm by 30 cm.

Scale 1 : 6

Example 1

Part of a house plan drawn to a
scale of 1 : 100 is shown.

Bedroom 1 is 5 cm by 5 cm on the plan.

  (i) Find the actual length of the
      bedroom in metres.

(ii) The kitchen in the house is
      6.5 metres by 4.8 metres.
      What are the dimensions of the
      kitchen in the drawing?

5 cm

Bedroom 1

5 cm

  (i) On the plan, 1 cm = 100 cm ... 1:100 scale
              5 cm = 500 cm
                   = 5 metres.
      The length of the bedroom is 5 metres.

(ii) The kitchen is 6.5 m by 4.8 m or 650 cm by 480 cm.
      Since the scale is 1 : 100, we divide 650 cm and 480 cm by 100 to find the
      dimensions in the plan.
$$\text{Dimensions in the plan} = \frac{650}{100} \text{ cm by } \frac{480}{100} \text{ cm}$$
$$= 6.5 \text{ cm by } 4.8 \text{ cm}$$

Example 2

The scale on a map is 1 : 100 000.

  (i) Find the distance in kilometres between two towns which are 7 cm apart on
      the map.

(ii) Two train stations are 25 km apart.
      How many centimetres are they apart on the map?

(i) Scale $= 1 : 100\,000$

$\therefore\quad 1\,\text{cm} = 100\,000\,\text{cm}$

$7\,\text{cm} = 700\,000\,\text{cm}$

$= \dfrac{700\,000}{100}\ \text{metres} = 7000\,\text{m} = 7\,\text{km}$

The towns are 7 km apart.

(ii) $25\,\text{km} = \dfrac{25}{100\,000}\ \text{km on the map}$

$= \dfrac{25 \times 1000}{100\,000}\ \text{metres}$

$= \dfrac{25}{100}\,\text{m} = 0.25\,\text{m} = 25\,\text{cm}$

The train stations are 25 cm apart on the map.

Exercise 6.6

1. Express each of the following in the form $1 : n$, where $n \in N$.

    (i) 1 cm to 40 cm   (ii) 1 cm to 1 metre   (iii) 1 cm to 600 m

    (iv) 5 cm to 100 m   (v) 10 cm to 1 km   (vi) 1 mm to 10 m

2. Use the scales given to find the indicated heights of the animals below:

    $1 : 30$ $1 : 90$ $1 : 45$

3. The scale on a building plan is $1 : 100$.

    Find the actual lengths in the building that are represented on the plan by:

    (i) 5 cm   (ii) 11 cm   (iii) 8.5 cm   (iv) 14.8 cm

4. Find the actual lengths of the following lines on a building plan for which the scale is given:

    (i) 2 cm, scale is $1 : 300$ (ii) 5 cm, scale is $1 : 400$

    (iii) 8 cm, scale is $1 : 500$ (iv) 1.8 cm, scale is $1 : 200$

    (v) 3.6 cm, scale is $1 : 800$ (vi) $5\tfrac{3}{4}$ cm, scale is $1 : 250$

5. This is the scale drawing of a lorry.
The scale is 1 : 100.
Measure the length of this drawing
and hence write down the actual
length of the lorry.
Find also the maximum height of the lorry.

Scale 1:100

6. A walking map has a scale of 1 : 25 000.

   (i) Find the actual distance for each of these scaled distances:
     (a) 2 cm   (b) 5 cm   (c) 8.5 cm   (d) 6.75 cm

  (ii) Find the distances on the map for these actual distances:
     (a) 10 km   (b) 4 km   (c) 6.5 km   (d) 12.75 km

7. A map has a scale of 1 : 500 000.

   (i) The distance between two service stations
     on the map is 3.4 cm.
     What is the actual distance?

  (ii) The next emergency phone is 22 km away.
     How many centimetres would this be on the map?

8. A surveyor needs to draw an accurate
plan of this awkwardly-shaped field.
The scale he will use is 1 cm = 10 m.

   (i) What lengths will these lines have on the plan?
     (a) [AB]   (b) [BC]

  (ii) Construct an accurate scale drawing of this field
     using the given scale.

9. The scale on a map is 5 cm to 2 km. Express this in the form 1 : n.
Find also the distance in cm on the map between two towns, A and B, which are in
reality 30 km apart.

10. A girl made this scale drawing to calculate
the height, |AB|, of a triangular wall.

   (i) Measure the distance |CB| on the scale drawing
     and calculate the scale of the drawing.

  (ii) By measurement and calculation,
     find the real height |AB|.

 (iii) Find the area of this triangular wall.

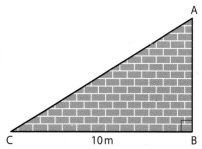

Test yourself 6

1. (a) Find the area of the figure shown on the right.

(b) The volume of the given solid is 1320 cm³. Find the height h of the solid.

(c) Find   (i) the volume

(ii) the total surface area of the given triangular prism.

2. (a) Taking $\pi = 3.14$, find the area of the sector shown.

(b) Find the area of the given parallelogram. Hence find the value of h.

(c) This cuboid can be made from a piece of card shaped like this.

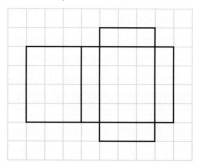

If each square on the grid for the net is 3 cm in length, find
- (i) the volume of the cuboid
- (ii) the total surface area of the cuboid.

3. (a) The given figure consists of a square and a semicircle.
Taking $\pi = 3.14$, find correct to 1 decimal place,

- (i) the area of the figure
- (ii) the perimeter of the figure.

(b) (i) A $1:50$ scale model of a yacht is to be built.
If the yacht is 25 m long, how long will the model yacht be?
- (ii) A scale drawing is to be made of a car.
If the car is 6.25 m long and the model is to be 25 cm long, what should the scale be?

(c) (i) Show that prisms Ⓐ and Ⓑ have the same volume.

- (ii) Find the surface area of each prism.
Are the surface areas the same?

- (iii) Prism Ⓑ represents a large tent (with a floor) made of canvas.
Find the cost of the canvas used if each square metre of canvas costs €24.50.

4. (a) The diagram shows a quadrant, AOB, of a circle of radius 14 cm.

Taking $\pi = \frac{22}{7}$, find the area of the shaded portion of the figure.

(b) The figure shown is made from two identical overlapping rectangles which are 20 cm long and 15 cm wide.
Calculate the area of the figure.

(c) When the minute-hand of a clock moves through an angle of 75°, it covers an area of 88 cm². What is the length of the minute-hand?
Give your answer correct to 2 decimal places and use the π key on your calculator.

5. (a) Find the total length of ribbon used to tie a box as illustrated. 15 cm extra is required for the knot and bow.

10 cm

15 cm

20 cm

(b) A map has a scale of 1 : 25 000.

   (i) What is the actual distance if the scaled distance is 4 cm?

   (ii) What is the scaled distance if the actual distance is 3.5 km?

(c) The volume of this prism is 245 cm^3.
Find the value of k.

5 cm

k cm

7 cm

6. (a) A farmer wants to sell his field. He wants more than €24 per square metre.
Mr Dunne offers him a total of €90 000 for the field.
Should the farmer accept this offer?
Give an explanation for your answer.

104 m

39 m

56 m

23 m

(b) The net shown will fold to make a prism.

Describe fully the prism it will make.

Now find (i) the volume

           (ii) the surface area of the prism.

1.7 cm

2 cm   2 cm

2 cm   2 cm

2 cm

4 cm

2 cm   2 cm

(c) The large circle has an area of 129 cm^2.

What is the area of the shaded region?

Give your answer correct to one decimal place.

Statistics 2 – Averages and Spread

Key words

average   mean   mode   median   outlier   frequency distribution
grouped frequency distribution   mid-interval value   range   variability
upper quartile   lower quartile   interquartile range

Section 7.1 Averages – Mode and Median

When we collect data such as the numbers of hours our classmates spend watching television each week or the ages of people living in an apartment block, one of the first things we would like to find is an **average**.

When we look for an average, we are trying to find a **single or typical value** that will represent the many values we have collected.

The idea of an average is extremely useful because it enables us to compare one set of data with another by comparing just two values, namely their averages.

There are several ways of expressing an average, but the most commonly-used averages are the **mode**, the **median** and the **mean**.

1. The Mode

The **mode** is the most common value in a set of data. The mode is very useful when one value appears much more often than any other. It is easy to find and can be used for non-numerical data such as the colours of cars sold by a garage.

> **Example 1**
>
> The ages of students on a school bus are:
>
> $$12, \ 15, \ 12, \ 13, \ 14, \ 16, \ 15, \ 11, \ 12$$
> $$16, \ 15, \ 16, \ 14, \ 10, \ 13, \ 17, \ 15, \ 17$$
>
> Placing these in order we get:
>
> $$10, \ 11, \ 12, \ 12, \ 12, \ 13, \ 13, \ 14, \ 14, \ 15, \ 15, \ 15, \ 15, \ 16, \ 16, \ 16, \ 17, \ 17$$
>
> The number in this list with the greatest frequency is 15.
>
> ∴   the mode = 15

2. The Median

To find the median of a list of numbers, put the numbers in order of size, starting with the smallest. The **median** is the middle number.

Example 2

(i) Find the median age of the Byrne family whose members' ages are:

$$19 \quad 31 \quad 21 \quad 3 \quad 6 \quad 14 \quad 19 \quad 24 \quad 11$$

(ii) Find the median of the following scores:

$$62 \quad 64 \quad 81 \quad 68 \quad 95 \quad 57$$

(i) Arrange the values in ascending order:

$$\underbrace{3 \quad 6 \quad 11 \quad 14}_{\text{4 values}} \Big| \overset{\uparrow}{19} \Big| \underbrace{19 \quad 21 \quad 24 \quad 31}_{\text{4 values}}$$

Since there are nine values, the middle one is the fifth value.
The median age is 19 years.

(ii) Arrange the six scores in order:

$$\underbrace{57 \quad 62 \quad 64}_{\text{3 values}} \overset{\uparrow}{\Big|} \underbrace{68 \quad 81 \quad 95}_{\text{3 values}}$$

Now there are two middle scores, 64 and 68.

Take the average of 64 and 68:

$$\frac{64 + 68}{2} = \frac{132}{2} = 66$$

The median is 66.

> There will always be two middle scores when there is an even number of scores.

Note:
> The median depends on the **number** of scores in the data set, but not the actual scores themselves.

> In a set with an **odd number** of scores, the median will always be one of the scores.

> In a set with an **even number** of scores, the median is the average of the two middle scores.

Exercise 7.1

1. Write down the mode of these sets of data:

   (i) 15, 12, 16, 19, 12, 14, 16, 12   (ii) 67, 43, 89, 45, 54, 86, 45, 76, 53

   (iii) 5.6, 5.4, 5.7, 5.5, 5.7, 5.6, 5.7   (iv) 3, 3, 7, 8, 7, 9, 8, 5, 7, 11, 12

   (v) bus, car, bus, walk, car, bus, cycle, car, bus, bus, walk, cycle, car, walk, bus

   (vi) $\frac{1}{2}, \frac{1}{4}, \frac{3}{4}, \frac{1}{4},$ 1, $\frac{1}{4}, \frac{3}{4},$ 1, 0, $\frac{1}{4},$ 0, $\frac{1}{4}, \frac{3}{4}, \frac{1}{2},$ 1, $\frac{1}{4}, \frac{1}{2}$

2. The mode of these numbers is 5. Find the value of *.

2, 3, 7, 5, 2, 6, *, 5, 3

3. Rewrite the following array of numbers in order of size:

3, 3, 7, 8, 7, 9, 8, 5, 7, 11, 12

Now write down   (i) the mode   (ii) the median.

4. Rearrange the following marks in order and then write down the median in each case.

(i) 9, 5, 8, 3, 2, 7, 6   (ii) 8, 12, 18, 9, 14, 7, 10, 6

5. A rugby team played 10 games.
Here are the numbers of points the team scored.

12, 22, 14, 11, 7, 18, 22, 14, 36, 14

(i) Write down the mode.
(ii) What is the median number of points scored?

6. Work out
(i) the mode
(ii) the median   for this set of data.

5, 7, 9, 9, 8, 7, 9, 10, 12, 11, 9, 9, 5

7. In this set of data, the mode is 9.

7, 4, 3, 3, 12, 9, x, 10, 9

(i) Find the value of x.
(ii) What is the median of the set?

8. Matthew's marks in eight tests are shown below.
What mark did he score in the ninth test if his median mark was then 6?

5   9   7   3   7   4   5   8

9. The hourly pay rates for 10 workers are as follows:

€12.40, €14.80, €10, €9.20, €14.20, €12.30, €15, €11.80, €15.20, €13.20.

Find the median hourly rate.

10. The following set of data has 2 modes.

2, 3, 4, 4, 5, 6, 7, 8, $a + 1$, 4, 3, 5

What are the possible values of a?

11. Joana did a survey to find the shoe sizes of pupils in her mixed class.
The bar chart illustrates her data.

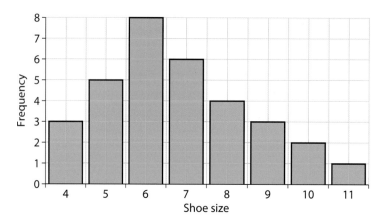

(i) How many pupils are there in Joana's class?
(ii) What is the modal shoe size?
(iii) Can you tell from the bar chart which are the boys or which are the girls in her class?
(iv) Joana then decided to draw a bar chart to show the shoe sizes of the boys and the girls separately. Do you think that the mode for the boys and the mode for the girls will be the same as the mode for the whole class? Explain your answer.

Section 7.2 The Mean

The **mean** of the numbers

  4, 5, 7, 9, 10

$$\text{Mean} = \frac{\text{Sum of the numbers}}{\text{Number of numbers}}$$

is the sum of these numbers divided by the number of numbers.

$\therefore \qquad \text{Mean} = \dfrac{4 + 5 + 7 + 9 + 10}{5} = \dfrac{35}{5} = 7$

In everyday language, the word 'average' is generally used instead of 'mean'.
The mean is a very important value in statistics as it takes into account all the values in the set of data.

Example 1

In five basketball matches, Joan scored 16 points, 10 points, 22 points, 18 points and 24 points. Calculate her mean score for the five matches.

$$\text{Mean} = \frac{16 + 10 + 22 + 18 + 24}{5} = \frac{90}{5} = 18$$

Example 2

The mean of four numbers is 7.
When a fifth number is added, the mean of the five numbers is 9.
Find the fifth number.

If the mean of four numbers is 7, then the sum of the four numbers is
4×7, i.e. 28.
The mean of five numbers $= 9 \Rightarrow$ sum of the five numbers $= 45$

$\therefore$ the fifth number $= 45 - 28$

$= 17$

Extreme values

Here are the marks scored by six pupils in a maths test:

26, 35, 34, 46, 52, 95

The mean mark is

$$\frac{26 + 35 + 34 + 46 + 52 + 95}{6} = \frac{288}{6} = 48$$

Notice that four out of the six pupils are below the mean mark.

This is caused by one mark, i.e. 95, which is much higher than all the other marks.

Such a mark is generally known as an **outlier** or **extreme value**.
When an outlier exists, the mean may not fully or accurately represent the set of data given.
This happens, in particular, when the number of data items is small.

Example 3

The mean of 10, 7, 3, 6, x is 8. Find the value of x.

There are 5 scores.

$\therefore$ $\dfrac{10 + 7 + 3 + 6 + x}{5} = 8$

$\dfrac{26 + x}{5} = 8$

$26 + x = 40$

$x = 40 - 26$

$x = 14$

Exercise 7.2

1. Find the mean of each of these arrays of numbers:
   (i) 2, 4, 5, 6, 8
   (ii) 14, 17, 21, 13, 6, 13
   (iii) 1, 0, 5, 7, 17, 12
   (iv) 19, 12, 6, 18, 40, 18, 5, 40

2. Ava's marks in six subjects were 47, 68, 62, 76, 59 and 54.
   Find her mean mark.

3. A snooker player scored 208 points in 8 visits to the table.
   What was his average number of points per visit?

4. The mean of six numbers is 14. Find the sum of the six numbers.

5. The mean of four numbers is 9.
   (i) What is the sum of the four numbers?
   (ii) If three of the numbers are 6, 11 and 14, find the fourth.

6. The three sides of this triangle have a
   mean length of 10 cm.
   Find the length of the side [AC].

7. The mean of three numbers is 8. When a fourth number is added, the mean is 9. Find
   the fourth number.

8. In the first three frames of a snooker match, a player got a mean score of 27.
   In the fourth frame he scored 19. Find his mean score for the four frames.

9. The mean of seven numbers is 12.
   One of the numbers is removed. Find its value if
   (i) the mean of the remaining numbers is reduced to 11.
   (ii) the mean of the remaining numbers is unchanged.
   (iii) the mean of the remaining numbers is increased to 14.

10. The mean price of five packets of biscuits is €1.80.
    The prices of two of the packets are €2.10 and €1.71.
    The other three packets are all the same price. Find this price.

11. Find the mean of these numbers: 1, 4, 7, 8, 10.
    Now increase each number by 4.
    Find the mean of these new numbers.
    What have you noticed?
    Now multiply each of the given numbers above by 5 and find their mean.
    What effect has multiplication by 5 had on the mean?

12. Write down five numbers so that the mode is 4, the mean is 6 and the median is 5.

☐ ☐ ☐ ☐ ☐

13. The mean height of a group of eight students is 165 cm.
   (i) What is the total height of all eight students?

   A ninth student joins the group. He is 168 cm tall.
   (ii) What is the mean height of all nine students?

14. The numbers 4, 8, 12, 17, x are arranged in order of size.
   If the mean of the numbers is equal to the median, find x.

15.   (i) The mean of 3, 7, 8, 10 and x is 6. Find x.
         (ii) The mean of   1, k, 3, 6 and 8 is 7. Find k.

16. The mean of five numbers is 39.
   Two of the numbers are 103 and 35 and each of the other three numbers is equal to x.

   Find   (i) the total of the five numbers
            (ii) the value of x.

17. Nicky's marks in four tests were:

         8, 4, 5, 3

   What mark did she get in her fifth and sixth tests if her modal mark was 4 and her mean mark was 5 after the six tests?

18. Here are two sets of data:

   (A)   19   31   21   3   6   14   19   24   11
   (B)   19   31   21   3   6   14   19   24   91

   (i)   Calculate the mean (to one decimal place) of each set.
   (ii) What is the only difference between the two sets of data?
   (iii) What effect does the difference identified in part (ii) have on the mean?

19. A basketball team scored 43, 55, 41 and 37 points in their first four matches.
   (i)   What is the mean number of points scored for the first four matches?
   (ii) What score will the team need to shoot in the next match so that they maintain the same mean score?
   (iii) The team shoots only 24 points in the fifth match. What is the mean number of points scored for the five matches?
   (iv) The team shoots 41 points in their sixth and final match. Will this increase or decrease their previous mean score? What is the mean score for all six matches?

20. Jane had seven spelling tests, each with twelve words, but could only find the results of five of them.

These were: 9, 5, 7, 9 and 10.

She asked her teacher for the other two results and the teacher said that the score which occurred most frequently was 9 and the mean was 8.

What are the two missing results, given that Jane knows that her worst result was a 5?

21. On four tests, each marked out of 100, my mean score was 85. What is the lowest mark I could have scored on any one test?

Section 7.3 Which average to use?

The three averages – the **mean**, the **mode** and the **median** – are all useful but depending on the data, one may be more suitable than the others.

We try to select the 'average' that is most representative of a set of data.

If you use the wrong average, your results may lead to an incorrect conclusion.

The mode   The **mode** is useful in situations where you want to know for example,
> which dress size is the most common
> which brand of dog food is most popular.

The mean   The **mean** is useful for finding a 'typical' value when most of the data is closely grouped. The mean may not give a typical value if the data is very spread out or if it includes a few values that are very different from the rest (outliers).

The median   Here are the monthly salaries of 8 people in a small company:

Director: €14 000 per month
5 people: €3500 per month
2 people: €2400 per month

The mean salary is $\dfrac{14\,000 + (3500 \times 5) + (2400 \times 2)}{8}$

$= €4537.50$

Here the mean monthly salary is €4537.50 which is not typical of most of the monthly salaries.

In situations like this, the **median** (€3500) is a more appropriate average.

Example 1

Here are the marks obtained by a group of ten students in a maths test.

6, 7, 83, 84, 85, 86, 86, 87, 88, 89

Find   (i) the mean   (ii) the median.

State which of these averages best represents the data.

(i) Mean $= \dfrac{6 + 7 + 83 + 84 + 85 + 86 + 86 + 87 + 88 + 89}{10}$

$= \dfrac{701}{10} = 70.1$

(ii) The median $= \dfrac{85 + 86}{2} = 85.5$

In the data, eight out of the ten marks are in the eighties.
Since the mean is only 70.1, the median is a more suitable average.

Exercise 7.3

1. The numbers of computers in eight classrooms are:

      3, 15, 1, 2, 1, 30, 2, 1

  (i) What is the median number of computers?

  (ii) What is the modal number of computers?

  (iii) Why would the mean not be a sensible average for this data?

2. For the set of numbers below, find the mean and the median.

      1, 3, 3, 3, 4, 6, 99

Which average best describes the set of numbers?

3. Find (i) the mean   (ii) the median of these numbers:

      9, 11, 11, 15, 17, 18, 94

Which of these two averages would you choose to best describe these numbers?

4. Jack and Daniel are backpacking in Australia and have recorded these midday temperatures for a week.

Day	1	2	3	4	5	6	7
Midday temperature (°C)	32	30	30	28	33	31	30

  (i) Find the mean midday temperature, correct to the nearest whole number.

  (ii) Give a reason why the mean is appropriate for this data.

5. (i) Find the mean of this set of numbers:

      37, 28, 37, 18, 18, 22, 26, 18, 37, 37, 19

  (ii) Why is the mode a bad choice of average in this case?

6. In March, Rachel and Dave sold five different types of jacket in their clothes shop in the amounts shown.

Jacket	Leather	Suede	Denim	PVC	Cotton
Amount sold	45	17	64	28	52

  (i) Find the modal type of jacket sold.

  (ii) Why is the mode appropriate for this data?

7. Decide which average you would use for each of the following.
   Give a reason for your choice.
   (i) The average mark in an examination.
   (ii) The average uniform size for all the pupils in a class.
   (iii) The average height of the players in a basketball team.
   (iv) The colours of the shirts sold by a department store.
   (v) The average salary of seven people who work for a small business.

8. There are 10 apartments in a block.
   On a particular day, the number of letters delivered to each of the apartments is
   $$2, 0, 5, 3, 4, 0, 1, 0, 3, 15$$
   Calculate the mean, mode and median number of letters.
   Which of these averages is the most suitable to represent this data?
   Give a reason for your answer.

9. A student wants to use an 'average' to show how he has performed in eight science tests.
   Here are his marks: 56   56   58   58   85   97   56   54
   Should he use the mean, mode or median to impress his parents?
   Give a reason for your answer.

10. A restaurant records the number of diners it has every day for a week. The numbers are as follows.
    28   40   28   38   110   170   33
    (i) Write down the mode.
    (ii) Work out the median number of diners.
    (iii) Work out the mean number of diners, correct to one decimal place.
    (iv) The manager wishes to sell the restaurant.
         What average is he likely to use when talking to prospective buyers?
         Give a reason for your answer.

Section 7.4 Frequency tables

The number of children in each of 50 families in a certain district was recorded in the following way:

1, 3, 4, 3, 2, 2, 4, 2, 6, 7, 6, 2, 4, 5, 5, 4, 3, 4, 3, 2, 1, 6, 2, 5, 1,
4, 4, 4, 3, 5, 3, 6, 2, 4, 5, 7, 2, 4, 3, 5, 5, 3, 3, 4, 1, 2, 5, 3, 4, 4.

This list could be much more useful and easier to read if it was presented in the form of a table, as shown below.

Number of children per family	1	2	3	4	5	6	7
Number of families	4	9	10	13	8	4	2

The table above is called a **frequency table** or **frequency distribution**.

This table shows the numbers of families (i.e. the frequency) with 1 child, 2 children and so on. For example, there are 13 families with 4 children per family.

Mean and mode of a frequency distribution

The frequency table below shows the numbers of children aged from 2 to 7 living on a certain road.

Age	2	3	4	5	6	7
Number of children	1	3	5	10	8	3

From the table it can be seen that the **mode** or **modal age** is 5 as it occurs more often than any other age.

To find the **mean** age of the children from the table, we perform these operations:

1. Find the sum of the ages of all the children.

2. Find the number of children.

3. Divide the sum of the ages by the number of children.

1. To find the sum of the ages, we multiply each age by the number of children of that age and add up the results.

$$\text{Sum of ages} = (1 \times 2) + (3 \times 3) + (5 \times 4) + (10 \times 5) + (8 \times 6) + (3 \times 7)$$
$$= 2 + 9 + 20 + 50 + 48 + 21 = 150$$

2. The number of children is $1 + 3 + 5 + 10 + 8 + 3 = 30$.

3. The mean age $= \dfrac{\text{Sum of all the ages}}{\text{Number of children}} = \dfrac{150}{30} = 5$

If x stands for the variable and f stands for the frequency, then the mean is given by

$$\text{Mean} = \frac{\Sigma f(x)}{\Sigma f}$$

where $\Sigma f(x)$ is the sum of all the variables multiplied by the corresponding frequencies and Σf is the sum of the frequencies.

$$\text{Mean} = \frac{\Sigma f(x)}{\Sigma f}$$

Example 1

A road-check on 30 motor vehicles yielded the following record of the number of occupants each carried:

2, 1, 3, 4, 5, 3, 2, 1, 2, 3, 1, 1, 2, 4, 6, 5, 4, 2, 2, 1, 1, 2, 4, 6, 5, 2, 6, 2, 5, 3

Make out a frequency table of the above data and find the mean and mode of the distribution.

Number of occupants per vehicle	1	2	3	4	5	6
Number of vehicles	6	9	4	4	4	3

$$\text{Mean} = \frac{(6 \times 1) + (9 \times 2) + (4 \times 3) + (4 \times 4) + (4 \times 5) + (3 \times 6)}{6 + 9 + 4 + 4 + 4 + 3}$$

$$= \frac{90}{30} = 3$$

Mode = 2, as 2 occurs with the greatest frequency.

Grouped frequency distributions

When dealing with a large number of variables, such as the ages of people in a certain district, it is often convenient to arrange the data in **groups** or **classes**.

Thus, when recording the ages of people, the results could be grouped (0–9) years, (10–19) years … etc.

The grouped frequency distribution table below shows the marks (out of 25) achieved by 50 students in a test.

Marks achieved	1–5	6–10	11–15	16–20	21–25
No. of students	11	12	15	9	3

While it is not possible to find the exact mean of a grouped frequency distribution, we can find an estimate of the mean by taking the **mid-interval value** of each class.

The mid-interval value in the (1–5) class is found by adding 1 and 5 and dividing by 2.

The mid-interval of the (1–5) class is $\dfrac{1 + 5}{2} = \dfrac{6}{2} = 3$.

The table given above is reproduced with the mid-interval values written in smaller size over each class interval.

	3	8	13	18	23
Marks achieved	1–5	6–10	11–15	16–20	21–25
No. of students	11	12	15	9	3

$$\text{Mean} = \frac{\Sigma f(x)}{\Sigma f} = \frac{11(3) + 12(8) + 15(13) + 9(18) + 3(23)}{11 + 12 + 15 + 9 + 3} = \frac{555}{50} = 11.1$$

For the **grouped** table above, we cannot give the exact mode, but we can say that the **modal class** is the interval (11–15) because this interval contains the greatest frequency.

Exercise 7.4

1. Thirty students in a class were given a test which was marked out of 10.
The results of the test are shown below.

4, 6, 7, 5, 9, 8, 6, 4, 3, 5, 6, 9, 8, 7, 6, 10, 1, 3, 6, 7, 9, 8, 5, 3, 2, 4, 7, 9, 10, 5

Copy and complete the frequency table shown below:

Marks per student	1	2	3	4	5	6	7	8	9	10
Number of students			3							

From the table, write down the number of students who got
(i) 5 marks   (ii) 8 marks   (iii) 10 marks.

What mark was got most frequently?

2. A factory produces 50 television sets per day.
Tests at the end of one day gave rise to the following data:

Number of faults per set	0	1	2	3	4	5	6
Number of sets	1	8	12	11	9	5	4

(i) How many sets had no fault?
(ii) How many sets had 6 faults?
(iii) What was the modal number of faults?
(iv) What was the total number of faults recorded in all the sets?
(v) Find the mean number of faults per set.

3. The table below shows the numbers of goals scored in a number of hockey matches on a Sunday morning.

Goals scored	1	2	3	4	5	6
Number of matches	14	16	8	8	6	8

(i) In how many matches were 6 goals scored?
(ii) What was the modal number of goals scored?
(iii) What was the total number of goals scored?
(iv) Find the mean number of goals scored.

4. The following frequency table shows the numbers of goals scored in 60 football matches.

Goals scored	1	2	3	4	5	6
Number of matches	15	14	9	6	10	6

(i) Find the mean number of goals scored per match.
(ii) What was the modal number of goals scored?
(iii) In what percentage of the matches were 3 or 4 goals scored?
(iv) Find the greatest number of matches which could have ended in a draw.

5. A dice was thrown 30 times.
The results are shown here.

Score	1	2	3	4	5	6
Frequency	3	4	6	8	7	2

Find the mean score.

6. Carol is trying to estimate how many words she has written in an essay.
She records the number of words she wrote on each line of one page.
Her results are given in the table below.

Words per line	10	11	12	13	14	15
No. of lines	1	3	6	9	7	4

(i)   How many lines in total were there on the page?
(ii) How many lines contained 14 words?
(iii) What was the modal number of words per line?
(iv) Calculate the mean of the distribution.

7. The marks of 36 students in third-year are given below:

31 49 52 79 40 29 66 71 73 19 51 47 81 67 40 52 20 84
65 73 60 54 60 59 25 89 21 91 84 77 18 37 55 41 72 38

Copy and complete the grouped frequency table below:

Marks	1–20	21–40	41–60	61–80	81–100
Number of students					

(i)   How many students scored between 21 and 60 inclusive?
(ii) What is the modal class?
(iii) Which class had the second largest number of students?
(iv) Name one disadvantage of a grouped frequency table.

8. People attending a course were asked to choose one of the whole numbers from
1 to 12. The results were recorded as follows:

Number	1–3	4–6	7–9	10–12
No. of people	3	17	2	8

(i) Write down the modal class of the distribution.
(ii) Use the mid-interval value of each class to estimate the mean of the distribution.

9. The frequency table shows the numbers of books bought by 20 pupils in the past year.

Number of books	0–4	5–9	10–14	15–19
Frequency	2	4	6	8

Find an estimate for the mean number of books bought by each pupil.

10. Use the mid-interval values to estimate the mean of the following frequency distribution:

Class	14–16	16–18	18–20	20–22	22–24
Frequency	1	5	12	3	0

Give your answer correct to one decimal place.

11. One hundred people were asked to record the numbers of mobile phonecalls they received on a particular day. The results are shown in the table below.

No. of calls	0–4	5–9	10–14	15–19	20–24
Frequency	45	29	17	8	1

   (i) What is the modal group?

   (ii) What is the greatest number of people who could have received more than 18 calls?

  (iii) What is the least number of people who could have received less than 8 calls?

  (iv) Use the mid-interval values to find an estimate for the mean number of phonecalls received.
        Give your answer correct to the nearest whole number.

12. The table below shows the distances travelled by seven paper aeroplanes after they were thrown.

Aeroplane	A	B	C	D	E	F	G
Distance (cm)	188	200	250	30	380	330	302

   (i) Find the median of the data.

   (ii) Find the mean of the data.

  (iii) Aeroplane D is thrown again and the distance it travels is measured and recorded in place of the original measurement. The median of the data remains unchanged and the mean is now equal to the median. How far did aeroplane D travel the second time?

  (iv) What is the minimum distance that aeroplane D would need to have travelled in order for the median to have changed?

Section 7.5 Range and variability

Range

The **range** for a set of data is the highest value of the set minus the lowest value.

For the data   3, 7, 9, 15, 21, 28

          Range = 28 − 3 = 25

The range shows how **spread out** a set of data is.

> The range is largest value minus smallest value.

It is very useful when comparing two sets of data.

The marks, out of 20, scored by Ava and Sean in 6 maths tests are given below:

Ava   12, 10, 18, 14, 8, 10

Sean   12, 10, 16, 13, 11, 10

For **Ava**:   Mean $= \frac{72}{6} = 12$ Range $= 18 - 8 = 10$

For **Sean**:   Mean $= \frac{72}{6} = 12$ Range $= 16 - 10 = 6$

Notice that the mean mark for both is the same but Sean's marks have a smaller range. Since Sean's marks are less **spread out**, it shows that Sean's results are more **consistent** than Ava's.

This spread-out nature of Ava's marks compared to Sean's marks illustrates the variability of data and how important it can be.

The **range** is generally used as a measure of variability as it is easy to find and easy to understand.

Comparing data

To compare two sets of data, we use the **range** and either the **mean**, the **mode** or the **median**.

In the example above comparing Ava's and Sean's marks, we used the range and the mean.

Quartiles and Interquartile range

When data is arranged in order of size, we have already learned that the **median** is the value half-way into the data.
So we can say that the median divides the data into two halves.
The data can also be divided into four quarters.

When the data is arranged in ascending order of size:

> the **lower quartile** is the value one quarter of the way into the data
> the **upper quartile** is the value three quarters of the way into the data
> the upper quartile minus the lower quartile is called the **interquartile range**.

Consider the following data which is arranged in order of size. It contains 15 numbers.

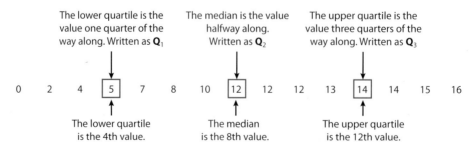

The lower quartile is the value one quarter of the way along. Written as Q_1

The median is the value halfway along. Written as Q_2

The upper quartile is the value three quarters of the way along. Written as Q_3

0   2   4   5   7   8   10   12   12   12   13   14   14   15   16

The lower quartile is the 4th value.

The median is the 8th value.

The upper quartile is the 12th value.

The lower quartile $Q_1 = 5$.
The median $Q_2 = 12$.
The upper quartile $Q_3 = 14$.
The interquartile range $= Q_3 - Q_1$

$$= 14 - 5 = 9$$

> The interquartile range is
> upper quartile − lower quartile
> $= Q_3 - Q_1$

Example 1

Find the median and interquartile range of this set of data:

8   2   9   6   7   10   12   13   5   12   10   8   10   4

We first re-arrange the data, starting with the smallest.

2   4   5   ⑥   7   8 $\boxed{8 \mid 9}$ 10   10   ⑩   12   12   13
$\quad\quad\quad Q_1$ $\qquad\qquad\qquad\qquad\qquad\qquad Q_3$

Since there is an even number of data points, there will be 2 middle terms.
These terms are boxed above.

$$\therefore \quad \text{the median} = \frac{8 + 9}{2} = \frac{17}{2} = 8\tfrac{1}{2}$$

The broken red line divides the data into two halves.
The lower quartile, Q_1, is the 4th term.
$\therefore$ the lower quartile is 6
Similarly, the upper quartile is 10.
The interquartile range $= 10 - 6 = 4$

Exercise 7.5

1. Find the range for each of the following sets of data:

   (i) 3, 7, 6, 8, 12, 6, 14

   (ii) 8, 2, 9, 6, 7, 10, 4, 18, 5, 23

2. Which of these two sets of data has the bigger range?

   (i) 23, 36, 42, 29, 34, 27

   (ii) 81, 74, 92, 77, 85, 89

3. Saskia's marks in six French tests were: 54, 82, 65, 72, 38, 66
John's marks in the same six tests were: 58, 62, 51, 66, 71, 64

   (i) Find the range of marks for Saskia and for John.
      Use your results to find which of the two had the more consistent marks.

   (ii) Which of the two had the higher mean mark?

4. In a golf competition between two clubs, the captain had to choose between Emer and Anna to play in the first round. In the previous eight rounds, their scores were as follows:

Emer: 80, 73, 72, 88, 86, 90, 75, 92
Anna: 88, 84, 79, 85, 76, 85, 87, 80

   (i) Calculate the mean score for each golfer.
   (ii) Find the range of scores for each golfer.
   (iii) Which golfer would you choose to play for you in the competition?
   Explain your answer. (Lower scores are better.)

5. Sinead has five cards. The five cards have a mean of 7 and a range of 4.

What are the missing numbers?

6. Miss Moore gave her class a maths test. Here are the marks for the girls:

7, 5, 8, 5, 2, 8, 7, 4, 7, 10, 3, 7, 4, 3, 6

What is   (i) the median mark   (ii) the range of marks?

The median mark for the boys in her class was 7 and the range of marks for the boys was 4. By comparing the results, explain whether the boys or girls did better in the test.

7. A set of cards has these numbers on them.

   (i) Find five cards from this set with median 6 and range 4.
   (ii) Find four cards with median 6 and range 3.

8. Eleven college students were asked to record the amount of time they spent on the internet one evening. Their times, in minutes, were:

38   42   50   56   60   62   65   70   70   75   80

   (i) Find the median time spent on the internet.
   (ii) Find Q_1, the lower quartile and Q_3, the upper quartile.
   (iii) Write down the interquartile range.

9. Nine students submitted their assignments which were marked out of 40. The marks obtained were:

37, 34, 34, 29, 27, 27, 10, 4, 34

   (i) Write down the range of marks.
   (ii) Write down the median mark.
   (iii) Find   (a)   the lower quartile
                (b)   the upper quartile
                (c)   the interquartile range.

10. Here are the times, in minutes, for a bus journey:

    15, 7, 9, 12, 9, 19, 6, 11, 9, 16, 8

   (i) Find the range of these times.
   (ii) Find the lower quartile.
   (iii) Find the upper quartile.
   (iv) Write down the interquartile range.

11. There are 5 children in a family. The youngest child is 8 years old and another child is 15 years old. The median child's age is 13. The range of the children's ages is 17. The mean age is 14. Find the ages of the 5 children.

12. A greengrocer sold boxes of apples from different countries.
   A box contained 9 French apples.

   The weight of each apple is given below, in grams.

       101, 107, 98, 109, 115, 103, 96, 112, 104

   (i) Calculate the mean weight of a French apple.
   (ii) Find the range of the weights of the French apples.

   Another box contained 9 South African apples.
   Their mean weight was 107 g and their range was 19 g.

   (iii) Make two comments on the weights of the apples in the two boxes.

13. As part of an ongoing research programme, the pups in a small colony of grey seals were weighed, to the nearest kilogram, at the age of four weeks. Their weights were as follows:

       42   40   45   47   50   48   39   47   42   50   49

   (i) Work out the range of the weights.
   (ii) Find the interquartile range.

14. Here are summaries of the data obtained from measuring the weights of two varieties of pear.

Variety A		Variety B	
Minimum	131 g	Minimum	139 g
Lower quartile	142 g	Lower quartile	150 g
Median	155 g	Median	160 g
Upper quartile	171 g	Upper quartile	173 g
Maximum	185 g	Maximum	182 g

   (i) What percentage of the pears of variety A weigh up to 142 g?
   (ii) What percentage of the pears of variety B weigh over 173 g?
   (iii) Use the median and range to compare the weights of the two varieties.

Test yourself 7

1. (a) The mean of 3, 7, 8, 10, x is 8. Find x.
   (b) Find   (i) the mean   (ii) the median   for the following set of data:
         3, 5, 4, 7, 29, 9, 2, 4, 10, 8

         Which of these two averages is the more suitable to represent the data?
         Give a reason for your answer.
   (c) Find   (i) the median   (ii) the upper quartile   (iii) the lower quartile
        for these numbers:
         12 6 4 9 8 4 9 8 5 9 10

2. (a) The mean height of six girls is 1.63 m.
        The mean height of five of the girls is 1.61 m.
        Find the height of the sixth girl.
   (b) A group of boys and girls took a Geography test. These are the marks which the
        boys got:
         13, 14, 14, 15, 14, 14, 15, 17, 16, 14, 16, 12

    (i) Find the range of the boys' marks.
   (ii) Calculate the mean mark of the boys.

   The mean mark for the girls in the class was 13.2 and the girls' marks had a range of 7.
   (iii) Make two statements about the differences between the boys' and girls' marks in
          the Geography test.

3. (a) Find a set of three numbers for which the median is 15, the mean is 13 and the range
        is 12.
   (b) The numbers of goals scored by the 11 members of a hockey team in 2009 were as
        follows:
         6   0   8   12   2   1   2   9   1   0   11
    (i) Find the median.
   (ii) Find the upper and lower quartiles.
  (iii) Find the interquartile range.

4. (a) Find the mean, correct to one decimal place, and the mode(s) of this set of numbers:
         34, 28, 38, 19, 19, 21, 28, 19, 37, 36, 19.
        Why is the mode a bad choice of average in this case?
   (b) A sample of 10 measurements has a mean of 15.7 and a sample of the other
        20 measurements has a mean of 14.3. Find the mean of all 30 measurements.
        Give your answer correct to one decimal place.
   (c) In a diving competition, the five judges gave scores of 8, 7.5, 8.5, 9 and 8.
    (i) Delete the highest and lowest scores and find the mean of the remaining
         three scores. Multiply this by the Degree of Difficulty of 2.8 to get the score for
         the dive.

(ii) Repeat the process above to find the score for a dive with a Degree of Difficulty of 3.2, if the judges' scores are 6, 6.5, 6.5, 7, 7.5.
Give each answer correct to two decimal places.

5. (a) The weekly wages of the employees of a fast-food takeaway are listed below:

€300, €250, €240, €220, €200, €1050.

Find   (i) the mean wage
       (ii) the median wage

Why can't you find the mode?

Which of the averages – mean or median – best represents the 'typical' wage?

(b) The range for eight numbers is 40 and seven of these numbers are shown.
Find two possible values for the missing number.

| 27 | 5 | 33 | 42 |

| 11 | | 13 | 19 |

(c) The frequency table shows the numbers of postage stamps bought by 20 people in the past month.

Number of stamps	0–4	5–9	10–14	15–19
Frequency	2	4	6	8

Use the mid-interval values to find an estimate of the mean number of stamps bought.

6. (a) Over the complete assessment period, Jenny averaged 35 out of a possible 40 marks for her maths tests. However, when checking her files, she could only find 7 of the 8 tests. For these she scored 29, 36, 32, 38, 35, 34 and 39. Determine how many marks out of 40 she scored for the eighth test.

(b) Ten men travelled to watch a rugby match. The mean age of the men was 25 years and the range of their ages was 6.
Write each statement below and then write next to it whether it is

(i) true (ii) could be true or (iii) false.

    (a) The youngest man was 18 years old.

    (b) All the men were at least 20 years old.

    (c) The oldest person was 4 years older than the youngest.

    (d) Every man was between 20 and 26 years old.

Quadratic equations

Key words

(
solutions   roots   satisfy the equation   parabola

quadratic formula   mathematical sentence   forming equations
)

Section 8.1 Solving quadratic equations using factors ⎯

Equations such as $x^2 - 4x + 3 = 0$ or $2x^2 - x - 3 = 0$ contain a term in x^2.
These are called **quadratic equations**.

Take the equation $x^2 - 5x + 6 = 0$.

When $x = 2$, then $x^2 - 5x + 6$ becomes
$$(2)^2 - 5(2) + 6, \text{ i.e., } 4 - 10 + 6 = 0$$
When $x = 3$, then $x^2 - 5x + 6$ becomes
$$(3)^2 - 5(3) + 6, \text{ i.e., } 9 - 15 + 6 = 0$$

When $x = 2$ or $x = 3$, both sides of the equation are zero.
When this happens, we say that $x = 2$ and $x = 3$
are **solutions** or **roots** of the equation.

> The **roots** of an equation
> are the values of x which
> satisfy the equation.

Multiplication by zero ⎯⎯⎯⎯⎯⎯⎯⎯

Any number multiplied by zero is zero.
For example, $4 \times 0 = 0$ or $0 \times 6 = 0$.
This illustrates a very important property of
real numbers which is given on the right.

> If the product of two numbers is zero,
> then at least one of them must be
> zero.
> e.g. if $ab = 0$, then $a = 0$ or $b = 0$.

Thus if $(x - 3)(x + 5) = 0$, then
$$x - 3 = 0 \text{ or } x + 5 = 0$$
i.e. $x = 3$ or $x = -5$.

Steps for solving quadratic equations ⎯⎯⎯⎯⎯⎯⎯⎯⎯⎯⎯⎯⎯⎯

> ❯ If necessary, rearrange the equation with one side being **zero**.

> ❯ Factorise fully the other side.

> ❯ Let each factor equal zero.

> ❯ Solve the resulting simple equations.

Example 1

Solve the equation $x^2 - 5x - 14 = 0$.

$x^2 - 5x - 14 = 0$

$(x - 7)(x + 2) = 0$ ... factorise the left-hand side

$x - 7 = 0$ or $x + 2 = 0$ ... let each factor $= 0$

$x = 7$ or $x = -2$

$\therefore \quad x = 7$ or $x = -2$

Example 2

Solve these equations:

  (i) $2x^2 - 9x = 0$

 (ii) $4x^2 - 25 = 0$

  (i) $2x^2 - 9x = 0$

    [This equation contains no number term (i.e. no constant) and is factorised by taking outside the brackets the highest factor common to both terms.]

$$2x^2 - 9x = 0 \Rightarrow x(2x - 9) = 0$$
$$x = 0 \quad \text{or} \quad 2x - 9 = 0$$
$$x = 0 \quad \text{or} \quad 2x = 9$$
$$\therefore \quad x = 0 \quad \text{or} \quad x = 4\tfrac{1}{2}$$

 (ii) $4x^2 - 25 = 0$

$$(2x - 5)(2x + 5) = 0 \quad \text{... the difference of two squares}$$
$$2x - 5 = 0 \quad \text{or} \quad 2x + 5 = 0 \quad \text{... both factors} = 0$$
$$2x = 5 \quad \text{or} \quad 2x = -5$$
$$x = \tfrac{5}{2} \quad \text{or} \quad x = -\tfrac{5}{2}$$
$$\therefore \quad x = 2\tfrac{1}{2} \quad \text{or} \quad x = -2\tfrac{1}{2}$$

Discussion

The curve on the right is called a parabola.

It is the graph of $y = x^2 + x - 2$.

> Factorise $x^2 + x - 2$ and then solve the equation $x^2 + x - 2 = 0$.

> Can you use the graph to solve the equation $x^2 + x - 2 = 0$?

> What is the link between the two sets of answers?

> Now explain the meaning of the roots of a quadratic equation.

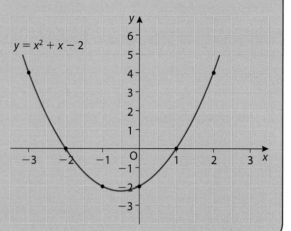

$y = x^2 + x - 2$

Exercise 8.1

Solve the following quadratic equations:

1. $(x - 2)(x - 4) = 0$

2. $(x - 4)(x + 2) = 0$

3. $(x - 6)(x + 4) = 0$

4. $(x - 4)(2x - 3) = 0$

5. $(x + 3)(6x - 9) = 0$

6. $(2x - 1)(x + 4) = 0$

7. $x(x - 3) = 0$

8. $x(x + 5) = 0$

9. $2x(x + 3) = 0$

10. $x^2 + 7x + 10 = 0$

11. $x^2 + 12x + 35 = 0$

12. $x^2 + 14x + 48 = 0$

13. $x^2 - 5x + 6 = 0$

14. $x^2 - 8x + 15 = 0$

15. $x^2 - 10x + 21 = 0$

16. $x^2 - x - 12 = 0$

17. $x^2 - 3x - 10 = 0$

18. $x^2 + 3x - 28 = 0$

19. $2x^2 - 5x + 2 = 0$

20. $2x^2 - 3x - 2 = 0$

21. $2x^2 - x - 6 = 0$

22. $2x^2 + 5x + 2 = 0$

23. $3x^2 - 7x + 2 = 0$

24. $3x^2 + x - 10 = 0$

25. $3x^2 + 10x - 8 = 0$

26. $3x^2 - 13x - 10 = 0$

27. $3x^2 + 19x - 14 = 0$

28. $4x^2 - 12x + 5 = 0$

29. $5x^2 - 13x - 6 = 0$

30. $5x^2 - 13x + 6 = 0$

31. $x^2 - 6x = 0$

32. $2x^2 - 5x = 0$

33. $3x^2 - 4x = 0$

34. $4x^2 - x = 0$

35. $5x^2 - 6x = 0$

36. $3x^2 - 7x = 0$

37. $x^2 - 9 = 0$

38. $x^2 - 25 = 0$

39. $4x^2 - 1 = 0$

40. $4x^2 - 25 = 0$

41. $9x^2 - 16 = 0$

42. $4x^2 - 49 = 0$

43. $2x(x - 2) = 3(x + 10)$

44. $(x - 2)(x - 3) = 20$

45. $(2x - 5)(x - 2) = 15$

46. Solve the equation $(x - 8)(x - 2) = 2x(x - 5)$.

47. Write down the roots of the equation $x^2 + 2x - 3 = 0$ by referring to the graph shown.

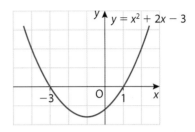

48. Write down the values of x where the graph of each of these functions crosses the x-axis. (You do not need to draw the graphs.)

    (i) $y = (x - 4)(x + 5)$ (ii) $y = (x + 2)(x + 4)$ (iii) $y = (x - 5)(x - 6)$

49. Three parabolas are shown here.

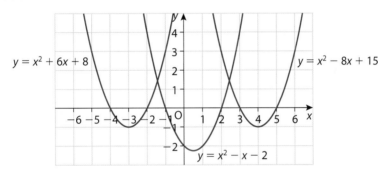

Use the graphs above to solve the following equations (each has two solutions).

    (i) $x^2 - 8x + 15 = 0$ (ii) $x^2 + 6x + 8 = 0$ (iii) $x^2 - x - 2 = 0$

50. (i) How many values of x make $(x + 2)^2 = 0$?

    (ii) One of these sketches shows $y = (x + 2)^2$.
    Which one?

    Explain your answer.

  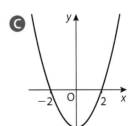

Section 8.2 Using the quadratic formula

In the previous section of this chapter, we used factors to solve quadratic equations of the form $ax^2 + bx + c = 0$.

If the expression $ax^2 + bx + c$ cannot be factorised, the equation can still be solved by using a special formula called the **quadratic formula**.
This formula is given below:

The quadratic formula

> The roots of the quadratic equation $ax^2 + bx + c = 0$ are
> $$x = \frac{-b \pm \sqrt{b^2 - 4ac}}{2a}$$

Example 1

Use the quadratic formula to find the roots of the equation $5x^2 + 7x - 3 = 0$, correct to two decimal places.

In the equation $5x^2 + 7x - 3 = 0$, $a = 5, b = 7$ and $c = -3$.

$$x = \frac{-b \pm \sqrt{b^2 - 4ac}}{2a}$$
$$= \frac{-7 \pm \sqrt{49 - 4(5)(-3)}}{2(5)}$$
$$= \frac{-7 \pm \sqrt{49 + 60}}{10}$$
$$= \frac{-7 \pm \sqrt{109}}{10} = \frac{-7 \pm 10.44}{10} = \frac{-17.44}{10} \text{ or } \frac{3.44}{10}$$

$\therefore \quad x = -1.744$ or $x = 0.344$

$\therefore \quad x = -1.74$ or $x = 0.34$

Note: When using the quadratic formula to solve a quadratic equation, remember that all terms must be on the left-hand side and zero only on the right-hand side, that is, the equation must be in the form,
$$ax^2 + bx + c = 0.$$

Exercise 8.2

Solve the following equations using the formula

$$x = \frac{-b \pm \sqrt{b^2 - 4ac}}{2a}$$

Give your answers correct to two decimal places.

1. $x^2 + 4x + 2 = 0$

2. $x^2 + 6x + 4 = 0$

3. $x^2 + 2x - 5 = 0$

4. $x^2 - 2x - 7 = 0$

5. $4x^2 + 2x - 1 = 0$

6. $3x^2 - x - 1 = 0$

7. $3x^2 - 6x + 2 = 0$

8. $3x^2 + 7x - 5 = 0$

9. $5x^2 - 4x - 2 = 0$

10. $3x^2 + 8x + 2 = 0$

11. $6x^2 - 9x - 4 = 0$

12. $3x^2 + 7x = 2$

13. $4x^2 + 3x = 5$

14. $2x^2 = 7x - 4$

15. $3x^2 + 5x = 3$

Section 8.3 Problems leading to quadratic equations

When a problem expressed in words is changed to a mathematical sentence, it often results in a quadratic equation.

To find the equation to represent a problem,

› where relevant, draw a diagram and put all the information you are given on it

› use x to represent the unknown you are asked to find

› look for the information in the question to form an equation in x

› solve the equation to find the value or values for x; you may sometimes have to reject a negative answer.

Example 1

The length of a rectangle exceeds its breadth by 6 cm.
If the area of the rectanlge is 160 cm², find its length and breadth.

Let the breadth of the rectangle be x cm.

∴ The length is $(x + 6)$ cm.

Area = 160 cm²

$$\therefore \quad x(x + 6) = 160 \quad \cdots A = \ell \times b$$
$$x^2 + 6x = 160$$
$$x^2 + 6x - 160 = 0$$
$$(x - 10)(x + 16) = 0$$
$$x - 10 = 0 \ \text{ or } \ x + 16 = 0$$
$$x = 10 \ \text{ or } \ x = -16$$

Naturally in this case, we reject the negative number -16.

$$\therefore \quad x = 10$$

∴ the length $(x + 6)$ cm = 16 cm and the breadth x cm = 10 cm

> **Example 2**
>
>   (i) Two numbers have a sum of 13. If one of them is x, what it the other number?
>
>   (ii) If the sum of their squares is 89, find the numbers.
>
>   (i) The other number is $(13 - x)$.
>
>   (ii) The two numbers are x and $(13 - x)$.
>
>   Sum of their squares $= 89 \Rightarrow x^2 + (13 - x)^2 = 89$
>
> $x^2 + (13 - x)^2 = 89$
>
> $x^2 + 169 - 26x + x^2 = 89$
>
> $2x^2 - 26x + 169 - 89 = 0$
>
> $2x^2 - 26x + 80 = 0$
>
> $x^2 - 13x + 40 = 0$ ... divide both sides by 2
>
> $(x - 8)(x - 5) = 0$
>
> $x - 8 = 0$ or $x - 5 = 0$
>
> $x = 8$ or $x = 5$
>
>   The two numbers are 8 and 5.

Exercise 8.3

1. When a number, x, is added to its square, the answer is 72.
   Write an equation in x and solve it to find two numbers.
   Verify that both numbers satisfy the equation.

2. If a positive number is subtracted from its square, the result is 90.
   What is the number?

3. One positive number is 3 bigger than another number. If the two numbers are multiplied together, the answer is 88. Find the two numbers.

4. When four times a positive number is taken from its square, the result is 60.
   Find the number.

5. One positive number is 3 greater than another positive number. When 12 is added to the square of the smaller number, the result is the same as four times the larger number. Find the two numbers.

6. When 5 is added to a certain positive number and the result is squared, the answer is 81. Find the number.

7. The area of the given rectangle is 77 cm².
   Find its length and breadth.

$(x + 4)$ cm

x cm

8. State the *Theorem of Pythagoras*.
   Now use this theorem to find the value of x
   in the given right-angled triangle.

9. A rectangle has length 3 cm greater than its width.
   If it has an area of 28 cm², find the dimensions of the rectangle.

10. Alan is x years old. His mother's age is the square of his age.
    If Alan's father is two years older than his mother and the sum of all three ages is 80
    years, how old is Alan?

11. The sum of the squares of two consecutive integers is 41.
    (i) If x is one of the integers, show that $x^2 + x - 20 = 0$.
    (ii) Solve $x^2 + x - 20 = 0$ to find two pairs of
         consecutive integers.

    7 and 8 are
    consecutive integers.

12. The diagram shows a rectangular lawn
    surrounded on three sides by flower beds.
    Each flower bed is 2 m wide.
    The area of the lawn is 14 m².
    Find the length of the lawn.

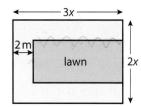

13. If the area of the given triangle is
    40 square units, find the value of x.

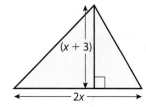

14. A baker making cakes finds that his profit per hour, €P, is given by the relationship
    $P = 20x - x^2$, where x is the number of cakes made per hour.
    Find the number of cakes baked when the company makes
    (i) €0 per hour profit
    (ii) €84 per hour profit.

15. When a cricket ball is hit directly upwards, its height (h) above the ground is given by
    $h = (30t - 5t^2)$ metres, where t is the time after the ball is hit (in seconds).
    After how many seconds is the ball at a height of:
    (i) 0 m above the ground
    (ii) 40 m ?

16. (i) A decorator's logo is rectangular and measures 10 centimetres by 6 centimetres.
It consists of three smaller rectangles: one red, one yellow and one blue.

The yellow rectangles measures 10 centimetres by x centimetres.
The length of the red rectangle is x centimetres.
Show that the area, A, of the blue rectangle is given by the expression
$A = x^2 - 16x + 60$.

(ii) The area of the blue rectangle is equal to $\frac{1}{5}$ of the total area of the logo.
Calculate the value of x.

17. The weight, W kilograms, of a giraffe is related to its age, M months,
by the formula
$$W = \tfrac{1}{4}(M^2 - 4M + 272)$$
At what age (in months) will a giraffe weigh 83 kilograms?

18. The closed rectangular box shown has a
square base of side x cm.
The height of the box is 5 cm.
The total surface area of the box is 288 cm^2.
Write an equation in x to represent this
information and use it to calculate x.

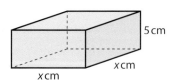

Section 8.4 **Forming a quadratic equation given its roots**

Examine the quadratic equation $x^2 + x - 6 = 0$.
The factors of the left-hand side are $(x + 3)(x - 2)$.
$\Rightarrow (x + 3)(x - 2) = 0$
$\quad x + 3 = 0 \quad$ or $\quad x - 2 = 0$
$\therefore \quad x = -3 \quad$ or $\quad x = 2$
i.e. -3 and 2 are the roots of the equation.

We can now use the reverse of this method to form a quadratic equation when we are given the roots.

Form the quadratic equation with roots -4 and 5.

If the roots are -4 and 5, then

$(x + 4)(x - 5) = 0$ is the quadratic equation with these roots.

$\Rightarrow x^2 - x - 20 = 0$ is the equation

Exercise 8.4

Form the quadratic equation, given the two roots, in each of the following:

1. $2, 4$ **2.** $5, 1$ **3.** $3, 2$ **4.** $3, -1$

5. $4, -2$ **6.** $-3, -4$ **7.** $6, -2$ **8.** $5, 0$

9. $-2, \frac{1}{2}$ **10.** $-5, -4$ **11.** $-\frac{1}{2}, 4$ **12.** $\frac{1}{4}, 8$

13. $0, -4$ **14.** $\frac{1}{2}, -\frac{1}{2}$ **15.** ± 3 **16.** $0, \frac{1}{4}$

17. If the roots of the equation $x^2 + ax + b = 0$ are 2 and -1, find the values of a and b.

18. Here is the graph of a quadratic function.

Use the x-values of the points at which the graph crosses the x-axis to write the function that this graph represents.

Give your answer in the form $y = \ldots\ldots$.

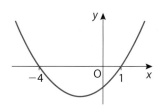

Test yourself 8

1. (a) Solve the equation $x^2 - 2x - 35 = 0$.

   (b) Given that $x^2 + y^2 + z^2 = 29$, find the two possible values of y when $x = 2$ and $z = -3$.

   (c)

   The length of a rectangle is $(x + 4)$ cm.
   The width is $(x - 3)$ cm.
   The area of the rectangle is 78 cm².
   Use this information to write down an equation in x.
   Solve this equation to find the value of x.

2. (a) Solve the equation $3x^2 + 10x = 8$.

   (b) Solve the equation $2x^2 - 7x + 4 = 0$, giving your answers correct to two decimal places.

   (c) The length of a rectangle is 4 cm more than its width.
   If the area of the rectangle is 96 cm², write an equation and solve it to find the length and width.

3. (a) If $x = 2$ is a root of the equation $x^2 - x + r = 0$, find the value of r.

   (b) The roots of a quadratic equation are -2 and 3.
   Write down an equation in x which has these 2 roots.

   (c) The diagram shows a shape in which all the corners are right angles.
   The area of the shape is 48 cm².

   (i) Form an equation, in terms of x, for the area of the shape.
   Show that the equation can be simplified to $x^2 + x - 12 = 0$.
   (ii) Solve the equation $x^2 + x - 12 = 0$ and hence calculate the perimeter of the shape.

4. (a) Solve the equations   (i) $2x^2 - 7x = 0$ (ii) $x^2 - 36 = 0$

(b) Which of the two graphs on the right gives the solutions to the equation $x^2 + 2x - 3 = 0$? Explain your answer.

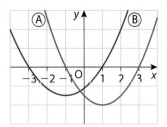

(c) The diagram on the right shows a carpet 10 m by 8 m placed in the centre of a hotel lounge so that there is a uniform border, x metres in width, all the way round.

  (i) Express the area of the lounge in terms of x.
  (ii) If the area of the lounge is 168 m², find the value of x.

5. (a) Solve the equation $x(x + 4) - (x - 2) = 20$.

(b) The square of a number is subtracted from the original number and the result is -110.
Find the number.

(c) A projectile is launched directly upwards and its height, H metres above the ground, is given by $H = 20t - 5t^2$ where t is the time in seconds.
After how many seconds will the projectile be 20 metres above the ground?

6. (a) Solve the equation $12x^2 - 4x - 5 = 0$.

(b) Form the quadratic equation whose roots are 2 and -5.

(c) A rectangle of area 72 cm² is divided into 4 smaller rectangles. The measurements of the sides are shown in the diagram. Write an equation in x to represent this information and hence solve the equation.

(d) A hurley-maker finds that his profit, €P per day, is given by the formula $P = 100x - 4x^2$, where x is the number of hurleys made.
How many hurleys does he need to make in order to have a profit of €400 a day?

chapter 9

Geometry 1 – Triangles and Quadrilaterals

Key words

> line   line segment   intersect   collinear   perpendicular
> straight angle   acute   obtuse   reflex   vertically opposite
> corresponding   alternate   interior   exterior   isosceles   equilateral
> quadrilateral   rhombus   diagonal   congruent   converse

Section 9.1 Revision of lines and angles

The diagrams below will help you recall some of the facts and terms you will have met in your study of geometry so far.

1. Lines

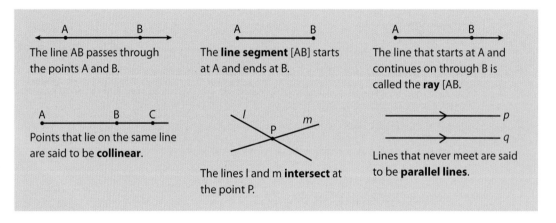

The line AB passes through the points A and B.

The **line segment** [AB] starts at A and ends at B.

The line that starts at A and continues on through B is called the **ray** [AB.

Points that lie on the same line are said to be **collinear**.

The lines l and m **intersect** at the point P.

Lines that never meet are said to be **parallel lines**.

2. Angles

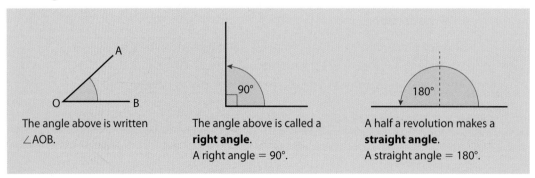

The angle above is written $\angle$AOB.

The angle above is called a **right angle**.
A right angle = 90°.

A half a revolution makes a **straight angle**.
A straight angle = 180°.

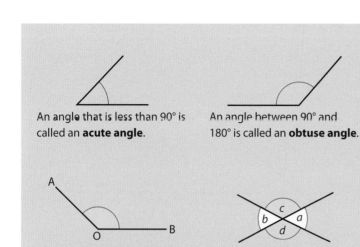

An angle that is less than 90° is called an **acute angle**.

An angle between 90° and 180° is called an **obtuse angle**.

An angle between 180° and 360° is called a **reflex angle**.

The shaded angle, which is less than 180°, is generally referred to as an **ordinary angle**.

Vertically opposite angles are equal in measure.

Angles at a point add up to **360°**.

3. Angles and parallel lines

Angles formed when a straight line crosses a pair of parallel lines have the following properties:

Corresponding angles are equal. So $a = b$. You can find them by looking for an F shape.

Alternate angles are equal. So $a = b$. Look for a Z shape.

The **interior angles** x and y sum to 180°. So $x + y = 180°$.

Exercise 9.1

1. Describe in words each of the following diagrams:

 (i) A   B

 (ii) A   B

 (iii) A

 B

2. Find the measure of the angle marked with a letter in each of the following diagrams:

151

3. Work out the angles marked with a letter in each of the following diagrams:

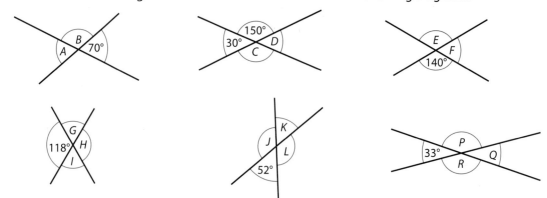

4. In each of the following diagrams, write down the number of the angle that **corresponds** to the shaded angle:

(i)　　　　　　　　　(ii)　　　　　　　　　(iii)

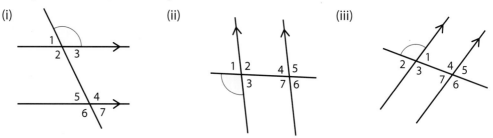

5. Write down the sizes of the angles marked with letters in each of the following diagrams, where arrows indicate parallel lines.

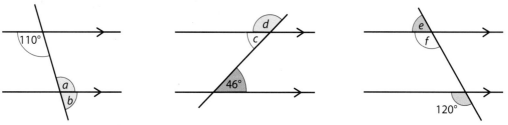

6. In each of the following, work out the size of the angle marked with a letter. Arrows indicate parallel lines.

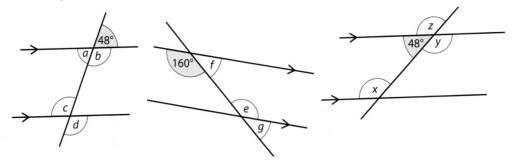

152

7. Find the measures of the angles marked with letters in the given diagram, where the arrows indicate parallel lines.

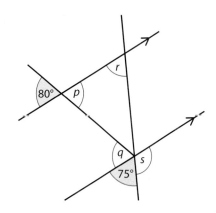

8. Find the sizes of the angles marked a, b, c, d, e, f and g in the given figure, where arrows indicate parallel lines.

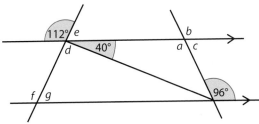

9. Find the value of n in each of the figures below:

(i)   (ii)   (iii)

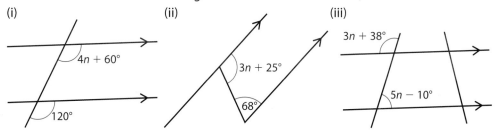

Arrows indicate parallel lines.

Section 9.2 Angles of a triangle

The diagrams below will help you recall some important facts about the angles of a triangle.

The angles of a triangle sum to 180°.
$$|\angle A| + |\angle B| + |\angle C| = 180°$$

The **exterior angle** of a triangle is equal to the sum of the interior opposite angles.
$$|\angle C| = |\angle A| + |\angle B|$$

153

An **equilateral triangle** has
3 equal sides
3 equal angles
Each angle is 60°.

An **isosceles triangle** has
2 equal sides
base angles equal.

A **right-angled triangle** has
an angle of 90°.
$$a^2 = b^2 + c^2$$

It is stated in the box above that in an isosceles triangle, the angles opposite the equal sides are also equal.

Conversely, it can be shown that if a triangle contains two equal angles, then that triangle is isosceles.

Example 1

In the given figure, MN is parallel to PO.
If $|\angle NPO| = 29°$, find
  (i) $|\angle MNP|$
  (ii) $|\angle PMN|$.

  (i) $|\angle MNP| = 29°$... alternate angles as PO‖MN

  (ii) $|\angle MPN| = 29°$... isosceles triangle as $|PM| = |MN|$
      $|\angle PMN| = 180° − 29° − 29°$
      $|\angle PMN| = 122°$

Exercise 9.2

1. Find the size of the angle marked with a letter in each of the following triangles:

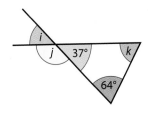

2. Work out the sizes of the missing angles in each of these isosceles triangles:

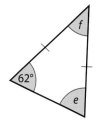

3. Find the size of the angle marked with a letter in the following figures:

4. Calculate the size of each angle marked with a letter:

5. In the given figure, BD, AE and BE are straight lines.
|BC| = |CE|,
|∠ACD| = 130° and |∠BAC| = 72°.

Work out the sizes of the angles marked *a*, *b* and *c*.

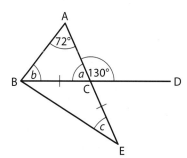

6. Find the values of *a*, *b*, *c* and *d* in the following triangles:

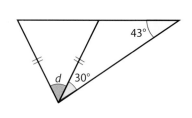

7. In the given diagram, AC is parallel to BE.
If $|\angle BCA| = 80°$ and $|\angle CAB| = 55°$, find
   (i) *x*
   (ii) *y*.
Give a reason for your answer in each case.

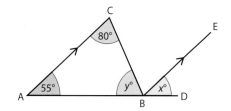

8. Find the sizes of the angles marked with letters in these diagrams:

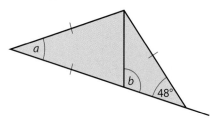

9.

Discussion

Abbie drew this diagram. The line parallel to CA
cuts angle *d* into two angles, *x* and *y*.
How could Abbie use this diagram
to prove that
$a + b = d$?
Discuss.

10. In the given figure, two right angles are marked.
Find the sizes of the angles marked with letters.
Give reasons for your answers.

11. Find the measure of the angle marked with a letter in each of the following diagrams, where the arrows indicate parallel lines:

  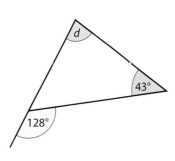

12. In the given figure, $|\angle AED| = |\angle DCB|$.
Explain why $|\angle ADE| = |\angle EBC|$.

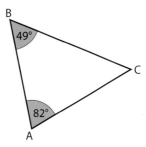

13. Explain why the given triangle is isosceles.

Section 9.3 Quadrilaterals

A figure which has four sides is called
a **quadrilateral**.
In the quadrilateral shown, the sides have different
lengths and the angles have different sizes.

However, there are quadrilaterals with special properties which you should recognise. Some of these special quadrilaterals are shown below.

A square
In a square,
> all four sides are the same length
> opposite sides are parallel
> all four angles are right angles.

A rectangle

In a rectangle,
> each pair of opposite sides are parallel and equal in length
> all four angles are right angles.

A parallelogram

In a parallelogram,
> the opposite sides are parallel
> the opposite sides are equal in length
> the opposite angles are equal.

A rhombus

In a rhombus,
> there are 4 equal sides
> opposite sides are parallel
> opposite angles are equal.

The angles of a quadrilateral

The quadrilateral shown is divided into two triangles.
The angles in each triangle add up to 180°.
So the angles in a quadrilateral add up to 360°.

The interior angles in a quadrilateral add up to 360°.

Diagonals

In the special quadrilaterals shown below, the diagonals bisect each other.

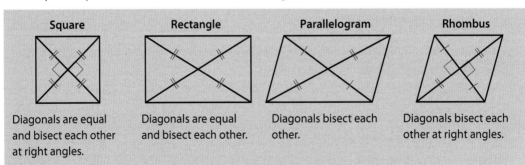

Square	Rectangle	Parallelogram	Rhombus
Diagonals are equal and bisect each other at right angles.	Diagonals are equal and bisect each other.	Diagonals bisect each other.	Diagonals bisect each other at right angles.

Theorem   The diagonals of a parallelogram bisect each other.

Example 1

In the given parallelogram ABCD,
$|\angle BAD| = 115°$ and $|\angle BDC| = 28°$.
Find (i) $|\angle BCD|$ (ii) $|\angle ABD|$
(iii) $|\angle ADC|$ (iv) $|\angle DBC|$
Give a reason for each answer.

(i) $|\angle BCD| = 115°$... opposite angles are equal
(ii) $|\angle ABD| = 28°$... alternate angles
(iii) $|\angle ADC| = 180° - 115°$... interior angles sum to 180°
$= 65°$
(iv) $|\angle DBC| = 180° - 115° - 28°$... $|\angle BCD| = 115°$ from (i) above
$= 37°$

Exercise 9.3

1. Find the measure of the angle marked with a letter in each of these parallelograms.

2. Find the size of the angle marked with a letter in each of these parallelograms:

3. Find the size of the angle marked with a letter in each of these parallelograms:

4. In the given quadrilateral, all the sides are equal, as marked.

Calculate the values of x, y, z and r.

(This figure is called a rhombus.)

5. ABCD is a parallelogram with the diagonals intersecting at the point O.
Write down the length of
   (i) [OB]
   (ii) [AB]
   (iii) [AC]
   (iv) [BC]

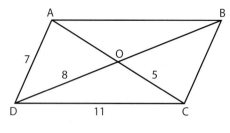

6. In the given parallelogram ABCD, parallel lines are drawn, as shown.
Find the values of the angles marked x, y and z.

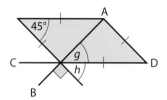

7. In the given parallelogram, all the sides are equal in length.
AB and CD are straight lines.
Find the sizes of the angles marked g and h.

8. Find the size of the angle marked with a letter in each of these figures.

9. Find the value of x in each of the diagrams below:
   (i)
   (ii)
   (iii)

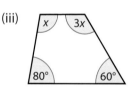

10. Find the value of y in each of the diagrams below:
   (i)
   (ii)

Section 9.4 Congruent triangles

Figures which are exactly the **same size and shape** are said to be **congruent**.
The following diagrams illustrate some congruent shapes, even though some of these shapes are turned over or upside down.

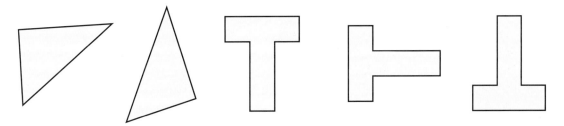

The two triangles below are congruent because all the angles and sides of one triangle are exactly the same as the angles and sides of the other triangle.

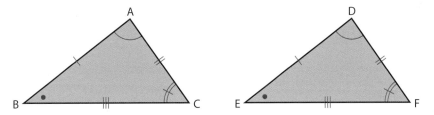

These two triangles are in fact congruent but it is not as immediately obvious.

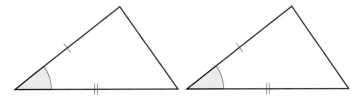

To help us identify congruent triangles, at least one of the following conditions must exist:

1. Two triangles are congruent if three sides in one triangle are equal in measure to three sides in the other triangle (SSS).

Case 1
SSS.

In the diagram below, each pair of triangles is congruent.

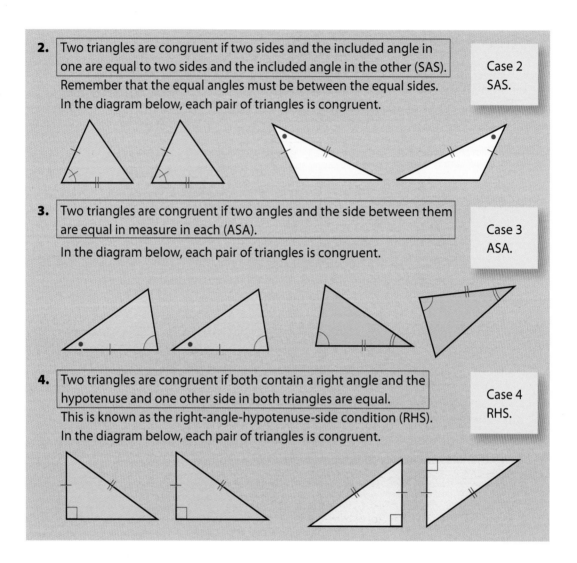

2. Two triangles are congruent if two sides and the included angle in one are equal to two sides and the included angle in the other (SAS). Remember that the equal angles must be between the equal sides. In the diagram below, each pair of triangles is congruent.

Case 2
SAS.

3. Two triangles are congruent if two angles and the side between them are equal in measure in each (ASA).

In the diagram below, each pair of triangles is congruent.

Case 3
ASA.

4. Two triangles are congruent if both contain a right angle and the hypotenuse and one other side in both triangles are equal. This is known as the right-angle-hypotenuse-side condition (RHS). In the diagram below, each pair of triangles is congruent.

Case 4
RHS.

Corresponding sides and angles

The two triangles below are congruent (ASA).

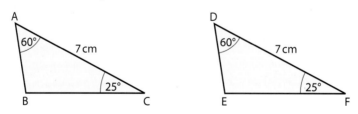

The side [DE] corresponds to the side [AB] as they are both opposite the 25° angle.

Similarly, [EF] corresponds to [BC] as they are both opposite the 60° angle.

The angle ABC corresponds to the angle DEF as they are both opposite the side of length 7 cm.

Since the triangles are congruent, it also implies that [BC] and [EF] are equal in length.

In mathematics, the word **implies** means that when one statement is made, another statement follows on logically from the first statement.

Note: If the triangles ABC and DEF are congruent, it can be written as △**ABC** ≡ △**DEF**.

Example 1

Explain why the two triangles shown are congruent.

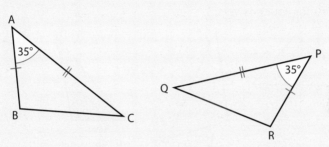

The triangles are congruent because two sides and the included angle in one triangle are equal to two sides and the included angle in the other triangle.

Many geometry theorems and other geometric problems are solved by showing that two triangles are congruent.

The worked example below shows how congruent triangles can be used to prove a very important property of equilateral triangles.

Example 2

Given the triangle ABC in which
$|AC| = |AB|$ and [AD] bisects ∠CAB.
Prove that $|∠ACD| = |∠ABD|$.

In the triangles ACD and ABD,
$\quad |AC| = |AB|$ ... given
$\quad |AD| = |AD|$ ... common side
$\quad |∠CAD| = |∠BAD|$ ... given [AD] is bisector of ∠CAB
∴ $\quad$ △ACD ≡ △ABC ... SAS
∴ $\quad$ $|∠ACD| = |∠ABD|$ ... corresponding angles, both opposite [AD].

Exercise 9.4

1. Explain why the two triangles shown are congruent.

2. State why each of the following pairs of triangles are congruent, using SSS, SAS, ASA or RHS as reasons for your answers:

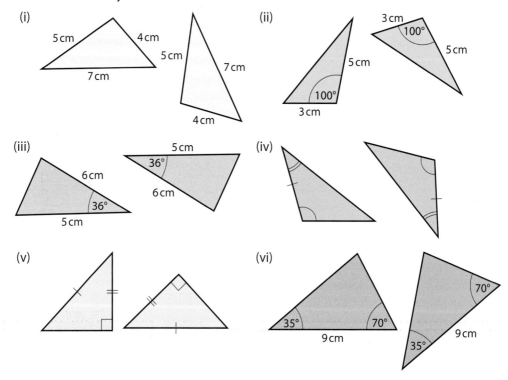

3. Which two of these triangles are congruent to each other?
Give a reason for your answer.

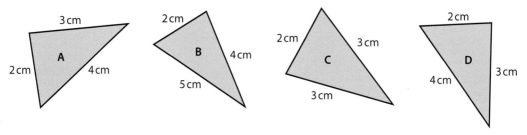

4. State whether the following pairs of triangles are congruent.
Give reasons for your answers.

(i)

(ii)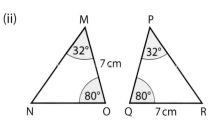

5. Are the triangles ABD and BCD on the right congruent?
Give a reason for your answer.

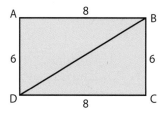

6. Explain why the triangles AOB and COD are congruent.

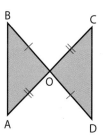

7. Explain why the two triangles shown below are congruent.

   (i) Which side corresponds
       to [BC]?

  (ii) Which side corresponds
       to [DE]?

  (iii) Find $|\angle DEF|$.

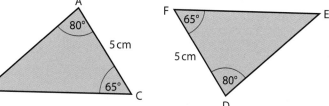

8. These triangles are congruent.
Write down the values of x and y.

9. ABCD is a parallelogram.

Show that the triangles ABC and ACD are congruent.

Hence explain why the angles ABC and ADC are equal in size.

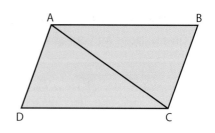

10. The straight lines [AB] and [CD] are equal in length and parallel.

Prove that triangles AEB and DEC are congruent.

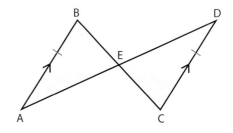

11. PQR is an isosceles triangle with $|PQ| = |PR|$.

M is the midpoint of [PQ].

N is the midpoint of [PR].

Prove that triangle PQN is congruent to triangle PRM.

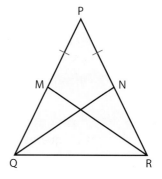

12. ABCD is a quadrilateral with $|AD| = |AB|$.

Angle ADC = angle ABC = 90°.

Prove that triangles ADC and ABC are congruent.

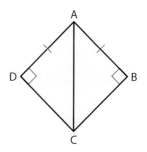

13. ABC is an isosceles triangle with $|AB| = |AC|$.

Prove that triangles ACD and ABE are congruent.

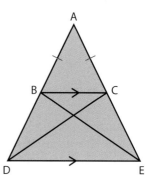

14. ABCD is a parallelogram and M is the midpoint of [CD].

    (i) Prove that the triangles ADM and PCM are congruent.

    (ii) Hence show that $|AM| = |MP|$.

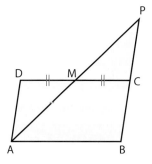

Section 9.5 The Theorem of Pythagoras

The diagram on the right shows a right-angled triangle of sides 3, 4 and 5 cm.

Squares are drawn on each of the three sides.

By counting the number of cm² in each of these squares, you will notice that the area of the square on the hypotenuse is 25 cm², while the other two squares have areas 16 cm² and 9 cm².

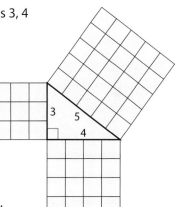

This diagram illustrates that the square on the hypotenuse is equal to the sum of the squares on the other two sides.

This important theorem is called the **Theorem of Pythagoras**.

Pythagoras was a Greek philosopher and mathematician who died about 500 BC.

> **Theorem of Pythagoras**
> In a right-angled triangle, the square on the hypotenuse is equal to the sum of the squares on the other two sides.

The Theorem of Pythagoras can be expressed very neatly through algebra, as shown.

The converse of the Theorem of Pythagoras is also true and is stated below.

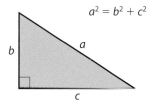

> **Converse of Theorem of Pythagoras**
> If the square on one side of a triangle is equal to the sum of the squares on the other two sides, then the angle opposite the first side is a right angle.

The triangle shown is right-angled since

$$10^2 = 8^2 + 6^2$$

i.e. $100 = 100.$

Example 1

Find the lengths of the sides marked x in the following right-angled triangles.

(i)

(ii)

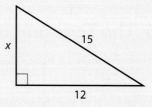

By the Theorem of Pythagoras:

(i) $x^2 = 3^2 + 2^2$
        $x^2 = 9 + 4$
$\therefore$ $x^2 = 13$
$\therefore$ $x = \sqrt{13}$
$\therefore$ $x = 3.6$

(ii) $15^2 = 12^2 + x^2$
            $225 = 144 + x^2$
    $225 - 144 = 144 + x^2 - 144$
            $x^2 = 81$
    $\therefore$ $x = \sqrt{81}$
    $\therefore$ $x = 9$

Example 2

Calculate the lengths marked x and y.

First $x^2 = 3^2 + 4^2$
        $x^2 = 9 + 16 = 25$
        $x = \sqrt{25}$
        $x = 5\,cm$

Then $y^2 + x^2 = 13^2$
        $y^2 + 5^2 = 13^2$
        $y^2 + 25 = 169$
            $y^2 = 169 - 25 = 144$
            $y = \sqrt{144}$
            $y = 12\,cm$

Exercise 9.5

1. Work out the length of the hypotenuse in each of these triangles:

(i)
(ii)
(iii)

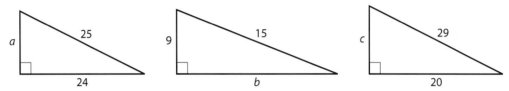

2. Find the length of the side marked with a letter in each of the following right-angled triangles.

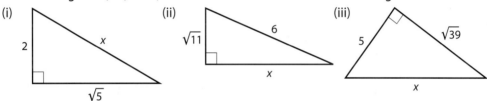

3. Remembering that $(\sqrt{2})^2 = 2$, find the value of x in each of these triangles:

(i)
(ii)
(iii)

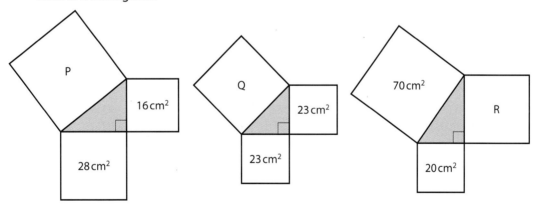

4. Use the **Theorem of Pythagoras** to find the area of the square marked with a letter in each of these figures:

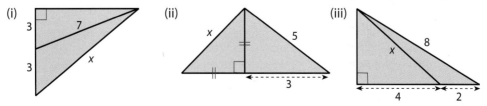

5. Find the length of the side marked x in each of the following right-angled triangles:

(i)
(ii)
(iii)

6. Find |AB| in the given right-angled triangle.

Now find the area of the triangle ABC.

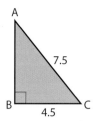

7. Find the value of x and y in each of the figures.
Where necessary, give your answer correct to the nearest whole number.

(i)

(ii)

(iii)

8. Find the values of x and y in the given diagram.

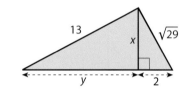

9. The diagram shows the side-view of a car ramp.
The ramp is 110 cm long and 25 cm high.
The top part of the ramp is 40 cm long.
Calculate the length of the sloping part of
the ramp, correct to the nearest cm.

10. In the given figure, $|\angle ACB| = |\angle CDB| = 90°$.

Find the lengths of the sides marked x and y.

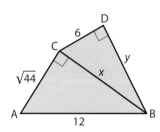

11. ABCD represents one end of a garden shed.
$|AB| = 2.30$ m, $|AD| = 2.25$ m and $|BC| = 3.15$ m.
Calculate
  (i) the length of [CD]
  (ii) the perimeter of ABCD
  (iii) the area of ABCD.
Give each answer correct to 2 decimal places.

12. A suitcase is 80 cm long and 60 cm wide.
Jane has an umbrella of length 1.05 m.
Will it fit in the bottom of her suitcase? Explain.

13. Use Pythagoras' theorem to decide whether or not these triangles have a right angle.

(i)

(ii)

14. Two right-angled triangles are joined together
to make a larger triangle ACD.
  (i) Show that the perimeter of triangle
      ACD is 78 cm.
 (ii) Show that triangle ACD is also a
      right-angled triangle.
      Explain why.

15. This glass tank is a cuboid. It has length 12 cm,
width 5 cm and height 8 cm.

  (i) Work out the length of the diagonal [HF].
 (ii) Hence work out the length of the
      diagonal [BH], in cm, correct to
      1 decimal place.

16. Semicircles are drawn on the sides of the given
right-angled triangle. Investigate if the area of
the semicircle on the hypotenuse is equal to
the sum of the areas of the semicircles on
the other two sides.

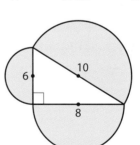

> Area of circle $= \pi r^2$

17. ABCD is a quadrilateral in which AC $\perp$ BD.
Explain why $|AB|^2 = |AM|^2 + |BM|^2$.
Hence show that
      $|AB|^2 + |CD|^2 = |AD|^2 + |BC|^2$.

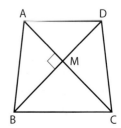

Test yourself 9

1. (a) Find the size of each angle marked with a letter in the figures below, where the arrows indicate parallel lines:

  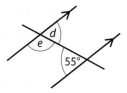

(b) Find the size of the angle marked with a letter in each of these triangles:

2. (a) Find the measures of the angles marked *a* and *b* in the triangles below, where equal sides are marked.

(b) Find the measure of each angle marked with a letter in the following parallelograms:

3. (a) Find the measure of each angle marked with a letter in each of the following figures, where the arrows indicate parallel lines.

(b) Find the value of x in the given triangle.
    What can be deduced about the triangle?

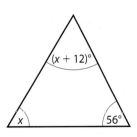

(c) If l∥m, find the sizes of the angles
    a, b, and c in the given figure.

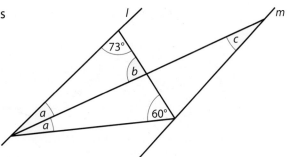

4. (a) In the given figure, equal sides are
       indicated. Find the sizes of the angles
       marked a and b.

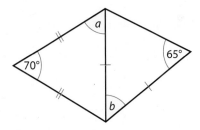

(b) Which two of the following triangles are congruent?
    Give a reason for your answer.

(c) ABC is an isosceles triangle with |AB| = |AC|.
    AE is parallel to BC.
    [BA] is produced to D.

    (i) Prove that AE bisects ∠DAC.
    (ii) Would the result in part (i) still apply if |AB| and
         |AC| were not equal?
         Give a reason for your answer.

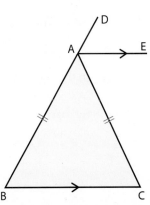

5. (a) Find the value of the angle marked *x* in each of the following diagrams, where the arrows indicate parallel lines.

(i)   (ii) (iii)

(b) A 4.5 m long pipe rests on a 2 m high fence.
One end of the pipe is on the ground,
3 m from the base of the fence.
How much of the pipe overhangs the fence?
Give your answer in metres, correct
to one decimal place.

(c) LMNP is a trapezium.
$|LP| = |MN|$ and $|\angle PLM| = |\angle NML|$.
Prove that the triangle PLM is
congruent to the triangle NML.

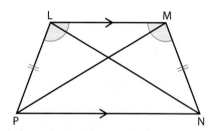

6. (a) Find the values of *x* and *y* in each of the following triangles.

(i)   (ii)   (iii)

(b) A room has floor dimensions 5 m by 4 m, as shown.
The height of the room is 3 m.
  (i) Find $|BD|$ in metres, correct to
       1 decimal place.
  (ii) Find the distance from the corner-point D
       on the floor to the opposite corner-point A
       on the ceiling, correct to the nearest metre.

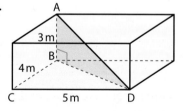

(c) In the given diagram,
$|AX| = |XC| = |BX|$.
By marking equal angles,
explain why $|\angle ABC| = 90°$.

Probability

Section 10.1 Listing outcomes

Here is a spinner with 8 sectors.
It has 8 different numbers and 3 different colours.
If the spinner is spun, you may get any of the numbers
1, 2, 3, 4, 5, 6, 7 or 8.
These are called **outcomes**.
If we are interested in colours only, then the possible
outcomes are green, blue and yellow.

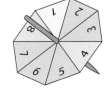

For the spinner above, we **listed** all the **possible outcomes** for numbers and for colours.

We will now consider the outcomes when this spinner is spun and a coin is tossed.

Here is the list of the possible outcomes:

   1H, 2H, 3H, 4H, 5H, 6H, 7H, 8H, 1T, 2T, 3T, 4T, 5T, 6T, 7T, 8T.

where H stands for head and T stands for tail.
Notice that there are **16** outcomes.

The number of outcomes can be found much more easily by multiplying **8** (number of
outcomes for the spinner) and **2** (number of outcomes for the coin), i.e. 8 × 2 = 16.

The preceding example illustrates the
Fundamental Principle of Counting
which is given on the right.

If one event has **m** possible outcomes and a
second event has **n** possible outcomes, the
two events have **m** × **n** possible outcomes.

Two-way tables

When the two spinners on the right are spun, the possible outcomes can be shown in an organised way by means of a **two-way table**, as shown below.

Numbers

	3	**4**	**5**	**6**
R	3R	4R	5R	6R
B	3B	4B	5B	6B
G	3G	4G	5G	6G

Colours

Number of possible outcomes is

$$4 \times 3 = 12$$

The **Fundamental Principle of Counting** can be extended to any number of events.

If a boy has to choose a shirt, a tie and a jacket from 5 shirts, 3 ties and 4 jackets he has,

$5 \times 3 \times 4$ choices

Exercise 10.1

1. An 'early-bird' menu consists of 3 starters and 4 main courses.
   How many different 2-course meals can you have?

2. Two coins are tossed.
   List all the possible outcomes using H for head and T for tail.

3. This spinner is spun and the dice is thrown.
   (i) How many different outcomes of colour
       and number can you have?
   (ii) How many of these outcomes will have
        the colour yellow?
   (iii) How many of the outcomes will have the number 3?

4. A code consists of one of the letters A, B, C or D followed by a digit from 1 to 9.
   How many different codes are possible?

5. A lunch menu consists of 3 starters, 4 main courses and 2 desserts.
   How many different 3-course meals can a person have?

6. A car manufacturer produces different types of cars as follows:
   › the model can be Saloon, Estate or Hatchback
   › the colours can be silver, black or red
   › the style can be Standard, Deluxe or Premium.
   How many different choices of car does a buyer have?

7. A game consists of spinning the given spinner and throwing a dice.

   (i) If the outcome of the game is a letter and a number, how many different outcomes are possible?

   (ii) If the game consists of a colour and a number, how many different outcomes are possible?

8. A pupil must choose one subject out of each of the following subject groups:

   › Group A has 3 modern language subjects.
   › Group B has 2 science subjects.
   › Group C has 2 business subjects.

   How many different subject selections are possible?

9. A restaurant advertises its lunch menu using the sign shown on the right.

   (i) The menu has a choice of five starters and nine main courses.
   How many items must appear on the dessert menu to justify the claim of 180 different lunches?

   (ii) On a particular day, one of the starters and one of the main course are not available.
   How many different three-course lunches is it possible to have on that day?

> **Lunch Menu**
> **3 courses for €18**
> Choose from our range of starters, main courses and desserts.
> 180 different lunches to choose from.

Section 10.2 Chance and the probability scale

You will already be familiar with words such as

Impossible   **Unlikely**   **Even chance**   **Likely**   **Certain**

to describe the **chance** or **probability** of something happening.

If we want to be more specific, we use numbers to describe how likely something is to happen.

An event which is **certain to happen** has a **probability of 1**.

An event which **cannot happen** has a **probability of 0**.

All other probabilities will be a number greater than 0 and less than 1.

The more likely an event is to happen, the closer the probability is to 1.

The line shown below is called a **probability scale**.

There is an **even chance** that the next person you meet on the street will be a male.

It is **certain** that the sun will rise tomorrow.

It is **impossible** to get 7 when a normal dice is rolled.

Exercise 10.2

1. Which of these labels best describes the likelihood of each of the events below occurring?

| Impossible | Unlikely | Even Chance | Likely | Certain |

   (i) A coin will show 'tails' when you toss it.

   (ii) You are more than ten years old.

   (iii) The sun will not rise in Ireland tomorrow.

   (iv) You will win an Olympic medal.

   (v) The next person you meet on the street will be Irish.

   (vi) You will get an even number when an ordinary dice is thrown.

   (vii) You will get less than 5 winning numbers when playing the *Euromillions* some Friday.

   (viii) It will snow later today.

   (ix) I draw a red card from a standard pack of cards.

   (x) You will get homework tonight.

2. For each of the events given below, choose one of these words:

   impossible   unlikely   even chance   likely   certain

   (i) A dice is to be thrown.

   Event 1:   A 6 will be thrown.

   Event 2:   A number less than 4 will be thrown.

   Event 3:   A number greater than 3 will be thrown.

   Event 4:   A zero will be thrown.

   Event 5:   A number less than 7 will be thrown.

   (ii) One card is to be chosen at random from these five.

   Event 1:   The card will be a *heart*.

   Event 2:   The card will be less than 8.

   Event 3:   The card will be a *diamond*.

   Event 4:   The card will be a 2.

   Event 5:   The card will not be a 3.

3. Here are four spinners with different colours:

A   B   C   D

If the spinners are spun,
  (i)   Which spinner has an even chance of showing blue?
  (ii) Which spinner has an even chance of showing red?
  (iii) Which spinner has the least chance of showing yellow?
  (iv) Which spinner has one chance in three of showing yellow?
  (v)   Which spinner has one chance in four of showing red?
  (vi) Which spinner has the greatest chance of showing red?

4. Order each of the events below from least likely to most likely:
  (i)   A dice is to be thrown.
    (a)   The number showing will be even.
    (b)   The number showing will be larger than 4.
    (c)   The number showing will be less than 6.

  (ii) One card is to be chosen at random from these six.
    (a)   The card will be a 2.
    (b)   The card will be a 7.
    (c)   The card will be greater than a 3.

5. The jar shown contains red, blue and green marbles.
When a marble is taken from the bag, the chances of
obtaining each of the three colours are shown in the
probability scale below.

Link each colour to either (a), (b) or (c):

6.

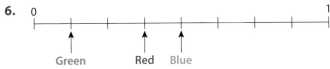

In a game, Todd spins an arrow.
The arrow stops in one of sixteen equal sectors of a circle.
Each sector of the circle is coloured.
The probability scale shows how likely it is for the arrow to
stop on any one colour.

How many sectors are

(i) coloured red (ii) coloured blue (iii) coloured green?

Section 2.3 Probability and equally likely outcomes

Before you can start a certain game, you must throw a dice and get a six.

The act of throwing a dice is called a **trial**.

The numbers 1, 2, 3, 4, 5 and 6 are all the possible **outcomes** of the trial.

The list of all possible outcomes is called a **sample space**.

The desired result is called an **event**.

If you require an even number when throwing a dice, then the **events** or **successful outcomes** are the numbers 2, 4 and 6.

> The result we want is called an **event**.

Equally likely outcomes

Two events are **equally likely** if they have the same chance of happening.

The chance of getting a red with this spinner is the same as the chance of getting a blue. Getting a red and getting a blue are **equally likely**.

The chances of getting a red or getting a blue with this spinner are **not** equally likely. The probability of getting a red when this spinner is spun is one chance in four.

We write this as Probability (red) $= \frac{1}{4}$.
This is shortened to P(red) $= \frac{1}{4}$.

The outcome we want is generally called a **favourable outcome**.

> A favourable outcome is an outcome that you want.

> For **equally likely outcomes**, the probability of event E occurring is given as
>
> $$P(E) = \frac{\text{Number of favourable outcomes}}{\text{Number of possible outcomes}}$$

For the spinner on the right,

P(green) $= \frac{1}{5}$, because 1 of the 5 sections is green

P(yellow) $= \frac{2}{5}$, because 2 of the 5 sections are yellow.

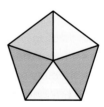

Example 1

Below is a number of lettered tiles.

| P | A | R | A | L | L | E | L | O | G | R | A | M |

One of these tiles is selected at random.
Work out the probability of getting:
  (i) an A   (ii) an L   (iii) an O
(iv) an A or an L   (v) an A or an O   (vi) an L or an O

  (i) There are 3 tiles lettered A out of the 13 tiles.
$$P(A) = \frac{\text{number of As}}{\text{total number}} = \frac{3}{13}$$

 (ii) $P(L) = \dfrac{\text{number of Ls}}{\text{total number}} = \dfrac{3}{13}$

(iii) $P(O) = \dfrac{1}{13}$

(iv) $P(A \text{ or } L) = \dfrac{\text{number of As} + \text{Ls}}{\text{total number}} = \dfrac{6}{13}$

 (v) $P(A \text{ or } O) = \dfrac{4}{13}$ (vi) $P(L \text{ or } O) = \dfrac{4}{13}$

Exercise 10.3

1. (i) State the sample space for each of these spinners:

    (a)   (b)   (c)

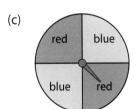

    (ii) For each of the spinners, write down the probability that the spinner ends on red.

2. What is the probability of getting a 6 on each of these spinners?

    (i)   (ii)   (iii)

What is the probability of getting a 2 or a 6 on spinner (iii)?

3. A fair dice is rolled.

What is the probability of getting

    (i)   a 5

    (iii) 4 or more

    (v)   less than 3

    (ii)   a 1 or a 2

    (iv) an odd number

    (vi) a prime number?

4. Here is a selection of shapes.

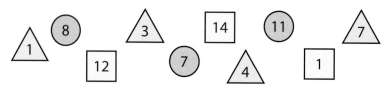

One of these shapes is chosen at random. Work out the probability that the shape will be:

    (i)   a square

    (iv) an odd number

    (ii)   a triangle

    (v)   a 2-digit number

    (iii) a square or a triangle

    (vi) a green odd number.

5. A letter is chosen at random from the word *PROBABILITY*.

Write down the probability that it will be

    (i)   *A*   (ii)   *B*   (iii) *I*   (iv) a vowel   (v) a *B* or an *I*.

6. For each of the following spinners, find the probability that the outcome of one spin will be a four.

    (i)   (ii)   (iii)

7. A dart board has 36 sectors, labelled 1 to 36.
Determine the probability that a dart thrown at the board hits:

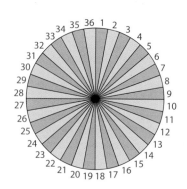

    (i)   a multiple of 4

    (ii)   a number between 6 and 9 inclusive

    (iii) a number greater than 20

    (iv) 9

    (v)   a multiple of 13

    (vi) an odd number that is a multiple of 3.

8. A standard pack of cards has 4 suits; hearts (♥), diamonds (♦), clubs (♣) and spades (♠). There are 13 cards in each suit and 52 cards altogether.

The first of these cards is called an **Ace**. The last three cards are the *picture* or *court* cards: the **Jack**, the **Queen** and the **King**.

From the 13 cards shown above, one card is to be chosen at random. What is the probability that the card chosen will be:
   (i)   the 7
   (ii) the Ace
   (iii) a picture card
   (iv) a heart
   (v)   a spade
   (vi) either a 9 or a 10?

9. From a standard pack of 52 cards, a card is chosen at random.
   What is the probability that the card will be:
   (i)   a diamond
   (ii) a red card
   (iii) a black card
   (iv) a 3
   (v)   a picture card
   (vi) either an Ace or a King?

10. A box contains twelve green marbles, six blue marbles and eight white marbles.
   A marble is selected at random.
   What is the probability that the marble selected is:
   (i)   green or white
   (ii) blue or white
   (iii) not green
   (iv) orange?

11. A square dart board is divided into sixteen smaller squares. Fourteen of the squares are painted as shown.
   (i) What colour(s) should the remaining squares be painted so that the probability of landing on red is $\frac{3}{8}$ and it is impossible to land on black?
   (ii) What colour(s) should the remaining squares be painted so that the probability of landing on red is twice the probability of landing on blue?

red	yellow	red	blue
white	red	white	blue
red	blue	white	red
white	yellow	?	?

12. What is the probability that the pointer of these spinners lands in the blue section?
   (i)
   (ii)
   (iii)
   (iv)

13. Design a spinner for which the probability of the pointer landing in the blue section is:
   (i)   half
   (ii) less than half
   (iii) three times as likely as on red

14. Assuming that a person is equally likely to be born on any day of the week or in any month of the year, what is the probability that a randomly-chosen person has his/her birthday
    (i) on a Tuesday
    (ii) on a Saturday or Sunday
    (iii) in January or February?

15. A bag contains five red discs with the numbers 1 to 5 painted on them and seven blue discs painted with the numbers 1 to 7. If a disc is chosen at random, what is the probability of choosing
    (i) a red disc
    (ii) a disc numbered 3
    (iii) a disc numbered 6
    (iv) the blue disc numbered 1
    (v) an even numbered disc
    (vi) an odd numbered disc?

    Explain why the probabilities in (v) and (vi) sum to 1.

16. In a pre-election poll of 400 people, 120 supported the A party, 140 supported the B party and the rest were undecided. If a person is selected at random from this group, what is the probability that they:
    (i) support the A party
    (ii) support the B party
    (iii) support a party
    (iv) are undecided?

17. At the end of a Summer Camp, 50 boys and girls were asked to name their favourite game at the camp. The results are given in the table below:

	Tennis	Basketball	Volleyball
Girls	15	10	5
Boys	6	12	2

    If a person was selected at random from the group of 50, find the probability that the person
    (i) was a boy
    (ii) was a girl who named tennis as her favourite game
    (iii) named basketball as her/his favourite game.

    If a girl was selected, find the probability that she had named volleyball as her favourite game.

18. Of 100 tickets sold in a raffle, Luke bought 10, Heather bought 5 and Alan bought 1. A ticket was chosen at random to determine who won the prize.
    What is the probability that the prize was won by:
    (i) Alan
    (ii) Luke
    (iii) Heather
    (iv) none of these three people?

    How many of the 100 tickets would I need to buy for the probability of my winning to be:
    (v) $\frac{3}{10}$
    (vi) 0.2
    (vii) 25%
    (viii) 100%?

19. There are 8 counters in a box.
    The probability of taking a green counter out of the box is $\frac{1}{2}$.
    A green counter is taken out of the box and put to one side.
    Gerry now takes a counter at random from the box.
    What is the probability it is green?

20. A game is played by picking a card at random from
    a pack of 52 playing cards.
    The table shows the results of picking various cards.

Card	Result
Ace	Win €2
K, Q or J	Win 50c
6, 7, 8, 9, 10	No result
2, 3, 4, 5	Lose 50c

    If Eileen picks a card, what is the probability that she will
    (i)   lose money   (ii) win money
    (iii) neither win nor lose   (iv) not lose money?

21. This table shows information about a group
    of children.

	Boys	Girls
Blue eyes	3	6
Brown eyes	12	9

    (i)   How many children are in the group altogether?
    (ii) If a child is chosen from the group at random,
          what is the probability of that child
          (a)   having blue eyes   (b)   being a boy?
    (iii) If a boy is chosen from the group, what is the probability that he has blue eyes?

22. Naomi approaches a roundabout from the west.
    She chooses one of the other exit roads at random
    when leaving the roundabout.
    (i)   What is the probability that she chooses
          the dead end?
    (ii) What is the probability that she chooses
          a road that leads to (X)?

Section 10.4 Two events – Use of sample spaces

When a dice is thrown and a coin is tossed, the set of possible
outcomes is as follows:

   {H1, H2, H3, H4, H5, H6, T1, T2, T3, T4, T5, T6}.

This set of possible outcomes is called a **sample space**.

Using the sample space above, we can write down the probability of getting a head and a 6,
for example.

   $P(H, 6) = \frac{1}{12}$

The probability of a head and an even number can be found by counting the required
outcomes.
These are H2, H4 and H6.

∴ $P(H \text{ and even number}) = \frac{3}{12} = \frac{1}{4}$

An experiment such as throwing two dice has a large number of possible outcomes, so we need to set out the sample space in an organised way, as shown in the following example.

Example 1

If two dice are thrown and the scores are added, set out a sample space giving all the possible outcomes. Now find the probability that

   (i) the total is exactly 7   (ii) the total is 4 or less

(iii) the total is 11 or more   (iv) the total is a multiple of 5.

The sample space is set out on the right.
There are 36 outcomes.

   (i) There are 6 totals of 7.

$$\Rightarrow \quad P(7) = \frac{6}{36} = \frac{1}{6}$$

  (ii) There are 6 totals of 4 or less.

$$\Rightarrow \quad P(4 \text{ or less}) = \frac{6}{36} = \frac{1}{6}$$

(iii) There are 3 totals of 11 or more.

$$\Rightarrow \quad P(11 \text{ or more}) = \frac{3}{36} = \frac{1}{12}$$

(iv) The multiples of 5 are 5 and 10.
     There are 7 totals of 5 or 10.

$$\Rightarrow \quad P(\text{multiple of 5}) = \frac{7}{36}$$

Total = 4 or less

	1	2	3	4	5	6
1	2	3	4	5	6	7
2	3	4	5	6	7	8
3	4	5	6	7	8	9
4	5	6	7	8	9	10
5	6	7	8	9	10	11
6	7	8	9	10	11	12

Total = 7

Exercise 10.4

1. These are the possible outcomes when two coins are tossed:

     HH, HT, TH, TT

Write down the probability of getting

   (i) 2 tails   (ii) 2 heads   (iii) a head and a tail.

2. When these two spinners are spun and the scores are added, you get the results shown on the right.

Number on 1st spinner

Number on 2nd spinner		1	2	3	4
	1	2	3	4	5
	2	3	4	5	6
	3	4	5	6	7
	4	5	6	7	8

Use the table to write down the following probabilities:

   (i) The total score is 6   (ii) the total score is an odd number

(iii) the total score is 7 or more   (iv) the total score is 2 or 3.

3. A fair three-sided spinner has sections labelled 2, 4 and 6.
The spinner is spun once and a fair
six-sided dice is thrown once.

The number that the spinner lands
on is added to the number that the
dice shows. This gives the score.

Copy and complete the table to show all
possible scores.

Use the table to write down the probability
that the score is

   (i) 4   (ii) 5
  (iii) 7   (iv) 9 or more
  (v) 5 or less   (vi) a multiple of 4

Dice

+	1	2	3	4	5	6
2	3					
4						
6						12

Spinner (left axis label)

4. Karl has two fair spinners, numbered as shown.
He spins them and finds the **product** of the
two scores.
  (i) Copy and complete the grid, to show all
      possible outcomes of the two spins.
  (ii) What is the probability that the product is
     (a) 12   (b) greater than 10   (c) a multiple of 3?

Second spinner				
6				
5			15	
4				
3				
	1	2	3	4

First spinner

5. The ace, king, queen and jack of clubs and the
ace, king, queen and jack of diamonds are put
into two piles. The sample space diagram shows
all the possible outcomes when a card is taken
from each pile.

J	AJ	KJ	QJ	JJ
Q	AQ	KQ	QQ	JQ
K	AK	KK	QK	JK
A	AA	KA	QA	JA
	A	K	Q	J

Clubs (left label)

Diamonds

Write down the probability that
  (i) both cards will be kings
  (ii) one card will be a club
  (iii) only one of the cards will be a queen
  (iv) the cards will make a matching pair
  (v) at least one of the cards will be a queen
  (vi) neither card will be a jack.

6. Three fair coins are tossed.
Make out a sample space for all
the possible outcomes.

Now write down the probability
that the outcome will be
  (i) three heads   (ii) two heads and one tail
  (iii) no heads   (iv) at least one head.

7. Two dice are thrown and the scores obtained are added. The resulting outcomes are shown in the given sample space. Find the probability that the sum of the two numbers is

    (i) 9   (ii) 10

    (iii) 3 or less   (iv) 10 or 11.

8. Chloe is playing a word game and chooses a vowel and a consonant at random from her letters.

    (i) Show all the possible choices she can make on a sample space diagram.

    (ii) What is the probability of choosing A and R?

    (iii) What is the probability of choosing I and L?

    (iv) What is the probability of choosing I and not choosing L?

Section 10.5 Estimating probabilities from experiments

So far we have calculated probabilities on the basis that all outcomes are equally likely to happen. However, in real-life situations, events are not always equally likely and some other way must be found to make an estimate of the probability.

In such cases we carry out an **experiment** or **survey** to estimate the probability of an event happening.

Experiment

John suspected that a coin was biased.

In an experiment, he tosses the coin 1000 times with the help of his friends.

He counted the number of heads obtained after 10, 20, 100 … and 1000 times.

The results are shown in the table on the right:

As the number of tosses increases, the values of the number of heads divided by the number of tosses gets closer to 0.5, i.e. $\frac{1}{2}$.

The value of the number of heads divided by the number of tosses is called the **experimental probability** or **relative frequency**.

It gives an **estimate** of the true probability.

Number of tosses	Number of heads	Heads ÷ tosses
10	6	0.6
20	11	0.55
100	53	0.53
200	108	0.54
400	194	0.485
500	242	0.484
1000	490	0.49

As the number of trials or experiments increases, the value of the experimental probability gets closer to the true or theoretical probability.

Since the probability of getting a head after tossing the coin 1000 times is very close to the true probability of $\frac{1}{2}$, John concludes that the coin is not biased.

Thus an estimate of the probability that an event will occur by carrying out a survey or experiment is given by

$$\text{Relative frequency} = \frac{\text{Number of successful trials}}{\text{Total number of trials}}$$

Example 1

Derek collects data on the colours of cars passing the school gate.
His results are shown in the table.

Colour	Tally	Frequency
White	IIII IIII IIII IIII IIII	24
Red	IIII IIII IIII IIII IIII IIII II	32
Black	IIII IIII IIII	14
Blue	IIII IIII IIII I	16
Green	IIII IIII	10
Other	IIII	4

  (i)   How many cars did Derek survey?
 (ii)   What was the relative frequency of blue cars?
(iii)   What was the relative frequency of red cars?
          Give your answer as a decimal.
 (iv)   Write down an estimate of the probability that the next car passing the
          school gate will be green.
  (v)   How can the estimate for the probability of green cars be made more
          reliable?

  (i)   The number of cars in the survey is the sum of the frequencies.
          This is 100 cars.
 (ii)   Relative frequency of blue cars $= \frac{16}{100} = \frac{4}{25}$
(iii)   Relative frequency of red cars $= \frac{32}{100} = 0.32$
 (iv)   Probability of next car green $=$ relative frequency of green cars
$$= \frac{10}{100} = \frac{1}{10}$$
  (v)   The estimate for the probability of green cars can be made more reliable by
          increasing the number of cars observed. Five hundred cars would give a very
          accurate estimate of the true probability.

Expected frequency

This bag contains 5 red discs and 3 blue discs.

A disc is chosen at random from the bag and then replaced.

The probability of getting a blue disc is $\frac{3}{8}$.

This means that, on average, you expect 3 blue discs in every 8 chosen or 30 blue discs in every 80 chosen.

To find the expected number of blue discs when you choose a disc 400 times,

 (i) Work out the probability that the event happens once.

 (ii) Multiply this probability by the number of times the experiment is carried out.
      Thus the expected number of blue discs is

$$\tfrac{3}{8} \times \tfrac{400}{1} = 150.$$

> Expected frequency is:
>
> probability × number of trials.

Example 2

This spinner is biased.
The probability that the spinner will land on each of the numbers 1 to 4 is given in the table below.

Number	1	2	3	4	5
Probability	0.35	0.1	0.25	0.15	

The spinner is spun once.
  (i)   Work out the probability that the spinner will land on 5.
  (ii) Write down the number on which the spinner is most likely to land.
  (iii) If the spinner is spun 200 times, how many times would you expect it to land on 3?

  (i)   The sum of all the probabilities is 1.
        Let x be the probability of the spinner landing on 5.
        $\therefore \qquad x + 0.35 + 0.1 + 0.25 + 0.15 = 1$
        $\qquad\qquad\qquad\qquad x + 0.85 = 1 \quad \Rightarrow \quad x = 0.15$
        $\therefore \qquad$ P(spinner lands on 5) = 0.15
  (ii) This spinner is most likely to land on 1 as it has the highest probability.
  (iii) P(landing on 3) = $0.25 = \frac{1}{4}$

        In 200 spins, the number of times you would expect the spinner to land on
        3 is $\frac{1}{4} \times 200 = 50.$

Exercise 10.5

1. A fair coin is tossed 100 times.
   How many heads would you expect to get?

2. A fair six-sided dice is thrown 60 times.
   (i)   How many sixes would you expect to get?
   (ii) How many twos would you expect to get?
   (iii) How many even numbers would you expect to get?

3. One ball is selected at random from the bag
   shown and then replaced. This procedure
   is done 400 times.
   How many times would you expect to select:
   (i) a blue ball,
   (ii) a red ball?

4. 50 cars are observed passing the school gate. 15 of these cars are red.
   Use these results to estimate the probability that the next car to pass the school gate
   will be red.

5. Jane and Nicky both did the 'dropping a drawing pin' experiment.
   Here are their results.

Jane
Trials	20
'Point up'	10

Nicky
Trials	100
'Point up'	75

   Another drawing pin is dropped.
   (i)   For Jane, what is the probability of getting 'point up'?
   (ii) For Nicky, what is the probability of getting 'point up'?
   (iii) Whose result is likely to be more reliable? Explain your answer.

6. Ciara surveyed the colours of vehicles passing her home. Here are her results.

Colour	Red	Black	Silver	Green	White	Other
Frequency	6	10	24	4	12	8

   Calculate an estimate of the probability that the next vehicle to pass will be
   (i) silver
   (ii) not black.

7. Eoin is carrying out an experiment – 'dropping a spoon'.   Up
   He records whether the spoon lands up or down.
   (i) Copy and complete this table of Eoin's results.   Down

Number of drops	5	10	20	25	50	100
Number of times landed up	3	7	11	15	32	63
Probability	0.6	0.7				

(ii) What do you think could be a reasonable estimate for the true probability of a spoon landing up? Give your answer as a decimal, correct to 1 decimal place.

(iii) If Eoin dropped the spoon 300 times, how many times is it likely to land up? (i.e., the expected frequency.)

8. A bag contained coloured beads. Darren randomly selects a bead and then replaces it. He does this 60 times. Here are the results.

Colour	White	Green	Blue
Frequency	10	30	20

Estimate the probability that on his next draw he will select:

(i) a white bead (ii) a green bead (iii) a white bead or a blue bead

9. A bag contains eight counters. Each counter is blue or red or yellow.
Helena takes a counter at random from the bag. She records the colour of the counter and then puts the counter back in the bag.
She performs this experiment 400 times. The table shows her results.

Colour of counter	Blue	Red	Yellow
Frequency	210	98	92

(i) Estimate how many of the eight counters are blue.
Give an explanation for your answer.

(ii) Estimate how many of the eight counters are yellow.
Give an explanation for your answer.

10. Olivia, Ben and Joe each rolled a different dice 360 times.

Only one of the dice was fair. Whose was it?
Explain your answer.
Whose dice is the most biased?
Explain your answer.

Number	Olivia	Ben	Joe
1	27	58	141
2	69	62	52
3	78	63	56
4	43	57	53
5	76	56	53
6	67	64	5

11. A fair six-sided dice has its faces painted red, white or blue.
The dice is thrown 36 times.
Here are the results:

Colour	Frequency
Red	7
White	11
Blue	18

Based on the results, how many faces do you think are painted each colour?

12. Lyra made a spinner with three colours – yellow, blue and red.
She tested it by spinning it 500 times.
Her results were: yellow   240
                     blue   160
                     red   100

    (i) Estimate the probability of the spinner landing on yellow.
    (ii) She then spun the spinner 100 times.
         About how many times would you expect the spinner to land on yellow?

13. Carol spins a red and a green spinner 50 times each. She records whether or not each spinner lands on a 1. The tables show her results.

Red spinner

Lands on a 1	Does not land on a 1
7	43

Green spinner

Lands on a 1	Does not land on a 1
24	26

    (i) Work out the relative frequency of getting a 1 on each spinner.
    (ii) Both spinners are fair six-sectored spinners.

    How many sides of each spinner do you think will have a 1 on them?
    Give an explanation for your answers.

14. The probability of having to wait for more than 5 minutes at a post office is $\frac{2}{7}$.
350 people use the post office in one day.
Work out an estimate for the number of people who have to wait for more than 5 minutes.

15. These are the results of an experiment to test a spinner:

    (i) Explain what the spinner could look like.
    (ii) Draw a possible sketch of the spinner.

	Result of spins
Red	50
White	30
Blue	20
Total	100

16. David and Rory are keen golfers
Out of their last 20 rounds, Rory has won 14.
    (i) Based on these results, give and estimate of the probability that David will win the next round.
    (ii) Given that David wins the next five rounds, give an estimate of the probability that Rory wins the next round after that.

Section 10.6 Probability using Venn diagrams

If information is presented in the form of a Venn diagram, it is easy to write down the probability of different events occurring.

The diagrams below illustrate the main regions when two Venn diagrams intersect.

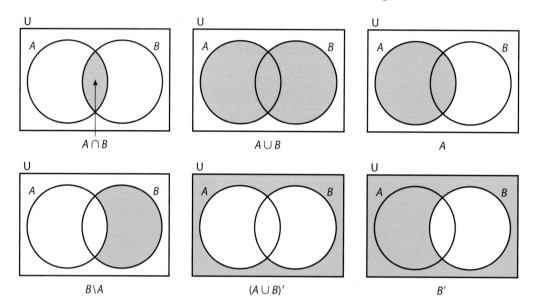

Example 1

The Venn diagram shows the sports played
by members of a club.
How many members played
  (i) both football and tennis
  (ii) tennis but not football
  (iii) neither of these two games
  (iv) football or tennis?
Now write down the probability of each of the above.

  (i) Both football and tennis = 10
  (ii) Tennis but not football = 35
  (iii) Neither of these two games = 45
  (iv) Football or tennis = 40 + 10 + 35 = 85

$$P(i) = \frac{10}{\text{total membership}} = \frac{10}{130} = \frac{1}{13} \qquad P(ii) = \frac{35}{130} = \frac{7}{26}$$

$$P(iii) = \frac{45}{130} = \frac{9}{26} \qquad P(iv) = \frac{85}{130} = \frac{17}{26}$$

Three sets

The diagram on the right shows the sports played by
a group of second-year students.

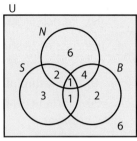

The probabilities of various events are given below.
Verify these probabilities by examining the diagram.

(i) P(student plays all three games) $= \dfrac{1}{25}$

(ii) P(student plays netball) $= \dfrac{6 + 2 + 1 + 4}{25} = \dfrac{13}{25}$

(iii) P(student doesn't play soccer) $= \dfrac{6 + 4 + 2 + 6}{25} = \dfrac{18}{25}$

(iv) P(student plays two games only) $= \dfrac{2 + 4 + 1}{25} = \dfrac{7}{25}$

N = netball
B = basketball
S = soccer

Exercise 10.6

1. In the given Venn diagram,

> U represents the houses in a given street,
>
> C represents those which have a cat and
>
> D represents those which have a dog.

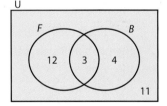

If a household is selected at random,
what is the probability that it has

(i) a cat   (ii) a cat and a dog   (iii) a dog but not a cat

(iv) a cat or a dog   (v) neither a cat nor a dog?

2. In the given Venn diagram,

> U = the students in class 1K
>
> F = the students in the class who play football
>
> B = the students in the class who play badminton.

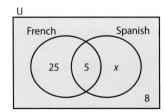

(i) How many students are there in the class?

(ii) How many students play badminton?

If a student is selected at random from the class, find the probability that the student

(iii) plays both games   (iv) plays neither game

(v) plays badminton but not football   (vi) plays one game only.

3. The given Venn diagram shows the modern languages,
if any, taken by a group of 50 students.

(i) Find the value of x.

If a student is selected at random, find the probability that the student takes
(ii) French
(iii) both French and Spanish
(iv) French or Spanish
(v) one of these languages only.

4. In a class of 28 students, 25 were wearing blazers or ties or both.
   Seven wore blazers with no tie and eight wore blazers and ties.
   (i) Show this information on a Venn diagram.
   (ii) Find the probability that a student selected at random was wearing a tie but not a blazer.
   (iii) Find the probability that a student selected at random was wearing neither a tie nor a blazer.

5. In a class of 40 children, a survey was carried out to find out how many children liked chocolate and how many liked ice-cream. The Venn diagram shows the results but the region marked A is not filled in.
   (i) What is the number in region A?
   (ii) What can you say about the children in region A?
   (iii) If one child is chosen at random, what is the probability that the child liked ice-cream but not chocolate?
   (iv) One of the children who liked chocolate is chosen at random. What is the probability that the child also liked ice-cream?

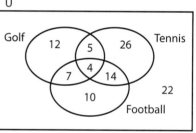

6. The Venn diagram on the right shows the results of a survey of a number of adults to find out which of the games golf, tennis or football, if any, they play.
   (i) How many adults were surveyed?

   If an adult was selected at random, find the probability that the person plays
   (ii) golf
   (iii) both golf and tennis
   (iv) all three games
   (v) football only
   (vi) football and tennis
   (vii) football and tennis but not golf.

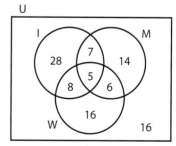

7. The given Venn diagram shows the results of a survey in which 100 people were asked to name which of the papers – *Independent* (I), *Mail* (M) or *World* (W) they had bought the previous Sunday.

   If a person was selected at random, find the probability that he/she had bought
   (i) the *Independent*
   (ii) the *World* and *Mail*
   (iii) one paper only
   (iv) two papers only
   (v) the *Mail* and *Independent* but not the *World*.

8. 35 people coming back from America were asked if they had visited New York, Boston or San Francisco. The results were as follows:

20 had visited New York.
13 had visited Boston.
16 had visited San Francisco.

7 had been to all three cities.

3 had been to both New York and San Francisco, but not Boston.
1 had been to both New York and Boston, but not San Francisco.
8 had been to Boston and San Francisco.

(i) Display this information in a Venn diagram.

(ii) If one person is chosen at random from the group, what is the probability that the person had not visited any of the three cities?

(iii) If one person is chosen at random, what is the probability that the person had visited New York only?

(iv) If one person is chosen at random, what is the probability that the person had visited Boston or New York?

(v) A person who visited New York is chosen at random.
What is the probability that the person also visited Boston?

Section 10.7 Tree diagrams ————————————

The possible outcomes of two or more events can be shown in a particular type of diagram called a **tree diagram**.
The branches of the tree represent all possible outcomes for each event.

The tree diagram below represents all possible outcomes in a three-child family.

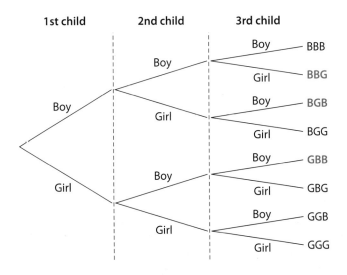

From the tree diagram, it can be seen that there are 8 possible outcomes.
The three highlighted results represent the families that have one girl.
$\therefore$ P(one girl) $= \frac{3}{8}$
From the diagram, it can be seen that P(3 boys) $= \frac{1}{8}$.

The diagram on the right shows
a tree diagram of the outcomes
when two coins are tossed.
We can see that P(HH) $= \frac{1}{4}$.

We will now redraw the tree diagram
and write the probabilities on the branches.
The P(HH) is found by multiplying the
probabilities along the relevant branches, i.e.,
$\frac{1}{2} \times \frac{1}{2} = \frac{1}{4}$.

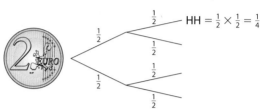

Example 1

Each of the spinners shown on the right is
spun once.
Draw a tree diagram to represent these spins.
Use the tree diagram to write down these
probabilities:

Spinner A   Spinner B

   (i) P(A red, B red)   (ii) P(both the same colour).

The tree diagram and the probabilities along each branch are shown below.

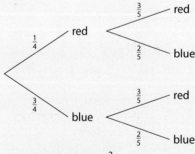

Spinner A   Spinner B

     $\frac{3}{5}$ red   probability of (A red, B red) $= \frac{1}{4} \times \frac{3}{5} = \frac{3}{20}$

     $\frac{2}{5}$ blue   probability of (A red, B blue) $= \frac{1}{4} \times \frac{2}{5} = \frac{2}{20}$

     $\frac{3}{5}$ red   probability of (A blue, B red) $= \frac{3}{4} \times \frac{3}{5} = \frac{9}{20}$

     $\frac{2}{5}$ blue   probability of (A blue, B blue) $= \frac{3}{4} \times \frac{2}{5} = \frac{6}{20}$

  (i) P(red, red) $= \frac{3}{20}$
 (ii) P(both the same colour) = probability of (A red, B red) + probability of
                  (A blue, B blue)
                $= \frac{3}{20} + \frac{6}{20} = \frac{9}{20}$

(Notice that the sum of the probabilities at the end of the four branches adds up
to 1.)

Exercise 10.7

1. When a motorist approaches any traffic lights, there is an even chance that they will be red or green.
   If a motorist has to go through two sets of lights, copy and complete the tree diagram on the right.
   Write down the probability of each of these:
   (i) P(both green)   (ii) P(one red, one green).

   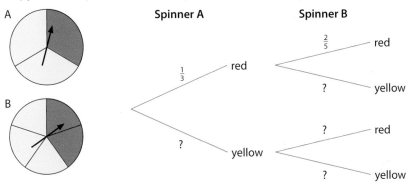

2. Copy and complete the tree diagram for these two spinners.

   What is the probability that A and B show
   (i) the same colour   (ii) different colours?

3. Paula has a dice with 5 red faces and 1 green face.
   She rolls the dice twice.
   (i) Copy and complete the tree diagram.
   (ii) Find the probability that the dice shows the same colour each time.
   (iii) Find the probability that the dice shows green and red in that order.

   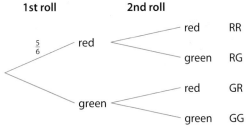

4. A bag contains 4 **red** beads and 2 **blue** beads.
   A second bag contains 2 **red** beads and 4 **blue** beads.
   Jack takes one bead at random from each bag.
   (i) Complete the probability tree diagram.
   (ii) Find the probability that Jack takes
       (a) 2 red beads
       (b) red and blue in that order
       (c) red and blue in any order.

   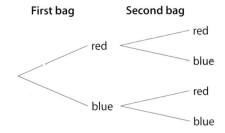

5. Gerry has a coin which is weighted so that the probability that it lands 'head' is $\frac{3}{5}$ and 'tail' $\frac{2}{5}$.

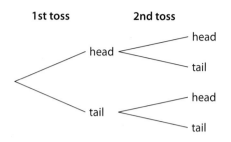

   (i) Copy and complete the tree diagram for two tosses of the coin, writing the probabilities on the branches.

   (ii) Find the probability of getting one 'head' and one 'tail'.

6. A bag contains 10 coins.

There are 6 gold coins and the rest are silver.

A coin is taken at random from the bag.
The type of coin is recorded and the coin is then returned to the bag.
A second coin is then taken at random from the bag.

   (i) The tree diagram shows all the ways in which two coins can be taken from the bag. Copy the diagram and write the probabilities on it.

   (ii) Use your tree diagram to calculate the probability that one coin is gold and one coin is silver.

7. Silvia throws an ordinary dice twice.

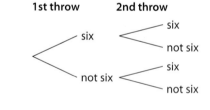

   (i) Copy and complete this tree diagram.

   (ii) Use the tree diagram to write down the probability that Silvia gets

   (a) two sixes

   (b) one six only.

8. Helen tosses a fair coin three times.

Draw a tree diagram for the three tosses.

Find the probability that

   (i) all three tosses give the same result

   (ii) two tosses give 'head' and the other 'tail'.

9. Two fair dice, each having faces numbered 1, 1, 2, 2, 2, 2, are thrown.

Draw up a probability tree and use the tree to find the probabilities of these events:

   (i) the total score is 4

   (ii) the total score is 3

   (iii) at least one dice shows a 2.

Test yourself 10

1. (a)

A

B

C

For which of these spinners is the probability of spinning a 3 equal to:
(i) 20%   (ii) 25%   (iii) $\frac{1}{3}$?

(b) The first 100 vehicles to pass a checkpoint gave the results in the table. If these figures truly represent the traffic at any time past this checkpoint, determine the experimental probability that the next vehicle will be:
(i) a car   (ii) a motor cycle
(iii) a bus   (iv) *not* a car
(v) *not* a car or truck

Type of vehicle	Frequency
Cars	70
Trucks	15
Motor cycles	10
Buses	5

(c) In a class of 30 students, 8 study music (M), 14 study art (A) while 6 study both music and art.
(i) Represent this information on a copy of the given Venn diagram.

If a student is selected at random, what is the probability that the student studies
(ii) both music and art   (iii) art but not music
(iv) neither music nor art   (v) music or art?

2. (a) A bag contains 50 marbles: 20 are red, 12 are green and 18 are black.
What is the probability that a marble selected at random is:
(i) red   (ii) green   (iii) not black?

(b) Ken has two spinners, each numbered 1 to 4.
Only one of them is a fair spinner.
These tables show the results of spinning each spinner 80 times.
Which spinner do you think is fair, spinner **A** or spinner **B**?
Explain your decision.

A

Score	Frequency
1	19
2	22
3	21
4	18

B

Score	Frequency
1	15
2	18
3	15
4	32

(c) These are two sets of cards.

SET P   SET Q

A card is taken at random from set P and another from set Q.

     (i) List all the possible outcomes.

     (ii) What is the probability of getting two even numbers?

     (iii) What is the probability of getting two consecutive numbers?

3. (a) The contents of 20 matchboxes were examined and the results recorded.

Number of matches	48	49	50	51	52	53
Number of boxes	1	5	8	3	2	1

If the contents of a similar box of matches were counted, what would be the experimental probability that it would contain 50 matches or more?

(b) There are 5 green beads and x golden beads in a bag.
What is the value of x if the probability of drawing a golden bead is $\frac{2}{3}$?

(c) The Venn diagram on the right shows the numbers of students who take Maths (M), English (E) and History (H).

If a student is selected at random, find the probability that the student takes

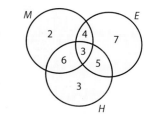

    (i) English   (ii) both Maths and History

    (iii) Maths or English   (iv) Maths only

    (v) all three subjects   (vi) English or History.

4. (a) Explain what is meant by a probability of

     (i) 0   (ii) 0.5   (iii) 75%   (iv) 1.

(b) The colours of flags flying at an international sports tournament are recorded in the given table.
Find the probability that a flag selected at random from these flags is

Red	240
Blue	160
White	320
Other	80

     (i) white   (ii) not blue   (iii) either blue or white.

(c) A biased dice is rolled.
This table gives the probability that it will land on each of the numbers 1, 2, 4, 5 and 6.

	1	2	3	4	5	6
Probability	0.1	0.1		0.2	0.3	0.1

     (i) Work out the probability that the dice will land on 3.

     (ii) Work out the probability that the dice will land on an even number.

5. (a) An ordinary pack of playing cards is shuffled well and a card is drawn out.
Determine the probability that it is:

     (i) a red card   (ii) the ace of spades

    (iii) a number less than ten and greater than four

    (iv) a black picture card   (v) an ace

    (vi) a number between four and ten inclusive.

(b) Jenny tossed four coins 30 times and the number of heads was recorded each time. The bar chart shows the results.

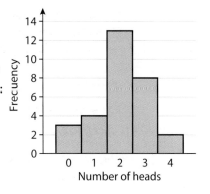

(i) From this experiment, what is the probability that when four coins are thrown there will be:
   (a) no heads
   (b) two heads
   (c) at least three heads?

(ii) If this experiment were to be repeated, would you expect the same results? Explain your answer.

(c) In a group of 25 students, 18 study Maths, 12 study Science and 5 study neither Maths nor Science.
Illustrate this information on a Venn diagram.
If a student is selected at random, what is the probability that the student studies
   (i) Mathematics only   (ii) Science only
   (iii) Mathematics or Science or both   (iv) both Mathematics and Science?

6. (a) The probability that a biased dice will land 3 up is 0.4.
Mark rolls the biased dice 200 times.
Work out an estimate for the number of times that the dice will land 3 up.

(b) Tom has a four-sided dice.
He rolls the dice 100 times.
The table shows the outcomes.

Outcome	1	2	3	4
Frequency	18	44	19	19

Is the dice fair? Explain your answer.

(c) A drawing pin can land 'point up' or 'point down'.
Nelson dropped it first 10, then 20, then 30, … times.
Which of these graphs of relative frequency of landing 'point up' versus number of trials is most likely to show Nelson's results?

'point up'   'point down'

A
Drawing pin landing 'point up'

B
Drawing pin landing 'point up'

C
Drawing pin landing 'point up'

(d) On his way to work, Nick goes through a set of traffic lights and then passes over a level crossing.
Over a period of time, Nick has estimated the probability of stopping at each of these.
The probability that he has to stop at the traffic lights is $\frac{2}{3}$.
The probability that he has to stop at the level crossing is $\frac{1}{5}$.
   (i) Construct a tree diagram to show this information.
   (ii) Calculate the probability that Nick will not have to stop at either the lights or the level crossing on his way to work.

11 Coordinate Geometry – The Line

Section 11.1 Revision of formulae

In your study of coordinate geometry so far, you will have learned how to plot points in the coordinated plane. You will also have used formulae for finding the distance between two points and the midpoint of a line segment. These two important formulae are given below and should be memorised.

1. Distance between two points

The given diagram shows the points $A(x_1, y_1)$ and $B(x_2, y_2)$.

$$|BC| = y_2 - y_1 \quad \text{and} \quad |AC| = x_2 - x_1$$

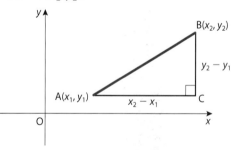

Using the Theorem of Pythagoras:

$$|AB|^2 = |AC|^2 + |BC|^2$$
$$= (x_2 - x_1)^2 + (y_2 - y_1)^2$$
$$\therefore \quad |AB| = \sqrt{(x_2 - x_1)^2 + (y_2 - y_1)^2}$$

The distance between $A(x_1, y_1)$ and $B(x_2, y_2)$ is

$$|AB| = \sqrt{(x_2 - x_1)^2 + (y_2 - y_1)^2}$$

2. The midpoint of a line segment

The midpoint, M, of the line segment joining $A(x_1, y_1)$ and $B(x_2, y_2)$ is

$$\left(\frac{x_1 + x_2}{2}, \frac{y_1 + y_2}{2} \right)$$

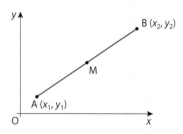

Example 1

If A(-1, 3) and B(5, 7) are two points in the plane, find

(i) $|AB|$ (ii) the midpoint of [AB].

(i) $|AB| = \sqrt{(x_2 - x_1)^2 + (y_2 - y_1)^2}$ A(-1, 3)   B(5, 7)

$= \sqrt{(5 + 1)^2 + (7 - 3)^2}$ $\downarrow$ $\downarrow$

$= \sqrt{36 + 16}$ (x_1, y_1) (x_2, y_2)

$= \sqrt{52}$

(ii) Midpoint of [AB] $= \left(\dfrac{x_1 + x_2}{2}, \dfrac{y_1 + y_2}{2} \right)$

$= \left(\dfrac{-1 + 5}{2}, \dfrac{3 + 7}{2} \right)$

$= (2, 5)$

Exercise 11.1

1. Write down the coordinates of each of the points marked in the coordinated plane on the right:

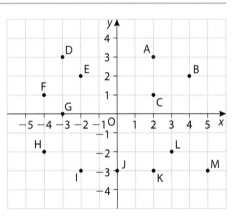

2. Draw a coordinated plane from -5 to 5 on the x-axis and from -4 to 4 on the y-axis. Now plot each of the following points:

(i) A(3, 4)   (ii) B(-1, 3)   (iii) C(4, -3)   (iv) D(-4, -3)   (v) E(1, -3)

3. The four quadrants are shown on the right. In which quadrant does each of the following points lie?

(i) (3, 5)

(ii) (-2, -3)

(iii) (1, -4)

(iv) (-3, 1)

(v) (3, -3)

(vi) (-1, -3).

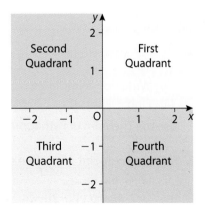

4. On which axis does each of the following points lie?

    (i) (4, 0)   (ii) (−3, 0)   (iii) (0, 4)   (iv) (0, −3)   (v) (0, 0).

5. The points A, B, C and D are shown.

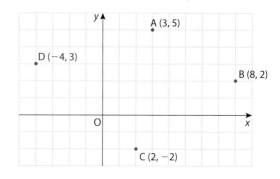

    Find (i) $|AB|$

           (ii) $|AC|$

          (iii) $|AD|$.

    Is $|DC| = |BC|$?

6. Find the distance between each of the following pairs of points:

    (i) (2, 1) and (3, 4)   (ii) (1, 5) and (2, 3)   (iii) (−1, 4) and (2, 6)
    (iv) (3, −2) and (−5, 3)   (v) (−6, −1) and (1, −3)   (vi) (4, −2) and (0, −5)

7. A(1, 1), B(3, 6) and C(5, 1) are the vertices of a triangle. Show that $|AB| = |BC|$.

8. The centre of a circle is (−3, 1) and (4, 3) is a point on the circle.
    Find the length of the radius of the circle.

9. The points A(2, 1), B(6, 1), C(5, −2) and D(1, −2) are the vertices of a parallelogram.
    Plot the parallelogram on a coordinated plane.
    Find   (i) $|AC|$ (ii) $|BD|$.
    Are the diagonals equal in length?

10. The given diagram shows the points D, E and F.

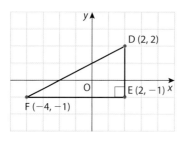

    (i) Write down the lengths of [FE] and [ED].
    (ii) Find $|DF|$.
    Use the Theorem of Pythagoras to show that the triangle DEF is right-angled.

11. Find the midpoint of the line segment joining these points:

    (i) (2, 4) and (6, 2)   (ii) (2, 4) and (0, 2)   (iii) (2, −1) and (4, 3)
    (iv) (−2, 4) and (4, −2)   (v) (2, −3) and (0, −1)   (vi) (−3, 4) and (−1, −4).

12. Find the midpoint of the line segment joining $(-3, 4)$ and $(3, 7)$.
On which axis does the midpoint lie?

13. The points $(-2, 3)$ and $(6, 5)$ are the end points of the diameter of a circle.
Find the coordinates of the centre of the circle.

14. $A(4, 3)$, $B(1, -3)$, $C(-2, -2)$ and $D(1, 4)$ are the vertices of a parallelogram.
Draw a sketch of this parallelogram.
Find the midpoint of [AC].
Verify that the midpoint of [AC] is also the midpoint of [BD].

15. Find M, the midpoint of the line segment joining $A(-3, 4)$ and $B(1, -6)$.
Now show that $|AM| = |MB|$.

16. The given diagram shows the
points $A(1, 2)$, $M(3, 5)$ and B.
If M is the midpoint of [AB], find
by inspection the coordinates of
the point B.

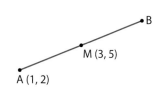

17. $A(5, 2)$, and $B(x_1, y_1)$ are two points.
If $M(2, 4)$ is the midpoint of [AB], find the coordinates of B.

Section 11.2 The slope of a line

The slope of the line AB is defined as

$$\frac{\text{vertical change}}{\text{horizontal change}} \quad \text{or} \quad \frac{\text{rise}}{\text{run}}$$

The slope of $AB = \frac{3}{6} = \frac{1}{2}$.

In the diagram on the right, the slope
of AB is found by getting the

$$\frac{\text{vertical change}}{\text{horizontal change}} = \frac{y_2 - y_1}{x_2 - x_1}$$

Thus the slope, m, of AB is $= \dfrac{y_2 - y_1}{x_2 - x_1}$.

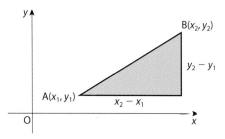

The slope, m, of the line passing through (x_1, y_1) and (x_2, y_2) is

$$m = \frac{y_2 - y_1}{x_2 - x_1}$$

Example 1

If A = (3, −1) and B = (5, 2), find the slope of the line AB.

$$m = \frac{y_2 - y_1}{x_2 - x_1}$$

$$= \frac{2 + 1}{5 - 3} = \frac{3}{2}$$

(3, −1)	(5, 2)
↓	↓
(x_1, y_1)	(x_2, y_2)

The slope of AB $= \frac{3}{2}$.

Positive and negative slopes

As we go from left to right, the slope is positive if the line is rising and the slope is negative if the line is falling.

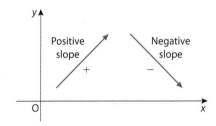

Parallel lines

The lines a and b in the given diagram both have the slope $\frac{3}{2}$.

These lines are **parallel**.

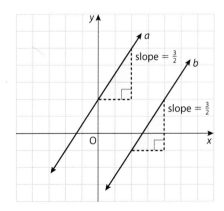

Parallel lines have equal slopes.

Perpendicular lines

The given lines a and b are perpendicular.

The slope of $a = \frac{3}{2}$.

The slope of $b = -\frac{2}{3}$.

Notice that one slope is minus the reciprocal of the other.

Notice also that the product of the two slopes is -1, i.e.,

$$-\frac{2}{3} \times \frac{3}{2} = -1$$

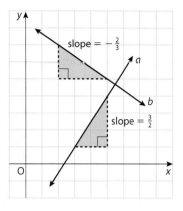

If two lines are perpendicular, the product of their slopes is -1, i.e.,

$$m_1 \times m_2 = -1$$

Example 2

A$(-1, 0)$, B$(3, 2)$, C$(-1, 4)$ and D$(2, -2)$ are four points in the plane.
Show that AB is perpendicular to CD.

Let m_1 be the slope of AB and m_2 be the slope of CD.

$$
\begin{array}{cccc}
\text{A}(-1,0) & \text{B}(3,2) & \text{C}(-1,4) & \text{D}(2,-2) \\
\downarrow & \downarrow & \downarrow & \downarrow \\
(x_1, y_1) & (x_2, y_2) & (x_1, y_1) & (x_2, y_2)
\end{array}
$$

$$m_1 = \frac{y_2 - y_1}{x_2 - x_1} \qquad\qquad m_2 = \frac{y_2 - y_1}{x_2 - x_1}$$

$$= \frac{2 - 0}{3 + 1} \qquad\qquad = \frac{-2 - 4}{2 + 1}$$

$$= \frac{2}{4} = \frac{1}{2} \qquad\qquad -\frac{-6}{3} = -2$$

$$m_1 \times m_2 = \frac{1}{2} \times (-2)$$

$$= -1$$

AB is perpendicular to CD as the product of the slopes is -1.

Exercise 11.2

1. The diagram shows four lines a, b, c and d.

   (i) Which lines have positive slopes?

  (ii) Which lines have negative slopes?

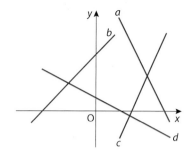

2. Write down the slope of each of the lines shown on the grid below:

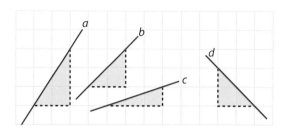

3. Three lines a, b and c are drawn on the grids below:

  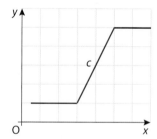

   (i) Which line has a slope of $\frac{3}{2}$?

  (ii) What is the slope of line a?

 (iii) What is the slope of line c?

4. Why is the slope of the given line negative?
Use the grid to work out the slope of the line.

5. Find the slope of the line AB in each of the following:

   (i) A(3, 1) and B(5, 3)   (ii) A(−1, 2) and B(3, −4)

 (iii) A(−1, −3) and B(0, 5)   (iv) A(3, 0) and B(−1, −4)

  (v) A(−3, 2) and B(−5, 0)   (vi) A(−5, 1) and B(−2, 3).

6. Show that the line passing through A(−1, −2) and B(3, 0) has the same slope as the line passing through C(2, 3) and D(−2, 1).
   What can you say about the lines AB and CD?

7. The line ℓ contains the points (1, 1) and (2, 4).
   The line m contains the points (4, 1) and (3, −2).
   Investigate if ℓ is parallel to m.

8. A(−2, −4), B(5, −1), C(6, 4) and D(−1, 1) are the vertices of a quadrilateral.
   Draw a rough sketch of the figure.
   Now verify that AB∥CD and AD∥BC.

9. The given diagram shows three lines a, b, and c.
   Match the lines with these slopes:
    2, $\frac{1}{2}$, 1.

   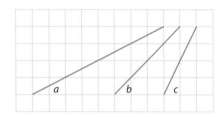

10. The slope of a line ℓ is $\frac{3}{4}$.
    (i) Write down the slope of a line m if m is parallel to ℓ.
    (ii) Write down the slope of a line n if n is perpendicular to ℓ.

11. The slopes of five lines are given below.
    Write down the slope of any line that is perpendicular to each of these lines:
    (i) $\frac{2}{3}$ (ii) $\frac{4}{5}$ (iii) $-\frac{3}{4}$ (iv) $-\frac{2}{5}$ (v) $-\frac{1}{2}$

12. The line m contains the points (3, −1) and (4, −2).
    (i) Find the slope of any line parallel to m.
    (ii) Find the slope of any line perpendicular to m.

13. A(−1, 1), B(1, 3), C(6, 2) and D(4, 4) are four points in the plane.
    Find the slope of   (i) AB   (ii) CD. Verify that AB ⊥ CD.

14. If the slope of the line through the points (3, 2) and (8, k) is $\frac{3}{5}$, find the value of k.

15. The slope of the line through (3, −2) and (1, k) is $\frac{1}{3}$. Find the value of k.

16. The line ℓ contains the points (−2, 0) and (4, 3).
    The line m contains the points (1, −1) and (k, 1).
    (i) Find the slope of ℓ.
    (ii) Find, in terms of k, the slope of m.
    (iii) If $\ell \| m$, find the value of k.

17. A county council uses the rule that the gradient of a wheelchair ramp must not be above 0.08.
Which of these ramps would be suitable for wheelchairs?

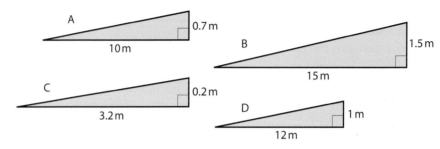

18. Given the points A(3, 2), B(2, 3), C(−2, −1) and D(k, 5).
Find the value of k if AB∥CD.

Section 11.3 **The equation of a line**

In the given line ℓ, the sum of the x and y values of each point is 5, e.g. $2 + 3 = 5$.

For this reason we say that the equation of the line ℓ is

$x + y = 5$.

$x + y = 5$ is called the **equation of a line**, or a **linear equation**.

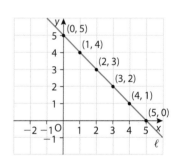

The equation was found by observing the relationship between the x and y values of each point and discovering that for all the points, $x + y = 5$.

We will now consider the figure on the right.

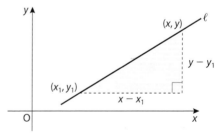

The line ℓ contains the point (x_1, y_1) and has slope m.

Let (x, y) be any other point on ℓ.

From the diagram, the slope of ℓ is $\dfrac{y - y_1}{x - x_1} = m$.

If we multiply both sides by $(x - x_1)$ we get,

$$y - y_1 = m(x - x_1)$$

> The equation of the line through (x_1, y_1), with slope m, is found by using
>
> $$y - y_1 = m(x - x_1)$$

Example 1

Find the equation of the line containing the point $(-3, 2)$ and whose slope is $\frac{2}{3}$.

Equation of the line is: $\quad y - y_1 = m(x - x_1)$ $\qquad\qquad\qquad\qquad m = \frac{2}{3}$

$$y - 2 = \frac{2}{3}(x + 3) \qquad\qquad\qquad (x_1, y_1) = (-3, 2)$$

$$y - 2 = \frac{2x}{3} + \frac{6}{3}$$

Multiply each term by 3: $\qquad\qquad\qquad 3y - 6 = 2x + 6$

$$2x - 3y + 12 = 0$$

$\therefore$ the equation of the line is: $\qquad 2x - 3y + 12 = 0$

Equation of a line when given two points on the line

To find the equation of a line containing two points, we first find the slope of the line using

the formula $\dfrac{y_2 - y_1}{x_2 - x_1}$.

We then use the formula $\quad y - y_1 = m(x - x_1)\quad$ to find the equation of the line.

You may then use either of the two points as (x_1, y_1).

Example 2

Find the equation of the line containing the points $(-2, 3)$ and $(3, 1)$.

Slope of line: $\quad m = \dfrac{y_2 - y_1}{x_2 - x_1}$ $\qquad\qquad (-2, 3) \qquad (3, 1)$

$$= \frac{1 - 3}{3 + 2} = \frac{-2}{5} \qquad\qquad (x_1, y_1) \qquad (x_2, y_2)$$

We now use the slope $-\frac{2}{5}$ and the point $(-2, 3)$ $\quad$ ...you may use either of the 2 points

Equation of line: $\quad y - y_1 = m(x - x_1)$

$$y - 3 = -\frac{2}{5}(x + 2)$$

$$y - 3 = -\frac{2x}{5} - \frac{4}{5}$$

$$5y - 15 = -2x - 4 \qquad \text{...multiply each term by 5}$$

$$\Rightarrow \quad 2x + 5y - 11 = 0 \ \text{ is the equation of the line.}$$

1. Find the equations of the following lines, given the slope and a point on the line in each case:
    (i) slope = 2; point = (3, 4)
    (ii) slope = 4; point = (1, 5)
    (iii) slope = 5; point = (−2, 3)
    (iv) slope = −3; point = (−2, 0)
    (v) slope = −5; point = (−3, −2)
    (vi) slope = $\frac{2}{3}$; point = (3, −1).

2. Find the equations of the following lines, given the slope and a point on the line in each case:
    (i) slope = $\frac{3}{4}$; point = (1, −4)
    (ii) slope = $\frac{3}{5}$; point = (−4, 2).

3. Find the equation of the line through (−2, 3) with slope
    (i) 4
    (ii) −2
    (iii) $\frac{3}{4}$
    (iv) $-\frac{2}{3}$

4. Find the equation of the line through (0, 0) and whose slope is −3.

5. Find the equation of the line through (0, 0) and whose slope is
    (i) 3
    (ii) −5
    (iii) $\frac{1}{3}$
    (iv) $-\frac{3}{2}$
    What do you notice about the equation of each of these lines?

6. Find the slope of the line through A(3, −4) and B(1, 2).
    Hence find the equation of the line AB.

7. Find the equations of the lines through the following pairs of points:
    (i) (2, 3) and (4, 6)
    (ii) (−1, 2) and (2, −4)
    (iii) (−5, 1) and (1, 0)
    (iv) (−2, 3) and (3, −1)
    (v) (2, 7) and (0, 5)
    (vi) (−3, −5) and (−1, −1).

8. Find the equation of the line through (−2, 3) and the midpoint of the line segment joining (1, −3) and (3, −1).

9. Using any two points on each line, find the slopes of the lines shown below. Hence find the equation of each line.
    (i)

    (ii)

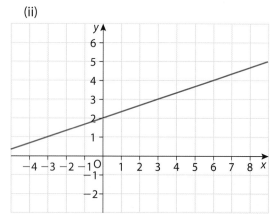

10. Use two different ways to find the slope of the given line AB.

Hence find the equation of the line.

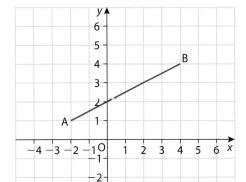

Section 11.4 The equation $y = mx + c$

Consider the two parallel lines shown on the right.

The slope of each line is 2.

Notice that **2** is the coefficient of x in each line.

Each line is in the form $y = mx + c$.

m represents the slope of the line.

The line $y = 2x + 4$ intersects the y-axis at $(0, 4)$

The line $y = 2x - 3$ intersects the y-axis at $(0, -3)$

From these two examples we can see that if the equation of a line is in the form

$y = mx + c,$ then

(i) the slope of the line is m

(ii) the line intersects the y-axis at $(0, c)$.

The point $(0, c)$ is called the **y-intercept**.

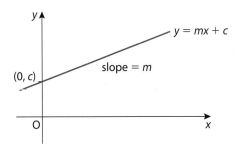

If a line is in the form $3x + 2y - 8 = 0$, change the equation to the form $y = mx + c$.

The slope is the value of m.

Example 1

Find the slope of the line $3x - 2y - 9 = 0$.

We write the equation in the form $y = mx + c$.

$$3x - 2y - 9 = 0$$

$\Rightarrow \quad -2y = -3x + 9 \qquad$ ...leave the y term only on left-hand side

$\Rightarrow \quad 2y = 3x - 9 \qquad$ ...multiply each term by -1

$\Rightarrow \quad y = \frac{3}{2}x - \frac{9}{2} \qquad$ ...divide each term by 2

$\therefore \quad$ the slope of the line is $\frac{3}{2}$

Example 2

ℓ is the line $2x - 3y + 6 = 0$ and k is the line $3x + 2y - 4 = 0$.
Show that ℓ is perpendicular to m.

Slope of ℓ:

$$2x - 3y + 6 = 0$$

$\Rightarrow \quad -3y = -2x - 6$

$\Rightarrow \quad 3y = 2x + 6$

$\Rightarrow \quad y = \frac{2}{3}x + 2$

$\Rightarrow \quad$ slope of $\ell = \frac{2}{3}$

Slope of k:

$$3x + 2y - 4 = 0$$

$\Rightarrow \quad 2y = -3x + 4$

$\Rightarrow \quad y = -\frac{3}{2}x + 2$

$\Rightarrow \quad$ slope of $k = -\frac{3}{2}$

Slope of $\ell \times$ slope of $k = \frac{2}{3} \times \left(-\frac{3}{2}\right)$

$$= \frac{-6}{6} = -1$$

Since the product of the two slopes $= -1$, the lines are perpendicular.

Exercise 11.4

1. Write down the slope of each of these lines:
   (i) $y = 3x + 5$
   (ii) $y = 2x - 3$
   (iii) $y = \frac{1}{2}x + 4$

2. Write down the coordinates of the point where each of the lines in Question 1 above intersects the y-axis.

3. Express each of the following lines in the form $y = mx + c$ and hence write down the slope of the line:
   (i) $x + y - 4 = 0$
   (ii) $3x + y - 5 = 0$
   (iii) $2x + 3y - 7 = 0$
   (iv) $5x - 2y + 3 = 0$
   (v) $3x + 4y - 2 = 0$
   (vi) $3x - 4y + 6 = 0$.

4. Express the line $\ell: 2x + 3y - 7 = 0$ in the form $y = mx + c$.
   (i) Write down the slope of ℓ.
   (ii) What is the slope of any line parallel to ℓ?
   (iii) What is the slope of any line perpendicular to ℓ?

5. Show that the lines $x - 2y + 1 = 0$ and $3x - 6y - 7 = 0$ are parallel.
   What is the slope of any line perpendicular to these lines?

6. Show that the lines $2x + 3y - 4 = 0$ and $3x - 2y + 1 = 0$ are perpendicular to each other.

7. If the equation of the line ℓ is $y = 3x - 4$, write down the equation of any line, in the
   form $y = mx + c$, that is
   (i) parallel to ℓ (ii) perpendicular to ℓ.

8. Investigate if the lines $y = \frac{2}{3}x + 4$ and $2x - 3y - 5 = 0$ are parallel.

9. (i) Match the equations below to give four pairs of parallel lines:

(A) $y = \frac{1}{2}x + 1$ **(B)** $y = \frac{1}{3}x + 5$ **(C)** $y = -\frac{3}{4}x + 3$ **(D)** $y = \frac{x}{5} - 1$ **(E)** $y = 9 + \frac{1}{2}x$

(F) $y = \frac{x}{3} - 2$ **(G)** $y = \frac{1}{5}x + 3$ **(H)** $y = \frac{4}{3}x + 2$ **(I)** $y = 1 - \frac{3}{4}x$

   (ii) Which equation is the odd one out?

10. (i) Write down the slope of the
   given line k.

   (ii) Write the equation of k in the
   form $y = mx + c$.

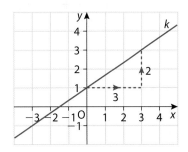

11. The lines labelled p, q, and r match these equations:

   $y = 2x + 5$

   $y = x + 5$

   $y = x - 2$

   Match each line to its correct equation.

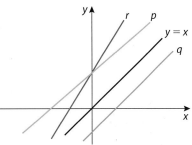

12. By finding the slope and y-intercept,
   write down the equation of the
   given line.

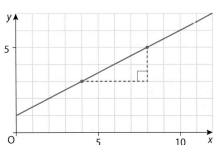

13. The equations of six lines are given below:

a: $y = 2x - 3$ c: $y = x + 3$ e: $y = -\frac{1}{2}x + 4$

b: $y = \frac{1}{2}x + 5$ d: $y = -2x - 4$ f: $y = 2x - 2$

(i) Name a pair of parallel lines.   (ii) Name a pair of perpendicular lines.

(iii) Which line crosses the y-axis at $(0, 4)$?   (iv) Which line crosses the y-axis at $(0, -3)$?

14. If the line $x + 2y - 6 = 0$ is parallel to the line $2x + ky - 5 = 0$, find the value of k.

15. If the line $2x - 3y + 7 = 0$ is perpendicular to the line $3x + ky - 4 = 0$, find the value of k.

16. Find the equation of each line sketched below:

(i)

(ii)

(iii)
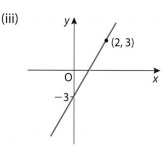

17. Which two of these lines are parallel to $y = \frac{1}{2}x - 3$?

(A)

$2y = x + 2$

(B)

$2x = y + 10$

(C)

$2y + 8 = x$

(D)
$y - 2x = 9$

Section 11.5 Parallel and perpendicular lines

If we are given the equation of a line ℓ, such as $2x + 3y - 4 = 0$, we can find the slope of the line by expressing the equation in the form $y = mx + c$.

If we are also given a point (x_1, y_1), we can then find the equation of a line through (x_1, y_1) and which is parallel to or perpendicular to ℓ.

> **Example 1**
>
> Find the equation of the line through the point $(-2, 3)$ which is perpendicular to the line $2x - y + 5 = 0$.
>
> To find the slope of $2x - y + 5 = 0$, we express it in the form $y = mx + c$.
>
> $\qquad 2x - y + 5 = 0$
> $\Rightarrow \quad -y = -2x - 5$
> $\Rightarrow \qquad y = 2x + 5 \qquad$ …multiply each term by -1
> $\Rightarrow \quad$ the slope is 2
>
> The slope of the line perpendicular to this line is $-\dfrac{1}{2}$

Equation of line through $(-2, 3)$ with slope $-\frac{1}{2}$ is:

$$y - y_1 = m(x - x_1) \qquad\qquad (x_1, y_1) = (-2, 3)$$

$$y - 3 = -\frac{1}{2}(x + 2) \qquad\qquad m = -\frac{1}{2}$$

$$y - 3 = \frac{-x}{2} - 1$$

$\Rightarrow \quad 2y - 6 = -x - 2 \qquad$ ...multiply each term by 2

$\Rightarrow \quad x + 2y - 4 = 0 \quad$ is the required equation.

Exercise 11.5

1. Find the slope of the line $2x + y - 4 = 0$.
   Now find the equation of the line through the point $(2, 4)$ and which is parallel to the line $2x + y - 4 = 0$.

2. Find the equation of the line through the point $(1, -6)$ and which is parallel to the line $3x - y + 4 = 0$.

3. Find the slope of the line $2x - 3y + 1 = 0$.
   What is the slope of any line perpendicular to $2x - 3y + 1 = 0$?
   Now find the equation of the line through the point $(4, -1)$ and which is perpendicular to the line $2x - 3y + 1 = 0$.

4. Find the equation of the line through $(-2, 1)$ and which is perpendicular to the line $3x + 2y - 4 = 0$.

5. Find the equation of the line through $(-4, 0)$ and which is parallel to the line $y = 3x - 5$.

6. The given diagram shows the lines a and b intersecting at the point $(5, 2)$.

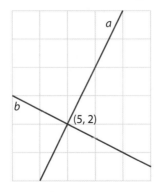

   (i)   Use the grid to find the slopes of a and b.
   (ii) Investigate if a and b are perpendicular to each other.
   (iii) Find the equation of the line a.

7. The given diagram shows the points A(-1, 5), B(2, -1) and C(0, 5).

The line ℓ is parallel to AB and contains the point C.

Find the equation of ℓ.

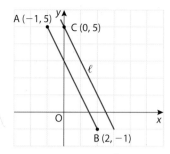

8. Which one of the following lines is parallel to $3x + y - 4 = 0$?

A: $y = 3x - 2$ B: $y = \frac{1}{3}x + 4$ C: $6x + 2y + 7 = 0$ D: $x + 3y + 2 = 0$

9. The point A has coordinates (1, 7) and the point B has coordinates (3, 1).

The midpoint of [AB] is P.

Find the coordinates of P.

Now find the equation of the line which passes through P and which is perpendicular to the line $x + 5y - 7 = 0$.

10. The line $y = 2x + 5$ intersects the y-axis at the point P.

   (i) Write down the slope of the line and the coordinates of P.

   (ii) Find the equation of the line through P and which is perpendicular to $y = 2x + 5$.

11. Use the grid in the given diagram to write down the slope of the line a.

Now write down the equation of a in the form $y = mx + c$.

Write down the coordinates of the point P and hence find the equation of the line through P which is perpendicular to a.

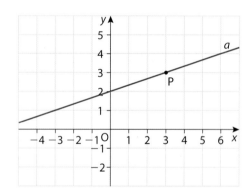

12. The equation of the line AB is $5x - 3y = 26$.

   (i) Find the slope of AB.

   (ii) The point A has coordinates (4, -2) and a point C has coordinates (-6, 4).

      (a) Prove that AC is perpendicular to AB.

      (b) Find the equation of the line AC, expressing your answer in the form $ax + by = c$.

Section 11.6 Graphing lines

To draw a line such as $2x + 3y = 6$, we need to know at least two points on the line.

The easiest points to find are those at which the line crosses the x-axis and y-axis.

On the x-axis, $y = 0$; on the y-axis, $x = 0$.

Take the line $2x + 3y = 6$

When $x = 0$, then
$$2(0) + 3y = 6$$
$$3y = 6$$
$$\Rightarrow \quad y = 2$$

$\therefore$ $(0, 2)$ is one point on the line

When $y = 0$, then
$$2x + 3(0) = 6$$
$$2x = 6$$
$$x = 3$$

$\therefore$ $(3, 0)$ is a second point on the line

A sketch of the line is shown on the right.

Sketch of line $2x + 3y = 6$

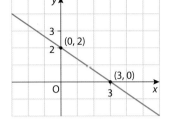

Lines parallel to the axes

The lines $x = 2$ and $x = 4$ are shown.

Notice that the x-value of each point on the line $x = 4$ is 4.

Similarly, the x-value of each point on the line $x = 2$ is 2.

All lines with equations of the form $x = a$ will be parallel to the y-axis.

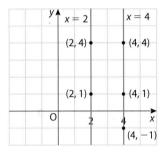

The diagram on the right shows the line $y = 2$.

Again, notice that the y-value of each of the points on this line is 2.

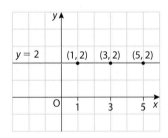

Lines containing the origin

A line such as $x + 2y = 0$, with no independent term, always contains the origin $(0, 0)$.

To plot the line $x + 2y = 0$, we know that it contains the origin.

To find a second point, we select a value for x and then find the corresponding y-value.

Let $x = 2$:
$$2 + 2y = 0$$
$$2y = -2$$
$$y = -1$$

$\therefore$ $(2, -1)$ is a second point on the line.

A sketch of the line containing $(0, 0)$ and $(2, -1)$ is shown.

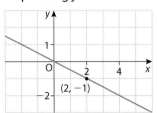

To verify that a point is on a given line

To investigate if the point $(3, -2)$ is on the line $x + 2y + 1 = 0$, we substitute 3 for x and -2 for y in the equation.

$$x + 2y + 1 = 0$$
$$x = 3 \text{ and } y = -2$$

Test: $3 + 2(-2) + 1$
$3 - 4 + 1$
$= 0$

> If a point is on a line, then the coordinates of the point will satisfy the equation of the line.

Since $(3, -2)$ **satisfies** the equation $x + 2y + 1 = 0$, it shows that the point is on the line.

However $(-3, 4)$ is not on the line $x - 3y + 7 = 0$, since $-3 - 12 + 7 \neq 0$, i.e. it does not satisfy the equation.

Example 1

If the point $(k, 3)$ is on the line $4x - 3y + 1 = 0$, find the value of k.

We substitute k for x and 3 for y in the equation $4x - 3y + 1 = 0$.
$\Rightarrow \quad 4k - 3(3) + 1 = 0$
$\Rightarrow \quad 4k - 9 + 1 = 0$
$\Rightarrow \quad 4k - 8 = 0$
$\Rightarrow \quad 4k = 8 \Rightarrow k = 2$

Exercise 11.6

1. Write down the equations of the lines a, b, c and d shown on the right.

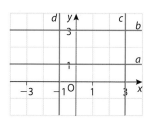

2. Draw a pair of axes and sketch these four lines:
   (i) $x = 4$ (ii) $y = 2$ (iii) $x = -2$ (iv) $y = -3$

3. Use the graph of the line $2x + y = 6$ to write down
   (i) the value of x when $y = 0$
   (ii) the coordinates of the point where the line crosses the y-axis
   (iii) the value of y when $x = 1$
   (iv) the value of x when $y = 2$
   (v) the area of the triangle formed by the line, the x-axis and the y-axis.

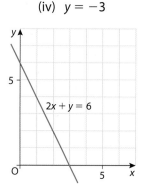

4. A straight line has equation $x + y = 5$.
  (i) By substituting $x = 0$, find the coordinates of the point where the line crosses the y-axis.
  (ii) By substituting $y = 0$, find the coordinates of the point where the line crosses the x-axis.
  (iii) Draw a graph of the line $x + y = 5$.

5. A straight line has equation $3x + y = 6$.
  (i) By substituting $x = 0$, find the coordinates of the point where the line crosses the y-axis.
  (ii) By substituting $y = 0$, find the coordinates of the point where the line crosses the x-axis.
  (iii) Draw a graph of the line $3x + y = 6$.

6. Find the coordinates of the points at which the line $x - 2y - 6 = 0$ intersects the x-axis and y-axis.
Now use these points to draw a sketch of the line.

7. Find the coordinates of the points where the line $x - 2y = 5$ intersects the x-axis and y-axis. Hence draw a sketch of the line.

8. Draw these graphs on the same diagram.
  (i) $x + y = 2$ (ii) $x + y = 3$ (iii) $x + y = 5$
  What do they all have in common?

9. Draw a sketch of the line $2x - y + 6 = 0$.
Hence write down the area of the triangle formed by the x-axis, the y-axis and the line.

10. The equations of the lines a and b are:

  a: $y = \frac{2}{3}x + 2$
  b: $3x + 5y - 15 = 0$
  (i) Which line intersects the y-axis at $(0, 2)$?
  (ii) Which line intersects the x-axis at $(5, 0)$?
  (iii) Use the slopes of the two lines to investigate whether the lines are perpendicular to each other.
  (iv) Write down the area of the triangle formed by the line $3x + 5y - 15 = 0$, the x-axis and the y-axis.

11. The diagram shows a sketch of the line $2y = x + 4$
  (i) Find the coordinates of points A and B.
  (ii) What is the gradient of the line?

Gradient is another word for slope.

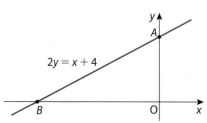

$2y = x + 4$

12. Each of the following lines contains the origin $(0, 0)$.
By taking a value for x and then finding the corresponding y-value, sketch each of the lines on separate diagrams:

  (i) $x - 2y = 0$ (ii) $x + 3y = 0$ (iii) $3x - y = 0$ (iv) $x - 4y = 0$.

13. The lines a, b, c and d are graphed in the given diagram.
Match each line with one of these equations:

  (i) $x = -2$
  (ii) $x - y = 0$
  (iii) $2x + 5y = 10$
  (iv) $y = 4$

14.   (i) Verify that $(2, -5)$ is on the line $2x + y + 1 = 0$.
  (ii) Verify that $(2, -3)$ is on the line $y = x - 5$.
  (iii) Show that $(-3, 1)$ is not on the line $x - 3y + 1 = 0$.
  (iv) Investigate if $(2, 0)$ is on the line $2x - y + 3 = 0$.

15. Show that $(-3, 1)$ is on the line $2x + 4y + 2 = 0$.

16. If $(1, 4)$ is on the line $2x + y + k = 0$, find the value of k.

17. If $(2, -3)$ is on the line $x + ky + 7 = 0$, find the value of k.

18.   (i) Find the value of k if the line $2x + ky - 8 = 0$ contains the point $(3, 1)$.
  (ii) If $(1, t)$ lies on the line $y = 2x + 3$, find the value of t.

Section 11.7 Intersection of two lines

A sketch of the lines $x + y = 4$ and $x + 3y = 6$ is shown below.

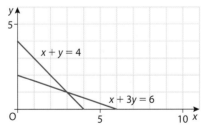

The point of intersection of the two lines can be read from the diagram.

This point is $(3, 1)$.

The point of intersection of any two lines can be found by sketching the lines on a grid and then reading their point of intersection from this grid.

However, the point of intersection of two lines may be found more easily by using simultaneous equations, as shown in the following example.

> Simultaneous equations can be used to find the point of intersection of two lines.

> **Example 1**
>
> Use simultaneous equations to find the point of intersection of the lines
>
> $x + y = 5$ and $2x - y = 4$.
>
> $$x + y = 5 \dots ①$$
> $$2x - y = 4 \dots ②$$
>
> Adding: $3x \quad = 9 \Rightarrow x = 3$
>
> From ①: $3 + y = 5 \Rightarrow y = 2$
>
> ∴ the point of intersection is (3, 2).

Exercise 11.7

1. Using the one diagram, sketch the lines

$x + y = 5$ and $x + 4y = 8$.

Use your sketch to write down the point of intersection of the two lines.

2. Use the diagram to solve these simultaneous equations:

$$x + y = 4$$
$$2x - y = -1$$

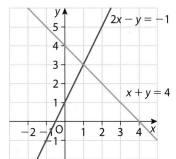

3. A sketch of the lines $2x + y = 6$
and $x + y = 5$ is shown.
Use the sketch to write down the point
of intersection of the two lines.
Now use simultaneous equations to
verify your answer.

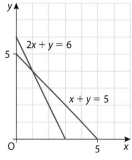

Use simultaneous equations to find the point of intersection of the following pairs of lines:

4. $x + y = 5$
  $2x - y = 1$

5. $x - y = 2$
  $2x + y = 7$

6. $2x + 5y = 1$
  $x - 3y = -5$

7. $x + 2y = -1$
  $2x - 3y = -9$

8. $x + 3y = 7$
  $2x - y = -7$

9. $x - 7y = 4$
  $3x - y = -8$

10. $2x - 3y = 4$
  $2x + 3y = -8$

11. $3x - 2y = 17$
  $4x + 3y = 0$

12. $x + 3y = 13$
  $2x + 5y = 21$

13. Use simultaneous equations to verify that the lines

$$2x + 3y = 12 \quad \text{and} \quad 3x - 4y = 1$$

intersect at the point (3, 2).

14. In the diagram, the lines *AB* and *CD* are perpendicular to each other and intersect at the point (1, 4). The line *AB* crosses the *x*-axis at (3, 0).

Calculate the coordinates of the points *P* and *Q*.

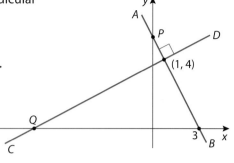

Section 11.8 Interpreting slope

In the previous sections of this chapter we learned how to find the slope of a line. In this section we will show how to interpret what the slope means in different real-life situations.

Water is poured into a container at a steady rate over a period of 8 minutes. The graph on the right shows the volume of water in the container during these 8 minutes.

For a horizontal **increase** of 6 mins, there is a vertical **increase** of 60 litres.

The **slope** is $\dfrac{60}{6} = 10$.

> 60 **litres** in 6 **minutes**, so 10 **litres per minute**.

So the rate of flow of the water is **10 litres per minute**.
Since the slope is also 10, we can see that the slope in this example represents **the rate of flow**.

This sketch shows the volume of water in a bath over a period of 4 minutes.
For a horizontal **increase** of 3 minutes, there is a vertical **decrease** of 30 litres.

So the slope is $\dfrac{-30 \text{ litres}}{3 \text{ minutes}} = -10$ litres per minute.

The negative slope shows that the volume of water is decreasing.

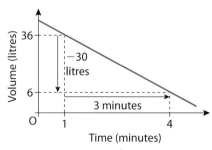

226

Time–distance graphs

The distance–time graph given shows Emer's 3-hour journey.

The slope of the line segment marked a has slope $\dfrac{30}{1} = 30$.

The line segment a shows that Emer travelled 30 km in 1 hour.
Thus her speed is 30 km/hr.
From these two results we can see that the **slope** of the line represents the **speed**.
The line segment marked b shows that Emer has stopped travelling.
Here the speed is zero and the slope is zero.

Now verify that the slope of the line segment marked c represents the speed for that part of Emer's journey.

> In a distance–time graph the slope of the line represents speed.

Exercise 11.8

1. What rates of flow, in litres per minute, are shown by the following graphs?

   (i) (a)   (b)

 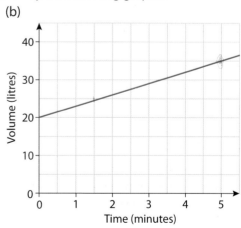

  (ii) Write down the slope of the line in each graph.

 (iii) What is the meaning of the slope in each case?

2. (i) Write down the rate of flow, in litres per second, in each of the diagrams below.

(a)

(b)
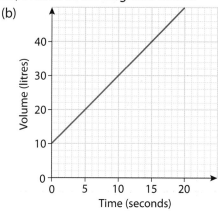

(ii) Find the slope of each of the lines drawn above.

(iii) Show that the slope of each line corresponds to the rate of flow in the diagram.

3. The graph opposite shows the distance Stephen travelled in the first 24 minutes of his journey.

(i) Work out the slope of the line.

(ii) Which of the following statements is true?

    A: The slope represents the speed in km per hour.

    B: The slope represents the speed in metres per minute.

    C: The slope represents the speed in km per minute.

4. The graph below can be used to change pints to litres and litres to pints.

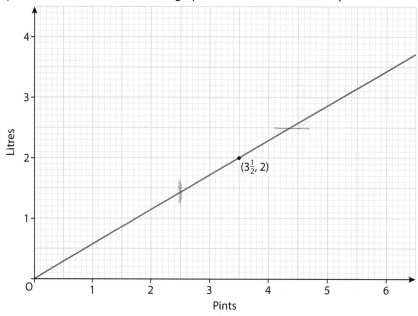

(i) Use the graph to convert
    (a) 4 pints to litres   (b) 3.5 pints to litres   (c) 2.5 litres to pints
(ii) Use the origin and the point $(3\frac{1}{2}, 2)$ to find the slope of the line.
(iii) Find the equation of the line.
(iv) Use the equation of the line to find how many litres are equivalent to 12 pints.

5. This graph shows the volume of oil in a tank.

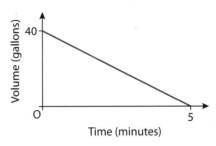

(i) Calculate the slope of the line.
(ii) What happens to the oil in the tank during these 5 minutes?
(iii) What is the rate of flow of oil from the tank?
(iv) Explain what the slope of the line means in this diagram.

6. The following is a conversion graph between kilograms (kg) and pounds (lb).

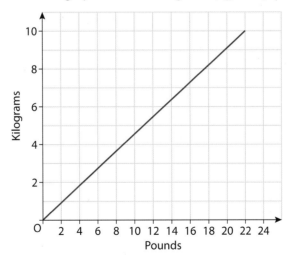

(i) Use the graph to convert
    (a) 20 lb to kg   (b) 4 kg to pounds
(ii) Use the grid to work out the slope of the line.
(iii) Explain what the slope means in the context of the question.
(iv) Work out the equation of the given line.
(v) Use the equation to estimate the number of pounds in 20 kilograms.

7. A hire firm hires out industrial blow heaters.
The following graph is used to find the approximate charge for the hiring of one of
these heaters.

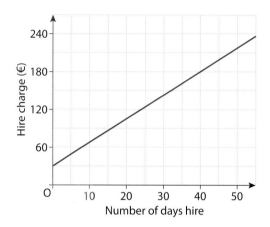

   (i) Use the graph to find the approximate charge for hiring a heater for
      (a)   40 days   (b)   25 days.
  (ii) Use the graph to find the number of days hire you would get for a cost of
      (a)   €120   (b)   €210.
 (iii) Use the grid to work out the slope of the line.
 (iv) Explain the meaning of the slope in the context of the graph.
  (v) Use the graph to write down the fixed charge you are required to pay as well as the
      daily hire charge.

8. The graph below show the relationship between distances travelled and fuel
consumption for John's car. The segments l_1 and l_2 represent the fuel consumption at
steady speeds of 60 km/h and 100 km/h respectively.

   (i) Find the slopes of l_1 and l_2.
  (ii) What do these slopes tell you about the fuel consumption of the car at these
      speeds?
 (iii) Fuel costs €1.45 per litre.
      John drives a distance of 200 km at a steady speed.
      How much cheaper is the journey at 60 km/h than at 100 km/h?

Test yourself 11

1. The equation of a line is $y = 2x - 4$.
   - (i) Write down the slope of this line.
   - (ii) At what point does the line intersect the y-axis?
   - (iii) At what point does the line intersect the x-axis?
   - (iv) What is the slope of any line that is perpendicular to $y = 2x - 4$?

2. (i) Use the grid on the right to write down the slope of the line p.
   Now write down the equation of p in the form $y = mx + c$.

   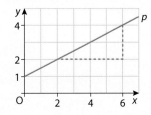

   - (ii) Which of these lines is parallel to $2y - x = 3$?

    $2y + x = 5$
    $4y - 1 = 2x$
    $y = 2x + 3$
    $x = \frac{1}{2}y + 1$

3. $A(-3, 1)$ and $B(3, 9)$ are two points in the plane.
   - (i) Find M, the midpoint of [AB]. On which axis does M lie?
   - (ii) Find the slope of AB.
   - (iii) Write down the slope of any line perpendicular to AB.
   - (iv) Now find the equation of the line through the origin and which is perpendicular to AB.

4. (i) This diagram shows three parallel lines.
      - (a) Write down equations for lines A and B.
      - (b) Write down an equation of any other line that is parallel to these three.

   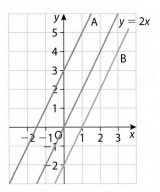

   - (ii) ℓ is the line $x - 2y + 2 = 0$.
      m is the line $3x + y - 8 = 0$.
      Use simultaneous equations to find the coordinates of P, the point of intersection of ℓ and m.

5. (i) If the line $2x + y - 7 = 0$ is parallel to the line $4x + ky - 3 = 0$, find the value of k.
   - (ii) The line $2x + 3y - 6 = 0$ intersects the x-axis at A and the y-axis at B.
      Find the coordinates of A and B and hence find the area of the triangle OAB, where O is the origin.

6. A graph of the line
$y = ax + b$ is shown.

Find the values of a and b.

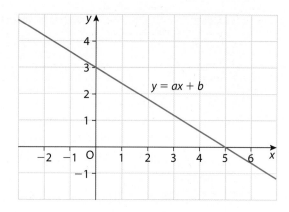

7. The given graph shows three lines a, b and c.

    (i) Which line(s) have negative slopes?

   (ii) Use the grid to find the slope of the line a.

  (iii) Associate each of the lines with one of these
equations:

         D: $y = 2x + 1$

         E: $x + y = 10$

         F: $2x + 5y = 17$.

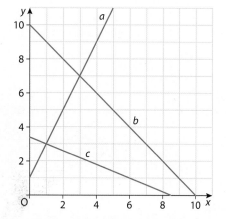

8.   (i) What is the equation of the line parallel to $y = 3x + 2$ that crosses the y-axis at
$(0, -1)$?

  (ii) This is a sketch of a child's slide.

      (a) Find the gradient of the sloping part of the slide.

      (b) For safety reasons, the gradient of the slide
should be no greater than 0.7.
Is this a safe slide?
Explain your answer.

9.   (i) Copy the given diagram and using the same scale on the x-axis and y-axis, draw
lines through A with slope

      (a) $\frac{1}{2}$ (b) -2.

(ii) The line $ax + y + 1 = 0$ passes through the point of intersection of the lines $x = 2$ and the x-axis. Find the value of a.

10. (i) Find the equation of the straight line through (0, 1) and (3, 7).

(ii) Another line has equation $y = 7 - 2x$.
Without drawing the lines, explain how you can tell whether or not this line is perpendicular to the line in part (i).

11. The map below shows part of a town containing a park and some streets. Distances are measured (in kilometres) horizontally and vertically from the Town Hall and shown in coordinate form.

(i) How long is the path from B(3, 10) to C(10, 9)?
Give your answer correct to three significant figures.

(ii) E(6, 6) is the centre of *Round Park*.
How much shorter is it to walk directly from B to C rather than take the path to E and then on to C?
Give your answer correct to the nearest km.

(iii) The points A(1, 8.5) and B(3, 10) are on Tangent Street.
Find the equation of Tangent Street.

(iv) Perpendicular Avenue in perpendicular to Tangent Street and passes through D(17, 8).
Find its equation.

(v) The Museum is located at the intersection of Tangent Street and Perpendicular Avenue.
Find the coordinates of the museum.

(vi) John is at the Town Hall and wants to get to the Museum.
Give one possible route he might take and calculate the total distance he must travel if he takes that route.

Ratio – Time – Speed

Key words

Section 12.1 Ratio and proportion

1. Ratio

We use ratios to compare two quantities.

The ratio of blue discs to yellow discs is $5:3$.

The ratio $12:8$ can be simplified by dividing each term by 4.

Thus, $12:8 = 3:2$.

$3:2$ is called the **simplest form** of the ratio.

A ratio is normally expressed as whole numbers.

The ratio $\frac{1}{3}:\frac{5}{6}$ can be expressed as whole numbers by multiplying each term by 6.

$$\therefore \frac{1}{3}:\frac{5}{6} = \frac{6}{3}:\frac{5 \times 6}{6} = 2:5$$

Example 1

A sum of money is divided in the ratio $1:3:5$.
If the smallest part is €250, find the sum of money.

If a sum of money is divided in the ratio $1:3:5$, we divide the total into 9 parts.

$\frac{1}{9}, \frac{3}{9}, \frac{5}{9}$ ... nine parts in total

$\Rightarrow \frac{1}{9} = $ €250

$\Rightarrow \frac{9}{9} = $ €250 $\times 9 = $ €2250

$\therefore$ the sum of money is €2250

---

2. Proportion

While ratios compare one part to another part, proportion compares a part to the total.

The proportion of the given circle that is shaded red is $\frac{2}{6}$ or $\frac{1}{3}$.

Proportion is generally expressed as a fraction, decimal or percentage.

If 1 litre of petrol costs €1.60, 2 litres cost €3.20 and 3 litres cost €4.80.
Here the costs of 1 litre, 2 litres and 3 litres are in **direct proportion**.

Example 2

A car travels 78 km on 9 litres of petrol.
- (i)   How far is it likely to travel on 21 litres of petrol?
- (ii) How many litres would be required for a journey of 390 km?

- (i) Here we are looking for **distance**, so we keep distance last.

    9 litres do 78 km

    1 litre does $\frac{78}{9}$ km

    21 litres do $\left(\frac{78}{9} \times \frac{21}{1}\right)$ km $= 182$ km.

- (ii) Here we are looking for litres, so we keep litres last.

    78 km require 9 litres

    1 km requires $\frac{9}{78}$ litres

    390 km require $\left(\frac{9}{78} \times \frac{390}{1}\right)$ litres $= 45$ litres

    $\therefore$ 390 km would require 45 litres.

3. Inverse proportion

When a dog eats 200 g of dogfood each day, a container lasts him 10 days.
If he eats 400 g each day, the container will last him only 5 days.
Notice that as the quantity of food eaten **increases**, the time that the food
lasts **decreases**.
This is an example of of **inverse proportion**.

Example 3

Five painters can paint an office block in 12 days.
- (i)   How long would it take three painters to paint the block?
- (ii) If the office block had to be painted in 3 days, how many painters would
  be needed?

(i) 5 painters take 12 days

   1 painter takes $12 \times 5 = 60$ days … 5 times as long

   3 painters take $\frac{60}{3} = 20$ days …$\frac{1}{3}$ as long as 1 painter

(ii) To be painted in 12 days requires 5 painters.

   To be painted in 1 day requires 60 painters … 12 times quicker so multiply 5 by 12

   To be painted in 3 days requires $\frac{60}{3} = 20$ painters

   $\therefore$ 20 painters would be required to paint the office block in 3 days.

Exercise 12.1

1. Express each of these ratios in its simplest form:

   (i) $6 : 18$ (ii) $25 : 45$ (iii) $28 : 98$ (iv) $50c : €2$

   (v) $80c : €2.40$ (vi) $50\,cm : 4\,m$ (vii) $3\,days : 3\,weeks$ (viii) $40\,min : 3\,hours$

2. Express each of these ratios in its simplest form:

   (i) $\frac{1}{2} : \frac{1}{4}$ (ii) $\frac{3}{4} : \frac{1}{4}$ (iii) $\frac{1}{3} : \frac{1}{2}$ (iv) $\frac{1}{3} : \frac{1}{4}$

   (v) $\frac{2}{5} : \frac{1}{2}$ (vi) $\frac{3}{5} : \frac{7}{10}$ (vii) $3\frac{1}{2} : 1\frac{1}{2}$ (viii) $1\frac{3}{4} : 5\frac{1}{4}$

3. Divide €288 between Ann and David in the ratio $5 : 3$.

4. Divide €2800 between three people in the ratio $4 : 2 : 1$.

5. Divide €1300 in the ratio $\frac{3}{4} : 1\frac{3}{4}$.

6. €1575 was shared among three people in the ratio $1 : 2 : \frac{1}{2}$.
   Calculate the smallest share.

7. (i) Find two pairs of matching statements here.
   (ii) Write your own statement that matches the odd one out.

   A 20% of the class are girls.

   B The ratio of girls to boys is 1:5.

   C One sixth of the class are girls.

   D 25% of the class are girls.

   E The number of boys is 4 times the number of girls.

8. In a school, the ratio of girls to boys is $7 : 2$.
   If there are 735 girls in the school, how many boys are there?

9. A prize fund is divided between A, B and C in the ratio 4 : 3 : 2 respectively.
   If C's share is €1224, find the total fund.

10. Brass is made from copper and zinc in the ratio 5 : 3 by weight.
    (i) If there are 6 kg of zinc, work out the weight of copper.
    (ii) If there are 25 kg of copper, work out the weight of zinc.

11. In a school, the ratio of the number of students to the number of computers is $1 : \frac{2}{5}$.
    If there are 100 computers in the school, work out the number of students in the school.

12. Susan has 375 g of butter and adapts her
    apple pie recipe so that she can use all the butter.

    (i) What quantities of the other ingredients would
        she need?
    (ii) How many people would this serve?

    > **Apple Pie (for 4)**
    > 3 large apples
    > 25 g brown sugar
    > 200 g flour
    > 75 g butter (or margarine)
    > 50 g caster sugar
    > 1 tablespoon water to mix

13. A glass contains alcohol and water in the ratio 1 : 4. A second glass has the same
    quantity of liquid but this time the ratio of alcohol to water is 2 : 3.
    Each glass is emptied into a third glass.
    What is the ratio of alcohol to water for the final mixture?

14. When a car is moving at 108 km/hr, it travels 18 km on a litre of petrol.
    If petrol costs €1.62 a litre, work out the cost of petrol per minute when driving the
    car at 108 km/hr.

15. Alice builds a model of a house. She uses a scale of 1 : 20.
    The height of the real house is 10 metres.

    (i) Work out the height of the model.
    The width of the model is 80 cm.
    (ii) Work out the width of the real house.

16. The number of pages in a comic book was increased from 48 to 80. If the price, which
    was previously €6.00, is increased in the same ratio, what should the new price be?

17. A pastry mix is made from 2 parts butter mixed
    with 3 parts flour.

    (i) How much of each ingredient is needed to
        make one kilogram of pastry mix?
    (ii) Rachel has 200 g of butter and 400 g of flour.
         What is the most pastry mix she can make?
    (iii) Gina has 1.5 kg of butter and 1125 g of flour.
         What is the most pastry mix she can make?

18. A motorist driving 90 km per day has enough diesel to last her 8 days. If she reduces her driving to 72 km per day, how long should the diesel last?

19. 12 blocklayers can build a wall in 15 days.

    (i) How long would it take 20 blocklayers working at the same rate to do so?
   (ii) How many blocklayers would be needed to build the wall in 10 days?

20. What is the ratio of the shaded area to the area of the largest square?

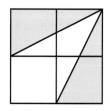

21. One full glass contains vinegar and water in the ratio of 1 : 3. Another full glass of twice the capacity of the first has vinegar and water in the ratio 1 : 4. If the contents of both glasses were mixed together, what then is the ratio of vinegar to water?

22. A male punky fish has 9 stripes and a female punky fish has 8 stripes. I count 86 stripes on the fish in my tank. What is the ratio of male fish to female fish?

23. In the diagram, $\frac{5}{6}$ of the circle is shaded and $\frac{2}{3}$ of the triangle is shaded. What is the ratio of the area of the circle to the area of the triangle?

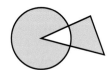

Section 12.2 Time and timetables

The clock on the right shows the time to be 9.20.

This could be 9.20 a.m. or 9.20 p.m..

When we give a time containing a.m. or p.m. we are expressing it in **12-hour clock time**.

The letters **a.m.** are used to indicate times between midnight and noon.

Times between noon and midnight are indicated by **p.m.**.

The **24-hour clock** is another way of telling the time. This method uses 4 digits, e.g. 10.24.

> a.m. means *ante meridiem*
>   – before noon
> p.m. means *post meridiem*
>   – after noon

The first two digits give the hour after midnight and the second two digits give the number of minutes after the hour.

The table below shows times expressed in 12-hour and 24-hour clock times.

12-hour clock	10 a.m.	4.30 p.m.	4.20 a.m.	9.16 p.m.	12.10 a.m.
24-hour clock	10.00	16.30	04.20	21.16	00.10

In most bus and train timetables, for example, the decimal point in the 24-hour time is omitted and 21.16 is written as 2116.

Example 1

A film begins at 20.45 and ends at 22.14. How long does it last?

We subtract 20.45 from 22.14 as follows:
$$\begin{array}{r} 22.14 \\ -20.45 \end{array}$$

When subtracting a larger number of minutes from a smaller number, change the top line by adding 60 to the minutes and taking away one hour as follows:

$$\begin{array}{r} 22.14 \\ -20.45 \end{array} = \begin{array}{r} 21.74 \\ -20.45 \\ \hline 1.29 \end{array}$$ ... 14 minutes after 10 = 74 minutes after 9

The film lasts 1 hour 29 minutes.

Exercise 12.2

1. Perform the following additions and subtractions:

(i)
```
  hr  min
   4   38
+  3   46
```
(ii)
```
  hr  min
   4   53
−  2   17
```
(iii)
```
  hr  min
   3   12
+  1   46
```
(iv)
```
  hr  min
   5   35
−  3   54
```

2. Express each of these in minutes:

(i) 3 hours 24 min   (ii) 5 hours 36 min   (iii) 7 hours 54 min

3. Express each of these in 12-hour clock time:

(i)

a.m.

(ii)

p.m.

(iii)

a.m.

(iv)

p.m.

4. Write the following using a.m. or p.m. :

    (i) 11.40   (ii) 15.35   (iii) 12.20   (iv) 00.30   (v) 22.15

5. Write in 24-hour clock time:

    (i) 6 a.m.   (ii) 10.45 a.m.   (iii) 4 p.m.   (iv) 10.12 p.m.   (v) 12 noon

6. How many hours and minutes from

    (i) 9.45 a.m. to 2.15 p.m.   (ii) 8.45 p.m. to 3.50 a.m.

   (iii) 08.30 to 16.45   (iv) 06.42 to 15.10 ?

7. How many hours and minutes from

    (i) 10.35 to 14.45   (ii) 12.48 to 16.20   (iii) 10.36 to 18.45 ?

8. The times shown below give hours, minutes and seconds:
Match the times on the clocks to the digital times in the blue boxes:

9. A woman works from 08.45 to 12.30 and from 13.45 to 17.15 for 5 days each week.
Calculate how many hours she works in the week.

10. A play started at 8.20 p.m. and lasted 2hr 35 min. At what time did it finish?

11. A train leaves Tralee at 10.52 and arrives in Dublin at 14.40.
How long does the journey take?

12. A turkey needs to be cooked for dinner at 18.30.
The cooking time is 28 minutes per kg, plus an extra 20 minutes.
If the turkey weighs 8 kg, at what time should it be put in the oven?

13. The following is an extract from the Dublin to Westport train timetable:

		Train 1	Train 2
Dublin Heuston	dep.	08.30	17.10
Athlone	arr.	10.08	18.43
Athlone	dep.	10.10	18.45
Claremorris	arr.	11.25	20.08
Claremorris	dep.	11.44	20.11
Westport	arr.	12.05	20.38

(i)   How long does it take Train 1 to go from Dublin to Westport?

(ii)   For how long does Train 1 stop in Claremorris?

(iii) How long does it take Train 2 to go from Athlone to Westport?

(iv)   Which is the faster train from Dublin to Athlone?

(v)   How long does it take Train 1 to go from Dublin to Claremorris?

(vi)   For how long does Train 2 stop in Athlone?

(vii) If I arrive at Heuston Station in Dublin at 07.52, how long do I have to wait for Train 1 to Westport?

(viii) Which is the faster train from Dublin to Westport?

14. A car journey began at 10.40 and finished at 13.25.
If the car used 6 litres of petrol per hour and each litre costs €1.65, calculate the cost of petrol for the journey.

Section 12.3 Speed – Distance – Time

If a car travels 100 km in 2 hours, then we say that the average speed of the car for the journey is 50 kilometres per hour (written as **50 km/hr**).

Again, if a train does 300 km in 3 hours, its average speed is 100 km/hr.

In each of these examples, the average speed $= \dfrac{\text{distance travelled}}{\text{time taken}}$.

The examples above could also be used to show that

(i) Time $= \dfrac{\text{Distance}}{\text{Speed}}$ (ii) Distance $=$ Speed $\times$ Time

The triangle on the right could help you to remember the formulae given.

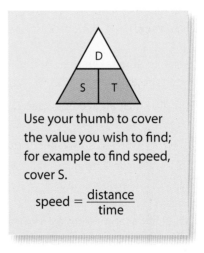

Speed $= \dfrac{\text{Distance}}{\text{Time}}$

Time $= \dfrac{\text{Distance}}{\text{Speed}}$

Distance $=$ Speed $\times$ Time

Use your thumb to cover the value you wish to find; for example to find speed, cover S.

$$\text{speed} = \dfrac{\text{distance}}{\text{time}}$$

Example 1

A train travels a journey of 210 km in $2\frac{1}{2}$ hours. Find its average speed.

Average speed $= \dfrac{\text{Distance}}{\text{Time}} = \dfrac{210}{2\frac{1}{2}} = \dfrac{210 \times 2}{2\frac{1}{2} \times 2} = \dfrac{420}{5} = 84$

$\therefore$ the average speed $= 84$ km/hr.

Example 2

A motorist travelled 500 kilometres in six hours.
Her average speed for the first two hours was 100 km/hr.
Find her average speed in kilometres per hour for the last four hours.

Distance travelled in the first 2 hours is $100 \text{ km} \times 2 = 200 \text{ km}$.

Therefore she travelled 300 km in the last 4 hours.

Average speed $= \dfrac{\text{Distance}}{\text{Time}}$

$\qquad = \dfrac{300}{4}$ ... 500 km − 200 km = 300 km and 6 hr − 2 hr = 4 hr.

$\qquad = 75$

$\therefore$ average speed for the last 4 hours $= 75$ km/hr.

Exercise 12.3

1. How far will a car travel

    (i) in 3 hours at an average speed of 75 km/hr

    (ii) in $2\frac{1}{4}$ hours at an average speed of 88 km/hr ?

2. Find the time taken to travel

    (i) 200 km at an average speed of 80 km/hr

    (ii) 48 km at an average speed of 64 km/hr.

3. Find the average speed, in km/hr, of a car if it does

    (i) 120 km in 2 hours   (ii) 90 km in $1\frac{1}{2}$ hours

    (iii) 25 km in 30 minutes   (iv) 90 km in 40 minutes.

4. A racing car completes a 15 km lap of a track in 5 minutes.
Express this speed in km/hr.

242

5. A speedboat travels at 60 km/hr for two hours and then at 90 km/hr for one hour. Find its average speed over the three hours.

6. A journey takes 3 hours at an average speed of 120 km/hr. How long, in hours, will the journey take if the average speed is reduced to 80 km/hr?

7. A journey of 276 km began at 1040 hrs and ended on the same day at 1430 hrs. Find the average speed in km/hr.

8. It takes 4 hours and 20 minutes to travel a journey at an average speed of 120 km/hr. How many hours and minutes will it take to travel the same journey if the average speed is reduced to 100 km/hr?

9. A motorist travelled 320 km in five hours. Her average speed for the first 160 km was 80 km/hr. What was her average speed for the second 160 km?

10. A distance of 18 km is travelled in 25 minutes. Find the average speed in metres per second.

11. A cyclist started a journey of 56 km at 1015 hours and finished the journey at 1135 hours. Calculate the average speed of the cyclist in km/hr.

12. A distance of 600 metres is travelled in 30 seconds. Find the average speed in km/hr.

13. A car journey of 559 kilometres took 6 hours and 30 minutes.
   (i) Calculate the average speed, in km/hr, for the journey.
   (ii) If the average petrol consumption for the journey was 8.3 km per litre, calculate the number of litres used, correct to the nearest litre.

14. A runner sets out at midday to run to the next village, a distance of 12 km. She wants to arrive at this village at 1330 hours. At what average speed should she run?

15. A cheetah can run 100 m in 5.4 seconds. A train takes 12 minutes to travel 7.7 km between two stations. Which has the faster average speed, the train or the cheetah? Express the difference in metres per minute.

16. Anne walks a distance of 1.7 km to school from home. She walks at an average speed of 5.1 km/hr. What is the latest she can leave home to be in school at 8.55 a.m.?

17. The table on the right shows the times taken by some very fast animals to travel the distances given.
Arrange the animals in order, starting with the fastest.

Animal	Time taken	Distance in metres
Cheetah	18 seconds	500 m
Racehorse	16 seconds	300 m
Antelope	$4\frac{1}{2}$ min	6 000 m
Deer	42 min	32 000 m

18. A train is scheduled to make a journey of 300 km at an average speed of 120 km/hr.
It leaves six minutes late and its average speed is increased so that it arrives on time.
Find the new average speed.

19. Barbara's rule for mountain walkers is:

Allow 1 hour for every 5 km you must walk.
Add $\frac{1}{2}$ hour for every 300 metres you must climb.

Jasmine started a 4 km walk at 0800 hours.
The path climbed 1800 m from start to finish.
Jasmine wanted to work out at about what time she would finish the walk.
If she allows $2\frac{1}{2}$ hours for stops along the way, at about what time should she arrive?

Test yourself 12

1. (a) Simplify these ratios as far as possible:
      (i) 28 : 35   (ii) 20 cm : 1 m   (iii) 250 g : 3 kg   (iv) 40c : €2

   (b) A train left Dublin at 0945 and reached Limerick at 1215.
      (i) How long did the journey take?
      (ii) If the length of the journey is 220 km, find the average speed of the train
          in km/hr.

   (c) A rectangle is divided into four triangles, as shown.
      Find the ratio of
          smallest triangle : largest triangle.

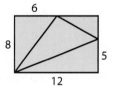

2. (a) The ratio of sailing dinghies to motor cruisers moored in a harbour is 4 : 1.
      If there are 24 dinghies in the harbour, how many motor cruisers are there?

   (b) A motorist travels at an average speed of 60 km/hr for $2\frac{1}{4}$ hours.
      If his car has an average fuel consumption of 1 litre of petrol per 15 km, find how
      many litres of petrol are used.

   (c) A large ball of wool is used to knit a scarf.
      The scarf is 40 stitches wide and 120 cm long.
      If the same size ball of wool is used to knit a scarf 25 stitches wide, work out the
      length of the new scarf.

3. (a) (i) For this almond cake recipe, write the ratio of
             butter to sugar to flour to ground almonds in
             its simplest form.
         (ii) In another recipe, the ratio of flour to sugar is 3 : 2.
             How much sugar is needed to mix with 1.2 kg
             of flour?

Rich Almond Cake
0.25 kg butter
350 g sugar
0.5 kg flour
150 g ground almonds

   (b) A school's lessons begin at 9.00 a.m. and end at 3.40 p.m. with an hour's break at
      lunchtime and 20 minutes break mid-morning.
      If there are 8 lessons of equal length, how long is a lesson?

   (c) A T.G.V. travels 567 km from Bordeaux to Paris at an average speed of 252 km/hr.
      Find the arrival time in Paris, if it leaves Bordeaux at 1410.

4. (a) A bus travels for 2 hours at an average speed of 90 km/hr and then for a further
      hour at a speed of 60 km/hr.
      Find   (i) the total distance travelled   (ii) the total time taken
             (iii) the average speed of the bus for the whole journey in km/hr.

(b)   An alloy consists of copper, zinc and tin in the ratio $1:3:5$.
If there are 45 kg of tin in the alloy, find its total mass.

(c)   An aeroplane was due to take off from Shannon airport at 18:42 but it was 35 min late. During the flight, thanks to a tail wind, the plane made up the time and in fact landed 16 min before its scheduled arrival time of 00:05. (Assume that the plane did not cross any time zones on its journey.)
  (i)   What time did the aeroplane take off?
 (ii)   What time did it land?

5. (a)   A prize fund was divided between *A*, *B* and *C* in the ratio $5:2:1$.
If *B* received €520, find the total prize fund.

(b)   The Grand Old Duke of York, he had ten thousand men, he marched them up to the top of the hill, ...
By 2 p.m. they were one third of the way up.
By 4 p.m. they were three quarters of the way up.
When did they set out?

(c)   A 500 ml jug is filled with orange squash and lemonade in the ratio $1:4$.
Another 1 litre jug is filled with orange squash and lemonade in the ratio $1:3$.
Both jugs are poured into one large jug.
What is the ratio of orange squash to lemonade in the large jug?

6. (a)   The largest square is divided into 4 squares, as shown.
What proportion of this diagram is shaded?
Give your answer as a fraction.

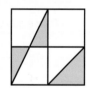

(b)   A contractor estimated that he could do a certain job in 1 year with 280 men.
If he was asked to do the work in 10 months, how many more men would he need to employ?

(c)   A man walks 15 kilometres at an average speed of 6 km/hr.
He then runs 9 kilometres at an average speed of 18 km/hr.
Find (i)   the total time taken for the two journeys
      (ii)   his average speed for the two journeys.

(d)   In a grand prix, the winning car passed the chequered flag 0.3 seconds ahead of the next car.
Both cars were travelling at 84 m/s.
What was the distance between the two cars?

Key words

line plot	outlier	clustered	bar chart	pie chart
sector	histogram	normal distribution		positive skew
negative skew	stem and leaf plot		misleading graphs	
median	quartiles	interquartile range		

Section 13.1 Line plots and bar charts revisited

1. Line plots

The following data shows the daily maximum temperatures (in °C) in Barcelona during the month of June.

```
27  28  26  25  26  27  22  30  28  29
28  26  24  22  28  24  27  29  28  27
19  25  26  29  29  26  28  28  31  25
```

These temperatures are shown in the line plot below:

Each temperature is represented by a dot

The **range** is 19°C to 31°C, i.e., 12°C.

The **mode** is 28°C as it occurs most frequently.

19°C is referred to as an **outlier** as it is significantly different from the rest of the scores.

The temperatures are bunched or **clustered** between 25°C and 29°C.

2. Bar charts

Bar charts are a simple but effective way of displaying data.

A bar chart consists of a series of bars of the same width, drawn either vertically or horizontally from an axis.

The heights (or lengths) of the bars always represent the frequencies.

The bars are generally separated by narrow gaps of equal width.

The bar chart below shows the numbers of text messages received by a group of students on a particular Saturday.

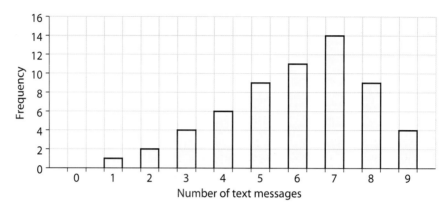

The total number of text messages received was

$$1 + 2 + 4 + 6 + 9 + 11 + 14 + 9 + 4 = 60.$$

The modal number is 7 and the range is 1 to 9.

Exercise 13.1

1. The line plot below illustrates the number of goals scored per match by a hockey team.

Goals scored

(i)   How many matches have the team played?
(ii) Which number of goals scored is the mode?
(iii) What is the range of the number of goals scored?
(iv) What percentage of their matches were scoreless?

2. The daily maximum temperatures (in °C) at the Eiffel Tower during April are shown in this line plot:

(i)   What is the mode?
(ii) What is the outlier?
(iii) On how many days was the maximum temperature 25°C?
(iv) On what percentage of days did the maximum temperature drop below 20°C?
(v)   If a day is selected at random, what is the probability that the maximum temperature is less than 18°C?

3. This line plot shows the scores (out of 50) of a group of students in a maths exam:

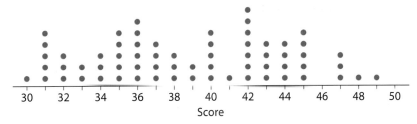

Score

(i)   Which score was the most common?
(ii) How many students scored 34?
(iii) How many students scored 45 or more?
(iv) What percentage of students scored 35 or less?
(v)   If a student was selected at random, what is the probability that he scored 40?

4. This bar chart shows the number of pictures remembered by each student in a memory experiment.

(i)   How many students took part in the experiment?
(ii) What is the modal number of pictures remembered?
(iii) How many students remembered less than 7 pictures?
(iv) What is the range of the number of pictures remembered?
(v)   What is the median number of pictures remembered?

5. The bar chart shows the numbers of hours spent on homework each week by a group of second-year students.

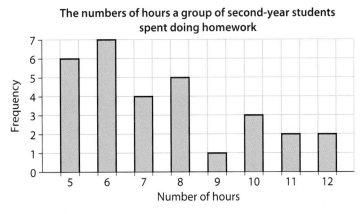

The numbers of hours a group of second-year students spent doing homework

(i)   How many students spent 6 hours doing homework?
(ii) What was the greatest number of hours a student spent doing homework?

(iii) How many students spent less than 7 hours doing homework?

(iv) How many students spent more than 10 hours doing homework?

(v) How many students were surveyed?

(vi) What percentage of students spent 8 hours doing homework?

(vii) If a student is selected at random, what is the probability that the student spent 10 hours doing homework?

6. Six coins were tossed 30 times and the number of heads showing each time was recorded.

The results are shown in the given bar chart.

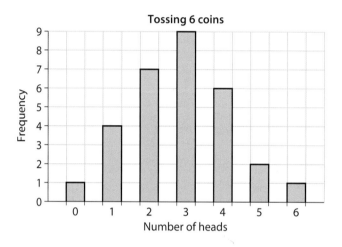

(i) How many times were 4 heads showing?

(ii) What was the modal number of heads showing?

(iii) If, for a particular toss, there were 2 heads, how many tails showed?

(iv) Write down the experimental probability of getting 4 heads.

7.

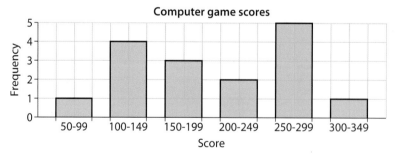

This graph shows scores in a computer game.

(i) Scores of 250 or more won a prize. How many people won a prize?

(ii) How many people played altogether?

(iii) What is the greatest number of people who could have scored more than 220?

(iv) What is the smallest number of people who could have scored less than 160?

8. The numbers of goals scored in a series of football matches is represented in the bar chart shown on the right.

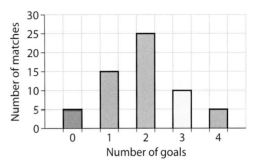

   (i) How many matches were played?
   (ii) Calculate the total number of goals scored.
   (iii) Calculate the mean number of goals scored per match, correct to one decimal place.

9. A survey was conducted to determine the numbers of hours students spent on the Internet per week. The results were as follows:

17	14	9	28	8	27	23	16	10	18
15	23	5	38	27	19	6	25	24	36
16	5	7	17	8	9	3	4	27	28
16	7	8	18	9	4	9	8	6	35

   (i) Arrange this information in a frequency distribution table using class intervals (1–10), (11–20), (21–30) and (31–40).
   (ii) Draw a bar chart to represent this information.
   (iii) How many students used the Internet for more than 30 hours per week?
   (iv) What percentage of students used the Internet for 25 hours or more per week?
   (v) What percentage of students used the Internet for fewer than 21 hours per week?

10. A group of 20 male and 20 female teenagers were asked their opinion on whether physical education should be compulsory. The results are displayed in this double-column bar chart.

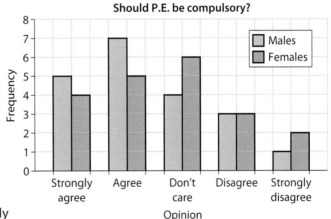

Should P.E. be compulsory?

   (i) How many females strongly agree with compulsory physical education?
   (ii) How many males strongly agree with compulsory physical education?
   (iii) What is the total number of students who strongly disagree with compulsory physical education?
   (iv) If a student was selected at random, what is the probability that the student strongly agreed that physical education should be compulsory? Give your answer as a decimal.

Section 13.2 Pie charts

A **pie chart** is a good way of displaying
information when we want to show how a
given quantity is shared out or divided
into different categories. The 'pie' or circle
represents the total quantity and each
'slice' or **sector** represents the size of the share.

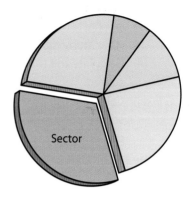

The size of each 'slice' or sector is in proportion to the
size of the angle at the centre of the sector.

The angle at the centre of a circle or pie is 360°.
A half share will have an angle $\frac{1}{2} \times 360° = 180°$.

The diagram on the right shows how different shares
are represented by sectors in a pie chart.

If the fraction of a share is $\frac{1}{6}$, the angle at the centre is
found by getting $\frac{1}{6}$ of 360°.

$\frac{1}{6}$ of 360° = 360° ÷ 6 = 60°.

Similarly, if the fraction is $\frac{1}{10}$, the angle at the centre
is $\frac{1}{10}$ of 360° = 36°.

Example 1

120 first-year girls were asked to name their favourite
sport. The result is shown in the given pie chart.

How many girls named
  (i)   tennis
  (ii) athletics
  (iii) hockey
  (iv) netball
as their favourite sport?

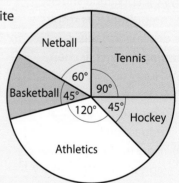

Here we express each of the angles in the sectors required as a fraction of 360°.

  (i) **Tennis:**   90°; $\dfrac{90°}{360°} = \dfrac{1}{4}$ and $\dfrac{1}{4}$ of 120 = 30

    ∴   30 girls named tennis

252

(ii) **Athletics:** 120°; $\dfrac{120°}{360°} = \dfrac{1}{3}$ and $\dfrac{1}{3}$ of 120 = 40

∴ 40 girls named athletics

(iii) **Hockey:** 45°; $\dfrac{45°}{360°} = \dfrac{9}{72} = \dfrac{1}{8}$ and $\dfrac{1}{8}$ of 120 = 15

∴ 15 girls named hockey

(iv) **Netball:** 60°; $\dfrac{60°}{360°} = \dfrac{1}{6}$ and $\dfrac{1}{6}$ of 120 = 20

∴ 20 girls named netball

Example 2

In a survey, 72 people were asked what type of heating they had in their homes. The results are given in the table below:

Type of heating	Oil	Gas	Electricity	Solid fuel
Number of households	30	24	12	6

Draw a pie chart to illustrate this information.

The angle in each sector is found as follows:

Oil: $\dfrac{30}{72} = \dfrac{5}{12}$ and $\dfrac{5}{12}$ of 360° $= \dfrac{5}{{}_1\cancel{12}} \times \dfrac{\overset{30}{\cancel{360}}}{1} = 150°$

Gas: $\dfrac{24}{72} = \dfrac{1}{3}$ and $\dfrac{1}{3}$ of 360° = 120°

Electricity: $\dfrac{12}{72} = \dfrac{1}{6}$ and $\dfrac{1}{6}$ of 360° = 60°

Solid fuel: $\dfrac{6}{72} = \dfrac{1}{12}$ and $\dfrac{1}{12}$ of 360° = 30°

The results are represented by the pie chart on the right.

Exercise 13.2

1. Find the value of x in each pie chart shown.

(i)

(ii)

(iii)

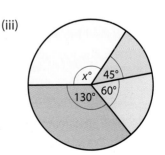

253

2. The pie chart below shows the different types of accommodation in a holiday village.

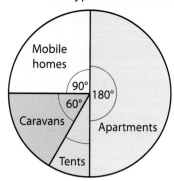

If the total number of 'units' in the village was 600, find
   (i) the number of apartments in the village
   (ii) the number of mobile homes in the village
   (iii) the number of caravans in the village
   (iv) the angle in the sector representing tents.

3. On returning to Dublin, 240 holiday makers were asked to name countries they had visited.
   The results are shown in the pie chart on the right.
   (i) What is the size of the angle marked $x°$?
   (ii) How many people visited Portugal?
   (iii) Which country was visited by the most people?
   (iv) Which country was visited by $\frac{1}{4}$ of the people questioned?
   (v) Which two countries combined accounted for one half of the holiday makers questioned?

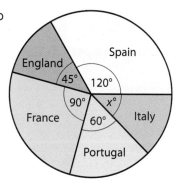

4. A packet of breakfast cereal weighing 600 g contains 4 ingredients as follows:

Oats	Barley	Wheat	Rye
150 g	100 g	75 g	275 g

In the pie chart on the right, find the angle in the sector representing
   (i) oats   (ii) wheat   (iii) rye.

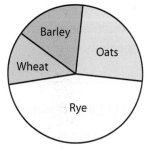

5. Sixty people were asked how they generally travel to work and the results are given in the following table:

Transport	Bus	Car	Train	Walk	Bicycle
Number of people	20	15	12	8	5

   (i) Calculate the angle in each of the sectors.
   (ii) Draw a pie chart to illustrate the data.

6. The pie chart shows how the cost of a holiday was shared between various items.

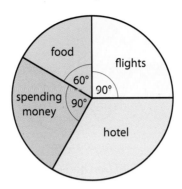

The flights cost €450.
  (i) Calculate the total cost of the holiday.
 (ii) (a) Calculate the size of the angle which represents the cost of the hotel.
        (b) Calculate the cost of the hotel.

7. 100 people were asked to spell 'hypotenuse'.

40 spelt it correctly, 35 would not try and 25 spelt it incorrectly.

Select the pie chart below that correctly matches the information given.

Spelling   **Spelling**   **Spelling**

8. In a survey, some small children were asked to name their favourite pet.

The given pie chart shows information about their answers.

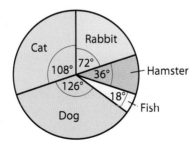

  (i) What fraction of the children named hamster as their favourite pet?
 (ii) If 20 children named rabbit, work out the number of children who took part in the survey.

9. These pie charts show what sorts of cards were in two stationery shops.

Cardworld

200 Cards

Card Den

600 Cards

Cardworld had 200 cards and *Card Den* had 600 cards.
 (i) Approximately how many birthday cards were at *Card Den*?
 (ii) Jenny thought the pie charts above showed there were more *Congratulations* cards at *Cardworld* than at *Card Den*.
 Explain why the pie charts show that this is not so.

10. An ice cream stall sells vanilla, strawberry and chocolate ice creams. The pie chart illustrates the sales of ice cream for last Saturday. The number of vanilla and the number of chocolate ice creams sold were the same. The stall sold 60 strawberry ice creams. How many chocolate ice creams were sold?

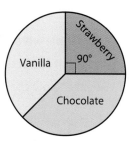

11. The pie chart illustrates the sales of four brands of crisps.
 (i) What percentage of total sales does *Tayto* have?
 (ii) If *Walkers* accounts for 35% of total sales, calculate the angles *x* and *y*.

Section 13.3 Histograms

One of the most common ways of representing a frequency distribution is by means of a **histogram**.

Histograms are very similar to bar charts but there are some important differences:
> there are no gaps between the bars in a histogram
> histograms are used to show **continuous data**
> the data is always **grouped**; the groups are called **classes**
> the **area** of each bar or rectangle represents the frequency.

Histograms may have equal or unequal class intervals.

For our course, we will confine our study to histograms with **equal class intervals**.

When the class intervals are equal, drawing a histogram is very similar to drawing a bar chart.

Example 1

Fifty children were asked to solve a puzzle.
The table below records the time, in minutes, taken by the children.

Time (in mins)	0–5	5–10	10–15	15–20	20–25
Number of children	6	10	16	12	6

All the groups have the same interval of 5 minutes.
To draw the histogram, you start by drawing the two axes.

The horizontal axis shows the time. Each group or class is 5 minutes.
The vertical axis is labelled 'Number of children'.
We now draw the rectangles or bars for each class.
Notice that the heights of the bars represent the frequencies.
The **modal class** is (10–15) minutes because there are more children in this class
than any other class.

The shape of a distribution

All the histograms drawn below have different shapes.

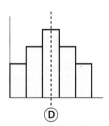

Only histogram D appears balanced or symmetrical as it has an axis of symmetry.
The other three histograms are less balanced or **skewed** in some way.

Histograms are very useful when you want to see where the data lies and so get a clear
picture of the shape of the distribution. For example, in histogram A above, we can see that
most of the data is concentrated at the lower values. In histogram C, the data is concentrated
at the higher values.

There are some shapes that occur frequently in statistics and you should be able to recognise and name them.

1. Symmetrical distributions

This distribution has an axis of symmetry down the middle.
The data is equally distributed about this axis.
It is generally referred to as a **normal distribution**.

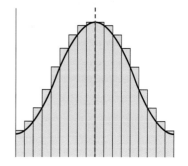

2. Positive skew

When a distribution has most of the data at the lower values, we say it has a **positive skew** or is **skewed to the right**.

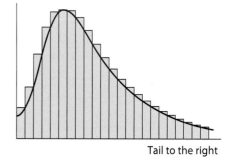

Tail to the right

3. Negative skew

When a distribution has most of the data at the higher values, we say that the distribution has a **negative skew** or is **skewed to the left**.

In a distribution with a **positive** skew, the tail is to the **right**; with a **negative** skew, the tail is to the **left**.

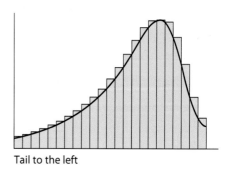

Tail to the left

Here are two line plots, one with a positive skew and the other with a negative skew.

Positively skewed

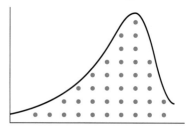

Negatively skewed

Exercise 13.3

1. The histogram on the right shows the distances, in kilometres, travelled to work by people in an office block.

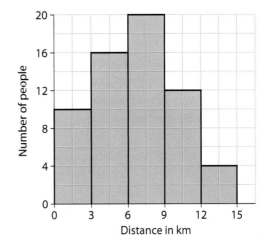

(i) How many people travelled between 6 km and 9 km to work?

(ii) How many people had to travel more than 9 km?

(iii) What is the modal class?

(iv) What is the total number of people included in the survey?

2. The histogram shows the number of people who used a snack bar before lunch one weekday.

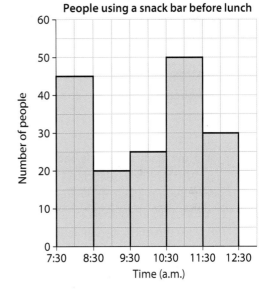

(i) At what time do you think the snack bar opened?

(ii) How many people used the snack bar during the first hour?

(iii) Why do you think that the people used the snack bar at this time?

The snack bar had another busy hour.

(iv) When was it busy again?

(v) Why do you think that the snack bar was busy for a second time?

3. A Garda officer recorded the speeds of cars passing a school.

The table below shows the speeds that he recorded.

Speed (in km)	20–30	30–40	40–50	50–60
Number of cars	8	20	16	12

(i) Draw a histogram to illustrate this data.

(ii) How many cars were travelling at less than 40 km/hour?

(iii) If the speed limit was 55 km/hr, what is the maximum number of cars that could have exceeded this limit?

259

4. The histogram below shows the times taken by a group of students to solve a problem.

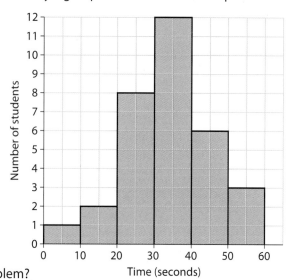

  (i)   How many students were in the group?
 (ii)   Write down the modal class.
(iii)   What percentage of students took between 20 seconds and 30 seconds to solve the problem?
(iv)   What is the greatest number of students who could have solved the problem in less than 35 seconds?
 (v)   If a student is selected at random, what is the probability that the student took longer than 40 seconds to solve the problem?

5. At the end of their journeys, 30 motorists were asked how many kilometres they had travelled. Their responses are shown in the table below:

Distance (in km)	0–20	20–40	40–60	60–80	80–100
Frequency	6	12	7	4	1

[0–20 means ⩾0 and <20]

  (i)   Draw a histogram to illustrate this data.
 (ii)   How many motorists had travelled 40 km or more?
(iii)   What is the modal class?
(iv)   If the median is the value that is halfway into the distribution, in which interval does the median lie?
 (v)   Use the mid-interval values to estimate the mean of the distribution.

6. The histogram opposite shows the annual salaries of a group of graduates in their first year of employment.

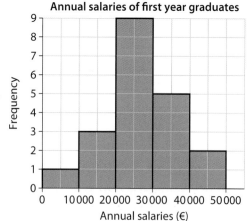

Annual salaries of first year graduates

  (i)   How many graduates earned more than €40 000?
 (ii)   What is the modal class for the salaries?
(iii)   What is the greatest number of graduates who could have earned more than €35 000?
(iv)   How many graduates were surveyed?
 (v)   If a graduate was selected at random from the group, what is the probability that he/she earned between €10 000 and €20 000?

7. The histogram below shows the ages of people living in a village.

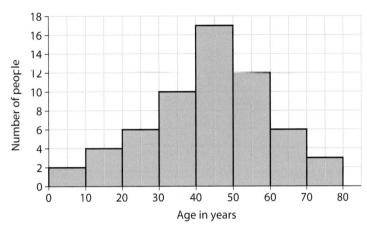

Age in years

  (i)   How many people are aged under 30 years?
 (ii)   How many people live in the village?
(iii)   Which interval contains 20% of the people?
(iv)   If a person is selected at random, what is the probability that he/she is aged between 60 and 70 years?
 (v)   What is the greatest number of people who could be older than 55 years?
(vi)   Use the mid-interval values to find an estimate of the mean age.

8. Here are three distributions.

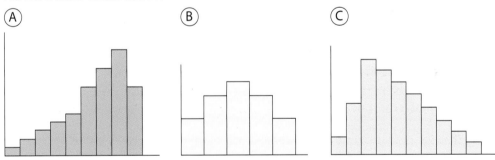

  (i)   Which of these distributions is symmetrical?
 (ii)   Which distribution is positively skewed?
(iii)   Which distribution is negatively skewed?

Section 13.4 Stem and leaf plots

A **stem and leaf diagram** is a very useful way of presenting data. It is useful because it shows all the original data and also gives you the overall picture or shape of the distribution.

It is similar to a horizontal bar chart, with the numbers themselves forming the bars.

Stem and leaf diagrams are suitable only for small amounts of data.

If data consists of 2 digits, the first digit is used as the stem and the second digit as the leaf.

The number 42 is written as 4|2.

A typical stem and leaf diagram is shown below.

```
0 | 6  9
1 | 2  5  (7) ←──────── This represents 17.
2 | 3  3  6  8
3 | 0  2  7
4 | 1  2  6
5 | 3                    Key: 3|2 = 32
```

> You must always add a key to show how the stem and leaf combine.

The data represented above is:

6, 9, 12, 15, 17, 23, 23, 26, 28, 30, 32, 37, 41, 42, 46, 53

Notice that all the numbers are in order of size, starting with the smallest and finishing with the largest.

This is called an **ordered** stem and leaf plot.

Example 1

Use a stem and leaf plot to show the following ages of the 21 musicians in an orchestra:

25	35	28	47	52	33	50	28	33	35	48
55	29	50	39	41	32	29	56	26	35	

(i) What is the mode of the data?

(ii) What is the median age?

The ages range from 25 to 56.

We write 2, 3, 4 and 5 down the first column to make the stem.

The leaves are the single digits written next to the stem:

25 is shown by writing a 5 next to the 2 stem.

Stem	Leaf
2	5 8 8 9 9 6
3	5 3 3 5 9 2 5
4	7 8 1
5	2 0 5 0 6

This is an unordered stem and leaf plot.

> In a stem and leaf plot, the numbers must align beneath one another.

It is more useful to rearrange the scores so they are in order, from smallest to largest.

This results in an **ordered** stem and leaf plot.

Stem	Leaf
2	5 6 8 8 9 9
3	2 3 3 5 5 5 9
4	1 7 8
5	0 0 2 5 6

Key: $3|2 = 32$

(i) The mode is 35 as it occurs most frequently.

(ii) The median is the value that is halfway through the distribution.
There are 21 values altogether.
The median value is the 11th value.
This value is 35, i.e., the median is 35.

Back-to-back stem and leaf plots

Two stem and leaf diagrams can be drawn using the same stem.

These are known as back-to-back stem and leaf diagrams.

The leaves of one set of data are put to the right of the stem.

The leaves of the other set of data are put on the left.

A back-to-back stem and leaf diagram is very useful to compare two sets of data.

This is illustrated in the following example.

Example 2

The Science teacher decided to give her class a test on a particular topic. The class performed poorly. One week later she gave the class a similar test after a thorough revision of the topic.

The results are shown in the back-to-back stem and leaf plot below.

Leaf	Stem	Leaf
9 8 6 6 0	3	
9 7 7 3 1 1 1	4	3 6 6 8
9 8 8 5 3 3 0	5	1 7 9 9
9 8 7 5 3	6	3 8 9
	7	0 5 5 5 8 9
	8	2 6 7 7
0	9	0 0 1 3

Key: $3|6 = 63$

Key: $8|2 = 82$

(i) What does the diagram show about the performance of the class in the two tests?
(ii) Find the median mark in each test.
(iii) Write down the range of the marks in each test.
(iv) Do the median marks and the ranges support your conclusion in (i) above?
(v) Identify any outliers in the test results.

(i) The diagram shows that the class scored far better in the second test.
14 students scored 70 marks or higher in the second test while there was only one student with a mark higher than 70 in the first test.
(ii) There are 25 students in the class.
The median mark in each test is the 13th mark.
The median mark in the first test is 50.
The median mark in the second test is 75.
(iii) The range in the first test is 90–30, i.e. 60.
The range in the second test is 93–43, i.e. 50.
(iv) Since the median mark in the second test is 75 and only 50 in the first test, it confirms the conclusion that the students did better in the second test.
Also the range is higher in the first test and this shows that the marks were more spread out (i.e. less consistent) in the first test.
(v) In the first test, the score 90 is an outlier.
In the second test, there are no outliers.

Finding the interquartile range from a stem and leaf diagram

In Chapter 4, we found that the **lower quartile** is the value in the data that is one quarter way through the distribution. The **upper quartile** is the value that is three quarters way through the distribution. The difference between the upper quartile and the lower quartile is the **interquartile range**.

We will now show how to find the two quartiles and the interquartile range of a distribution presented as a stem and leaf diagram.

Example 3

The stem and leaf diagram on the right shows the marks, out of 50, obtained in a maths test.

Find
(i) the median mark
(ii) the lower quartile
(iii) the upper quartile
(iv) the interquartile range.

Marks obtained

1	2	8			
2	1	4	7	7	8
3	1	4	5	7	
4	1	2	8		
5	0				

Key: $2|1 = 21$

(i) The median mark is the mark that is halfway through the distribution.

There are 15 data values.

The halfway value is the 8th value.

Starting at the lowest value, the 8th value is 31

∴ the median = 31

(ii) The lower quartile is the value that is one quarter way through the distribution.

This value is the 4th value.

This value is 24.

∴ the lower quartile = 24

(iii) The upper quartile is the value that is three quarters of the way through the distribution.

This value is the 12th value.

This value is 41.

∴ the upper quartile = 41

(iv) The interquartile range = upper quartile minus lower quartile

$$= 41 - 24$$
$$= 17$$

Exercise 13.4

1. The stem and leaf diagram below shows the ages, in years, of 25 people who wished to enter a 10 km walking competition.

```
1 | 4  4  6  9
2 | 1  3  7  7  7  8
3 | 3  6  6  7  9
4 | 0  2  3  3  8  8
5 | 1  3  4  7
```
Key: 1|6 means 16 years old

(i) How many people were less than 20 years old?

(ii) Write down the modal age.

(iii) How many people were between 35 and 45 years old?

(iv) What was the median age?

2. The stem and leaf diagram on the right shows the marks obtained by a group of students in a Spanish test.

    (i) How many students took this test?

    (ii) How many students got between 70 and 79 marks?

    (iii) What is the range of the marks obtained?

    (iv) Find the median mark.

stem	leaf					
5	1	4	6			
6	2	3	3	6		
7	2	3	5	7	8	
8	0	0	2	4	6	6
9	3	4				

Key: 7|3   means 73 marks

3. The number of points scored per match by the Dragons basketball team are shown below:

85	67	56	69	99	97	59	65	84	97
49	72	89	78	66	81	92	88	53	73

Copy and complete the stem and leaf plot on the right.

    (i) Write down the range of the scores.

    (ii) Find the median score.

    (iii) Find Q_1, the lower quartile.

    (iv) Find Q_3, the upper quartile.

    (v) Write down the interquartile range.

4	9	
5	3	6
6		
7		
8		
9		

4. Twenty four pupils were asked how many CDs they had in their collection. The results are shown below:

23	2	18	14	7	4	25	21	32	26	31	6
17	6	18	19	31	21	12	1	0	8	14	15

    (i) Draw a stem and leaf diagram to represent this information.

    (ii) How many pupils had more than 20 CDs?

    (iii) What is the median number of CDs in the collections?

    (iv) What is the mean number of CDs in the collections? Give your answer to the nearest whole number.

5. The stem and leaf plot below shows the marks achieved by 19 students in a test.

stem	leaf				
2	2				
3	4	6			
4	2	7	9		
5	3	4	5	8	9
6	0	2	6	7	
7	2	6			
8	1	4			

Key: 4|2 = 42 marks

    (i) Write down the range of the marks.   (ii) Find the value of the lower quartile.

    (iii) What is the upper quartile?   (iv) What is the interquartile range?

6. These are the speeds, in km/hr, of vehicles crossing a city-centre bridge one afternoon:

15	17	12	16	24	29	36	25	38	42	17
53	44	49	53	29	21	11	38	14	29	

   (i) Draw a stem and leaf diagram to show these speeds.

   (ii) What is the lower quartile?

   (iii) Find the upper quartile.

   (iv) What is the interquartile range?

7. The results for examinations in Maths and History for a class of students are shown in the back-to-back stem and leaf diagram below:

```
            Maths   |   | History
              7 5 | 2 |
              8 0 | 3 | 6
              5 5 | 4 | 0 5 7 8
      9 5 4 3 2 | 5 | 1 5 8
          9 7 5 | 6 | 2 4 4 5 7
          3 1 | 7 | 2 4 5 6
          6 3 | 8 | 3 5
            1 | 9 |
```

Key: 1|7 = 71 marks   Key: 3|6 = 36 marks

   (i) How many students took the examinations?

   (ii) What is the range of marks in Maths?

   (iii) What is the median mark in History?

   (iv) What is the interquartile range of the marks in Maths?

8. The back-to-back stem and leaf plot below shows the pulse rates of a class at the beginning and end of a PE lesson.

Pulse rates (beats per minute)

```
         Before PE       |   |    After PE
             8 7 | 4 |
       7 4 2 1 0 0 | 5 | 3 5
     8 8 6 5 5 3 1 | 6 | 0 3 6 8 9
         7 5 5 1 0 | 7 | 1 4 4 7 9 9
             6 2 1 | 8 | 3 3 6 6 7 8 9 9
               5 0 | 9 | 0 3 5 8
```

Key: 1|8 = 81 bpm   Key: 8|3 = 83 bpm

   (i) Write down the range of the pulse rates before and after the PE lesson.

   (ii) Find the median of the pulse rates before and after the PE lesson.

   (iii) Use your answers to (i) and (ii) to write a brief statement about the pulse rates of the class before and after the PE lesson.

9. Two different brands of batteries were tested in the same toy to determine which lasted longer. The back-to-back stem and leaf plot below shows the two sets of data, recorded to the nearest hour.

	Dynamo			Energy Plus
	4 1	1	3 3 7 7 8 8 9	
	8 8 6 3	2	5 6 8 9 9 9	
8 7 6 6 5 4 4		3	2 4 6 7 7 8 8 9	
7 5 4 3 2 2		4	0 1	
	3 2 2 0	5		

Key: 8|2 = 28 hours   Key: 4|1 = 41 hours

  (i)   How many batteries of each brand were tested?
  (ii) Find the median length for each brand.
  (iii) By comparing the medians and ranges for the two brands, which brand do you think is better? Explain your answer.

10. The data below shows the average male life expectancy (in years) of the main countries in Africa in the year 2000.

Algeria	68	Madagascar	57	South Africa	62
Angola	45	Mauritius	68	Sudan	54
Ethiopia	48	Nigeria	51	Tunisia	68
Ghana	56	Rwanda	41	Uganda	40
Kenya	52	Sierra Leone	36		

  (i)   Put this data into a stem and leaf plot with the data in order.

The data for the female life expectancy in the same African countries is given on the right.

  (ii) Compare the life expectancies of males and females in these African countries using the median and range for each set of data.

Female life expectancy (years)

3	9
4	2 3 8
5	2 4 6 6
6	0 0 8
7	0 1 5

Key: 5|2 = 52

11. Martina and Jack took part in several tests and their results are shown below.

	Martina			Jack
	2 1	1	x	
6 5 z		2	3 7 8	
6 2 1		3	2 y 7	
	7 4	4	0 1 3	

Key: 1|3 = 31   Key: 4|0 = 40

  (i)   In how many tests did they each participate?
  (ii) In how many tests did Martina obtain marks below 30?
  (iii) If the range of Jack's marks is 31, find the value of x.
  (iv) If the median mark for Jack is 34, find the value of y.
  (v)   If the lower quartile mark for Martina is 23, find the value of z.

Section 13.5 Misleading graphs

Because graphs and tables are based on information gathered and presented, people tend to believe the impressions they give. However, graphs can be used by unscrupulous people to give a false or misleading impression.

The following three graphs were used by *Munchies* dog food to compare its sales figures to those of *Doggo's* dog food.

We will use these graphs to highlight some of the more common ways of drawing graphs that may be used to give a false impression.

1. This graph does not have a scale on the vertical axis. You cannot tell how big the difference is between *Munchies* sales and *Doggo's* sales.

    > The vertical axis must be labelled.

2. This graph shows only **part** of a scale. The scale does not start at 0. This makes the difference between *Munchies* sales and *Doggo's* sales look much bigger than it actually is.

    > If an axis does not start from zero, or the zero is put in the wrong place, it can mislead people.

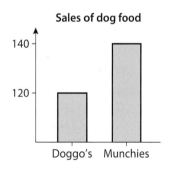

3. This graph uses pictures instead of columns. The *Munchies* dog is twice as tall as the *Doggo's* dog, but it is also twice as wide, making it seem much bigger (four times bigger).

    > Using area or volume will mislead when only height is needed.

4. This graph shows the information correctly.
The scale is regular and begins at 0.
Notice that the difference in sales figures is
not as large as it seemed in the misleading
graphs on the previous page.

Exercise 13.5

1.

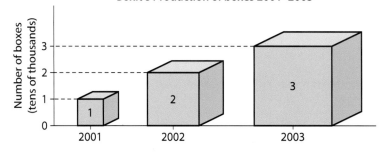

Boxit's Production of boxes 2001–2003

   (i)   How many times greater is the height of box 2 than the height of box 1?
   (ii) How many times greater is the area of box 2 than the area of box 1?
   (iii) How many times greater is the volume
         of box 2 than the volume of box 1?
   (iv) How many times greater is the height
         of box 3 than the height of box 1?
   (v)   How many times greater is the area of
         box 3 than the area of box 1?
   (vi) How many times greater is the volume
         of box 3 than the volume of box 1?
   (vii) Draw a vertical bar chart to represent
         the information shown here.

- Box 2 is meant to represent
  twice what box 1 represents,
  but it appears to be 8 times
  as big.
- Box 3 is meant to represent 3
  times what box 1 represents,
  but it appears to be 27 times
  as big.

2. Give one reason why the graph
on the right is misleading.

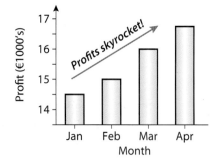

3. Describe the misleading or poor features of each of the following graphs:

(i)

Fish sold at markets

(ii)

Milk production

(iii)

Interstate bus fares

(iv)

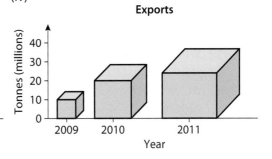

Exports

4. The bar chart on the right gives the correct representation of the sales of three soft drinks.

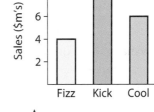

The company produced the following graph to represent the sales.

Name two ways in which this graph is misleading.

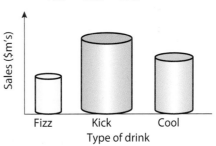

5. The Government releases the following graph showing the increase in employment in the tourism industry over recent years.

(i) Explain why the graph is misleading.
(ii) Redraw the graph in a way that more accurately indicates the increase in employment.

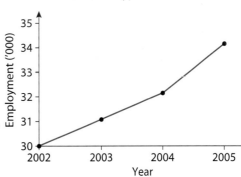

6. The two graphs below show the sales of *Nu-Choc* chocolates over a 7-year period.

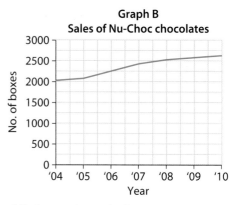

(i) Which graph gives the impression of rapidly increasing sales?

(ii) Have sales in fact rapidly increased over this 7 year period?

(iii) According to graph A, the sales for 2007 appear to be roughly double those of 2006.

Is this actually true?

7. Draw a graph that gives a misleading impression for the data in the table below.

Then draw another graph that illustrates the data correctly and accurately.

School sport	Hockey	Netball	Soccer
Number of players	14	12	10

Test yourself 13

1. (a) The pie chart shows how 180 boys at *Superfit Academy* chose five sports options.

    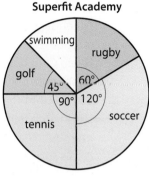

    Superfit Academy

    (i) Find the angle in the sector representing swimming.
    (ii) How many boys chose soccer?
    (iii) What percentage chose golf?

   (b) Neil records the number of emails he receives every day for 35 days.
   The data he collects is shown in the stem and leaf diagram.

0	6 7 9 9
1	4 7 7 8 8 9 9
2	2 3 5 5 6 7 8 9 9 9
3	1 5 6 6 6 6 7
4	3 6 8 9
5	2 3 3

   Key: $3|1 = 31$

    (i) Write down the mode of the data.
    (ii) Find the median.
    (iii) Find the lower quartile and the upper quartile of the data. Hence write down the interquartile range.

2. (a) The histogram below shows information about the training times taken by some 100 m runners before the Olympic Games.

    (i) Write down the reason why there are no gaps between bars.
    (ii) Write down the number of runners that took between 10 and 12 seconds.
    (iii) Work out the number of runners that took 12 seconds or more.
    (iv) Work out how many runners there were altogether.

    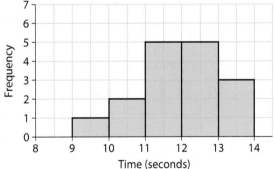

   (b) These are the weights (in kg) of 24 babies born in a hospital.

   4.1 3.7 2.8 4.3 4.7 4.6 2.8 5.2 3.9 3.7 3.7 4.8
   3.8 3.4 4.9 4.6 4.7 4.2 3.0 3.1 2.5 5.0 4.5 4.5

    (i) Draw a stem and leaf plot for this data.
    (ii) Work out the mode and the median of the data.

(c) These pie charts show the numbers of members in two tennis clubs.
Greendale Club had 250 members altogether.
Nevin Club had 100 members altogether.
Lee thought the charts showed that Nevin Club had more senior female members than Greendale Club.
Is this correct?
Give a reason for your answer.

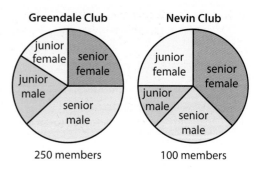

Greendale Club

250 members

Nevin Club

100 members

3. (a) The numbers of drinks dispensed by a vending machine in one day are shown in the table.
A pie chart is to be drawn to illustrate this data.

Type of drink	Tea	Black coffee	Hot chocolate	Orange	Coke	Latte
Number of drinks	54	42	18	30	12	24

  (i) Find the angle in the sector representing orange.
  (ii) Find the angle in the sector representing black coffee.

(b) Explain what is misleading about each of these diagrams.

  (i)

  (ii)

Mobile phone sales have doubled!

(c) Here are the maximum bench presses (in kg) of the members of an under-age rugby team.

54	42	61	47	24	43	55	62	30	27
28	43	54	46	25	32	49	73	50	

  (i) Construct a stem and leaf diagram to show these results.
  (ii) Write down the range of the weights. (iii) What is the lower quartile?
  (iv) What is the upper quartile? (v) Write down the interquartile range.

4. (a) The total cost of a holiday was €2400.
The pie chart shows how this cost was made up.

  (i) How much was spent on food?

  (ii) How much was spent on travel?

  (iii) How much was spent on the hotel?

  (iv) How much was spent on other items?

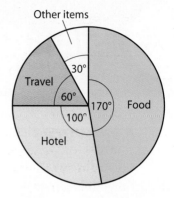

(b) The following back-to-back stem and leaf plot show the points scored by *Sparks* and *Dynamos* in a series of matches.

Sparks			Dynamos
4 3	7		
8 7	8	9	
5 0	9	5 7 8 9	
4	10	0 2 6	
9 3	11	0 2	
2	12		

Key: 4|10 = 104   Key: 9|8 = 98

  (i) Find the median score for each team.
  (ii) Write down the range of the scores for each team.
  (iii) Which team is the more consistent? Explain your answer.
  (iv) Write one sentence about the scoring pattern of the *Sparks*.

5. John's third-year Physical Education class did a fitness test. The number of sit-ups that each student did in one minute is recorded below.

59 48 27 53 36 29 52 46 45 37 49 51
33 45 38 52 40 51 37 44 47 45 60 41

The students practiced this exercise for the next three weeks and then repeated the test in the same order. The data for the second test is as follows:

61 52 33 51 39 40 50 49 46 37 59 49
38 48 39 58 44 52 38 44 49 51 62 44

  (i) Represent the data from the two tests in a back-to-back stem and leaf diagram.
  (ii) How many students are there in the class?
  (iii) What is the range of sit-ups for each test?
  (iv) Based on the data and the diagram, do you think that practice improves the ability to do sit-ups? Give a reason for your answer.
  (v) John did 41 sit-ups in Test 1 and 44 in Test 2.
  How did his performance compare with that of the rest of the class?

14 Simultaneous equations

Key words

satisfy the equation   simultaneous equations   elimination method

solving simultaneous equations graphically

Section 14.1 Solving simultaneous equations

Consider the equation

$$3x + y = 9.$$

The values $x = 2$ and $y = 3$ satisfy this equation.

The values $x = 1$ and $y = 6$ also satisfy the equation.

In fact, there are many pairs of values for x and y which satisfy the equation.

Now we take a second equation

$$2x - y = 1.$$

The values $x = 2$ and $y = 3$ satisfy this equation also.

Thus, the values $x = 2$ and $y = 3$ satisfy both equations

$$3x + y = 9 \text{ and } 2x - y = 1.$$

> When two equations are both satisfied by the same values for x and y, they are said to be simultaneous equations.

Only **one** set of values for x and y will satisfy a pair of simultaneous equations.

There are many ways of solving simultaneous equations.

One method is called the **elimination method**.

In this method, we 'eliminate' one of the variables.

This method is discussed in the box below.

Discussion

$\begin{aligned} 5x + 3y &= 23 \\ 2x - 3y &= 5 \end{aligned}$ are simultaneous equations.

We can illustrate them using scales.

If we add the left-hand sides and add the right-hand sides, would the scales still balance? **Discuss.**

What is the left-hand side total?

What is the right-hand side total?

How can you use this to find x? **Discuss.**

What is the value of x?

How can you use this to find y? **Discuss.**

| $5x + 3y$ | 23 |
| $2x - 3y$ | 5 |

| $5x + 3y$ | |
| $2x - 3y$ | $23 + 5$ |

From the 'discussion' on the previous page, it can be seen that it is easy to solve simultaneous equations if one of the variables can be eliminated by adding or subtracting the two equations.

If a variable cannot be eliminated by adding or subtracting, then we have to multiply one or more of the equations by a number to make the elimination possible.

Example 1

Solve the simultaneous equations
$$x + 2y = 10$$
$$2x - y = 5$$

(To solve these equations, we must make the number of x's or the number of y's equal. We then add or subtract as necessary.

For convenience, we call the first equation ① and the second equation ②.)

Equation ①: $\qquad x + 2y = 10$
Equation ② $\times$ 2: $\qquad 4x - 2y = 10$
Adding: $\qquad 5x \qquad = 20$
$$\therefore \quad x = 4$$

Substituting $x = 4$ in ① we get: $\quad 4 + 2y = 10$
$$2y = 6$$
$$\therefore \quad y = 3$$

The solution is $x = 4$ and $y = 3$.

(Note: It is important to check that $x = 4$ and $y = 3$ satisfy both equations.)

Example 2

Solve the simultaneous equations
$$2x - 5y = 9$$
$$3x + 2y = 4$$

We number the equations $\qquad 2x - 5y = 9 \qquad$ ①
① and ② for convenience. $\qquad 3x + 2y = 4 \qquad$ ②

We now multiply equation ① by 3 and equation ② by 2 to equate the number of x's.

① $\times$ 3: $\qquad 6x - 15y = 27$
② $\times$ 2: $\qquad \underline{6x + 4y = 8}$
Subtract: $\qquad -19y = 19$
$$19y = -19$$
$$y = -1$$

We now substitute -1 for y in equation ①
$$2x - 5y = 9$$
$$y = -1 \quad \Rightarrow \quad 2x + 5 = 9$$
$$\Rightarrow \quad 2x = 4 \quad \Rightarrow \quad x = 2$$
$$\therefore \quad x = 2 \text{ and } y = -1 \text{ are the solutions.}$$

Equations containing fractions

Here are two simultaneous equations:

$$3x - 2y = 19 \dots \text{①}$$

$$\frac{x}{3} + \frac{y}{2} = 5 \quad \dots \text{②}$$

To solve these equations, we 'get rid of the fractions' in equation ② by multiplying each term by 6 (the LCM of 3 and 2).

Thus, equation ② becomes: $\quad 6\left(\frac{x}{3}\right) + 6\left(\frac{y}{2}\right) = 6 \times 5$

$$\text{i.e.} \qquad 2x + 3y = 30$$

The simultaneous equations can now be solved as in Example 2, on the previous page.

Exercise 14.1

1. $2x + y = 8$
$3x - y = 2$

2. $3x + y = 14$
$2x - y = 6$

3. $3x + y = 7$
$x + y = 5$

4. $4x + y = 17$
$2x + y = 11$

5. $8x - 2y = 10$
$5x - 2y = 4$

6. $3x - 2y = 8$
$x + y = 6$

7. $3x + y = 13$
$x - 2y = -5$

8. $x + 2y = 12$
$3x - 5y = 3$

9. $3x - y = 3$
$x + 3y = 11$

10. $2x - 3y = 14$
$2x - y = 10$

11. $3x + y = 5$
$5x - 4y = -3$

12. $2x - y = 12$
$3x + 2y = 11$

13. $x + 2y = 12$
$3x - 5y = 3$

14. $x - 3y = 1$
$4x + y = 30$

15. $3x + 7y = 20$
$x - 2y = -2$

16. $3x - 2y = 17$
$4x + 3y = 0$

17. $4x + 3y = 22$
$5x - 4y = 43$

18. $5x + 2y = 5$
$6x - y = 23$

19. $3x + 4y = 23$
$y = 2x + 3$

20. $5y = 16 - 4x$
$6x = 13 - 2y$

21. $5x + y = 19$
$2x - y = 2y - 2x$

22. $2x - 3y = 24$
$\dfrac{5x}{3} - \dfrac{y}{2} = 12$

23. $2x - y = 18$
$\dfrac{x}{3} - \dfrac{y}{4} = 2$

24. $x + y = 5$
$\dfrac{4x}{3} - \dfrac{y}{2} = -8$

25. $3x - 2y = 19$
$\dfrac{x}{3} + \dfrac{y}{2} = 5$

26. $9 = 2x - 3y$
$3y + x = 9$

27. $3x = y - 4$
$3y = 34 - 2x$

28. $\dfrac{x}{2} + \dfrac{y}{5} = 4$
$\dfrac{x}{4} + \dfrac{y}{2} = 6$

29. $4x + y = 17$
$\dfrac{x - 3}{4} + \dfrac{y}{2} = \dfrac{5}{2}$

30. $3x + y = 19\frac{1}{2}$
$x - 2y = 3$

Section 14.2 Solving simultaneous equations graphically

Discussion

Here are two lines: $x + y = 1$ ... ①
                        $2x - y = -4$ ... ②

We can draw each line by taking two points on the line.

For line ①: $x = 0 \Rightarrow y = 1$
                $y = 0 \Rightarrow x = 1$

∴ $(0, 1)$ and $(1, 0)$ are two points on the line.

For line ②: $x = 0 \Rightarrow -y = -4 \Rightarrow y = 4$
                $y = 0 \Rightarrow 2x = -4 \Rightarrow x = -2$

∴ $(0, 4)$ and $(-2, 0)$ are two points on the line.

The two lines are drawn on the right.

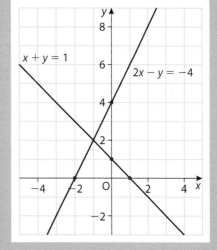

What are the coordinates of the point which lies on *both* lines?

Solve the simultaneous equations
$x + y = 1$
$2x - y = -4$ using the adding or
subtracting equations method.

Compare the values of x and y you found with the coordinates of the point where these lines meet.

What do you notice? **Discuss**.

From the 'discussion' above, you will have discovered that two simultaneous equations may be solved by drawing graphs of the two equations (lines) and then reading the x-value and y-value of their point of intersection.

Using simultaneous equations to solve problems

Simultaneous equations are particularly useful for solving problems which have two unknowns. Generally, two different pieces of information enable us to write down two equations.

The following examples illustrate this procedure.

Example 1

The sum of two numbers is 19.
When twice the second number is taken from three times the first number, the result is 22.
Find the two numbers.

Let x and y be the numbers.

Equation ①: $x + y = 19$
Equation ②: $3x - 2y = 22$

Equation ① × 2: $2x + 2y = 38$
Equation ②: $3x - 2y = 22$
Add: $5x = 60$
  $x = 12$

Substituting 12 for x in equation ①, we get: $12 + y = 19$
  $y = 19 - 12$
  $y = 7$

The two numbers are 12 and 7.

Example 2

Tickets to a movie cost €8 or €10.
If 300 tickets were sold and the total amount of money collected was €2640, how many of each type of ticket were sold?

Let x = number of €8 tickets sold, and
  y = number of €10 tickets sold.

① Number: $x + y = 300$
② Money: $8x + 10y = 2640$

① × 8: $8x + 8y = 2400$
②: $8x + 10y = 2640$
Subtract: $-2y = -240$
  $\Rightarrow 2y = 240$
  $\Rightarrow y = 120$

Substituting 120 for y in equation ①, we get:

  $x + y = 300$
$y = 120$: $x + 120 = 300$
  $x = 180$
  $\therefore x = 180$ and $y = 120$

$\therefore$ 180 €8 tickets and 120 €10 tickets were sold.

Exercise 14.2

1. The given diagram shows the graphs of the lines $x - y = 1$ and $x + 2y = 4$.

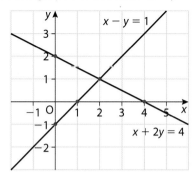

- (i) Write down the point of intersection of the two lines.
- (ii) Solve the simultaneous equations $x - y = 1$ and $x + 2y = 4$.
- (iii) Explain the connection between your answers in (ii) to the answer you found in (i) above.

2. Graph the lines $2x - y = 1$ and $x - y = -1$.
Hence write down the point of intersection of the two lines.

3. Solve these simultaneous equations by drawing graphs:
- (i) $2x - y = -1$
  $x - y = 1$
- (ii) $2x - y = 1$
  $x - y = -2$

4. Use graphs to solve each pair of simultaneous equations.
- (i) $x + y = 6$
  $x - y = 2$
  Draw axes for x and y
  from -3 to 7.
- (ii) $y + 2x = 5$
  $x - y = 1$
  Draw axes for x and y
  from -2 to 6.

Check each solution by substituting into the equations.

5. Use the given graphs to solve each pair of simultaneous equations.

- (i) $x + y = 10$
  $y - 2x = 1$
- (ii) $2x + 5y = 17$
  $y - 2x = 1$
- (iii) $x + y = 10$
  $2x + 5y = 17$

Check each solution by substituting into the equations.

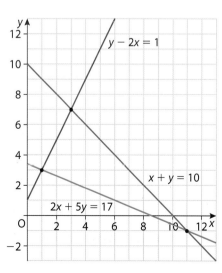

6. (i) Use the graphs to solve each pair of simultaneous equations.

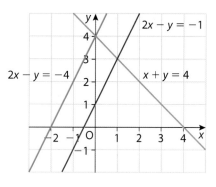

    (a) $\quad 2x - y = -4$ (b) $\quad 2x - y = -1$
        $x + y = 4$ $x + y = 4$

    Check each solution by substituting into the equations.

  (ii) How do you know there is no solution to the following pair of simultaneous equations?

$$2x - y = -4$$
$$2x - y = -1$$

7. The sum of two numbers is 9. If twice the first number is added to three times the second, the answer is 15. Find the two numbers.

8. The difference of two numbers is 7. When three times the smaller number is taken from twice the larger, the result is 11. Find the two numbers.

9. Find two numbers such that the first number added to three times the second is 31, while three times the first less twice the second is 16.

10. Examine the rectangle shown and write down two equations in x and y.

Now solve these equations to find the value of x and the value of y.

11. Three nuts and six bolts have a combined weight of 72 g.
Four nuts and five bolts have a combined weight of 66 g.
Find the combined weight of one nut and one bolt.

12. Three chocolate bars and four chocolate eggs weigh 465 grams.
Three chocolate bars and two chocolate eggs weigh 315 grams.

  (i) Which of these pairs of equations is correct for the chocolate bars and eggs?

    A
    $3b + 2e = 465$
    $3b + 4e = 315$

    B
    $b + 4e = 465$
    $b + 2e = 315$

    C
    $3b + 4e = 465$
    $3b + 2e = 315$

  (ii) Solve the pair of simultaneous equations that is correct to find the values of b and e.

13. A bag contains 34 coins, all of them either 5c or 10c coins. If the value of the money in the bag is €2.40, find how many of each coin the bag contains.
[Hint: Convert €2.40 to cents.]

14. Two small mugs and one large mug weigh 758 grams.
Four small mugs and three large mugs weigh 1882 grams.

The weight of a small mug is *s* grams and the weight of a large mug is *l* grams.

Write down two equations connecting *s* and *l*.
Solve these simultaneous equations to find the weight of each size of mug.

15. In the given two figures, all the angles are right angles and the distances are in centimetres. If the area of the figure on the left is 45 cm² and the area of the second figure is 25 cm², find the values of *x* and *y*.

 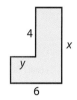

16. The length of a blue rod is *x* cm.

The length of a yellow rod is *y* cm.

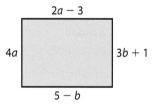

    (i) The total length of 2 blue rods and 3 yellow rods is 33 cm.

        Write an equation for this diagram.

   (ii) The total length of 4 blue rods and 2 yellow rods is 46 cm.

        Write an equation for this diagram.

  (iii) Solve your equations simultaneously to find the values of *x* and *y*.

  (iv) What is the total length of 1 blue and 6 yellow rods?

17. The diagram shows a rectangle.
All sides are measured in centimetres.

    (i) Write down a pair of simultaneous equations in *a* and *b*.

   (ii) Solve your pair of simultaneous equations to find *a* and *b*.

18. A car-hire company charges €*x* per day to hire a car and then adds a charge of €*y* for each kilometre travelled.

John hires a car for 2 days and travels 250 km. He is charged €200.

Emer hires a car for 5 days and travels 620 km. She is charged €498.

Write two equations in *x* and *y* and solve them to find the charge per day and the charge for each kilometre.

19. The sum of the ages of a father and a son is 52 years.

Eight years ago, the father was eight times as old as his son.

If the father is now x years and the son y years of age, write two equations and solve them to find the values of x and y.

20. A person has €60 made up of €1 and 50 cent coins.

He has 78 coins altogether.

If the number of €1 coins is x and the number of 50 cent coins is y, write down two equations in x and y to represent this information.

Solve the equations to find the values of x and y.

21. In this puzzle, each different symbol stands for a number.

What does each symbol stand for?

$$\blacksquare + \heartsuit + \blacksquare + \heartsuit + \heartsuit = 68$$
$$\heartsuit + \blacksquare + \blacklozenge + \blacklozenge = 28$$
$$\heartsuit + \blacksquare + \blacksquare = 28$$

22. Write down the pair of simultaneous equations that are solved by the coordinates of the point of intersection of the two lines shown in the given diagram.

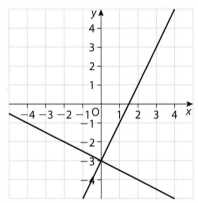

Challenge

The rate at which cylindrical candles burn depends on the diameter of the candle.

Thinner candles burn more quickly than fatter ones.

Consider the two candles shown.

The first is 400 mm long and burns at a rate of 5 mm per hour.

The second is 490 mm long and burns at a rate of 8 mm per hour.

(i) Explain why the first candle's height in millimetres, after t hours, is given by $h_1 = 400 - 5t$.

(ii) Write an equation in the form $h_2 = \boxed{} - \boxed{}\,t$ to give the height of the second candle after t hours.

(iii) Use the equations to find how long each candle will last.

(iv) On the same set of axes, graph each equation on graph paper.

(v) At what time do the candles have the same height?

(vi) If you want the candles to 'go out' together, which candle would you light first and how long after this would you light the other one?

Test yourself 14

1. (a) Solve these simultaneous equations:
$$x + 2y = 13$$
$$3x - 5y = 6$$

(b) The weight of a blue brick is b grams.
The weight of a red brick is r grams.

4 blue bricks and 3 red bricks weigh 58 grams.
5 blue bricks and 6 red bricks weigh 86 grams.

(i) Write two equations to represent these diagrams.

(ii) Solve the equations to find the weight of a blue brick and the weight of a red brick.

(iii) Find the total weight of 3 blue bricks and 6 red bricks.

58 grams

86 grams

2. (a) Solve the simultaneous equations:
$$3x = 5y + 13$$
$$2x + 5y = -8$$

(b) ABC is an equilateral triangle.
All lengths are in centimetres.

(i) Form two simultaneous equations and solve them to find the value of x and the value of y.

(ii) Now find the length of the side of the triangle.

A

$3x + 2y$ $3y - 1$

B $11 + x - 2y$ C

3. (a) Solve these simultaneous equations:

$$2x + 3y = 17$$
$$3x - 2y = 6$$

(b) The graphs of three lines are shown opposite:

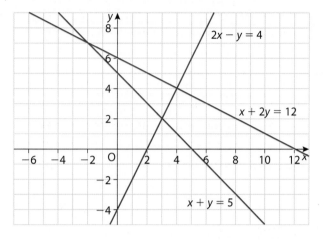

(i) Use the graph to find the solution of the simultaneous equations $x + 2y = 12$ and $x + y = 5$.

(ii) Use the graph to write down two simultaneous equations which have the solution $x = 3$, $y = 2$.

(c) A woman is paid €x per hour for a 30-hour week and is paid €y for each hour overtime worked. In a particular week, she worked 35 hours and received €660. The following week, she worked 42 hours and received €828.
Write two equations in x and y and solve them to find their values.

4. (a) Solve the simultaneous equations:

$$2x - y = 18$$
$$\frac{x}{3} - \frac{y}{4} = 2$$

(b) The cost €C of hiring a car for n days is given by the formula $C = a + bn$, where $a, b \in N$. It costs €420 for 5 days and €870 for 11 days to hire a car.
Write two equations in a and b and solve them to find their values.
Hence find the cost of hiring a car for 15 days.

(c) At what point do the lines $2x + 3y = 1$ and $5x - 2y = 12$ intersect?

5. (a) Solve the simultaneous equations:

$$3x = 22 + 2y$$
$$5y = 2x$$

(b) The shape ABCD is a parallelogram. Write two equations in x and y and solve them to find their values.

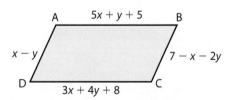

(c) A mother is x years old, her son is y years old and the sum of their ages is 58 years. Five years ago, the mother was five times as old as the son.
Write two equations in x and y and solve them to find the age of the mother and the age of the son.

Indices – Scientific Notation – Surds

chapter 15

Key words

index	indices	product	quotient	fractional indices
rational numbers	recurring decimals	irrational numbers	surds	
simplest form	standard form	scientific notation	significant figures	
approximation	reciprocals	squares	cube root	

Section 15.1 The laws of indices

$2^3 = 2 \times 2 \times 2 = 8$

2^3 is called '2 cubed' or '2 to the power of 3'.

3 is the **power** or **index** which tells us how many times the number 2 is multiplied by itself.

> **Power** is another word for **index**.

1. Multiplication

$4^2 \times 4^3 = (4 \times 4) \times (4 \times 4 \times 4)$

$\qquad\quad = 4^5$

Similarly, $x^2 \times x^3 = (x \times x) \times (x \times x \times x) = x^5$

So, $\qquad x^2 \times x^3 = x^{2+3} = x^5$

> To **multiply** powers of the same number, **add** the indices.

2. Division

$\dfrac{3^5}{3^2} = \dfrac{3 \times 3 \times 3 \times 3 \times 3}{3 \times 3} = 3^3$

Similarly, $\dfrac{x^5}{x^2} = \dfrac{x \times x \times x \times x \times x}{x \times x} = x^3$

Thus, $\qquad \dfrac{x^5}{x^2} = x^{5-2} = x^3$

> To **divide** powers of the same number, **subtract** the indices.

3. A power to a power

$(x^2)^3$ means $(x^2) \times (x^2) \times (x^2) = x^6$

$\Rightarrow (x^2)^3 = x^{2+2+2} = x^6$

$\qquad\qquad\quad = x^{2 \times 3}$

Similarly, $(x^4)^3 = x^{4 \times 3} = x^{12}$

> To **raise** a power to a further power, **multiply** the indices.

4. The power of zero

$\frac{2^3}{2^3} = \frac{8}{8} = 1$ and $\frac{2^3}{2^3} = 2^{3-3} = 2^0$

This shows that $2^0 = 1$.

> Any number to the power of zero is 1, i.e., $a^0 = 1$.

5. Negative indices

$\frac{4^3}{4^5}$ can be written as

$\frac{\cancel{4} \times \cancel{4} \times \cancel{4}}{\cancel{4} \times \cancel{4} \times \cancel{4} \times 4 \times 4} = \frac{1}{4^2}$

Also, $\frac{4^3}{4^5} = 4^{3-5} = 4^{-2} \Rightarrow \frac{1}{4^2} = 4^{-2}$

This shows that $\frac{1}{4^2} = 4^{-2}$.

> $a^{-n} = \frac{1}{a^n}$ e.g. $3^{-2} = \frac{1}{3^2}$

6. A product or quotient to a power

$(2 \times 3)^2 = 6^2 = 36$
Also, $(2 \times 3)^2 = 2^2 \times 3^2 = 4 \times 9 = 36$.

This illustrates that $(ab)^n = a^n b^n$.

Similarly, it can be shown that

$$\left(\frac{a}{b}\right)^n = \frac{a^n}{b^n}$$

> $(ab)^n = a^n b^n$
>
> $\left(\frac{a}{b}\right)^n = \frac{a^n}{b^n}$

Example 1

Express each of these as a single number without a power:

(i) $2^3 \times 2^2$ (ii) $\frac{3^5}{3^2}$ (iii) $(2^2)^3$ (iv) $\frac{1}{3^{-2}}$ (v) $(3 \times 4)^2$ (vi) 8^0

(i) $2^3 \times 2^2 = 2^{3+2} = 2^5 = 32$ (ii) $\frac{3^5}{3^2} = 3^{5-2} = 3^3 = 27$

(iii) $(2^2)^3 = 2^{2 \times 3} = 2^6 = 64$ (iv) $\frac{1}{3^{-2}} = 3^2 = 9$

(v) $(3 \times 4)^2 = 3^2 \times 4^2$ (vi) $8^0 = 1$
           $= 9 \times 16 = 144$

Exercise 15.1

1. Write each of these as a single number without an index:

(i) 7^2 (ii) 4^3 (iii) 2×2^3 (iv) $\frac{5^4}{5^2}$ (v) $\frac{6^5}{6^3}$

2. Write each of the following as a single number to a power:

(i) $2 \times 2 \times 2$ (ii) 2×2^3 (iii) $4^2 \times 4^3$ (iv) $5 \times 5^2 \times 5^3$

(v) $a \times a^5$ (vi) $2x^2 \times 3x$ (vii) $2x^2 \times 4x^3$ (viii) $\dfrac{a^5}{a^2}$

3. Express as a single number to a power:

(i) 9 (ii) 25 (iii) 27 (lv) 32 (v) 1000 (vi) 400

4. Express as a single number in index form:

(i) $\dfrac{5^4}{5^2}$ (ii) $\dfrac{3^5}{3}$ (iii) $\dfrac{7^5}{7^3}$ (iv) $\dfrac{3^8}{3^4}$ (v) $\dfrac{5^8}{5}$ (vi) $\dfrac{4^3 \times 4^2}{4}$

5. State whether each of the following statements is true or false:

(i) $5^2 = 5 \times 2$ (ii) $3^2 > 2^3$ (iii) $2^6 < 5^2$ (iv) $3^4 < 6^2$

6. Simplify each of these and express your answer as a whole number:

(i) $\dfrac{2^4 \times 2^2}{2^3}$ (ii) $\dfrac{4^3 \times 4}{4^2}$ (iii) $\dfrac{3^7 \times 3}{3^6}$ (iv) $\dfrac{7^6 \times 7^2}{7^5}$ (v) $\dfrac{3^7 \times 3^4}{3^8 \times 3}$

7. Express each of the following as a whole number or as a fraction:

(i) 3^{-2} (ii) $\dfrac{1}{2^{-3}}$ (iii) $\dfrac{3}{2^{-2}}$ (iv) $\dfrac{2^{-2}}{3}$ (v) $\dfrac{2^{-4}}{4^{-2}}$

8. Write down the numbers missing from these calculations:

(i) $8 \times 8^7 = 8^{\square}$ (ii) $7^5 \times 7^{\square} = 7^8$ (iii) $\dfrac{9^7}{9^{\square}} = 9^3$ (iv) $\dfrac{3^9}{3^{\square}} = 3$

9. What does the question mark (**?**) stand for in each of the following?

A $35 \times 3^{-2} = \mathbf{?}$

B $\dfrac{3^3}{3^5} = \mathbf{?}$

C $(2^3)^{-2} = \mathbf{?}$

D $6^{-1} \times 6^{-2} = \mathbf{?}$

E $\dfrac{7^2}{7^2} = \mathbf{?}$

F $2^{-5} \times 2^3 = \mathbf{?}$

G $(3^{-1})^{-2} = \mathbf{?}$

H $\dfrac{5^3}{5^{-2}} = \mathbf{?}$

10. Simplify each of these:

(i) $(2 \times 3)^2$ (ii) $\left(\frac{1}{2}\right)^3$ (iii) $\left(\frac{2}{3}\right)^2$ (iv) $(ab)^3$ (v) $\left(\dfrac{2a}{3b}\right)^2$

11. Copy and complete these:

(i) $3^2 \times 5^3 \times 5^4 \times 3^6 = 3^{\square} \times 5^{\square}$ (ii) $2 \times 9^2 \times 2^5 \times 9^3 = 2^{\square} \times 9^{\square}$

(iii) $4^7 \times 3^{\square} \times 4 \times 3^2 = 3^{10} \times 4^{\square}$ (iv) $3^4 \times 11^{\square} \times 3^{\square} \times 11^5 = 3^5 \times 11^8$

12. Which of these statements is false?

A $2^5 \times 3^4 \times 2^2 = 2^7 \times 3^4$

B $5^2 \times 6^3 \times 5^4 \times 6 = 5^6 \times 6^4$

C $2^2 \times 3^5 = 6^7$

13. Copy and complete these:

(i) $(4^2)^3 = 4^\square$ (ii) $(2^4)^\square = 2^{12}$ (iii) $(2^4)^n = 2^\square$ (iv) $(5^x)^\square = 5^{4x}$

14. Write each of these numbers as a power of 3:

(i) 9 (ii) 9^2 (iii) 27^3 (iv) 81^2 (v) 9^n

15. Find four matching pairs.

A 3^{-2} **B** 2^{-3} **C** 4^{-2} **D** 6^{-1} **E** -6 **F** $\dfrac{1}{6}$ **G** $\dfrac{1}{16}$ **H** $\dfrac{1}{8}$ **I** $\dfrac{1}{9}$

16. Simplify each of these:

(i) $a^4 \times a^{-5}$ (ii) $a^3 \times a^{-3}$ (iii) $3a^7 \times 2a^{-5}$ (iv) $\dfrac{a^{-2}}{a^{-6}}$

17. Copy and complete the following:

(i) $3^\square \times 3^{-2} = 3^6$ (ii) $\dfrac{4^{-1}}{4^\square} = 4^{-5}$ (iii) $a^2 \times a^\square \times a^{-4} = a^{-3}$

Section 15.2 Fractional indices

Fractional indices

We use the laws of indices to show that $2^{\frac{1}{2}} = \sqrt{2}$.

$2^{\frac{1}{2}} \times 2^{\frac{1}{2}} = 2^{\frac{1}{2}+\frac{1}{2}} = 2^1 = 2$.

Also, $\sqrt{2} \times \sqrt{2} = 2$.

This shows that $2^{\frac{1}{2}} = \sqrt{2}$.

Similarly, $2^{\frac{1}{3}} = \sqrt[3]{2}$.

$2^{\frac{1}{2}} = \sqrt{2}$

$2^{\frac{1}{3}} = \sqrt[3]{2}$

....

$2^{\frac{1}{n}} = \sqrt[n]{2}$

One of the laws of indices is $(a^m)^n = a^{mn}$.
From this rule it follows that

$27^{\frac{2}{3}} = (27^{\frac{1}{3}})^2 = (\sqrt[3]{27})^2 = 3^2 = 9$.

Similarly, $16^{\frac{3}{4}} = (16^{\frac{1}{4}})^3 = (\sqrt[4]{16})^3 = (2)^3 = 8$.

$8^{\frac{2}{3}} = (\sqrt[3]{8})^2$

$16^{\frac{3}{4}} = (\sqrt[4]{16})^3$

....

$x^{\frac{m}{n}} = (\sqrt[n]{x})^m$

Note: $16^{\frac{3}{4}}$ may also be expressed as $\sqrt[4]{16^3}$.

However, it is generally easier to get $\sqrt[4]{16}$ first and then raise your answer to the power of 3.

Example 1

Write as rational numbers:

(i) $16^{\frac{1}{4}}$ (ii) $25^{\frac{3}{2}}$ (iii) $81^{-\frac{3}{4}}$ (iv) $\dfrac{1}{27^{\frac{2}{3}}}$

(i) $16^{\frac{1}{4}} = \sqrt[4]{16} = 2$ (ii) $25^{\frac{3}{2}} = (\sqrt{25})^3 = 5^3 = 125$

(iii) $81^{-\frac{3}{4}} = \dfrac{1}{81^{\frac{3}{4}}} = \dfrac{1}{(\sqrt[4]{81})^3} = \dfrac{1}{3^3} = \dfrac{1}{27}$ (iv) $\dfrac{1}{27^{\frac{2}{3}}} = \dfrac{1}{(\sqrt[3]{27})^2} = \dfrac{1}{3^2} = \dfrac{1}{9}$

 When using a calculator to find $27^{\frac{2}{3}}$, key in

$27 \boxed{x^y} \boxed{(} 2 \boxed{\div} 3 \boxed{)} \boxed{=}$ The result is 9.

Similarly, to find $\left(\frac{27}{8}\right)^{\frac{2}{3}}$, key in

$\boxed{(} 27 \boxed{\div} 8 \boxed{)} \boxed{x^y} \boxed{(} 2 \boxed{\div} 3 \boxed{)} \boxed{=}$ The result is 2.25.

Note: $\boxed{x^y}$ may appear as $\boxed{x^\blacksquare}$ or $\boxed{y^x}$, depending on the calculator model.

Exercise 15.2

1. Write down the value of each of these:

(i) $\sqrt{25}$ (ii) $\sqrt{144}$ (iii) $\sqrt[3]{27}$ (iv) $\sqrt[3]{64}$ (v) $16^{\frac{1}{2}}$ (vi) $125^{\frac{1}{3}}$

2. Express each of these as a rational number:

(i) $25^{\frac{1}{2}}$ (ii) $64^{\frac{1}{3}}$ (iii) $216^{\frac{1}{3}}$ (iv) $\left(\frac{8}{27}\right)^{\frac{1}{3}}$ (v) $\left(\frac{16}{25}\right)^{\frac{1}{2}}$ (vi) $\left(\frac{16}{81}\right)^{\frac{1}{4}}$

3. Write each of the following without using the $\sqrt{}$ sign:

(i) $\sqrt{x}$ (ii) $\sqrt[3]{x}$ (iii) $\sqrt[4]{a}$ (iv) $\sqrt[3]{a^2}$ (v) $\sqrt{a^3}$ (vi) $\sqrt[4]{a^3}$

4. Find the value of each of these:

(i) $\left(\frac{1}{4}\right)^{\frac{1}{2}}$ (ii) $\left(\frac{1}{27}\right)^{\frac{1}{3}}$ (iii) $16^{-\frac{1}{2}}$ (iv) $\left(\frac{1}{9}\right)^{-\frac{1}{2}}$ (v) $(100)^{-\frac{1}{2}}$ (vi) $(0.01)^{\frac{1}{2}}$

5. Rewrite the following using the $\sqrt{}$ sign:

(i) $a^{\frac{1}{2}}$ (ii) $a^{\frac{1}{4}}$ (iii) $a^{\frac{2}{3}}$ (iv) $a^{\frac{5}{2}}$ (v) $a^{\frac{3}{4}}$ (vi) $\left(\frac{a}{x}\right)^{\frac{1}{2}}$

6. Find the value of each of the following:

(i) $81^{\frac{1}{2}}$ (ii) $8^{\frac{2}{3}}$ (iii) $16^{\frac{3}{4}}$ (iv) $4^{\frac{3}{2}}$ (v) $27^{\frac{2}{3}}$

(vi) $16^{\frac{3}{2}}$ (vii) $64^{\frac{2}{3}}$ (viii) $100^{\frac{3}{2}}$ (ix) $81^{\frac{3}{4}}$ (x) $125^{\frac{2}{3}}$

7. Evaluate each of these:

   (i) 3^{-1} (ii) 4^{-2} (iii) $8^{-\frac{1}{3}}$ (iv) $\dfrac{1}{16^{-\frac{1}{4}}}$ (v) $64^{-\frac{1}{3}}$

8. Find the value of each of the following:

   (i) $16^{-\frac{1}{2}}$ (ii) $\dfrac{1}{8^{-\frac{2}{3}}}$ (iii) $16^{-\frac{3}{4}}$ (iv) $100^{-\frac{3}{2}}$ (v) $32^{-\frac{3}{5}}$

9. Noting that $\left(\dfrac{2}{3}\right)^{-3} = \dfrac{2^{-3}}{3^{-3}} = \dfrac{3^3}{2^3} = \dfrac{27}{8}$, evaluate each of these:

   (i) $\left(\dfrac{2}{3}\right)^{-2}$ (ii) $\left(\dfrac{1}{4}\right)^{-2}$ (iii) $\left(\dfrac{3}{5}\right)^{-2}$ (iv) $\left(\dfrac{4}{9}\right)^{-\frac{1}{2}}$ (v) $\left(\dfrac{9}{25}\right)^{-\frac{1}{2}}$

10. Simplify each of these:

   (i) $49^{-\frac{3}{2}}$ (ii) $\left(\dfrac{9}{25}\right)^{-\frac{3}{2}}$ (iii) $\left(\dfrac{9}{4}\right)^{\frac{3}{2}}$ (iv) $\left(\dfrac{27}{125}\right)^{-\frac{2}{3}}$ (v) $\left(\dfrac{8}{1000}\right)^{-\frac{1}{3}}$

11. If $a = 64^{\frac{2}{3}}$ and $b = 3^{-2}$, write a and b as rational numbers.

   Hence find the value of $\sqrt{\dfrac{a}{b}}$.

12. Express as rational numbers: (i) $\left(\dfrac{8}{27}\right)^{\frac{2}{3}}$ (ii) $\dfrac{1}{(25)^{\frac{3}{2}}}$

13. If $K = 2a^{\frac{1}{2}}b^{-\frac{1}{3}}$, find the value of K when $a = 100$ and $b = 64$.

14. Simplify $\dfrac{4^2 \times 16^{\frac{1}{2}}}{64^{\frac{2}{3}} \times 4^3}$, giving your answer in the form 4^n, where $n \in Z$.

15. (i) Show that $8^{\frac{2}{3}} \cdot 16^{\frac{3}{4}} = 32$.

    (ii) Show that $\left(3\tfrac{3}{8}\right)^{\frac{1}{3}} + \left(11\tfrac{1}{9}\right)^{-\frac{1}{2}} = 1\tfrac{4}{5}$.

16. Express $\dfrac{81^{\frac{1}{2}} \times 9^{-1}}{27^{\frac{2}{3}}}$ in the form 3^x, where $x \in Z$.

Section 15.3 Equations involving indices

If $5^x = 5^2$, then $x = 2$.

Similarly, if $7^x = 7^{\frac{1}{2}}$, then $x = \tfrac{1}{2}$.

> In general, if $a^x = a^y$, then $x = y$.

If we are given the equation $25^x = 125$, we express each side as a power of the same base number. In this case, the base number is 5.

Thus, if $25^x = 125$, then $(5^2)^x = 5^3$
$$5^{2x} = 5^3$$
$$2x = 3$$
$$x = 1\tfrac{1}{2}$$

Example 1

Write each of these as whole numbers or fractions:

(i) $4^x = 16$ (ii) $16^x = 64$ (iii) $3^x = \dfrac{1}{27}$ (iv) $25^x = \dfrac{1}{125}$

(i) $4^x = 16$
$4^x = 4^2$
$x = 2$

(ii) $16^x = 64$
$(4^2)^x = 4^3$
$4^{2x} = 4^3$
$2x = 3 \Rightarrow x = 1\frac{1}{2}$

(iii) $3^x = \dfrac{1}{27}$
$3^x = \dfrac{1}{3^3}$
$3^x = 3^{-3}$
$x = -3$

(iv) $25^x = \dfrac{1}{125}$
$(5^2)^x = \dfrac{1}{5^3}$
$5^{2x} = 5^{-3}$
$2x = -3$
$x = -1\frac{1}{2}$

Example 2

Express   (i) 9^{2x-3} (ii) $\dfrac{1}{27}$ as powers of 3.

Hence solve the equation $9^{2x-3} = \dfrac{1}{27}$

(i) $9^{2x-3} = (3^2)^{2x-3} = 3^{4x-6}$

(ii) $\dfrac{1}{27} = \dfrac{1}{3^3} = 3^{-3}$

$9^{2x-3} = \dfrac{1}{27} \Rightarrow 3^{4x-6} = 3^{-3}$

$\Rightarrow 4x - 6 = -3$
$4x = 3$
$x = \dfrac{3}{4}$

Exercise 15.3

1. Express each of the following in the form 2^k, where k is an integer:

(i) 8   (ii) 16   (iii) $\frac{1}{4}$ (iv) $\frac{1}{8}$ (v) $\frac{1}{32}$

2. Express each of the following in the form 3^k, where k is an integer:

(i) 9   (ii) 27   (iii) 81   (iv) $\frac{1}{27}$ (v) $\frac{1}{81}$

293

3. Write each of the following as a power of 2:

(i) $2\sqrt{2}$ (ii) $8\sqrt{2}$ (iii) $\dfrac{4}{\sqrt{2}}$ (iv) $\dfrac{16}{\sqrt{2}}$ (v) $\dfrac{\sqrt{2}}{8}$

4. Solve these equations:

(i) $2^x = 8$ (ii) $3^x = 27$ (iii) $9^x = 27$ (iv) $8^x = 32$

(v) $4^x = 32$ (vi) $16^x = 64$ (vii) $25^x = 125$ (viii) $16^x = 32$

5. Solve each of these equations:

(i) $2^x = \dfrac{1}{4}$ (ii) $3^x = \dfrac{1}{27}$ (iii) $4^x = \dfrac{1}{8}$ (iv) $5^x = 125$

6. Solve each of these equations:

(i) $27^x = 81$ (ii) $\dfrac{1}{5^x} = 125$ (iii) $4^x = \dfrac{1}{32}$ (iv) $2^{x+1} = 16$

7. Find the value of x in each of the following:

(i) $3^{x-2} = 81$ (ii) $4^{x-1} = 2^{x+1}$ (iii) $4^{x-1} = \dfrac{1}{32}$ (iv) $25^{x-1} = \dfrac{1}{125}$

8. Express each of the following in the form 5^k, where k is a rational number:

(i) $\sqrt{5}$ (ii) $5\sqrt{5}$ (iii) $\dfrac{25}{\sqrt{5}}$ (iv) $125\sqrt{5}$ (v) $\dfrac{1}{25\sqrt{5}}$

9. Work out the value of x in each of these:

(i) $2^x = \dfrac{\sqrt{2}}{2}$ (ii) $3^x = \dfrac{1}{\sqrt{3}}$ (iii) $5^x = \dfrac{125}{\sqrt{5}}$ (iv) $2^{x+4} = \dfrac{8}{\sqrt{2}}$

10. Write $\dfrac{81}{\sqrt{3}}$ as a power of 3, and hence solve the equation $9^{x+1} = \dfrac{81}{\sqrt{3}}$.

11. Express $\dfrac{27}{\sqrt{3}}$ as a power of 3, and hence solve the equation $3^{2x+1} = \left(\dfrac{27}{\sqrt{3}}\right)^3$.

12. Express $\dfrac{16}{\sqrt{8}}$ as a power of 2, and hence solve the equation $2^{2x-2} = \dfrac{16}{\sqrt{8}}$.

13. Express $\dfrac{\sqrt{27}}{81}$ as a power of 3, and hence solve the equation $9^{3-x} = \dfrac{\sqrt{27}}{81}$.

14. Express (i) 16 (ii) $2\sqrt{2}$ as a power of 2.

Hence solve the equation $2^{2x-1} = \left(\dfrac{16}{2\sqrt{2}}\right)^3$.

Section 15.4 Irrational numbers – Surds

1. Rational numbers

Rational numbers are numbers that can be written in the form $\frac{a}{b}$, where a and b are integers.

The decimal equivalent of a rational number either **terminates** or **recurs**.

Rational numbers are denoted by the letter **Q**.

Here are some examples:

(i) $\frac{7}{8} = 0.875$

(ii) $\frac{1}{3} = 0.333$
$= 0.\dot{3}$

(iii) $\frac{3}{11} = 0.272727...$
$= 0.\dot{2}\dot{7}$

(iv) $\frac{7}{12} = 0.58333...$
$= 0.58\dot{3}$

> When using the dot notation in a recurring decimal, a dot is written above the first and last digit of a recurring group.
>
> Example: $0.454545... = 0.\dot{4}\dot{5}$

From the examples above and below it can be seen that rational numbers include whole numbers, fractions, and decimals which terminate (end) or recur (repeat).

Examples of rational numbers are

(i) $4 = \frac{4}{1}$ (ii) $\frac{2}{3}$ (iii) $-\frac{7}{8}$ (iv) $0.45 = \frac{45}{100}$ (v) $0.666... = \frac{2}{3}$

2. Irrational numbers

If you use your calculator to find $\sqrt{2}$, you will get $1.414213562...$
This number is never-ending and non-repeating.
Such numbers are called **irrational numbers**.
They are called irrational because they cannot be expressed as rational numbers, that is, in the form of a fraction.

The square root of any number that does not have an exact square root is an irrational number.
Thus $\sqrt{5}, \sqrt{11}, \sqrt{15}, ...$ are irrational numbers.
However $\sqrt{9}, \sqrt{16}, \sqrt{25}$ are rational numbers as they have exact square roots.

A well-known irrational number is π, since $\pi = 3.14159265 ...$, a non-repeating and non-terminating decimal.

Remember

> Any number which can be expressed as a fraction is called a **rational number**.
> Numbers such as $\sqrt{2}, \sqrt{5}, \pi, ...$ which cannot be expressed as fractions, are called **irrational numbers**.

When rational and irrational numbers are combined, they form the set of **real numbers**. The set of real numbers is denoted by the letter **R**.

The set of irrational numbers is denoted by **R\Q**, that is, the set of real numbers less the set of rational numbers.

3. Surds

Irrational numbers such as as $\sqrt{3}, \sqrt{8}, \sqrt{13}, \ldots$ are said to be expressed in **surd** form.

We will now consider $\sqrt{100}$ in two ways:

$\sqrt{100} = 10$. Also, $\sqrt{100} = \sqrt{25 \times 4} = \sqrt{25} \times \sqrt{4} = 5 \times 2 = 10$.

This illustrates a very important property of surds, as stated in the highlighted box.

$$\sqrt{ab} = \sqrt{a} \times \sqrt{b}$$

$$\sqrt{\frac{a}{b}} = \frac{\sqrt{a}}{\sqrt{b}}$$

We will now use these properties to show how a surd can be simplified if one of its factors is a **perfect square** such as $4, 9, 16, 25, \ldots$

(i) $\sqrt{8} = \sqrt{4} . \sqrt{2}$
   $= 2\sqrt{2}$

(ii) $\sqrt{27} = \sqrt{9} . \sqrt{3}$
   $= 3\sqrt{3}$

$2\sqrt{2}$ is said to be the **simplest form** of $\sqrt{8}$.

(iii) $\sqrt{48} = \sqrt{16} . \sqrt{3}$
   $= 4\sqrt{3}$

(iv) $2\sqrt{45} = 2 \times \sqrt{9} \times \sqrt{5}$
   $= 2 \times 3 \times \sqrt{5}$
   $= 6\sqrt{5}$

4. Adding and subtracting surds

Surds may be added or subtracted only when they have the same irrational parts. If the irrational parts are not the same, we reduce each surd to its simplest form, where possible.

Example 1

Simplify $\sqrt{5} + \sqrt{45} - \sqrt{20}$.

We first express each surd in its simplest form:
$$\sqrt{5} + \sqrt{45} - \sqrt{20} = \sqrt{5} + \sqrt{9}\sqrt{5} - \sqrt{4}\sqrt{5}$$
$$= \sqrt{5} + 3\sqrt{5} - 2\sqrt{5}$$
$$= 4\sqrt{5} - 2\sqrt{5} = 2\sqrt{5}$$

5. Multiplying surds

When multiplying surds, multiply separately the rational factors and the irrational factors.

Examples (i) $\sqrt{6} \times \sqrt{2} = \sqrt{12} = \sqrt{4}.\sqrt{3} = 2\sqrt{3}$

(ii) $2\sqrt{3} \times 3\sqrt{5} = 2 \times 3 \times \sqrt{3} \times \sqrt{5} = 6\sqrt{15}$

(iii) $\sqrt{32} \times \sqrt{48} = \sqrt{16}.\sqrt{2} \times \sqrt{16}.\sqrt{3}$

$= 4\sqrt{2} \times 4\sqrt{3} = 16\sqrt{6}$

> **Remember**
> $\sqrt{6} \times \sqrt{6} = 6$

Example 2

Simplify $(2\sqrt{5} - 3)(2\sqrt{5} + 3)$.

$(2\sqrt{5} - 3)(2\sqrt{5} + 3) = 2\sqrt{5}\,(2\sqrt{5} + 3) - 3(2\sqrt{5} + 3)$

$= (2\sqrt{5})(2\sqrt{5}) + (2\sqrt{5})3 - (3)(2\sqrt{5}) - (3)(3)$

$= 4(5) + 6\sqrt{5} - 6\sqrt{5} - 9$

$= 20 - 9 = 11$

Exercise 15.4

1. Which of these numbers are rational?

  (i) $\frac{4}{9}$ (ii) $2\frac{1}{2}$ (iii) $\sqrt{5}$ (iv) $\sqrt{9}$ (v) π (vi) $-1\frac{3}{4}$

2. Which of these numbers are irrational?

  (i) $\sqrt{7}$ (ii) $\sqrt{16}$ (iii) $4\sqrt{7}$ (iv) $0.\dot{4}$ (v) $\frac{\pi}{2}$ (vi) $\sqrt{3} + 2$

3. Write down the value of each of these:

  (i) $\sqrt{25}$ (ii) $\sqrt{400}$ (iii) $3\sqrt{16}$ (iv) $\frac{\sqrt{100}}{2}$ (v) $2 + 3\sqrt{81}$ (vi) $\sqrt{36} + 2\sqrt{4}$

4. Write down an irrational number between:

  (i) 3 and 4   (ii) 4 and 5   (iii) 10 and 11   (iv) 0 and 1

5. Write each of these in the form $\sqrt{n}$, where n is an integer:

  (i) $\sqrt{2} \times \sqrt{5}$ (ii) $\sqrt{3} \times \sqrt{7}$ (iii) $\sqrt{8} \times \sqrt{3}$ (iv) $\sqrt{5} \times \sqrt{11}$

6. Evaluate each of these:

  (i) $\sqrt{5} \times \sqrt{5}$ (ii) $(\sqrt{6})^2$ (iii) $(2\sqrt{3})^2$ (iv) $\sqrt{2} \times \sqrt{8}$ (v) $\left(\dfrac{\sqrt{8}}{\sqrt{2}}\right)^2$

7. Express each of these surds in its simplest form:

  (i) $\sqrt{8}$ (ii) $\sqrt{12}$ (iii) $\sqrt{18}$ (iv) $\sqrt{27}$ (v) $\sqrt{45}$

8. Express these surds in their simplest forms:

  (i) $\sqrt{75}$ (ii) $\sqrt{125}$ (iii) $2\sqrt{8}$ (iv) $4\sqrt{27}$ (v) $2\sqrt{48}$

9. Sort these into matching pairs of equivalent numbers. Which is the odd one out?

A $\sqrt{4} \times \sqrt{9}$ **B** $3\sqrt{2}$ **C** $\sqrt{4} \times \sqrt{6}$ **D** $\sqrt{8} + \sqrt{10}$ **E** $\sqrt{20}$

F $\sqrt{2} \times \sqrt{5}$ **G** $\sqrt{10}$ **H** $\sqrt{18}$ **I** $\sqrt{24}$ **J** $2\sqrt{5}$ **K** $\sqrt{36}$

10. Express each of the following in its simplest form:
 (i) $5\sqrt{3} + 4\sqrt{3} - \sqrt{3}$ (ii) $2\sqrt{2} + 6\sqrt{2} - 3\sqrt{2}$ (iii) $2\sqrt{2} + \sqrt{18}$
 (iv) $\sqrt{18} + \sqrt{32}$ (v) $\sqrt{27} + \sqrt{48}$ (vi) $\sqrt{75} + \sqrt{12} - \sqrt{48}$

11. How many times greater than $\sqrt{2}$ is $\sqrt{32}$?

12. Express each of these products as a whole number:
 (i) $2\sqrt{5} \cdot \sqrt{5}$ (ii) $2\sqrt{3} \times 3\sqrt{3}$ (iii) $3\sqrt{5} \times 4\sqrt{5}$ (iv) $3\sqrt{7} \times \sqrt{7}$

13. Simplify each of these:
 (i) $\sqrt{5}(\sqrt{5} - 2)$ (ii) $2\sqrt{3}(\sqrt{3} - 2)$ (iii) $\sqrt{2}(3\sqrt{2} - \sqrt{3})$

14. Express the following products in their simplest forms:
 (i) $2\sqrt{5}(\sqrt{2} - \sqrt{5})$ (ii) $(\sqrt{2} + 1)(\sqrt{2} - 1)$ (iii) $(5 + \sqrt{3})(5 - \sqrt{3})$
 (iv) $(\sqrt{7} - 4)(\sqrt{7} + 4)$ (v) $(1 - 2\sqrt{3})(1 + 2\sqrt{3})$ (vi) $(\sqrt{2} + \sqrt{5})(\sqrt{2} - \sqrt{5})$

15. Simplify each of these:
 (i) $(2 - \sqrt{3})(4 + 2\sqrt{3})$ (ii) $(1 - 3\sqrt{2})(5 + 2\sqrt{2})$ (iii) $(3 + 2\sqrt{2})(3 - 2\sqrt{2})$

16. Write $(2 - 2\sqrt{5})^2$ in the form $a + b\sqrt{5}$, where $a, b \in Z$.

17. Given that $p = \sqrt{5} + \sqrt{3}$ and $q = \sqrt{5} - \sqrt{3}$, simplify $p^2 - q^2$.

18. In the given right-angled triangle, find the value of $k, k \in Z$.

19. $p = 2 + \sqrt{3}$ $q = 2 - \sqrt{3}$
 (i) (a) Work out $p - q$.
   (b) State whether $p - q$ is rational or irrational.
 (ii) (a) Work out pq.
   (b) State whether pq is rational or irrational.

Section 15.5 Numbers in standard form

If you use your calculator to perform the operation $60\,000 \times 4\,600\,000$, the screen will display the number 2.76×10^{11}.

This represents the number 2.76 multiplied by 10 eleven times.

The number 2.76×10^{11} is written in **scientific notation** or **standard form**.

Standard form is a convenient kind of shorthand for writing large and small numbers.

Definition

A number in the form $a \times 10^n$, where $1 \leqslant a < 10$, and n is an integer, is said to be expressed in scientific notation or standard form.

Example

$$6.8 \times 10^4$$

This part is written as a number between 1 and 10.

This part is written as a power of 10.

Here are some numbers written in standard form:

(i) $5000 = 5 \times 1000 = 5 \times 10^3$

(ii) $64\,000 = 64 \times 1000 = 6.4 \times 10\,000 = 6.4 \times 10^4$

(iii) $380\,000 = 3.8 \times 10^5$

Notice that if you move the decimal point

(i)   1 place to the **left**, multiply by 10^1

(ii) 2 places to the **left**, multiply by 10^2

(iii) 3 places to the **left**, multiply by 10^3 ...

Numbers less than 1

To express a number such as 0.037 in standard form, move the decimal point 2 places to the right to get a number between 1 and 10, as shown below:

(i) $0.037 = \dfrac{3.7}{100} = \dfrac{3.7}{10^2} = 3.7 \times 10^{-2}$

(ii) $0.0045 = \dfrac{4.5}{1000} = \dfrac{4.5}{10^3} = 4.5 \times 10^{-3}$

In these examples, if you move the decimal point

(i)   2 places to the **right**, multiply by 10^{-2}

(ii) 3 places to the **right**, multiply by 10^{-3} ...

On your calculator there is an $\boxed{\text{EXP}}$ or $\boxed{\times 10^x}$ key which stands for 'exponential' or 10 to any power.

To change the number 2.54×10^3 to decimal form, key in $2.54 \boxed{\text{EXP}} 3 \boxed{=}$.

The calculator will display 2540.

Adding and subtracting numbers in standard form

To add or subtract numbers expressed in standard form, convert each number to a decimal number and perform the addition or subtraction. You may also use a calculator as shown in the following example.

Example 1

Express in standard form: $1.84 \times 10^2 + 8.7 \times 10^3$.

$1.84 \times 10^2 = 184$ and $8.7 \times 10^3 = 8700$

$\therefore \quad 1.84 \times 10^2 + 8.7 \times 10^3 = 184 + 8700$
$$= 8884$$
$$= 8.884 \times 10^3$$

 Key in $1.84 \boxed{10^x} 2 + 8.7 \boxed{10^x} 3 \boxed{=}$

The result displayed is 8884 which is 8.884×10^3.

Multiplying and dividing numbers in standard form

To multiply (or divide) numbers expressed in standard form, first multiply the 'a parts' and then multiply the numbers expressed as powers of 10.
The calculator is particularly useful in these operations.

Thus, $(3.8 \times 10^3)(9.4 \times 10^{-2}) = (3.8 \times 9.4) \times 10^3 \times 10^{-2}$
$$= 35.72 \times 10^1 \ \dots 3 - 2 = 1$$
$$= 3.572 \times 10^2$$

Or using a calculator, key in

$3.8 \boxed{10^x} 3 \boxed{\times} 9.4 \boxed{10^x} -2 \boxed{=}$

The result is 357.2

$357.2 = 3.572 \times 10^2$

Example 2

Express each of these in standard form:

(i) $2.76 \times 10^3 - 5.9 \times 10^2$

(ii) $\dfrac{(6 \times 10^3) \times (4.5 \times 10^4)}{1.2 \times 10^4}$

(i) $2.76 \times 10^3 - 5.9 \times 10^2 = 2760 - 590$

$$= 2170 = 2.17 \times 10^3$$

$\left[\text{or key in } 2.76 \boxed{10^x} 3 \boxed{-} 5.9 \boxed{10^x} 2 \boxed{=} \quad \text{The result is 2170.}\right]$

(ii) $\dfrac{(6 \times 10^3) \times (4.5 \times 10^4)}{1.2 \times 10^4} = \dfrac{6 \times 4.5 \times 10^3 \times 10^4}{1.2 \times 10^4}$

$$= \dfrac{27 \times 10^7}{1.2 \times 10^4}$$

$$= \dfrac{27}{1.2} \times \dfrac{10^7}{10^4} = 22.5 \times 10^3$$

$$= 2.25 \times 10^4$$

$\left[\text{or key in } 6 \boxed{10^x} 3 \boxed{\times} 4.5 \boxed{10^x} 4 \boxed{\div} 1.2 \boxed{10^x} 4 \boxed{=}\right.$

The result is 22 500.

This is then converted to 2.25×10^4. $\Big]$

Exercise 15.5

1. Which of the following numbers are written in standard form?

(i) 3.6×10^2 (ii) 14.3×10^4 (iii) 0.8×10^3 (iv) 9.8×10^4

2. Write each of the following as a decimal number:

(i) 6×10^2 (ii) 4.5×10^2 (iii) 6.8×10^3 (iv) 5.1×10^4

(v) 6.7×10^4 (vi) 5.16×10^2 (vii) 7.05×10^3 (viii) 1.86×10^4

3. Write each of these numbers in standard form:

(i) 400   (ii) 280   (iii) 840   (iv) 6200   (v) 8600

(vi) 127   (vii) 827   (viii) 76 000   (ix) 146.8   (x) 72 400

4. Express these numbers in standard form:

(i) 40×10^2 (ii) 320×10^3 (iii) 0.9×10^3 (iv) 94.3×10^2

5. Work these out and express your answers as decimal numbers:

(i) $3.8 \times 10^2 + 1.7 \times 10^3$ (ii) $1.76 \times 10 + 6.43 \times 10^2$

(iii) $8.4 \times 10^3 - 1.7 \times 10^2$ (iv) $6.64 \times 10^2 - 9.4 \times 10$

6. Evaluate each of the following and give your answer in standard form:

(i) $(3.6 \times 10^2) \times (1.5 \times 10^3)$ (ii) $(4.6 \times 10^2) \times (3.7 \times 10^{-1})$

(iii) $(3.64 \times 10^{-2}) \times (9 \times 10^4)$ (iv) $(1.8 \times 10^{-4}) \times (8 \times 10^5)$

7. Change these numbers to decimal form:

(i) 2.5×10^{-1} (ii) 6×10^{-2} (iii) 4.8×10^{-3} (iv) 9.2×10^{-4}

8. Write these numbers in standard form:

(i) 0.04   (ii) 0.062   (iii) 0.007   (iv) 0.0065

9. Write these numbers in standard form:

(i) 0.008   (ii) 0.0079   (iii) 0.0006   (iv) 0.00053

10. Write each of these in the form $a \times 10^n$, where $1 \leqslant a < 10, n \in Z$:

(i) $\dfrac{8.4 \times 10^5}{1.2 \times 10^2}$ (ii) $\dfrac{9 \times 10^4}{1.5 \times 10^2}$ (iii) $\dfrac{4.48 \times 10^3}{8 \times 10^{-1}}$ (iv) $\dfrac{8.4 \times 10^{-2}}{1.2 \times 10^3}$

11. Work out each of these without using a calculator.
Give your answer in standard form.

(i) $(5.4 \times 10^5) \times (3 \times 10^2)$ (ii) $\dfrac{4 \times 10^3}{8 \times 10^5}$ (iii) $\dfrac{4 \times 10^5}{5 \times 10^8}$

(iv) $\dfrac{1.6 \times 10^9}{8 \times 10^7}$ (v) $\dfrac{8 \times 10^4}{1.6 \times 10^5}$ (vi) $\dfrac{4.8 \times 10^{-2}}{3 \times 10^3}$

12. Write these in standard form:

(i) $\dfrac{1.4 \times 10^3 + 5.6 \times 10^2}{7 \times 10^{-1}}$ (ii) $\dfrac{(6.4 \times 10^2) + (8.2 \times 10^4)}{1.033 \times 10^2}$

13. Express $\dfrac{1.2 \times 10^8 \times 3.6 \times 10^5}{1.8 \times 10^9}$ in standard form.

14. Calculate the value of $\dfrac{5.1 \times 10^8 + 1.9 \times 10^7}{1.4 \times 10^9}$ and write your answer as a decimal number.

15. Write each of these as a decimal number:

(i) $\dfrac{6.8 \times 10^3 - 5.2 \times 10^2}{3.2 \times 10^2}$ (ii) $\dfrac{1.12 \times 10^{-2} \times 9.8 \times 10^5}{1.4 \times 10^2}$

16. The Earth's diameter is 1.27×10^4 km and the diameter of Mars is 6.8×10^3 km.

(i) Which planet has the larger diameter?

(ii) What is the difference between their diameters?

(iii) What is the total if the two diameters are added?
Give your answer in standard form.

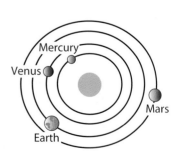

Section 15.6 Significant figures – Approximation

There are many occasions when it is either desirable or necessary to round off large or small numbers to a reasonable degree of accuracy. If there were 12 946 people at a football match, it would be reasonable to state that the attendance was about 13 000.
We say that 13 000 is given 'correct to the nearest thousand'.
Similarly, 1.823 could be rounded off to 1.8.

With the widespread use of calculators, it is important that we have some estimate of the answer we expect to get. Then we will know whether the answer shown on the calculator is reasonable or not. To make a rough estimate of a calculation, we generally give decimals correct to 1 or 2 decimal places and we round whole numbers to the nearest 10, 100 or 1000, as appropriate.

1. Decimal places

When writing a decimal correct to a given number of decimal places, count each digit, including zero, after the decimal point. If the last digit is 5 or more, increase the previous digit by 1. If the last digit is 4 or less, leave the previous digit as it is.

Thus, 6.8537 = 6.854, correct to 3 decimal places
= 6.85, correct to 2 decimal places
= 6.9, correct to 1 decimal place.

2. Significant figures

If the attendance at a football match was 34 176, it would be reasonable to write down 34 200 or 34 000.

34 200 is written correct to 3 significant figures.
34 000 is written correct to 2 significant figures.

When expressing a whole number correct to a given number of significant figures, zeros at the end of the number are not counted but must be included in the final result. All other zeros are significant.

Thus, 52 764 = 52 760, correct to 4 significant figures
= 52 800, correct to 3 significant figures
= 53 000, correct to 2 significant figures
= 50 000, correct to 1 significant figure.

The number 70 425 = 70 400, correct to 3 significant figures.
Notice here that the zero between the 7 and 4 is significant, but the two final zeros are not.

If a number is less than 1, then the zeros immediately after the decimal point are not significant.

Thus, (i) 0.07406 = 0.0741, correct to 3 significant figures.
(ii) 0.00892 = 0.0089, correct to 2 significant figures.

3. Making an Estimate

If a calculation involves a mixture of numbers greater than and less than 1, then to make an estimate of the answer,

(i) round numbers greater than 1 correct to one significant figure

(ii) round numbers less than 1 correct to one decimal place.

> ### Example 1
>
> Make a rough estimate of $\dfrac{10.25 + 29.83}{0.24 \times 46}$
>
> $\dfrac{10.25 + 29.83}{0.24 \times 46} \approx \dfrac{10 + 30}{0.2 \times 50} = \dfrac{40}{10} = 4$
>
> A rough estimate is 4.
>
> (The result using a calculator is 3.63…)

Exercise 15.6

1. Write each of these numbers correct to the nearest 10:

   (i) 76   (ii) 347   (iii) 1792   (iv) 7319   (v) 1608

2. Write these numbers to the nearest 100:

   (i) 87   (ii) 146   (iii) 1824   (iv) 2539   (v) 9829

3. Write each of these numbers correct to one decimal place:

   (i) 46.34   (ii) 8.753   (iii) 0.426   (iv) 0.456   (v) 0.074

4. How many significant figures are there in each of these numbers?

   (i) 3000   (ii) 28 000   (iii) 329 000   (iv) 309 000   (v) 607 100

5. Write each of these numbers correct to two significant figures:

   (i) 3184   (ii) 648   (iii) 2916   (iv) 28 936   (v) 40 673

6. Round these numbers to three significant figures:

   (i) 7136   (ii) 45 309   (iii) 3612   (iv) 159 762   (v) 700 713

7. Round these numbers to two significant figures:

   (i) 0.473   (ii) 0.06312   (iii) 2.384   (iv) 0.669   (v) 54.839

8. Round these numbers to three significant figures:

   (i) 0.7384   (ii) 8.372   (iii) 0.02843   (iv) 1.083   (v) 12.316

9. Write the number indicated by the arrow

    (i) correct to 3 significant figures

    (ii) correct to 2 significant figures

    (iii) correct to 1 significant figure.

10. Round each number correct to one significant figure and hence make an estimate of each of these:

    (i) $\dfrac{56 \times 18}{28}$
    (ii) $\dfrac{19.48 + 43.2}{10.4 \times 2.8}$
    (iii) $\dfrac{183 \times 46.4}{77.4}$

11. Round each number correct to one significant figure, or to one decimal place if the number is less than 1, to make a rough estimate of each of these:

    (i) $\dfrac{18.8 + 48.3}{11.3 - 2.75}$
    (ii) $\dfrac{0.231 \times 0.62}{0.419}$
    (iii) $\dfrac{0.86 + 0.734}{0.367 - 0.18}$

12. Round all the numbers to the nearest whole number and hence estimate the answer to each of these:

    (i) $\dfrac{2.75 \times 8.34}{5.24 + 2.74}$
    (ii) $\dfrac{0.73 \times 12.42}{1.75 + 2.38}$
    (iii) $\dfrac{6.28 + \sqrt{4.3}}{0.65 \times \sqrt{8.57}}$

13. By rounding numbers less than 1 correct to one decimal place and other numbers to one significant figure, make a rough estimate of these calculations:

    (i) $\dfrac{807}{391.3 \times 0.37}$
    (ii) $\dfrac{31.69 \times 6.25}{0.473}$
    (iii) $\dfrac{324 \times 2.76}{196 \times 0.54}$

14. By rounding appropriately, estimate the value of

    (i) $\dfrac{518.6 \times 8.32}{98.5}$
    (ii) $\dfrac{63.2 \times (9.8)^2}{48.7}$
    (iii) $\dfrac{0.79 \times 28.4}{0.372}$

15. Sally estimates the value of $\dfrac{42.8 \times 63.7}{285}$ to be 8.

Write down three numbers Sally could use to get her estimate: $\dfrac{\text{......} \times \text{......}}{\text{......}}$

Section 15.7 Reciprocals and use of calculator ───────

1. Reciprocals

The **reciprocal** of a number is $\dfrac{1}{\text{number}}$.

The reciprocal of 5 is $\frac{1}{5}$; the reciprocal of 1.8 is $\frac{1}{1.8}$.

When a number and its reciprocal are multiplied, the result is 1.

The reciprocal of 12.8 is $\frac{1}{12.8}$.

This can be found using your calculator by keying in $1 \boxed{\div} 12.8 \boxed{=}$.

The result is 0.078.

The reciprocal of a number may also be found by using the $\boxed{x^{-1}}$ key on your calculator.

Thus, to find the reciprocal of 12.8, key in $12.8 \boxed{x^{-1}} \boxed{=}$.

The result is 0.078, as found above.

2. Powers and roots

The examples below show the procedure for finding powers and roots of numbers on your calculator.

Operation	Example
(i) To find the **square root** of a number, use the $\boxed{\sqrt{\ }}$ key.	To find $\sqrt{28}$, key in $\boxed{\sqrt{\ }} 28 \boxed{=}$ The result is 5.29.
(ii) To find the **cube root** of a number, use the $\boxed{\sqrt[3]{\ }}$ key.	To find $\sqrt[3]{27}$, key in $\boxed{\text{SHIFT}} \boxed{\sqrt[3]{\ }} 27 \boxed{=}$ The result is 3.
(iii) To find the **square** of a number, use the $\boxed{x^2}$ key.	To find 24^2, key in $24 \boxed{x^2} \boxed{=}$ The result is 576.
(iv) To find 8^5 (or any power), use the $\boxed{x^\blacksquare}$ key.	To find 8^5, key in $8 \boxed{x^\blacksquare} 5 \boxed{=}$ The result is 32768.

3. Operations on the calculator

When using your calculator to find the value of $\frac{14 \times 15}{50 - 29}$, always enclose the denominator in brackets.

Now try $\frac{14 \times 15}{(50 - 29)}$. You should get 10.

Example 1

Use your calculator to evaluate $\frac{12.42 \times 23.47}{13.48 + 5.73}$, correct to two decimal places.

Insert brackets around the denominator and key in

$12.42 \boxed{\times} 23.47 \boxed{\div} \boxed{(} 13.48 \boxed{+} 5.73 \boxed{)} \boxed{=}$

The result is 15.17.

Example 2

Use your calculator to evaluate, correct to 1 decimal place,

$$(2.59)^2 - \frac{31}{14.6} + \frac{78.4}{5 \times \sqrt{60.4}}.$$

Key in 2.59 $\boxed{x^2}$ $\boxed{-}$ 31 $\boxed{\div}$ 14.6 $\boxed{+}$ 78.4 $\boxed{\div}$ $\boxed{(}$ 5 $\boxed{\times}$ $\boxed{\sqrt{}}$ 60.4 $\boxed{)}$ $\boxed{=}$.

The result is 6.6, correct to 1 decimal place.

Note: If you use the $\boxed{=}$ key at any stage in a calculation, it will give the result of all the operations done to that point.

Exercise 15.7

1. Write down the reciprocal of each of these numbers:

   (i) 6   (ii) $\frac{1}{2}$ (iii) $\frac{3}{4}$ (iv) $-\frac{2}{3}$ (v) $1\frac{1}{4}$

2. Use your calculator to work out the reciprocal of each of these, correct to 2 decimal places where necessary:

   (i) 2.6   (ii) 5.44   (iii) -2.8 (iv) 0.68   (v) -0.8

In the following questions, give all answers correct to two decimal places where necessary.

3. Use your calculator to verify that $\dfrac{48 \times 64}{16 + 24} = 76.8$.

4. Use your calculator to evaluate each of these:

   (i) $\dfrac{12.4 \times 5.9}{(3.7 \times 2.5)}$ (ii) $\dfrac{42.3 + 18.4}{16.7 \times 0.4}$ (iii) $\dfrac{81.73 - 21.4}{3.87 \times 1.25}$

5. Evaluate each of these:

   (i) $\sqrt{30.5}$ (ii) $\sqrt{348}$ (iii) $\sqrt{107.8}$ (iv) $(3.9)^2$ (v) $(16.34)^2$

6. Evaluate each of these:

   (i) $\dfrac{32}{14^2}$ (ii) $\dfrac{\sqrt{26}}{4}$ (iii) $\dfrac{2 \times \sqrt{40}}{3}$ (iv) $\dfrac{(12.8)^2}{3.7}$ (v) $\dfrac{15.4}{\sqrt{38}}$

7. Find the value of each of these:

   (i) $(3.4)^2 + \dfrac{3}{14.8} + \sqrt{108}$ (ii) $\sqrt{27} \times \dfrac{4}{3.8} + (9.62)^2$

   (iii) $\sqrt{73} + \dfrac{\sqrt{45}}{3} \times \dfrac{6.8}{14.9}$ (iv) $\dfrac{6}{15.9} \times \sqrt{136} - \dfrac{5}{18.7}$

8. Work out each of the following:

(i) $\dfrac{4.9 - (1.8)^2}{3.5}$

(ii) $6.84 + \dfrac{\sqrt{8.4}}{4.2}$

(iii) $\dfrac{5.84 \times \sqrt{17}}{2.5 - \sqrt{3.5}}$

9. Work out the value of $\dfrac{\sqrt{(12.3)^2 + 7.9}}{1.8 \times 0.17}$.

10. Evaluate $\dfrac{19.6}{(9.7)^2} + \dfrac{\sqrt{281}}{3.4} \times \dfrac{(1.83)^2}{7.3}$.

11. Find the value of $(3.73)^2 + \dfrac{16}{\sqrt{28}} \times \dfrac{6.7}{19.4}$.

12. Evaluate $p^2 - \sqrt{2q} - \dfrac{1}{r}$, where $p = 4.256, q = 0.327$ and $r = 0.45$.

Test yourself 15

1. (a) (i) Find the value of $16^{\frac{1}{2}} + \sqrt{4^3}$.

(ii) If $125^x = \frac{1}{5}$, find the value of x.

(b) (i) Express $\sqrt{50} - \sqrt{32} + 2\sqrt{8}$ in the form $k\sqrt{2}$, where $k \in N$.

(ii) Write down an irrational number between 6 and 7.

(c) By rounding appropriately, estimate the value of $\dfrac{28.6 \times 2\sqrt{17.3}}{(4.12)^2 + 3.84}$.

Now use your calculator to find its value, correct to two decimal places.

2. (a) (i) Which **two** of the following have the same value?

$$4^{\frac{1}{2}} \qquad 4^{-\frac{1}{2}} \qquad 16^{\frac{1}{4}} \qquad 2^0$$

(ii) Write 5300 in standard form.

(b) (i) Express $3\sqrt{12} - \sqrt{27}$ in the form $k\sqrt{3}$, where $k \in N$.

(ii) Find the value of $(8 \times 10^{-3})^{\frac{1}{3}}$ without using a calculator.

(c) Find the value of the variable in each of these equations:

(i) $2^x = 1$ (ii) $2^y = \frac{1}{4}$ (iii) $32^z = 2$ (iv) $16^{b+3} = 2^b$

3. (a) (i) Which **two** of the following numbers are equal?

$$16^{\frac{1}{2}} \qquad 4^{-1} \qquad 32^0 \qquad (-2)^4 \qquad 2^{-2}$$

(ii) Find a value of x for which $\sqrt{2} \times \sqrt{x}$ is rational.

(b) (i) Simplify $2x^4 \times 6x^3 \div 3x^5$.

(ii) Express $\dfrac{8.4 \times 10^4}{2.8 \times 10^{-1}}$ in the form $a \times 10^n$, where $1 \leqslant a < 10, n \in Z$.

(c) (i) Find the value of $25^{\frac{3}{2}}$.

(ii) Find the value of x for which $16^x = \frac{1}{8}$.

4. (a) Write each of these as a whole number or as a fraction:

(i) 2^5 (ii) 3^{-2} (iii) $4^{\frac{1}{2}}$ (iv) 7^0 (v) $27^{\frac{1}{3}}$

(b) (i) Express 0.04 in standard form.

(ii) Solve the equation $4^x = 8$.

(c) Decide if each of the following statements is true or false.
If the statement is false, give an example to show why.

(i) If $x^2 = x$, then the only possible value for x is 1.

(ii) If $a^2 = 64$, then the only possible value for a is 8.

(iii) $a^0 \times a^0 \times a^0 \times a^0 > 2$

(iv) $2^{-n} = (0.5)^n$

(v) $2^n < 0$, where n is a negative integer.

5. (a) Express each of these as a whole number or fraction:

(i) $\dfrac{1}{4^{-2}}$ (ii) $\left(\dfrac{1}{4}\right)^{\frac{1}{2}}$ (iii) $125^{\frac{1}{3}}$ (iv) $\dfrac{\sqrt{8}}{\sqrt{2}}$.

(b) (i) Express $\sqrt{40}.\sqrt{5}$ in the form $p\sqrt{2}$, where $p \in N$.

(ii) If $4^{2x+1} = 8$, find the value of x.

(c) Express $\dfrac{8.4 \times 10^4}{1.2 \times 10^{-2} \times 2.8 \times 10^3}$ in the form $a \times 10^n$, where $1 \leqslant a < 10, n \in Z$.

6. (a) (i) Find the value of $25^{\frac{1}{2}} + \left(\frac{1}{8}\right)^{\frac{1}{3}}$.

(ii) If $16^n = \frac{1}{4}$, find the value of n.

(b) If $x = \sqrt{a^2 + b^2}$, find the value of x when

(i) $a = \sqrt{2}$ and $b = \sqrt{7}$

(ii) $a = \frac{3}{7}$ and $b = \frac{4}{7}$

(c) Express $\sqrt{125}$ as a power of 5.

Hence find the value of x for which $25^x = \dfrac{\sqrt{125}}{5}$.

Chapter 16

Geometry 2: Similar Triangles – Circles – Theorems

Key words

similar triangles   equiangular   corresponding sides   theorem
converse   transversal   equal intercepts   parallel   semicircle
circumference   radius   chord   tangent   diameter   arc   sector
cyclic quadrilateral   corollary

Section 16.1 Similar triangles

The shapes A and B are similar.
All the corresponding angles are the same and all
the sides in shape B are twice as long as the
corresponding sides in shape A.

When two figures are **similar**:
> their **shapes** are the same
> their **angles** are equal
> corresponding **lengths** are in the **same ratio**.

All the sides in figure B are $1\frac{1}{2}$ times longer than
the corresponding sides in figure A.

Similar triangles

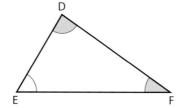

Similar triangles have
the same shapes but
different sizes.

The triangles ABC and DEF above have equal angles.
Notice that they have the same shape but are different in size.
These triangles are said to be **similar** or **equiangular** triangles.
The sides [BC] and [EF] are said to be **corresponding sides**
since they are opposite equal angles.
The sides [AB] and [DE] are also corresponding.

Equiangular means
all the corresponding
angles are equal.

Since each side in the triangle DEF is twice the length of the corresponding side in the triangle ABC, we say that the sides are in the same **ratio** or are **proportional**.

In the triangles above, |AB| is half |DE|.

Similarly, $|BC| = \frac{1}{2}|EF|$ and $|AC| = \frac{1}{2}|DF|$.

Thus, $\dfrac{|AB|}{|DE|} = \dfrac{|BC|}{|EF|} = \dfrac{|AC|}{|DF|} = \dfrac{1}{2}$

This important result for similar triangles is stated in the theorem on the right.

Theorem
If two triangles ABC and DEF are similar, then their sides are proportional, in order

$$\frac{|AB|}{|DE|} = \frac{|BC|}{|EF|} = \frac{|AC|}{|DF|}$$

The **converse** of this theorem is also true.

If the sides of two triangles are proportional, in order, then the triangles are similar.

Note: Two triangles are similar if two angles in one triangle are equal to two angles in the other triangle. The triangles are equiangular or similar because the third angles must be equal.

Example 1

The given triangles ABC and DEF are similar.
Find the lengths of the sides
 (i) [DE]
 (ii) [DF]

 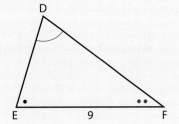

 (i) [DE] corresponds to [AB].
   Each side of the triangle DEF is $1\frac{1}{2}$ times the length of the corresponding side in the triangle ABC since 9 is $1\frac{1}{2}$ times 6.
   $\therefore\ |DE| = 1\frac{1}{2}|AB|$
   $\quad\ |DE| = 1\frac{1}{2}(4) = 6$

 (ii) $|DF| = 1\frac{1}{2}|AC|$
   $\quad |DF| = 1\frac{1}{2}(5) = 7\frac{1}{2}$

Example 2

(i) Show that triangle ABC is similar to triangle EFG.

(ii) Find the length of side [FG].

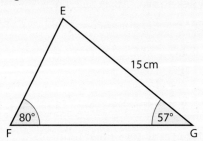

(i) Find the missing angles:

$$|\angle ACB| = 180° - 80° - 43° = 57°$$
$$|\angle FEG| = 180° - 80° - 57° = 43°$$

Since each triangle has angles measuring 80°, 57° and 43°, the triangles are similar.

(ii) [FG] corresponds to the side [BC].

Since $|EG| = 2\frac{1}{2}|AC| \Rightarrow |FG| = 2\frac{1}{2}|BC|$

$$= 2\frac{1}{2}(5 \text{ cm})$$
$$|FG| = 12.5 \text{ cm}$$

Exercise 16.1

1. In the given figures, each side in PQRS is twice the length of the corresponding side in KLMN.

   (i) What side corresponds to [NM]?

   (ii) What side corresponds to [QR]?

   (iii) If $|KL| = 4$, find $|PQ|$.

   (iv) If $|NM| = 8.2$, find $|SR|$.

   (v) If $|QR| = 15$, find $|LM|$.

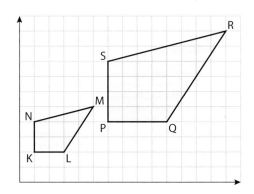

2. The triangles ABC and DEF are similar.

   (i) Complete this ratio:

      $|BC| : |EF| = 6 : 12 = \ldots : \ldots$

   (ii) If $|AC| = 7.2$, find $|DF|$.

   (iii) If $|DE| = 8$, find $|AB|$.

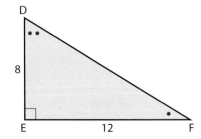

3. The given triangles are similar.
Find the lengths of the sides
marked *x* and *y*.

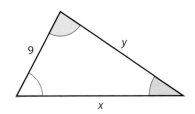

4. The shapes in (i) and (ii) below are similar.
Find the lengths of the sides marked with letters.

(i)

(ii)

5. The two given triangles are similar.

(i) Copy and complete this statement:
'Each side of the bigger triangle is … times
the length of the corresponding side of
the smaller triangle'.

(ii) Find the values of *x* and *y*.

6. Explain why the triangles ABC and DEF are similar.
Find the values of *x* and *y*.

7. The triangles ABC and PQR are similar.
In the triangle PQR, which side
corresponds to
(i) [AB]
(ii) [AC]
(iii) [BC]?

If $|AC| = 8$, $|PR| = 12$ and $|BC| = 6$, find $|PQ|$.

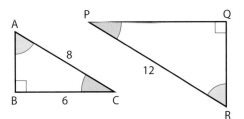

8. The triangles DEF and KLM are similar.

    (i)   Which side corresponds to [DF]?

    (ii) Which side corresponds to [ML]?

    (iii) Find |KM|.

9.

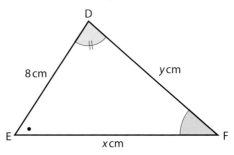

    (i)   Explain why the triangles ABC and DEF are similar.

    (ii) Which side of the triangle DEF corresponds to the side [AC]?

    (iii) Find the values of x and y.

10. The triangles ABC and XYZ are similar.

    (i)   Which side of the triangle XYZ corresponds to [AB]? Explain your answer.

    (ii) Find the values of d and e.

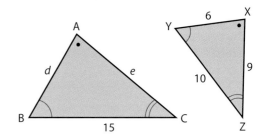

11. Which of these *shape families* are always similar?

    (i)   all squares   (ii) all rectangles

    (iii) all parallelograms   (iv) all circles

    (v) all equilateral triangles (vi) all isosceles triangles

12. Find the length of the side marked x in the figure below:

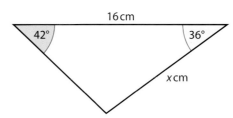

13. In the given figure, BC∥DE.

Draw the triangles ABC and ADE as separate diagrams.
Mark in the lengths of the known sides in each triangle.

   (i) Explain why the triangles ABC and ADE are similar.

  (ii) Now find |DE|.

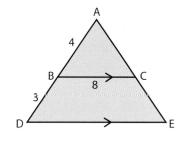

14. ABCD is a quadrilateral in which
AB∥DC and |∠DAB| = |∠CBD|.

   (i) Name two other equal angles in this figure.

  (ii) Now explain why the triangles ABD and
DCB are similar.

 (iii) Which side in △DCB corresponds to [DB]
in △ABD?

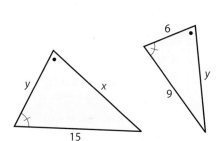

 (iv) Which side in △ABD corresponds to [BC] in △BCD?

  (v) If |DC| = 15 cm and |DB| = 12 cm, find |AB|.

15. Find the value of x and the value of
y in the given similar triangles.

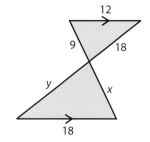

16. In the given triangles, the arrows
indicate that the lines are parallel.

Mark in the equal angles and hence
use similar triangles to find the values
of x and y.

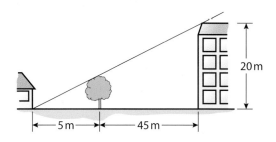

17. When James planted a tree 5 m from
a window, the tree just blocked from
view a building 50 m away.
If the building was 20 m tall, how tall
was the tree?

18. A tall man, who is sitting up straight in his seat, is completely blocking John's view at the cinema.
John is 10 m from the 4 m high screen.
The man is 1 m in front of John.
How far would the man need to lower his head and shoulders if John is to be able to see all of the screen?

19. In the given figure, JK||ML.

(i) Explain why triangles JKM and KLM are similar.

(ii) Find the length of [JK].

20. A swimming pool is being filled .
Find the length, *l*, of the surface of the water when the pool has been filled to a depth of 2 m.

21. A surveyor wants to calculate the distance across a lake. The lake is surrounded by woods. Three paths have been constructed to provide access to the lake from a road *AC* as shown in the diagram.

The lengths of the paths from the road to the lake are as follows.
$|AE| = 120$ m
$|BE| = 80$ m
$|CD| = 200$ m

(i) Explain how these measurements can be used to find $|ED|$.

(ii) Calculate $|ED|$, the distance across the lake.

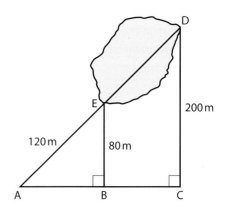

Section 16.2 Transversals and triangles

1. Transversals

The diagram on the right shows a
line p intersecting three parallel
lines ℓ, m and n.
The line p is called a **transversal**.
Since $|AB| = |BC|$, we say that the
parallel lines ℓ, m and n cut **equal
segments** on the transversal.

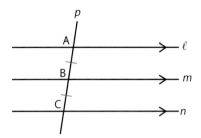

If another line q is drawn, it can be
shown that the parallel lines will
also cut equal segments on the line q,
that is, $|DE| = |EF|$.

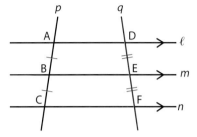

The same property holds for all other transversals.
This property is stated in the theorem below.

> **Theorem**
> If three parallel lines cut off equal segments on some transversal line,
> then they will cut off equal segments on any other transversal.

Example 1

In the given figure, the lines ℓ, m
and n cut equal intercepts of
9 cm from the transversal p.
If q is another transversal, find the
value of x.

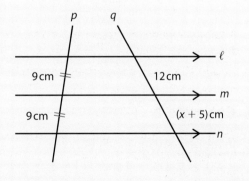

The lines ℓ, m and n also cut equal
intercepts on the line q.

$$\therefore \quad 12 \text{ cm} = (x + 5) \text{ cm}$$
$$x + 5 = 12$$
$$x = 12 - 5$$
$$x = 7$$

2. Line parallel to a side of a triangle

In the given triangle, the points D and E divide the side [AB] into 3 equal parts.

If lines through D and E are drawn parallel to [BC], then the points F and G will also divide the side [AC] into 3 equal parts.

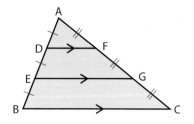

The example above can be extended to include any ratio $s : t$ as shown below.

In the given triangle, X divides the side [AB] in the ratio $s : t$.

If XY is parallel to BC, then Y will divide [AC] also in the ratio $s : t$.

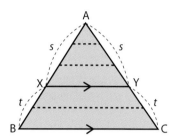

The diagram above illustrates a a very important and useful geometric result which is given on the right.

Theorem

A line drawn parallel to one side of a triangle divides the other two sides in the same ratio.

Remember

In a triangle ABC in which XY∥BC, the following ratios are always true:

(i) $\dfrac{|AX|}{|XB|} = \dfrac{|AY|}{|YC|}$

(ii) $\dfrac{|AB|}{|AX|} = \dfrac{|AC|}{|AY|}$

(iii) $\dfrac{|AB|}{|XB|} = \dfrac{|AC|}{|YC|}$

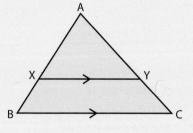

Example 2

In the given triangle, DE∥BC.
If $|AD| = 8$, $|DB| = 4$ and $|AC| = 9$, find $|AE|$.

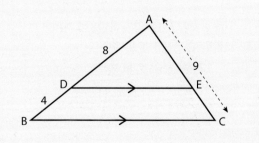

Generally we start the ratio with the side that we require.

$$\frac{|AE|}{|AC|} = \frac{|AD|}{|AB|}$$

$$\frac{|AE|}{9} = \frac{8}{12} \quad \dots \ |AB| = 8 + 4 = 12$$

$$12|AE| = 8 \times 9$$

$$|AE| = \frac{8 \times 9}{12} = \frac{72}{12} = 6 \quad \text{i.e. } |AE| = 6$$

The **converse** of the theorem on the previous page is also true and is stated on the right.

Converse of theorem

If a line cuts two sides of a triangle in the same ratio, then that line is parallel to the third side of the triangle.

Exercise 16.2

1. Find the value of x in each of the following figures where arrows indicate parallel lines.

(i)

(ii)

(iii)

2. In each of the given figures, the parallel lines ℓ, m and n cut equal intercepts on the transversals p and q.
   Find the values of x and y in each figure.

(i)

(ii)

(iii)

(iv)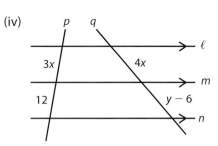

3. The given parallel lines ℓ, m and n cut equal intercepts on the transversals p and q, as shown.

   If $|BC| + |EF| = 3$ cm, find the value of a.

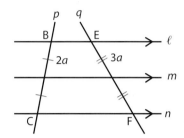

4. Examine the given diagram and then work out the values of x and y.

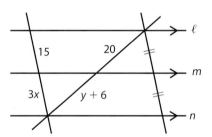

5. a, b and c are parallel lines.
   p, q and r are three transversals intersecting a, b and c.
   $|DE| = |EF|$, $|GH| = 8$ cm and $|JK| = 7$ cm.

   Find   (i) $|HI|$ (ii) $|GJ|$.

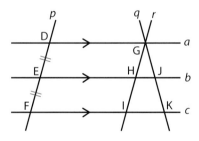

6. In each of the following triangles, the arrows indicate that the lines are parallel. Find the length of the line segment marked x in each triangle:

(i)

(ii)

(iii)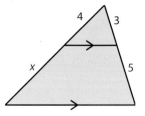

7. Find the length of the line segment marked *a* in each of the following triangles, where the arrows indicate parallel lines:

(i)

(ii)

(iii)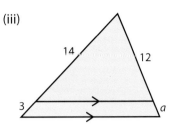

8. Find the values of *x*, *y* and *z* in the following triangles, where the arrows indicate parallel lines:

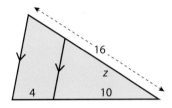

9. In the given triangle, DE∥BC.

|AD| = 8,
|DB| = 4,
|AC| = 9.
Find |AE|.

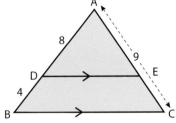

10. In the given diagram, DE∥BC.

If $\dfrac{|AD|}{|DB|} = \dfrac{2}{1}$ and |AE| = 14 cm,

find |EC|.

11. In the given triangle, XY∥BC.

If $\dfrac{|AY|}{|YC|} = \dfrac{7}{3}$ and |AB| = 15 cm,

find |AX|.

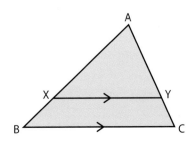

12. In the given triangle, MN∥QR.

If $\dfrac{|PR|}{|RN|} = \dfrac{8}{3}$ and $|PQ| = 33$ cm, find

(i) $|PM|$ (ii) $\dfrac{|PQ|}{|MQ|}$

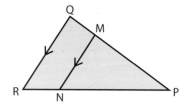

13. In the given triangle, XY∥ST.

If $|XS| = 5$ cm, $|YT| = 6$ cm and $|RS| = 12$ cm, find $|RT|$.

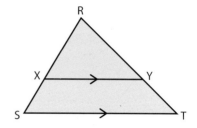

14. In the given figure, BC∥DE.

Find: (i) $|DE|$
        (ii) $|AE|$

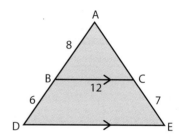

15. Explain why the triangles ABC and ADE are similar.

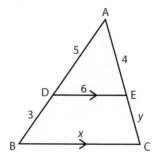

(i) Fill in the missing parts in these ratios:

$$\frac{|AD|}{|AB|} = \frac{|AE|}{\boxed{}} = \frac{|DE|}{\boxed{}}$$

(ii) Use these ratios to find the values of x and y.

16. A group of students were trying to find the distance between two trees on opposite sides of a river using pegs, a measuring tape and a large amount of string. They align the pegs in a particular way, take several measurements and sketch this diagram. On the diagram, A and B are the trees and C, D and E are the pegs.

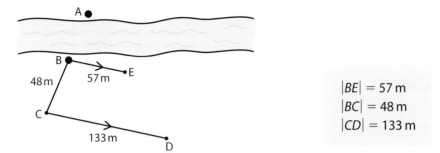

$|BE| = 57$ m
$|BC| = 48$ m
$|CD| = 133$ m

(i) In what way must the pegs and the trees be aligned if the students are to use these measurements to calculate $|AB|$?

(ii) Calculate the distance between the trees.

(iii) Another group of students repeats the activity. They have a similar diagram but different measurements. Their measurements are $|BE| = 40$ m and $|BC| = 9$ m. Based on the value of $|AB|$ that the first group got, what measurement will this second group have for $|CD|$?

Section 16.3 Angles and circles

The diagrams below will help you understand the meanings of the terms frequently used when dealing with circles.

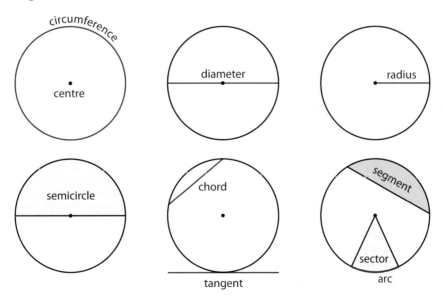

1. The angle in a semicircle

The shaded angle shown is called the angle in a semicircle because [AB] is a diameter. We will show below that the angle in a semicircle is a right angle.

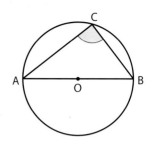

Explanation

In the given circle,

$$|OB| = |OA| = |OC| = \text{radius.}$$

The angles marked x are equal because the triangle AOB is isosceles.

Similarly, the angles marked y are equal.

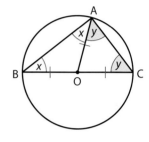

$2x + 2y$ make up the three angles of the △ABC.

$$\therefore \qquad 2x + 2y = 180°$$
$$\therefore \quad |\angle x| + |\angle y| = 90°$$
$$\text{Thus,} \qquad |\angle BAC| = 90°$$

The angle in a semicircle is a right angle.

Example 1

A, B and C are three points on a circle with centre O.
If $|\angle OCB| = 65°$, find

(i) $|\angle OBC|$ (ii) $|\angle AOB|$ (iii) $|\angle OBA|$.

(i) The triangle OCB is isosceles since $|OC| = |OB| = $ radius.
$$\therefore |\angle OBC| = |\angle OCB| = 65°$$

(ii) $|\angle BOC| = 180° - 65° - 65°$
$$\therefore |\angle BOC| = 50°$$
$$\therefore |\angle AOB| = 180° - 50° = 130°$$

(iii) Since $|OA| = |OB| = $ radius, $|\angle OAB| = |\angle OBA| = x°$
$$\therefore x + x + 130° = 180° \dots |\angle AOB| = 130°$$
$$2x = 50°$$
$$x = 25°$$
$$|\angle OBA| = 25°$$

Note: Many of the problems dealing with angles in circles will involve identifying isosceles triangles. These isosceles triangles occur when the two equal sides consist of radii. Two isosceles triangles are shown in the given circle.

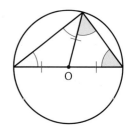

2. Angle at the centre of a circle and angle at the circumference

In the given diagram, O is the centre of the circle.
The angle AOB is said to be at the centre of the circle and **standing on the arc AB**.
The angle ACB is at the circumference of the circle, also standing on the arc AB.

A very important theorem linking the angle at the centre of a circle and the angle at the circumference is stated below.

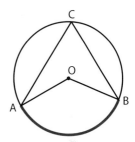

> **Theorem**
> The angle subtended at the centre of a circle is twice the angle at the circumference.

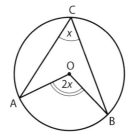

> The formal proof of this theorem is given in Section 7.4.

$$|\angle AOB| = 2|\angle ACB|$$

Corollaries

Some very important deductions or corollaries result from the theorem above.

> **Corollary 1**
> Angles in the same segment are equal.

Explanation
The angles x and y are both standing on the arc AB.

$$|\angle x| = \tfrac{1}{2}|\angle AOB| \quad \text{and} \quad |\angle y| = \tfrac{1}{2}|\angle AOB|$$

$$\therefore \ |\angle x| = |\angle y|$$

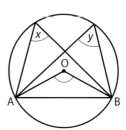

Cyclic quadrilaterals

The figure in the diagram on the right is called a **cyclic quadrilateral** because all the vertices are on the circle.

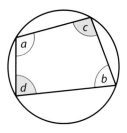

> **Corollary 2**
> The opposite angles of a cyclic quadrilateral add to 180°.

$a + b = 180°$
$c + d = 180°$

Explanation

The diagram shows that

$$2x + 2y = 360°$$
$$\therefore\ x + y = 180°$$
$$\therefore\ |\angle ABC| + |\angle ADC| = 180°$$

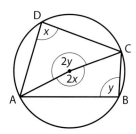

> **Corollary 3**
> The angle in a semicircle is a right angle.

Earlier in this section, we showed that the angle in a semicircle is a right angle.
Here is another way of showing the truth of this statement.

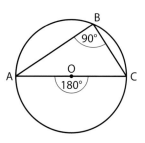

$$|\angle ABC| = \tfrac{1}{2}|\angle AOC|$$
$$\therefore\ |\angle ABC| = \tfrac{1}{2}(180°)$$
$$|\angle ABC| = 90°$$

> **Corollary 4**
> If the angle standing on a chord [BC] at some point of the circle is a right angle, then [BC] is a diameter.

Example 2

In the given diagram, O is the centre of the circle.
Find the measures of the angles *a* and *b*.

$|\angle a| = 48°$ ... angles standing on the same arc

$|\angle b| = 2 \times 48°$ ... angle at centre double angle at

$\quad\quad = 96°$ circumference standing on the same arc

Example 3

In the given figure, O is the centre of the circle
and $|\angle AOB| = 80°$.

Find   (i) $|\angle ACB|$ (ii) $|\angle ADB|$.

(i) $|\angle ACB| = \frac{1}{2}|\angle AOB|$ ... angle at centre

$\quad\quad\quad = \frac{1}{2}(80°) = 40°$

(ii) $|\angle ADB| + |\angle ACB| = 180°$... ADBC is a cyclic quadrilateral

$\quad |\angle ADB| + 40° = 180°$

$\quad |\angle ADB| = 140°$

Example 4

In the given diagram, O is the centre of the
circle, $|\angle AOB| = 110°$ and $|\angle OBC| = 30°$.

Find   (i) $|\angle ACB|$ (ii) $|\angle OAC|$.

(i) $|\angle AOB| = 2|\angle ACB|$ ...   angle at centre is twice angle

$\quad\quad 110° = 2|\angle ACB|$ at circumference

$\quad |\angle ACB| = \frac{1}{2}(110°) = 55°$

(ii) To find $|\angle OAC|$, join CO, as shown.

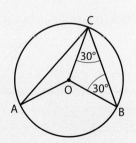

$\quad |\angle OBC| = |\angle OCB| = 30°$ ... $|OB| = |OC| = $ radius

$\quad |\angle ACB| = 55°$ ... from (i) above

$\quad \therefore |\angle OCA| = 55° - 30°$, i.e., $25°$

$\quad$ But $|\angle OAC| = |\angle OCA|$, since $|OA| = |OC| = $ radius

$\quad \therefore |\angle OAC| = 25°$

Exercise 16.3

1. [AB] is a diameter of the given circle.

    (i) Explain why ∠ACB is a right angle.

    (ii) Find |∠CAB|.

    (iii) Describe the triangle ABC in two ways.

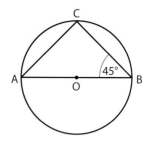

2. Find the value of x in each of these circles where O is the centre:

  (i)

  (ii)

  (iii)

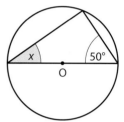

3. Write down the sizes of the angles marked with a letter in each of the following circles with O as centre:

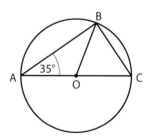

4. In the given circle, O is the centre.

    (i) Why is |OA| = |OB|?

    (ii) What is |∠ABC|?

    (iii) What is |∠ABO|?

    (iv) Now find |∠OBC|.

    (v) Explain why the triangle OBC is isosceles.

5. Find the value of the angle marked x in each of the following circles where O is centre:

  (i)

  (ii)

  (iii)

6. Find the measure of the angle marked with a letter in each of the following circles where O is the centre:

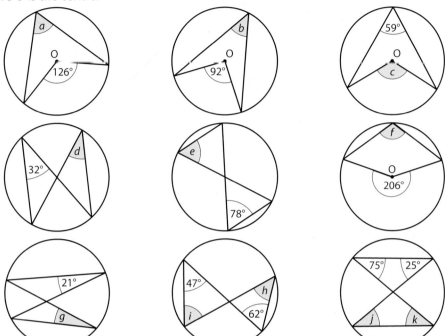

7. Find the measure of the angle marked with a letter in the following cyclic quadrilaterals:

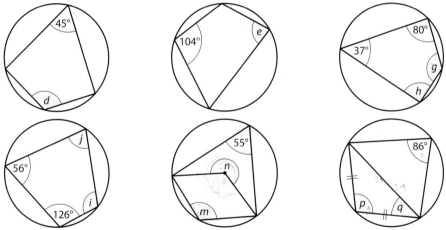

8. Find the measure of the angle marked with a letter in each of these circles.

9. In the given diagram, O is the centre of the circle, $|\angle AOB| = 140°$ and $|\angle OAC| = 30°$.

Find   (i) $|\angle ACB|$ (ii) $|\angle OCA|$

          (iii) $|\angle OCB|$ (iv) $|\angle OBC|$

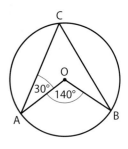

10. Find the measures of the angles marked x and y in the following circles with O as centre:

(i)

(ii)

(iii)

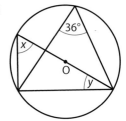

11. Calculate the measure of $\angle BDC$ in the given diagram.

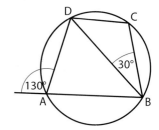

12. Find the measure of the angle marked x in each of the following circles with O as centre.

(i)

(ii)

(iii)

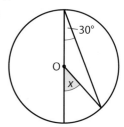

13. In the given diagram, $|\angle RPQ| = 30°$ and $|\angle PSQ| = 50°$.

   (i)   Name another angle that is 30°.

   (ii)   Hence find the measure of the angle marked x.

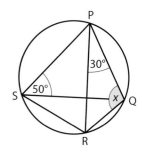

14. PQRS is a cyclic quadrilateral with PQ∥SR.
If $|\angle QSR| = 33°$ and $|\angle SQR| = 81°$,
show that $|PS| = |PQ|$.

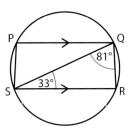

15. The diagonals of the cyclic quadrilateral
shown on the right meet at the point X.
If $|AX| = |XB|$, prove that AB is parallel to DC.

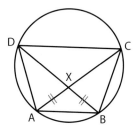

16. The indicated angles in the diagram
are equal in measure.
Prove that $\angle QPS$ is a right angle.

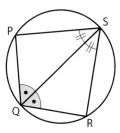

17. The chords [AC] and [BD] intersect at the
point X, as shown.
Prove that the triangles AXB and CXD
are similar.

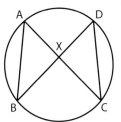

18. A, B, C and D are four points on a circle as shown.
[AD] bisects $\angle BAC$.
P is the point of intersection of AD and BC.

   (i) Show that the triangles ADB and APC are similar.

   (ii) Hence show that
$$|AC| \cdot |BD| = |AD| \cdot |PC|.$$

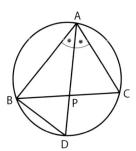

19. In the given diagram, O is the centre of the circle.

Prove that $x + y = 90°$.

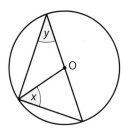

Section 16.4 Proofs of theorems 4, 6, 9, 14, 19 ————

Geometry results or **theorems** are proved in a formal or structured way by using previously established results and axioms to explain the steps that we take. This method of proving geometric results was first used by a Greek mathematician named Euclid about 300 BC.

The proofs of numerous theorems are contained in his famous book on geometry called *Elements*. Today, over 2000 years later, we still use Euclid's approach to solve many problems in geometry.

A result that follows logically from a theorem is called a **corollary**. An important circle theorem states that the angle at the centre of a circle is double the angle at the circumference of the circle. An obvious deduction or corollary to this theorem states that the angle in a semicircle is a right angle.

Pythagoras' theorem states that the square of the hypotenuse is equal to the sum of the squares of the other two sides. The **converse** of this theorem states that if the square of one side of a triangle is equal to the sum of the squares of the other two sides, then the angle opposite the first side is a right angle.

If $A > B$ and $B > C$, that **implies** that $A > C$.
We use $\Rightarrow$ to denote implies.
Thus, if $6 > 4$ and $4 > 2$
$\Rightarrow 6 > 2$

> An **axiom** is a statement accepted without proof. 'The angles in a straight line add to 180°' is an example of an axiom.

> A **theorem** is a statement that can be shown to be true through the use of axioms and logical argument.

> A **corollary** is a statement attached to a theorem which has been proven and follows obviously from it.

> The **converse** of a theorem is the opposite or reverse of the theorem.

> In mathematics, the word **implies** means that when one result is established, another result follows logically from it.

In this section, the formal proofs of five theorems on your course are given. You may be asked to reproduce these proofs in your examination. You will be familiar with the results of these theorems from the earlier sections of this chapter and also from Chapter 6. The various geometrical problems you solved used the results in these theorems.

Theorem 4	The angles in any triangle add to 180°.

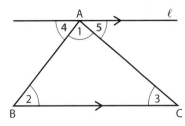

Given: The triangle ABC with angles marked 1, 2 and 3.

To prove: $|\angle 1| + |\angle 2| + |\angle 3| = 180°$.

Construction: Draw a line ℓ through A parallel to BC.
Mark the angles 4 and 5.

Proof: $|\angle 2| = |\angle 4|$ and $|\angle 3| = |\angle 5|$ … alternate angles

$|\angle 4| + |\angle 1| + |\angle 5| = 180°$ … straight angle

For $\angle 4$ and $\angle 5$, substitute $\angle 2$ and $\angle 3$.

$\therefore |\angle 2| + |\angle 1| + |\angle 3| = 180°$

i.e. $|\angle 1| + |\angle 2| + |\angle 3| = 180°$

Theorem 6	Each exterior angle of a triangle is equal to the sum of the interior opposite angles.

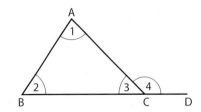

Given: A triangle ABC with the side [BC] extended to the point D.
The angles marked 1, 2, 3 and 4 are also given.

To prove: $|\angle 4| = |\angle 1| + |\angle 2|$

Proof: $|\angle 3| + |\angle 4| = 180°|$ … straight angle

$|\angle 1| + |\angle 2| + |\angle 3| = 180°$ … angles in a triangle

$\therefore |\angle 3| + |\angle 4| = |\angle 1| + |\angle 2| + |\angle 3|$

$\therefore |\angle 4| = |\angle 1| + |\angle 2|$ … subtract $\angle 3$ from each side

Theorem 9	In a parallelogram, opposite sides are equal and opposite angles are equal.

Given: A parallelogram ABCD.

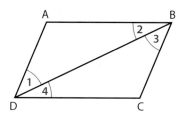

To prove: $|AB| = |DC|$ and $|AD| = |BC|$.

Construction: Draw the diagonal [BD] and mark in the angles 1, 2, 3 and 4.

Proof: In the triangles ABD and BCD,

$|\angle 1| = |\angle 3|$ ... alternate angles as AB∥DC

$|\angle 2| = |\angle 4|$ ... alternate angles

$|DB| = |DB|$ ... common side

∴ △s ABD and BCD are congruent ... ASA

∴ $|AB| = |DC|$ and $|AD| = |BC|$ ... corresponding sides

Also, $|\angle DAB| = |\angle DCB|$ ... corresponding angles

and $|\angle ABC| = |\angle ADC|$ ... $|\angle 2| + |\angle 3| = |\angle 1| + |\angle 4|$

Thus, opposite sides and opposite angles of a parallelogram are equal.

Theorem 14 **Theorem of Pythagoras**	In a right-angled triangle, the square of the hypotenuse is equal to the sum of the squares of the other two sides.

Given: A triangle ABC in which A is a right angle.

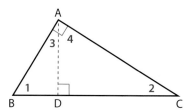

To prove: $|BC|^2 = |AB|^2 + |AC|^2$.

Construction: Draw AD ⊥ BC and mark in the angles 1, 2, 3 and 4.

Proof: Consider the triangles ABC and ABD.

∠1 is common to both △s

$|\angle BAC| = |\angle ADB| = 90°$

∴ △ABC and △ABD are similar.

∴ $\dfrac{|BC|}{|AB|} = \dfrac{|AB|}{|BD|} \Rightarrow |AB|^2 = |BC| \cdot |BD|$ ... Ⓐ

334

Now consider the triangles ABC and ADC.

∠2 is common to both.

$|\angle BAC| = |\angle ADC| = 90°$

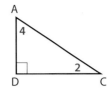

∴ △ABC and △ADC are similar.

$\therefore \dfrac{|AC|}{|DC|} = \dfrac{|BC|}{|AC|} \Rightarrow |AC|^2 = |BC| \cdot |DC| \dots$ Ⓑ

Adding Ⓐ and Ⓑ we get:

$$|AB|^2 + |AC|^2 = |BC| \cdot |BD| + |BC| \cdot |DC|$$
$$= |BC|\big[|BD| + |DC|\big]$$
$$= |BC|\big[|BC|\big] \dots \text{ } |BD| + |DC| = |BC|$$
$$|AB|^2 + |AC|^2 = |BC|^2$$

i.e. $|BC|^2 = |AB|^2 + |AC|^2$

Theorem 19	The angle at the centre of a circle standing on a given arc is twice the angle at any point of the circle standing on the same arc.

Given:

A circle k with centre O.

A, B and C are three points on k.

∠AOB is at the centre and

∠ACB is at the circumference.

Both stand on the arc AB.

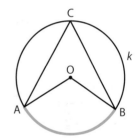

To prove: $|\angle AOB| = 2|\angle ACB|$.

Construction: Join C to O and extend to D.
Label the angles.

Proof: $|\angle 3| = |\angle 5|$ as △AOC is isosceles

and $|\angle 1| = |\angle 3| + |\angle 5| \dots$ exterior angle is equal to the sum of interior opposite angles

∴ $|\angle 1| = 2|\angle 3|$

Similarly, $|\angle 2| = 2|\angle 4|$

Adding: $|\angle 1| + |\angle 2| = 2|\angle 3| + 2|\angle 4|$

$|\angle 1| + |\angle 2| = 2\big[|\angle 3| + |\angle 4|\big]$

∴ $|\angle AOB| = 2|\angle ACB|$

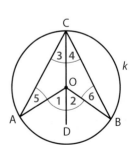

Test yourself 16

1. **(a)** In the given circle, O is the centre, $|\angle ACD| = 65°$ and $|AB| = |BC|$.

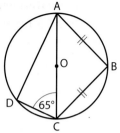

    (i) Name two right angles in the figure.

    (ii) Find $|\angle BAC|$.

    (iii) Find $|\angle BAD|$.

(b) In the given triangles, the marked angles are equal.

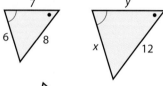

    (i) Explain why the two triangles are similar.

    (ii) Find the values of x and y.

(c) In the given diagram, the arrows indicate that the lines are parallel. Find the lengths of the line segments marked a and b.

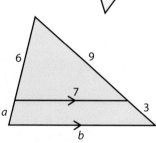

2. **(a)** Find the measures of the angles marked by letters in each of these circles:

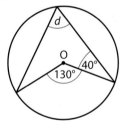

(b) In the given similar triangles, equal angles are marked. Find the values of a and b.

(c) In the given diagram, DE$\parallel$BC. Find the value of x and the value of y.

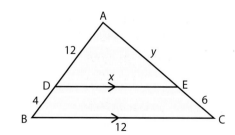

336

3. (a) In the diagram, ℓ, m and n are parallel lines. They make intercepts of the indicated lengths on the lines j and k.

AB is parallel to j.

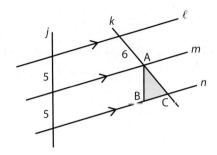

   (i) Write down the length of [AB].

   (ii) Write down the length of [AC].

(b) In the diagram, PRS is an equilateral triangle and $|\angle PRQ| = 36°$. Find

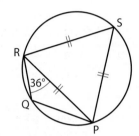

   (i) $|\angle QRS|$

   (ii) $|\angle PQR|$

   (iii) $|\angle QPS|$.

(c) A 3.5 m ladder leans on a 2.4 m fence. One end is on the ground and the other end touches a vertical wall 2.9 m from the ground. How far is the bottom of the ladder from the fence?

Give your answer in metres, correct to one decimal place.

4. (a) Find the value of x and the value of y in each of these circles with O as centre:

  (i)

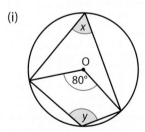

  (ii)

(b) In the diagram, VZ is parallel to WY.

Find   (i) $|WY|$

       (ii) $|VW|$

       (iii) $|VX|$.

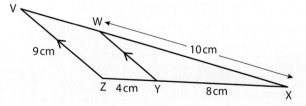

(c) Colin calculated the width, w, of a river by taking the measurements shown and then using similar triangles.
What answer should Colin get for the width?

4 m

16 m   62 m

5. (a) In the given triangle, DE∥BC.
Find |DE|.

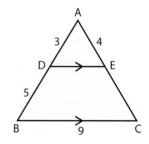

(b) A path up to the carpark from the beach has a constant slope of 2 in 7. This means that for every 7 m horizontally, the path rises 2 m. The carpark is 60 m horizontally from the beach end of the path. How high in the sand-dunes is the carpark?
Give your answer correct to the nearest whole number.

carpark
x m
2 m
53 m   7 m
beach

(c) In this circle, chords [PR] and [QS] intersect at T.
  (i) Prove that the triangles PQT and SRT are similar.
  (ii) Hence find |TS|.

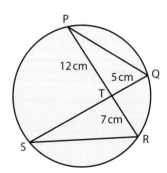

6. (a) Find the measure of the angles marked x and y in each of the following diagrams.

(i)

(ii)

(b) Sarah found the height of a tree by placing a 30 cm ruler upright in the shadow of the tree. She placed the ruler so that the end of its shadow was at the same place as the end of the shadow of the tree. How high was this tree? Give your answer in metres, correct to one decimal place.

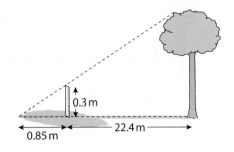

0.3 m
22.4 m
0.85 m

(c) In the diagram, ABCD is a parallelogram and $|\angle ABC| = 60°$.

Explain why $\triangle ADE$ is an equilateral triangle.

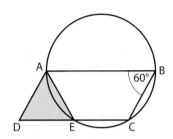

A
B
60°
D
E
C

7. (a) In the given figure, $|EC| = 9$ cm, $|AB| = 8$ cm and $|BE| = 15$ cm. Find $|DE|$.

A
8 cm
D
B
E
C
15 cm
9 cm

(b) A, B and C are pegs on the bank of a canal which has parallel straight sides. C and D are directly opposite each other. $|AB| = 30$ m and $|BC| = 140$ m. When I walk from A directly away from the bank, I reach a point E, 25 m from A, where E, B and D line up. How wide is the canal?

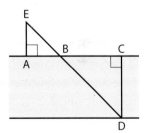

E
B
C
A
D

(c) Two surveyors estimate the height of a nearby hill. One stands 5 m away from the other on horizontal ground, holding a 3 m stick vertically. The other surveyor finds a "line of sight" to the top of the hill, and observes that this line passes the vertical stick at 2.4 m. The distance from the stick to the top of the hill is 1500 m (as measured by laser equipment).

How high, correct to the nearest metre, is their estimate of the height of the hill?

1500 m
x m
2.4 m
5 m

Key words

cylinder	prism	curved surface area	sphere
hemisphere	cone	vertical height	slant height

Section 17.1 The cylinder

When dealing with prisms in an earlier chapter, we found that the volume of a prism is the area of the base (cross-section) multiplied by the height.

Volume of prism = Area of base × height
$$= A \times h$$

> A cylinder can be thought of as a prism whose cross-section is a circle.

> Since we know how to find the area of a circle, we can use the above formula to find the volume of a cylinder.

> The formula $V = Ah$ becomes $V = \pi r^2 h$, since $A = \pi r^2$.

Curved surface area of cylinder

To calculate the area of the curved surface, imagine that the cylinder is hollow. If we cut the curved surface along the dotted line and flattened it out, it would form a rectangle.

The area of this rectangle would be the same as the area of the curved surface.

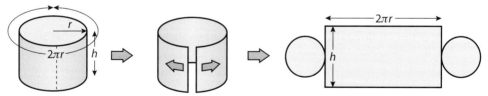

From the series of diagrams above, we see that the curved surface area is equivalent to a rectangle that has a length equal to the circumference of the circle and a width equal to the height of the cylinder. Using the formula for the area of a rectangle, we obtain:

Curved surface area $= 2\pi rh$

The total surface area = curved surface area + area of 2 circles
$$= 2\pi rh + 2\pi r^2$$

Cylinder	Volume $= \pi r^2 h$ Curved surface area $= 2\pi rh$ Total surface area $= 2\pi rh + 2\pi r^2$	

Example 1

Find   (i)   the volume
      (ii)   the total surface area
of the cylinder shown, taking $\pi = \frac{22}{7}$.

Volume $= \pi r^2 h$

$= \pi \times 7^2 \times 24 \quad \ldots r = \frac{14\,cm}{2},$ i.e. 7 cm

$= \frac{22}{7_1} \times \frac{7^1}{1} \times \frac{7}{1} \times \frac{24}{1}$

Volume $= 3696\,cm^3$

Total surface area $= 2\pi rh + 2\pi r^2$

$= 2 \times \frac{22}{7} \times 7 \times 24 + 2 \times \frac{22}{7} \times 7^2$

$= 1056 + 308$

Total surface area $= 1364\,cm^2$

Example 2

The volume of a cylinder is $1232\,cm^3$.
If its height is 8 cm, find the length of its radius taking $\pi = 3.14$.
Give your answer correct to the nearest centimetre.

Volume $= 1232\,cm^3 \Rightarrow \pi r^2 h = 1232$

$3.14 \times r^2 \times 8 = 1232$

$r^2 = \dfrac{1232}{3.14 \times 8}$

$r^2 = 49.04$

$r = \sqrt{49.04} = 7.0029$

$r = 7\,cm$

The radius $= 7$ cm

Exercise 17.1

1. Taking $\pi = \frac{22}{7}$, find the volume of each of the cylinders shown below:

(i)

12 cm

7 cm

(ii)

14 cm

16 cm

(iii)

30 cm

28 cm

2. Find the total surface areas of the solid cylinders in Question **1.** above, taking $\pi = \frac{22}{7}$.

3. Taking $\pi = 3.14$, find the volume of each of these cylinders.
Give your answers correct to the nearest whole numbers.

(i)   30 cm 24 cm

(ii)   8 m 4 m

(iii)   6 cm 50 cm

4. Taking $\pi = \frac{22}{7}$, find the volume of the cylinder shown on the right.

If 1 litre = 1000 cm³, find the capacity of the cylinder, correct to the nearest litre.

  40 cm 28 cm

5. The figure on the right shows a solid cylinder cut along its diameter.
Taking $\pi = 3.14$, find the volume of the figure in cm³.

  5 cm 18 cm

6. The volume of the given cylinder is 350π cm³.
   (i) Write down the formula for the volume of a cylinder.
   (ii) Write in all the known values in the formula, given that the height is 14 cm.
   (iii) Now find the length of the radius of the cylinder.

  14 cm Volume = 350π cm³

7. The volume of a cylinder is 288π cm³.
If the height of the cylinder is 8 cm, find its radius.

8. The volume of a cylinder is 360π cm³.
If the radius of the cylinder is 6 cm, find its height.

9. Write down the formula for the curved surface area of a cylinder.
The curved surface area of a certain cylinder is 110 cm².
If the height of the cylinder is 5 cm, find the length of the radius correct to 1 decimal place.

10. The area of the base of a cylinder is 154 cm².
If the volume of the cylinder is 770 cm³, find its height.

11. The volume of a cylinder is 1848 cm³.
If the height of the cylinder is 12 cm, find its radius, taking $\pi = \frac{22}{7}$.

12. A hole of radius 4 cm is bored through this
rectangular solid, as shown.
Using the π key on your calculator, find the
volume of the remaining solid, correct to
the nearest cm³.

13. A cylindrical metal pipe has an external diameter
of 6 cm and an internal diameter of 4 cm, as shown.
The pipe is 1 m long.
Taking $\pi = 3.14$, find

  (i) the volume of the pipe in cm³
  (ii) the mass of the pipe, in kg, if 1 cm³ of the metal has a mass of 9 g.

14. A cylindrical pencil holder has a diameter
4 cm and height 14 cm. Taking $\pi = \frac{22}{7}$,
find the volume of the holder in cm³.
Eight pencil holders are packed tightly
into a rectangular box as shown.
Find the volume of this box in cm³.

15. Rain falls into a flat rectangular container
88 cm by 42 cm by 6 cm. When the
container is full, it is poured into an empty
cylinder of radius 21 cm. The depth of
water in the cylinder is h cm.
Find the value of h.
Take $\pi = \frac{22}{7}$.

16. This is the metal frame of a greenhouse.
It consists of semicircles mounted on
rectangular frames.
  (i) Find the area of the material needed
       to cover this greenhouse.
       Exclude the floor and door.
  (ii) Calculate the volume of the greenhouse in
       cubic metres.
       Use the π key on your calculator and give
       each answer to the nearest whole number.

17. A semicircular shape of radius 9 cm is
cut from a solid cube of side 18 cm.

   Find   (i)   the volume of the remaining solid
          (ii) the surface area of the remaining solid.

   Give each answer correct to the nearest whole number.

Section 17.2 The sphere and hemisphere

The figure on the right is a sphere of radius r.
The Greek mathematician and engineer, **Archimedes** (born 287 BC),
found that the volume of a sphere is equal to two thirds the volume
of the smallest cylinder which encloses it.

Here is how Archimedes made his discovery.
He used a sphere of radius r and a cylinder of base radius r and height $2r$.

| He placed the sphere in the cylinder and filled it up with water. | He removed the sphere and found that the water filled only $\frac{1}{3}$ of the cylinder. |

$$\begin{aligned}
\text{Volume of sphere} &= \tfrac{2}{3}\text{ volume of cylinder} \\
&= \tfrac{2}{3} \times \pi r^2 h \\
&= \tfrac{2}{3} \times \pi r^2 (2r) \quad \ldots h = 2r \\
&= \tfrac{4}{3} \pi r^3
\end{aligned}$$

1. The sphere

Volume $= \frac{4}{3}\pi r^3$

Surface area $= 4\pi r^2$

2. The hemisphere

Volume $= \frac{2}{3}\pi r^3$

Surface area of solid hemisphere $= 3\pi r^2$

Example 1

Taking $\pi = 3.14$, find   (i)   the volume
                       (ii)   the surface area

   of the given sphere.

(i)   Volume $= \frac{4}{3}\pi r^3$

          $= \frac{4}{3} \times 3.14 \times 8^3$ ... $r = 8$ cm

          $= 2143.57$ cm^3

          $= 2143.6$ cm^3

(ii)   Surface area $= 4\pi r^2$

            $= 4 \times 3.14 \times 8^2$

            $= 803.84$ cm^2

            $= 803.8$ cm^2

Example 2

A sphere of radius 4 cm is dropped into a cylinder
partly filled with water. When the sphere is completely
submerged, the level of water rises h cm.
If the radius of the cylinder is 8 cm, find the value of h.

In the given diagram, the volume of the sphere is
equal to the volume of the shaded cylinder of
height h cm.

Volume of sphere $=$ Volume of cylinder

$\Rightarrow \quad \frac{4}{3}\pi r^3 = \pi r^2 h$

$\Rightarrow \frac{4}{3}\pi(4)^3 = \pi(8)^2 h$

$\Rightarrow \frac{4}{3} \times 64 = 64h$ ... divide both sides by π

$\Rightarrow \qquad \frac{4}{3} = h$ ... divide both sides by 64

$\therefore \quad h = \frac{4}{3} = 1\frac{1}{3}$

Note: In example 2 above, we are given two solids of equal volume, i.e., the volume of the
sphere equals the volume of the cylinder.

$$\Rightarrow \frac{4}{3}\pi(4)^3 = \pi(8)^2 h$$

Here both sides of the equation contain π.
When this occurs, we divide both sides by π and so there is no need to substitute a
value for π.

Exercise 17.2

1. Find the volume of each of these solids in cm^3.
   Take $\pi = 3.14$ and give each answer correct to 1 decimal place.

   (i)
   18 cm

   (ii)
   11 cm

   (iii)
   7 cm

2. Find the surface area of each of the figures above.
   Use the π key on your calculator and give each answer correct to the nearest whole number.

3. The length of the radius of a solid hemisphere is 5 cm.
   Find, in terms of π, (i) the volume
                              (ii) the total surface area
   of the hemisphere.

   5 cm

4. The volume of a sphere is 288π cm^3.
   (i) Find the length of the radius of the sphere.
   (ii) Find, in terms of π, its total surface area.

5. The surface area of a sphere is 616 cm^2. Taking $\pi = \frac{22}{7}$, find
   (i) the radius of the sphere   (ii) the volume of the sphere.

6. The surface area of a sphere is 36π cm^2.
   Find the volume of the sphere in terms of π.

7. A container is in the shape of a cylinder on top of a hemisphere, as shown. The cylinder has a radius of length 3 cm and the container has a total height of 15 cm.

   Calculate the volume of the container in cm^3, correct to the nearest whole number.

   3 cm
   15 cm

8. The cylinder and the sphere shown on the right have equal volumes.

Find the length of the radius of the cylinder, correct to the nearest centimetre.

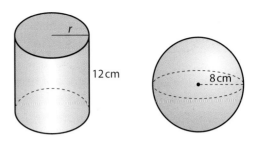

9. A cylinder has height $4\frac{1}{2}$ cm and radius length 2 cm. This cylinder has the same volume as a hemisphere. Find the radius of the hemisphere.

10. A basketball fits exactly into a cube which has sides equal in length to the diameter of the basketball. What percentage of the cube's volume does the basketball occupy?

Use the π key on your calculator and give your answer correct to the nearest whole number.

11. When a solid sphere of radius 6 cm is dropped into a cylinder partly filled with water, the level of the water rises h cm, as shown on the right.

If the diameter of the cylinder is 16 cm, find the value of h.

12. Three tennis balls, each of diameter 6 cm, just fit into a cylindrical can, as shown.

Find, in terms of π,
  (i) the volume of a tennis ball
  (ii) the volume of the cylindrical can
  (iii) the volume of the can not occupied by the tennis balls.

13. A sphere with radius of length 3 cm has a volume equal to eight times the volume of a sphere with radius of length r cm. Calculate r.

14. The height of a cylinder is equal to the length of its diameter.
The curved surface area of the cylinder is 100π cm². Calculate the height.

15. A wine glass is in the form of a hemisphere of radius 4 cm, as shown.
Find its volume in terms of π.

A full cylindrical container of wine is just sufficient to fill 21 of these wine glasses.
If the radius of the base of the cylinder is 8 cm, find its height.

16. Nine solid metal spheres, each of radius $1\frac{1}{2}$ cm, are dropped into a cylinder partly filled with water. If the spheres are totally immersed, find the increase in the height of the water if the radius of the cylinder is 3 cm.

17. (i) A container is in the shape of a cylinder on top of a hemisphere as shown. The cylinder has a radius of length 3 cm and the container has a total height of 15 cm. Calculate the volume of the container in terms of π.

(ii) If half the volume of the container is filled with liquid, calculate the height, h cm, of liquid in the container.

Section 17.3 The cone

The cone on the right is called a *right circular cone* as its vertex is directly above the centre of the base.
The perpendicular height $= h$
The slant height $= \ell$
The radius of the base $= r$
By the *Theorem of Pythagoras*, $\ell^2 = h^2 + r^2$

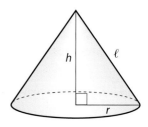

The diagram below shows three cones of base radius r and height h.
The cylinder has radius r and height h also.

If the three cones are filled and poured into the cylinder, they will exactly fill the cylinder.

$$\therefore \quad \text{volume of cone} = \tfrac{1}{3}\,\text{volume of cylinder}$$
$$= \tfrac{1}{3}\pi r^2 h$$

The Cone

Volume of a cone $= \tfrac{1}{3}\pi r^2 h$

Curved surface area $= \pi r \ell$

Total surface area of a solid cone $= \pi r \ell + \pi r^2$

Example 1

The height of a cone is 12 cm and the radius of the base is 5 cm.
Using the π key on your calculator, find correct to 1 decimal place,

(i) the volume (ii) the curved surface area of the cone.

By the Theorem of Pythagoras,
$$\ell^2 = 12^2 + 5^2$$
$$= 144 + 25 = 169$$
$$\therefore \quad \ell = \sqrt{169} = 13 \text{ cm}$$

Volume of cone $= \tfrac{1}{3}\pi r^2 h$
$$= \tfrac{1}{3} \times \pi \times 5^2 \times 12$$
$$= 314.2 \text{ cm}^3$$

Curved Surface Area $= \pi r \ell$
$$= \pi \times 5 \times 13$$
$$= 204.2 \text{ cm}^2$$

Example 2

A solid metal cylinder of radius 5 cm and height 12 cm is melted down and recast into a cone of base radius 10 cm.

Calculate the height of the cone.

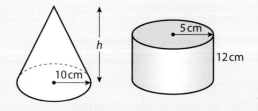

Volume of cone = volume of cylinder

$$\frac{1}{3}\pi r^2 h = \pi r^2 h$$

$$\frac{1}{3}\pi (10)^2 h = \pi \times (5)^2 \times 12$$

$$\frac{100h}{3} = 25 \times 12$$

$$100h = 3 \times 25 \times 12$$

$$h = \frac{3 \times 25 \times 12}{100} = 9 \text{ cm}$$

The height of the cone is 9 cm.

Exercise 17.3

In the following questions, take $\pi = 3.14$ or use the π key on your calculator unless otherwise stated.

1. (i) Find the volume of the cone shown on the right.
      Give your answer in cm³, correct to 1 decimal place.
   (ii) Use the Theorem of Pythagoras to find the slant height ℓ.
   (iii) Now find the total surface area of the solid cone, correct to the nearest cm².

2. Find, correct to the nearest whole number, the volume of a cone of base radius 8 cm and height 22 cm.

3. The given solid cone has base radius 5 cm and slant height 13 cm.
   (i) Find the height, h, of the cone.
   (ii) Find the curved surface area.
   (iii) Find the total surface area.
   (iv) Find the volume of the cone.

   Give your answers correct to 1 decimal place, where necessary.

4. The curved surface area of a cone is 112π cm².
   If the slant height of the cone is 14 cm, find the length of its radius.

5. The volume of a cone is 800π cm³.
   If the height of the cone is 24 cm, find the length of the radius.

6. A cone is attached to a hemisphere of radius 4 cm, as shown.
   If the total height of the object is 10 cm, find

   (i) the height of the cone
   (ii) the volume of the object in cm³, correct to
      one decimal place.

7. The volume of a cone is 6160 cm³.
   If the radius of the base of the cone is 14 cm, find its height. Take $\pi = \frac{22}{7}$.

8. The volumes of the given sphere and
   cone are equal.
   The dimensions of the cone are given.
   Find the length of the radius of the sphere.

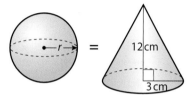

9. Express, in terms of π, the volume of a cylinder of height 12 cm and radius 4 cm.

   A cone of base radius 4 cm and height h cm has the same volume as the cylinder.
   Calculate the value of h.

10. A right circular cone of radius 6 cm and height 12 cm is
   totally immersed in a cylinder partly filled with water,
   as shown.

   Find, in terms of π, the volume of the cone.

   If the radius of the cylinder is 8 cm, find the value of h,
   the increase in the height of the water.

11. Work out the volume of the given shape.
   Leave your answer in terms of π.

12. The volume of a cone is $\dfrac{512\pi}{3}$ cm³.
   The height of the cone and its radius length are equal.
   Find the length of the radius.

13. A toy is made of a cone which fits exactly on top of a hemisphere, as shown in the diagram.
The radius length of the hemisphere is 6 cm and the volume of the cone is half the volume of the hemisphere.

    (i) Find the volume of the cone in terms of π and h, where h is the height of the cone.

    (ii) Find the height of the cone.

14. A cone has the same base radius as the radius of a sphere. If the volumes of the cone and the sphere are equal, by what factor is the height of the cone larger than its base radius?

15. A sphere has a radius of 5 cm.
A cone has a height of 8 cm.
The volume of the sphere is equal to the volume of the cone.

Calculate the radius of the base of the cone.
Give your answer, in centimetres, correct to two places of decimal.

16. Wax in the shape of a cylinder with radius of length 4 cm and height 36 cm is melted down. The resulting wax is formed into cone-shaped candles.
Each candle has height 6 cm and base of radius length 2 cm.

    (i) Calculate the number of candles that can be made, assuming that no wax is lost.

    (ii) The candles are placed, base down and in rows of six, in the smallest possible rectangular box.
Calculate, in cm^3, the volume (internal capacity) of the box.

17. The diagram shows a frozen yogurt cone enclosed in a paper wrapper. The area of the curved surface of the wrapper is 159 cm^2, and the radius of the base of the cone is 4 cm.

Find the slant height of the cone, giving your answer correct to one decimal place.

18. The diagram on the right represents the model of a rocket ship. The model is made from a solid cylinder and a solid cone. Both have a circular base of diameter 20 cm. The height of the cone is 24 cm.

    (i) Calculate the volume of the cone in terms of π.

    (ii) Find the height of the cylinder if the volume of the cylinder is 4 times the volume of the cone.

    (iii) Find the value of k if the volume of the cylinder of height k is half the volume of the whole solid model.

Test yourself 17

1. (a) Using $\pi = 3.14$, find

    (i) the volume

    (ii) the curved surface area of the given cylinder, correct to the nearest whole number.

(b) The cylinder and the cone shown below have equal volumes.

    (i) Find the volume of the cylinder in terms of π.

    (ii) Calculate h, the vertical height of the cone.

2. (a) (i) Soup is contained in a cylindrical saucepan which has an internal radius of length 12 cm. The depth of the soup is 18 cm.
Calculate, in terms of π, the volume of soup in the saucepan.

    (ii) A ladle, in the shape of a hemisphere with internal radius of length 6 cm, is used to serve the soup.
Calculate, in terms of π, the volume of soup contained in one full ladle.

    (iii) How many full ladles of soup does the saucepan contain?

(b) A loading chute in a flour mill loads directly into a feeding bin which is in the shape of a right circular cone as shown.

The curved surface area of the bin is 350 m² and its slant height is 18.2 m.

If a lid for the bin is needed, find the area of the lid required to cover the bin. Give your answer correct to the nearest m².

3. (a) The given shape consists of a cylinder and cone.

    (i) Find the volume of the cylinder in terms of π.

    (ii) Find the volume of the cone in terms of π.

    Hence find the volume of the shape, correct to the nearest cm³.

(b) A shape is made by joining a hemisphere of radius r cm to a cone of radius r cm. The height of the cone is $2r$ cm.
Find an expression, in terms of r and π, for the volume of the shape.

4. (a) (i) The volume of a sphere is 36π cm³.
Find the radius of the sphere.

(ii) When the sphere is fully immersed in a cylinder of water, the level of the water rises by 2.25 cm.
Find the radius of the cylinder.

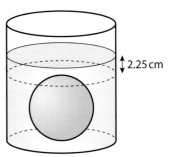

(b) The formula for the volume of a cone is $\frac{1}{3} \times$ area of base $\times$ height.
The volume of cone A is 33 cm³. It is 9 cm tall.
Cone B is 12 cm tall and the area of its base is the same as the area of the base of cone A.
What is the volume of cone B ?

5. (a) The radius of the base of a cone and the radius of a sphere are each 6 cm in length.
If the volume of the cone is equal to the volume of the sphere, find the height of the cone.

(b) The diagram below shows a solid rectangular block of metal, 75 cm by 11 cm by 6 cm. It is melted down and recast into cylindrical rods of length 25 cm and radius of length 1 cm, as shown.
Calculate the number of complete rods that can be made from the block.

6. **(a)** A cylindrical water tank has internal
diameter 40 cm and height 50 cm.
A cylindrical mug has internal diameter
8 cm and height 10 cm.

  (i) Find the volume of the tank
  in terms of π.

  (ii) Find the volume of the mug
  in terms of π.

  (iii) How many mugs can be filled from a full tank?

(b) A horse's drinking trough is 2 m long and
has a cross-section as shown alongside.
How long will it take to fill the trough if
water flows into it at a rate of 12 litres per minute?
Give your answer to the nearest minute.

7. **(a)** **(i)** What is the volume, correct to the nearest cm³,
  of this cylindrical can?

  (ii) Will it hold 1 litre of water?
   Explain your answer.

  (iii) If the height is doubled to 18 cm, how many complete litres would it hold?

  (iv) If the height was 9 cm, but the radius was doubled to 12 cm, how many
   complete litres would it then hold?

(b) A vitamin capsule is in the shape of a cylinder
with hemispherical ends. The length of the
capsule is 20 mm and the diameter is 6 mm.

  (i) Calculate the volume of the capsule, giving your
   answer correct to the nearest mm³.

A course of these vitamins consists of
24 capsules.
The capsules are stacked in three rows
of eight in a box, as shown in the diagram.

  (ii) How much of the internal volume of the box is not occupied by the capsules?

(c) Calculate the volume of a cylinder of height 7 cm and of radius 2 cm, correct to the
nearest cm³.
Water flows through a circular pipe of internal radius 2 cm at a rate of 7 cm/sec into
an empty rectangular tank that is 1.2 m long, 1.1 m wide and 30 cm high.
How long, in minutes, will it take to fill the tank?

18 Patterns and Sequences

Key words

sequence   term   position   term-to-term rule   repeating pattern
linear sequence   position-to-term rule   the *n*th term   quadratic sequence
first difference   second difference   exponential sequence

Section 18.1 Sequences

If we start at 0 and keep adding 4, we get this pattern:

   0, 4, 8, 12, 16, 20, 24, 28, 32, 36, 40, 44, …

If we take the last digit in each of these numbers, we get another pattern, as follows:

   0, 4, 8, 2, 6, 0, 4, 8, 2, 6, 0, 4, …

The first pattern continues on with each number 4 bigger than the number before it.
The second pattern is a little more complex.
The numbers repeat in **blocks** of 5 with a particular pattern in each block.

The number patterns above are called **sequences**.
A sequence is a set of numbers in a particular order.

   1, 3, 5, 7, 9, … is a sequence

   ↑   ↑   ↑

 1st term   4th term   the dots indicate that the sequence continues on.

Each number is called a **term**.
Each number's place in the sequence is called its **position**.

The pattern below is made of squares.

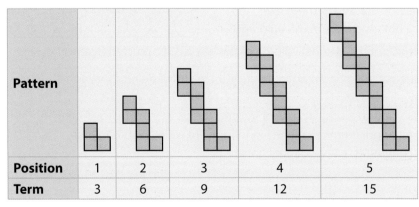

Pattern					
Position	1	2	3	4	5
Term	3	6	9	12	15

> The terms form the sequence.

The fifth term is 15. It is made of 15 squares.

The pattern increases by 3 each time.

The sixth pattern in the sequence is made of 18 squares.

Thus, the sixth term in the sequence is 18.

The **term-to-term rule** describes how to get from one term to the next.

The term-to-term rule for 4, 8, 12, 16, 20, ... is 'add 4'.

The term-to-term rule for 2, 6, 18, 54, ... is 'multiply by 3'.

The term-to-term rule for 30, 25, 20, 15, ... is 'subtract 5'.

A sequence is generally **described in words** by giving the first term and then the term-to-term rule.

Example 1

(i) A sequence starts at 7 and increases in steps of 4.
Write down the first six terms of the sequence.

(ii) Describe in words this sequence:
27, 24, 21, 18, ...

(i) The first six terms of the sequence are: 7, 11, 15, 19, 23, 27.

(ii) The sequence begins at 27 and goes down in steps of 3.

Exercise 18.1

1. Write down the next four terms of each of these sequences:

(i) 3, 5, 7, 9, 11, ...   (ii) 2, 5, 8, 11, 14, ...   (iii) 4, 8, 12, 16, 20, ...
(iv) 20, 18, 16, 14, ...   (v) 50, 45, 40, 35, ...   (vi) 12, 8, 4, ...

2. Write down the next three terms of each of these sequences:

(i) 1, 1.5, 2, 2.5, ...   (ii) −10, −8, −6, −4, ...   (iii) 2, 6, 18, 54, ...
(iv) $-\frac{1}{2}$, 1, $2\frac{1}{2}$, 4, ...   (v) −40, −20, −10, ...   (vi) 6, 3, 0, ...

3. Write down the first four terms of these sequences:

(i) Start with 2 and count forwards in steps of 4.
(ii) Start with 5 and count forwards in steps of 3.
(iii) Start with 3 and count forwards in steps of 5.
(iv) Start with 30 and count back in steps of 4.
(v) Start with −10 and count forwards in steps of 3.

4. Describe in words each of these sequences:

(i) 3, 6, 9, 12, ...   (ii) 0, 4, 8, 12, ...   (iii) 10, 15, 20, 25, ...
(iv) 16, 14, 12, 10, ...   (v) −6, −3, 0, 3, ...   (vi) $-2\frac{1}{2}$, −2, $-1\frac{1}{2}$, −1, ...

5. Write the term-to-term rule for each of these sequences:

(i) 4, 8, 12, 16, …   (ii) 1, 4, 7, 10, …   (iii) 2, 6, 10, 14, …

(iv) 22, 20, 18, 16, …   (v) $\frac{3}{4}$, 1, $\frac{5}{4}$, $\frac{3}{2}$, …   (vi) -12, -9, -6, -3, …

6. Copy and complete this table:

1st term	Term-to-term rule	2nd, 3rd, 4th and 5th terms
8	+5	
	+4	9, 13, 17, 21
		12, 15, 18, 21
0	−3	
−12		−7, −2, 3, 8
		$\frac{1}{7}$, $\frac{2}{7}$, $\frac{3}{7}$, $\frac{4}{7}$
$5\frac{1}{4}$	$-\frac{1}{4}$	

7. The first term of a sequence is 4.

The term-to-term rule is 'add 4'.

(i) What is the second term of the sequence?

(ii) What is the fifth term?

8. The sixth term of a sequence is 11.

The term-to-term rule is 'subtract 3'.

(i) What is the fifth term of the sequence?

(ii) What is the first term?

9. Here are three sequences:

(a) 7, 14, 21, 28, …   (b) 6, 11, 16, 21, 26, …   (c) 3, 7, 11, 15, 19, …

What goes in the box in each of the following?

(i) In sequence (a), the terms of the sequence are multiples of ☐.

(ii) In sequence (b), the terms are all ☐ more than a multiple of ☐.

(iii) In sequence (c), the terms are all ☐ less than a multiple of ☐.

10. Each table below shows patterns in a sequence.

Each term in the sequence is the number of squares in the pattern.

Copy and complete each table.

(i)

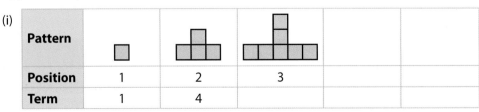

Pattern					
Position	1	2	3		
Term	1	4			

(ii)

Pattern					
Position	1	2	3		
Term	5	8			

(iii)

Pattern					
Position	1	2	3		
Term	3	7			

11. Two sequences have been mixed up.

The rule for one is 'add 4'.

The rule for the other is 'subtract 3'.

      7   15   11   15   21   9   3   12   19   18

What could the sequences have been?

12. Write down the first six terms of this sequence:

      I am thinking of a sequence.

      The 3rd term is 4.

      The rule is 'multiply by 2'.

13. In each of the sequences below, the difference between the terms is constant.

Copy each sequence and fill in the missing numbers.

   (i) 4, 6, ___, ___, ___, 14, ...   (ii) 25, ___, 19, ___, 13, 10, ...

  (iii) 1, ___, 11, ___, 21, ___, ...   (iv) ___, 10, ___, ___, 19, ___, ...

14. Examine these number patterns.

Write down the next line in each pattern without using a calculator.

Now use a calculator to check that you are correct.

(i)	$3 \times 11 = 33$	(ii)	$9 \times 1 = 9$	(iii) $7 \times 7 = 49$
	$33 \times 11 = 363$		$9 \times 12 = 108$	$67 \times 67 = 4489$
	$333 \times 11 = 3663$		$9 \times 123 = 1107$	$667 \times 667 = 444889$
	$3333 \times 11 = 36\,663$		$9 \times 1234 = 11\,106$	$6667 \times 6667 = 44448889$

     - - - - - - - - - - - - - - - - -   - - - - - - - - - - - - - - - - -   -

Section 18.2 Repeating patterns

The pattern of the coloured circles above is green, pink, blue, yellow, green, …
The pattern repeats in blocks of 4.
The pattern of green circles is 1, 5, 9, …
The pattern of yellow circles is 4, 8, 12, …

What colour is the 35th circle?
Since the pattern repeats every 4 circles, we find how many blocks of 4 there are in 35 and then how many circles are left over.

$35 \div 4 = 8$ and remainder 3

When the remainder is 3, we look for the colour of the 3rd circle in the block of 4.

This colour is blue.

Example 1

A repeating pattern is made up of letters as follows:

(i)   What is the 25th letter?
(ii) What is the 43rd letter?
(iii) What is the 61st letter?

(i)   The pattern repeats in blocks of 5.
      To find the 25th letter, divide 25 by 5.
      $25 \div 5 = 5$, i.e., five complete blocks.
      The 25th letter is therefore the last letter in the block.
      Thus, the 25th letter is E.

(ii) The 43rd letter is $43 \div 5$. This is 8 and remainder 3.
      Remainder 3 means it is the 3rd letter in the block.
      This letter is C.
      The 43rd letter is C.

(iii) The 61st letter is $61 \div 5$. This is 12 and remainder 1.
      Remainder 1 means the first letter in the block.
      The 61st letter is A.

Exercise 18.2

1. Here is a repeating pattern of geometric shapes:

□ ○ △ □ □ ○ △ □ ...

   (i)   What are the next two shapes?
  (ii) List the positions of the first three circles. Is there a pattern?
 (iii) Which shape forms the pattern 3, 7, …?
 (iv) What is the 21st shape?
  (v) What is the 37th shape?
 (vi) If the 61st shape is a square, what is the 62nd shape?

2. Here is a repeating pattern of coloured tiles:

□ ▣ ▣ ▦ ▦ □ □ ▣ ▦ ▦ □ □ ...

   (i)   What is the next colour in the pattern?
  (ii) What colour is the 30th tile?
 (iii) What colour is the 48th tile?
 (iv) If the 63rd tile is red, what colour is the 65th tile?
  (v) Write down the pattern formed by the blue tiles.
 (vi) In what position is the 6th blue tile?

3. The pattern below is the multiples of 6.

     6, 12, 18, 24, 30, 36, 42, 48, 54, 60, 66, 72, …

The last digit in each number forms this pattern:

     6, 2, 8, 4, 0, 6, 2, 8, 4, 0, 6, 2, …

Notice that this is a repeating pattern.

   (i)   What are the next two numbers of this pattern?
  (ii) What is the 24th number of the pattern?
 (iii) What is the 51st number of the pattern?
 (iv) What is the position of the fifth 8 of the pattern?

4. Write down the first ten multiples of 8.

   (i)   Show that the last digits of these multiples form a repeating pattern.
  (ii) After how many digits does the pattern start repeating?
 (iii) What number appears in the 100th position in the pattern?

Section 18.3 Linear sequences

Look at this sequence:

     12, 9, 6, 3, …   The term-to-term rule is −3 or 'subtract 3'.

When the term-to-term rule involves adding or subtracting a constant (a fixed number), it is known as a **linear sequence**.

A linear sequence is also known as an **arithmetic sequence**.

The following sequences are not linear because the term-to-term rule does not involve adding or subtracting a constant.

(i) 2, 4, 8, 16, 32, ...   The term-to-term rule is $\times 2$.
(ii) 27, 9, 3, 1, $\frac{1}{3}$, ...   The term-to-term rule is $\div 3$.

How to find any term of a sequence

We can calculate the value of a term from its position in the sequence by using a **position-to-term rule**. This helps us avoid having to add or subtract the constant a lot of times.

Examine the sequence below:

Position Term

Position	1	2	3	4	5	...	n
Term	7	10	13	16	19	...	$n \times 3 + 4$

The position-to-term rule may also be called the nth-term rule.

The example above shows that any term may be found by using the rule

From this the 6th term (T_6) is $6\ \boxed{\times 3}\ +\ \boxed{4}$, i.e. $T_6 = 22$.

The position-to-term rule for a sequence can be given by writing an expression for T_n, the nth term.

In the example above, $T_n = n\ \boxed{\times 3}\ +\ \boxed{4}$

$$\therefore T_n = 3n + 4$$

When we know T_n we can write down any term of the sequence.

Example 1

The nth term of a sequence is given by $T_n = 3n - 4$.
(i) Write down the first three terms of the sequence and also T_{20}.
(ii) Explain why the sequence is linear.

(i) $T_n = 3n - 4$
$T_1 = 3(1) - 4 = 3 - 4 = -1$ ... substitute 1 for n.
$T_2 = 3(2) - 4 = 6 - 4 = 2$
$T_3 = 3(3) - 4 = 9 - 4 = 5$
$T_{20} = 3(20) - 4 = 60 - 4 = 56$

The first three terms are $-1, 2, 5$ and $T_{20} = 56$.

(ii) Since the difference between the terms is a constant, i.e. 3, the sequence is linear.

Exercise 18.3

1. The nth terms of some sequences are given.
   Write out the first four terms of each sequence.

   (i) $T_n = 2n$ (ii) $T_n = 3n + 1$ (iii) $T_n = 4n - 3$
   (iv) $T_n = 2n + 5$ (v) $T_n = 5n - 4$ (vi) $T_n = 7 - 2n$

2. Write out the first three terms of these sequences defined by the given nth term:

   (i) $T_n = 1 - 3n$ (ii) $T_n = n^2 + 1$ (iii) $T_n = \dfrac{n + 1}{4}$

3. The nth term of a sequence is $T_n = 2n + 3$.

   (i)   Write down the first five terms of the sequence.
   (ii) Find T_{20} and T_{100}.

4. If $T_n = 2n - 6$, show that $T_1 + T_5 = 0$.

5. Explain why each of these sequences is linear:

   (i) $3, 8, 13, 18, \ldots$ (ii) $18, 14, 10, 6, \ldots$

6. Investigate whether each of these sequences is linear:

   (i) $-8, -10, -12, -14, \ldots$ (ii) $1, 3, 9, 27, \ldots$
   (iii) $20, 10, 5, 2\frac{1}{2}, \ldots$ (iv) $0.1, 0.3, 0.5, 0.7, \ldots$

7. The nth terms of six different sequences are:

   A $7n - 2$ **B** $10 - n$ **C** $\frac{1}{2}n - 3$ **D** $n^2 + 1$ **E** $\dfrac{60}{n}$ **F** 2^n

   (i)   Calculate the first four terms of each sequence.
   (ii) Calculate the 20th term of each sequence.
   (iii) Which of these sequences are linear?

8. The nth term of a sequence is $3n + 2$.

   (i)   Write down the first six terms of the sequence.
   (ii) Calculate the 100th term.

9. Linear sequences can be found on this grid.
   Two are shown on the diagram.

   (i)   Find seven more linear sequences that
         have four terms or more.

         Write down each sequence as an **increasing**
         sequence and find its next term.

44	34	24	14	4	3	6	9	12
40	30	5	20	10	11	5	8	1
44	37	30	23	16	9	2	7	3
4	11	23	21	22	12	1	6	9
1	7	26	20	28	9	8	5	0
3	31	10	15	34	30	12	4	8
36	6	11	13	40	0	1	3	2

(ii) The expressions below give the *n*th terms
of these sequences.
Match each expression to its sequence.

| $3n$ | $6n - 2$ | $10n - 6$ | $2n + 1$ | $4n$ |

| $3n + 1$ | $n + 2$ | $5n + 1$ | $7n - 5$ |

Section 18.4 Finding the *n*th term of a sequence

To find the *n*th term of a linear sequence, we look at the differences between terms.

$$7 \quad 10 \quad 13 \quad 16 \quad 19$$
$$+3 \quad +3 \quad +3 \quad +3$$

The sequence is linked to 3-times tables because the terms go up in 3s.
So $3n$ will be part of the *n*th term.
T_n will be $3n \pm$ some number.

To work out what to add to or subtract from $3n$, we compare the first term of $T_n = 3n$ and
the given sequence $7, 10, 13, \ldots$

For $T_n = 3n$, $T_1 = 3(1) = 3$.
We need to add 4 to this 3 to get 7, the first term of the given sequence.

$$\therefore T_n = 3n + 4 \qquad n \rightarrow \boxed{\times 3} \xrightarrow{3n} \boxed{+4} \rightarrow 3n + 4$$

Example 1

Find the *n*th term of the sequence $3, 7, 11, 15, \ldots$

In the sequence $3, 7, 11, 15, \ldots$, the difference between the terms is $+4$.
So $T_n = 4n \pm$ some number.
If $T_n = 4n$, then $T_1 = 4(1) = 4$.

What do I need to add to or subtract from 4 to get the first term 3 of the
given sequence?
I need to subtract 1, since $4 - 1 = 3$.
So $T_n = 4n - 1$.

Note: Having found an expression for T_n, always check that it works for T_2 or T_3,
for example.

Example 2

Find the nth term of the sequence $10, 7, 4, 1, -2, \ldots$
Hence work out T_{20} of the sequence.

In this sequence, the term-to-term rule is -3 or 'subtract 3'.
So $T_n = -3n \pm$ a number.
The first term of the sequence $T_n = -3n$ is $-3(1) = -3$.
What do I need to add to or subtract from -3 to get 10?
I need to add 13.
So $T_n = -3n + 13$.

$T_n = -3n + 13 \Rightarrow T_{20} = -3(20) + 13 = -60 + 13 = -47$

$\therefore T_{20} = -47$

If we know the nth term of a sequence, we can use this information to find which term of the sequence any given number is.

Example 3

The nth term of a sequence is given by $T_n = 5n - 4$.
Which term of the sequence is 21?

Let $T_n = 21$
$\therefore 5n - 4 = 21$
$\qquad 5n = 25$
$\qquad n = 5$

Thus 21 is the 5th term of the sequence.

Exercise 18.4

1. A given sequence is $5, 9, 13, 17, \ldots$

   (i) Write down the constant difference between the terms.

   (ii) If $T_n = \boxed{} n \pm$ number, what number goes in the box?

   (iii) Now find an expression for T_n, the nth term.

   (iv) Write down the value of T_{20}.

2. Find an expression for the nth term of each of these sequences:

   (i) $5, 7, 9, 11, \ldots$ (ii) $4, 7, 10, 13, \ldots$ (iii) $6, 10, 14, 18, \ldots$

3. Find an expression for the nth term of this sequence:

$$7, 11, 15, 19, \ldots$$

Use the expression for the nth term to find T_{10} and T_{20}.

4. Consider the sequence $12, 10, 8, 6, \ldots$.

    (i) What is the term-to-term rule for this sequence?

    (ii) If $T_n = \boxed{}\, n \pm$ a number, what number goes in the box?

    (iii) Use this to find an expression for T_n.

    (iv) Find T_{10} of the sequence.

    (v) Which term of the sequence is -14?

5. Find an expression for the nth term of these sequences:

    (i) $-3, 0, 3, 6, 9, \ldots$ (ii) $20, 15, 10, 5, \ldots$

6. Find an expression for T_n of the sequence $8, 5, 2, \ldots$

For what value of n is $T_n = -34$?

Section 18.5 Sequences formed from shapes

So far in this chapter we have dealt only with number patterns.

In this section we will examine some geometric figures and the patterns they form.

Example 1

The figure on the right shows some photo frames made with rods.

    1 photo   2 photos   3 photos

    (i) Draw the frame that holds 4 photos.

    (ii) How many rods are there in the frame that holds 5 photos?

    (iii) Find an expression for the number of rods in the nth frame.

    (iv) Which frame uses 41 rods?

    (v) Is it possible to make one of these frames using exactly 56 rods?

    (i) This is the frame that holds 4 photos:

    (ii) The sequence is $3, 5, 7, 9, 11, \ldots$

          The 5th frame has 11 rods.

    (iii) The difference between the terms is $+2$.

          Thus, the nth term will be $2n \pm$ a number.

          If $T_n = 2n$, $T_1 = 2$ and so 1 must be added to get the first term 3.

          $\therefore T_n = 2n + 1$

(iv) Let $T_n = 41 \Rightarrow 2n + 1 = 41$

$$2n = 40$$
$$n = 20$$

The 20th frame uses 41 rods.

(v) Let $T_n = 56$

$$2n + 1 = 56$$
$$2n = 55$$
$$n = 27\tfrac{1}{2}$$

Since $27\tfrac{1}{2}$ is not a whole number, no frame uses exactly 56 rods.

Exercise 18.5

1. Here is a pattern made from sticks.

    6 sticks   11 sticks   16 sticks

(i) Draw the 4th pattern in this sequence.

(ii) Write down the sequence of numbers generated by the sticks in the first six patterns.

(iii) Show that the number of sticks in the nth pattern is given by $T_n = 5n + 1$.

(iv) How many sticks are required for the 20th pattern?

(v) For which pattern are 51 sticks required?

2. Here are three diagrams made with triangles.

                Diagram 1   **Diagram 2**   **Diagram 3**

              3 triangles   5 triangles   7 triangles

(i) Draw diagram 4.

(ii) How many triangles will be in diagram 7?

(iii) Find an expression for the number of triangles in the nth diagram.

(iv) Which diagram will contain 33 triangles?

3. Complete the table of values for this sequence of matchstick patterns.

Number of squares	1	2	3	4	5
Number of matchsticks	4	7			

(i) How many matchsticks are required for the 6th pattern?
(ii) Find an expression in n for the number of matchsticks in the nth pattern.
(iii) Use the expression found to ascertain the number of matchsticks required for the 50th pattern.

4. Here is a pattern made with matchsticks.

Pattern 1   Pattern 2   Pattern 3

(i) How many matchsticks will be in Pattern 5?
(ii) Find an expression for the number of matchsticks in the nth pattern.
(iii) In which pattern are there 51 matchsticks?

5. Here is another pattern made with matchsticks.

Pattern 1   Pattern 2   Pattern 3

(i) How many matchsticks will there be in pattern 4?
(ii) What is the term-to-term rule for the pattern?
(iii) How many matchsticks will there be in the nth pattern?
(iv) Which pattern will contain exactly 66 matchsticks?
(v) Will any pattern use exactly 88 matchsticks?

6. Sharon drew these shapes on her bedroom wall.

Shape 1   Shape 2   Shape 3

(i) Draw shape 4.
(ii) Copy and complete this table.
(iii) Describe in words the sequence formed.

Shape number	1	2	3	4	5
Total number of circles	5	9			

(iv) Find an expression for the nth term of the sequence.
 (v) Which shape will contain exactly 81 circles?
(vi) Will any shape contain exactly 89 circles?

7. Tommy builds fences of different lengths using pieces of wood.

Fence length 1   Fence length 2   Fence length 3

 (i) Sketch fence length 5.
     Tommy counted how many pieces he needed to make each fence length.
     He then drew up the table below.

Fence length	1	2	3	4	5	6
Number of pieces	4	7	10			

 (ii) Complete the table to show how many pieces of wood he would use for fence
      lengths 4, 5 and 6.
(iii) Write down, in terms of n, an expression for the number of pieces of wood needed
      for fence length n.
(iv) How many pieces of wood are needed for fence length 40?
 (v) If 91 pieces of wood are needed, what is the number of the fence length?

Section 18.6 Quadratic sequences

1, 4, 9, 16, 25, ... is the sequence of square numbers.
Since $T_1 = 1^2, T_2 = 2^2, T_3 = 3^2, T_n = n^2$.

Sequences that have an nth term containing n^2 as the highest power are called **quadratic
sequences**.

Let us examine the first seven terms of the sequence $T_n = n^2$.

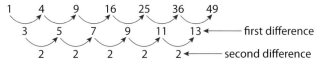

Notice that the second difference is a constant, i.e. 2.
Quadratic sequences always have a constant second difference.

Now let us look at the sequence with nth term $= 2n^2 - n$.
The first five terms of this sequence are

Here again the second differences are all the same, i.e., 4.

369

Notice that in each of the quadratic sequences above, the coefficient of n^2 in the nth term is half the second difference.

In a quadratic sequence, the coefficient of n^2 in the nth term is half the second difference.

Investigation

Write out the first five terms of the sequence with $T_n = 2n^2 + 3$.
Write out the first differences and the second differences between consecutive terms.
Investigate if the coefficient of n^2 in the nth term is half the value of the second difference.

Finding the nth term of a quadratic sequence

The nth term of a quadratic sequence will always be of the form

$$T_n = an^2 + bn + c$$

We now use a difference table to find the values of a, b and c, as shown in the following example.

Example 1

Find the nth term of the sequence 3, 10, 21, 36.

The terms and the 1st and 2nd differences are shown on the right.

Terms	3		10		21		36
1st differences		7		11		15	
2nd differences			4		4		

T_n will be of the form $T_n = an^2 + bn + c$
$a = 2$ ... half the value of the second difference, i.e., $4 \div 2$.

$\therefore T_n = 2n^2 + bn + c$

We now express T_1 and T_2 in terms of b and c.
$T_n = 2n^2 + bn + c \Rightarrow T_1 = 2 + b + c$
But $T_1 = 3 \Rightarrow 2 + b + c = 3 \Rightarrow b + c = 1 \dots$ ①
$T_2 = 8 + 2b + c$
But $T_2 = 10 \Rightarrow 8 + 2b + c = 10 \Rightarrow 2b + c = 2 \dots$ ②

We now solve the simultaneous equations ① and ②.

$$
\begin{array}{l|l}
b + c = 1 \dots ① & b + c = 1 \\
2b + c = 2 \dots ② & \Rightarrow 1 + c = 1 \\
\quad -b = -1 \Rightarrow b = 1 & \Rightarrow c = 0
\end{array}
$$

$\therefore T_n = 2n^2 + n$ ... $a = 2, b = 1, c = 0$

Exercise 18.6

1. Work out the first four terms of each of these quadratic sequences:

   (i) $T_n = n^2 + 4$ (ii) $T_n = n^2 - 2$ (iii) $T_n = 2n^2 - 1$ (iv) $T_n = 3n^2 - 4$

2. Find the next two terms of these quadratic sequences by finding the first and second differences:

   (i) 3, 4, 6, 9, 13, ...   (ii) 3, 6, 11, 18, 27, ...   (iii) 2, 7, 14, 23, 34, ...

3. Which of these sequences are quadratic?

   (i) 6, 8, 12, 18, 26, 36, ...   (ii) 6, 8, 10, 12, 14, 16, ...

   (iii) 3, 4, 7, 12, 19, 28, ...   (iv) 0, 3, 8, 15, 24, ...

4. If $T_n = n^2 + 2n - 4$, work out the tenth term.

5. The value of the second difference can tell us something about the formula for the nth term of a quadratic sequence.

   (i) Copy and complete this table.

nth term	First five terms	First differences	Second differences
$2n^2$	2, 8, 18, 32, 50, ...	6, 10, 14, 18, ...	4, 4, 4, ...
$3n^2$	3, 12, __, __, __, __, ...		
$4n^2$	4, __, __, __, __, __, ...		
$5n^2$	5, __, __, __, __, __, ...		

   (ii) What do you notice about the second difference and how it is connected to the quadratic formula for each sequence?

   (iii) If the second difference in a quadratic sequence is 12, and $T_n = an^2 + bn$, find the value of a.

6. Write the sequence 4, 7, 12, 19, 28, ... as follows

   $$4 \quad 7 \quad 12 \quad 19 \quad 28$$

       –   –   –   –   first difference

       –   –   –   second difference

   If $T_n = an^2 + bn + c$, use the second difference to write down the value of a.
   Hence find the expression for T_n.

7. Find an expression for the nth term of each of the quadratic sequences:

   (i) 7, 10, 15, 22, 31, ...   (ii) 2, 7, 14, 23, ...   (iii) 2, 8, 18, 32, 50, ...

8. Show that the nth term of the quadratic sequence 8, 15, 26, 41, 60, ... is given by $T_n = 2n^2 + n + 5$.

9. The given figures show a pattern of square tiles.

①

②

③

④

    (i)   How many tiles will there be in the fifth pattern?

    (ii) Explain why the numbers of tiles in the pattern do not form a linear sequence.

    (iii) Is the sequence of tiles used a quadratic sequence?
          Explain your answer.

    (iv) Use the second differences to find an expression for the nth term of the sequence.

    (v) Use the expression for the nth term that you found to work out the number of tiles in the twentieth pattern.

10. Here are the first 3 diagrams of a matchstick pattern.

    (i)   How many matchsticks will there be in Diagram 4?

    (ii) Using the sequence formed, write down the number of matchsticks in Diagram 5.

Diagram 1

Diagram 2

Diagram 3

    (iii) Explain why the sequence is quadratic.

    (iv) Find an expression for the nth term of the sequence.

    (v) Use the nth term to find the number of matchsticks in Diagram 10.

Section 18.7 Graphing sequences

1. Linear sequences

Here is a linear pattern: 1, 4, 7, 10, 13, ...

It can be seen that $T_1 = 1, T_2 = 4, T_3 = 7, ...$

These may be written as ordered pairs as follows:

$(T_1, 1), (T_2, 4), (T_3, 7), (T_4, 10), ...$

On the right, we have plotted the terms on the horizontal axis and the values of the terms on the vertical axis.

When the term and its value are plotted and the points joined, the result is a straight line.

This illustrates why the sequence is called **linear**.

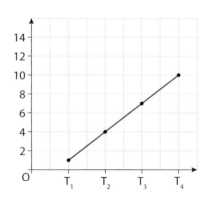

2. Quadratic sequences

Here is a quadratic sequence: 3, 4, 6, 9, 13, …

We will now start to plot these ordered pairs –
$(T_1, 3)$, $(T_2, 4)$, $(T_3, 6)$, $(T_4, 9)$, $(T_5, 13)$ – on a graph.

When the points are joined, the resulting
curve forms part of a **quadratic graph**.

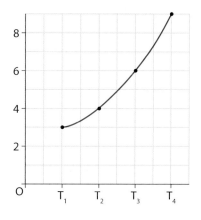

A quadratic graph takes one of the two shapes
shown on the right.

3. Exponential sequences

Here is a special type of sequence formed by powers of 2:

$2^1, 2^2, 2^3, 2^4, 2^5, \ldots$ or $2, 4, 8, 16, 32, \ldots$

Notice that the values of the terms increase very quickly.

This is an example of an **exponential sequence**.

If $T_n = 3^n$, then the sequence is

$3^1, 3^2, 3^3, 3^4, 3^5, \ldots$ or $3, 9, 27, 81, 243, \ldots$

> Exponent is another
> word for power.

In everyday language, **exponential growth** is used to indicate 'very fast growth'.

When the sequence 2, 4, 8, 16, … is plotted
on a graph, it can be seen that the curve
rises very steeply.

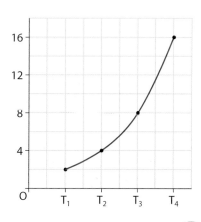

Example 1

Here are the fare structures of two taxi companies.

Company A has a fixed charge of €4 plus €2 per kilometre
Company B has no fixed charge but charges €2.50 per kilometre travelled.

Draw a graph to represent these two companies' charges.
Put the charges on the *x*-axis and the distances on the *y*-axis.
Use your graph to find

(i) how much Company A charges for a journey of 10 km
(ii) how far you could travel with Company B for €16
(iii) the distance for which both companies charge the same amount
(iv) the difference in the charges when the distance is 4 km.

Find the slope of the line that represents company B and explain its meaning.

We set out a table of charges for each company.

Ⓐ
Distance (km)	0	1	2	3
Cost (€)	4	6	8	10

Ⓑ
Distance (km)	0	1	2	3
Cost (€)	0	2.5	5	7.5

We now plot these charges on the same graph.

(i) Company A charges €24 for a journey of 10 km.
(ii) You could travel 6.4 km with company B for €16.
(iii) Both charges are equal where the lines intersect.
    This happens at 8 km.

(iv) For 4 km, Company A charges €12.
For 4 km, Company B charges €10.
The difference in the charges is €2.

The slope of the line B is $\frac{10}{4}$, as shown on the graph.

$\frac{10}{4} = \frac{5}{2} = 2\frac{1}{2}$ and €$2\frac{1}{2}$ is the charge for 1 km travelled.

Thus, the slope of the line B is the charge in euro for 1 km travelled.

Exercise 18.7

1. The table on the right shows the first
   four terms of a sequence and the values
   of these terms.

Term	1	2	3	4
Value	4	7	10	13

   Putting the terms on the horizontal axis and the values on the vertical axis, draw a
   graph of the sequence.
   Explain why the sequence is linear.

2. If $T_n = 2n + 1$, write out the first five terms of the sequence.
   Illustrate this sequence on a graph, putting the term numbers on the horizontal axis.
   Explain why the graph is a straight line.

3. The graph on the right shows a
   plumber's charges when called
   to do a repair job on a boiler.

   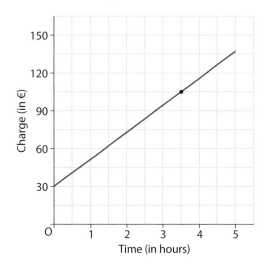

   (i)   What is the initial or 'call out' charge?
   (ii) How much does he charge for a
         job that lasts for $3\frac{1}{2}$ hours?
   (iii) If he charges €135, how many
         hours has he worked?
   (iv) Do his charges form a linear
         sequence?
         Explain your conclusion.
   (v)   Use the graph to work out what
         the plumber charges for each hour
         of actual work (i.e. excluding the
         'call out' charge).
   (vi) Investigate if the slope of the line is the same as the rate he charges for each
         hour's work.
   (vii) If the work lasted 10 hours, use the sequence to work out what the charge
         would be.

4. The table on the right shows the total amounts of money Cara has saved after weeks 1, 2, 3, ….
   Draw a graph to illustrate these savings, putting the week number on the x-axis.

Week number	Amount saved
1	€10
2	€20
3	€30
4	€40
5	€50
……	……

   (i)   Is the graph linear?
   (ii) Use the pattern to find the amount she will have saved at the end of the 12th week.
   (iii) Find the equation of the line you have drawn.
   (iv) Use the equation to find what Cara will have saved at the end of the 20th week.

5. This pattern is made from cubes.
   The outside faces of the cubes in each block are painted.

   The table below shows the number of faces painted in each block.

Block number (n)	1	2	3	4
Number of painted faces	6	10	14	18

   (i)   Explain why the sequence formed by the numbers of faces painted forms a linear sequence.
   (ii) Now find an expression for the nth term of the sequence.
   (iii) Draw a graph of the sequence, putting the block numbers on the horizontal axis.

6. A fast-growing plant is 4 cm in height when purchased. It grows 2 cm per day each day afterwards.
   Copy and complete the table on the right showing the height of the plant in its first seven days.

Day	Height (cm)
1	4
2	6
3	8
……	……

   (i)   Draw a graph to show the height of the plant for Day 1 ….. Day 7.
   (ii) How many days will it take for the plant to reach a height of 30 cm?
   (iii) The plant will stop growing when it reaches a height of 60 cm. How many days will this take?
   (iv) What is the slope of the line you have drawn?
   (v)   What is the rate of change of growth per day in the table?
   (vi) What is the connection between your answers in (iv) and (v) above?

7. The numbers of edges for the numbers of hexagons are shown in the pattern and table below:

Number of hexagons (n)	1	2	3	4
Number of edges (E)	6	11	16	21

   (i)   Find the number of edges when there are 5 hexagons.

  (ii)   Explain why the pattern in the numbers of edges is linear.

 (iii)   Find an expression for the *n*th term of the sequence 6, 11, 16, …

 (iv)   Draw a graph of the pattern, putting the numbers of hexagons on the *x*-axis.

  (v)   Find the equation of the line you have drawn in the form $E = \boxed{}\,n + \boxed{}$.

 (vi)   What is the slope of this line?

(vii)   Explain what the slope means in the context of the pattern.

8. A sequence of numbers begins 4, 7, 12, 19, 28, …

   (i)   Explain why this is a quadratic pattern.

  (ii)   What is the second difference between the terms?

 (iii)   Draw a graph of this pattern using the scales shown on the right.

 (iv)   Describe the shape of the graph.

9. Here are the first three terms of an exponential sequence:

      3, 9, 27, …

   (i)   Write down the next three terms.

  (ii)   Investigate if the second difference is a constant.

 (iii)   Explain why the sequence is not quadratic.

 (iv)   Describe one feature of an exponential graph.

10. Here are three graphs and three sequences.

Which sequence does each graph represent?

A: 2, 4, 8, 16, …

B: 3, 6, 10, 15, 21, …

C: 2, 5, 8, 11, …

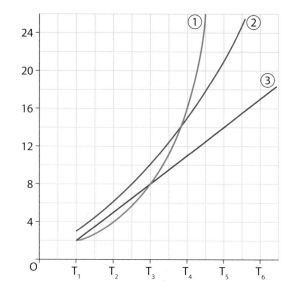

Test yourself 18

1. (a) Describe in words each of these three sequences:

    (i) 3, 7, 11, 15, …   (ii) −1, −3, −5, −7, …   (iii) 3, 6, 12, …

(b) Write out the first three terms of each of these sequences where T_n is the nth term:

    (i) $T_n = 3n + 1$ (ii) $T_n = 1 - 2n$ (iii) $T_n = 2n^2 - 1$

(c) Look at the sequence of these triangle patterns:

    (i) Draw the next triangle in the sequence.
    (ii) How many dots will there be in the 5th pattern?
    (iii) Find an expression for the nth term for this sequence.
    (iv) Use the expression for the nth term to find which pattern has 63 dots.

2. (a) Write the next three terms of these sequences:

    (i) 7, 4, 1, −2, …   (ii) 40, 20, 10, …   (iii) 1, 2, 4, 7, 11, …

(b) Here is a repeating pattern of coloured tiles:

(i) What are the colours of the next two tiles?

(ii) Write down the sequence formed by the positions of the yellow tiles in the pattern.

(iii) In what position is the 10th yellow tile?

(iv) What is the colour of the 72nd tile?

(c) (i) Write down the first three terms of the sequence if its nth term is given by $T_n = 2n^2 + 2$.

(ii) 2, 5, 10, 17, 26, … are the first five terms of a sequence.
Work out the second difference between the terms.
Explain why the sequence is quadratic.

3. (a) Which **one** of the following sequences is linear?

(i) 6, 4, 0, …   (ii) −3, −1, 3, 5, …   (iii) −5, −3, −1, 1, …

(b) Look at these matchstick shapes.

5 matchsticks   9 matchsticks

(i) Copy and complete the table below:

Shape number	1	2	3	4	5
Number of matchsticks	5	9	…	…	…

(ii) How many matchsticks are there in Shape 7?

(iii) Find an expression for the number of matchsticks in Shape n?

(iv) Which shape contains exactly 101 matchsticks?

4. (a) What number goes in the box in each of these sequences:

(i) 10, 7, 4, 1, ☐, …   (ii) −2, 1, ☐, 7, …

(iii) 81, 27, ☐, 3, …   (iv) 3, 5, 9, ☐, 23, …

(b) The first four terms of a sequence are 4, 7, 10, 13, …

(i) Explain why the sequence is linear.

(ii) Find an expression for the nth term of the sequence.

(iii) Use the expression you have found to work out the 40th term of the sequence.

(c) The first term of a quadratic sequence is 12.
The first 1st difference is 3 and the second difference is 2.
Write down the first six terms of the sequence.

5. (a) Write down the next three terms of each of these sequences, where the first two terms and the term-to-term rules are given:

(i) 1, 3, … Double the previous term and add 1.

(ii) 1, 3, … Multiply the previous term by 4 and take away 1.

(iii) 1, 3, … Add the two previous terms together.

(b)   Tess made this pattern with buttons around the hem of her dress.

Pattern 1   Pattern 2   Pattern 3

Pattern number	1	2	3	4	...
Number of buttons	4	7	10	?	...

(i)   Draw pattern 4.
      How many buttons are in pattern 4?
(ii) Describe the pattern and how it continues.
(iii) Find an expression for the number of buttons in the nth pattern.
(iv) Use the expression to find which pattern uses 25 buttons.

(c)   2, 6, 12, 20, ... are the first four terms of a quadratic sequence.
   (i)   Work out the second difference between the terms.
   (ii) Use this second difference to find an expression for the nth term of
         the sequence.

6. (a)   (i)   Write the next two terms in the sequence: 4, 5, 7, 10, 14, ...
        (ii) Describe in words this sequence: 2, 6, 18, 54, ...

   (b)   The first two terms of a sequence are 3, 9, ...
        (i)   If the sequence is linear, write down the next three terms.
        (ii) If the sequence is quadratic, write down what the next three terms could be.
        (iii) If the sequence is exponential, write down the next three terms.
        (iv) If the graphs of these sequences were drawn, which graph would rise
              the fastest?
        (v)   Explain why there is more than one quadratic sequence that satisfies the
              pattern 3, 6, ...

   (c)   A particular type of bacteria starts as a single cell and grows by doubling.

Stage 1   Stage 2   Stage 3   Stage 4
1 cell   2 cells   4 cells   8 cells

        (i)   How many cells will be present at stage 6?
        (ii) By studying the pattern, write down an expression in n for the number of cells
              present at stage n.

chapter 19

Functions

Key words

input	output	function machine	mapping diagrams	domain
range	function	codomain	couples	ordered pairs	parabola
coefficient	quadratic functions			

Section 19.1 Functions

Each term in the number sequence below is found by adding 4 to the previous term:

3   7   11   15   19
  +4   +4   +4   +4   ... 'Add 4' is the rule for finding the next term.

Now consider this sequence:

2   6   18   54
  ×3   ×3   ×3   ... Here the rule is 'multiply by 3'

The next number in the sequence is 54×3, i.e., 162.
When the operation '×3' is applied to 54, we get 162.
We use the term **input** for 54 and **output** for 162.

The chain of diagrams below shows how we can find the output if we are given the input by means of a **function machine** or **flow chart**.

(i)
$7 \rightarrow$ [multiply by 4] $\rightarrow$ [add 1] $\rightarrow 29$ If the input is 7, the output is $7 \times 4 + 1 = 29$.

(ii)
$4 \rightarrow$ [multiply by 3] $\rightarrow$ [add 6] $\rightarrow 18$

(iii)
$5 \rightarrow$ [multiply by 3] $\rightarrow$ [subtract 4] $\rightarrow 11$

If we call the input number x and the output number y, we can then write the 'rule' in terms of x and y.

$x \rightarrow$ [multiply by 3] $\rightarrow$ [add 2] $\rightarrow y$

The rule for this function machine is 'multiply by 3, then add 2'.
We can write this as $x \times 3 + 2 = y$ or $y = 3x + 2$.

Here are the rules for these function machines:

(i) $x \longrightarrow$ [multiply by 2] $\longrightarrow$ [add 4] $\longrightarrow y$ Rule: $y = 2x + 4$

(ii) $x \longrightarrow$ [multiply by 8] $\longrightarrow$ [subtract 7] $\longrightarrow y$ Rule: $y = 8x - 7$

The rule $y = 2x + 4$ may also be written as $x \rightarrow 2x + 4$.

Exercise 19.1

1. Find the output for each of these:

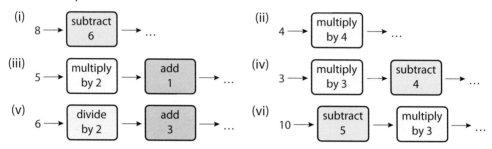

(i) $8 \longrightarrow$ [subtract 6] $\longrightarrow$ ...

(ii) $4 \longrightarrow$ [multiply by 4] $\longrightarrow$ ...

(iii) $5 \longrightarrow$ [multiply by 2] $\longrightarrow$ [add 1] $\longrightarrow$ ...

(iv) $3 \longrightarrow$ [multiply by 3] $\longrightarrow$ [subtract 4] $\longrightarrow$ ...

(v) $6 \longrightarrow$ [divide by 2] $\longrightarrow$ [add 3] $\longrightarrow$ ...

(vi) $10 \longrightarrow$ [subtract 5] $\longrightarrow$ [multiply by 3] $\longrightarrow$ ...

2. Describe in **words** what each function machine does to the input in Question **1.** above.

3. Find the outputs for these:

(i) $3 \longrightarrow$ / $7 \longrightarrow$ / $8 \longrightarrow$ [multiply by 2] $\longrightarrow$ [subtract 4] $\longrightarrow$ ...

(ii) $2 \longrightarrow$ / $1 \longrightarrow$ / $0 \longrightarrow$ [add 4] $\longrightarrow$ [multiply by 2] $\longrightarrow$ ...

4.

$x \longrightarrow$ [add 2] $\longrightarrow$ [multiply by 3] $\longrightarrow y$ is a function machine.

Use a copy of this table and fill in the values for y.

x	1	2	3	4	5
y					

Write in words what this function machine does.

5. Write the rules for these function machines as $y = ...$

(i) $x \longrightarrow$ [multiply by 2] $\longrightarrow$ [add 6] $\longrightarrow y$

(ii) $x \longrightarrow$ [multiply by 8] $\longrightarrow$ [subtract 9] $\longrightarrow y$

(iii) $x \longrightarrow$ [divide by 4] $\longrightarrow$ [subtract 3] $\longrightarrow y$

(iv) $x \longrightarrow$ [add 3] $\longrightarrow$ [multiply by 4] $\longrightarrow y$

6. Write the rules for these function machines in the form $x \rightarrow \dots$

(i)
$x \rightarrow$ [multiply by 3] $\rightarrow$ [add 2] $\rightarrow y$

(ii)
$x \rightarrow$ [multiply by 5] $\rightarrow$ [subtract 2] $\rightarrow y$

(iii)
$x \rightarrow$ [divide by 3] $\rightarrow$ [add 2] $\rightarrow y$

(iv)
$x \rightarrow$ [add 2] $\rightarrow$ [multiply by 7] $\rightarrow y$

7. Find the missing operation in each of these:

(i)
$3 \rightarrow$ [?] $\rightarrow 15$
$5 \rightarrow$ $\rightarrow 25$
$8 \rightarrow$ $\rightarrow 40$

(ii)
$9 \rightarrow$ [?] $\rightarrow 13$
$1 \rightarrow$ $\rightarrow 5$
$15 \rightarrow$ $\rightarrow 19$

(iii)
$24 \rightarrow$ [?] $\rightarrow 6$
$16 \rightarrow$ $\rightarrow 4$
$100 \rightarrow$ $\rightarrow 25$

8. Find the missing operations in these function machines:

(i)
$3 \rightarrow$ [multiply by 2] $\rightarrow$ [?] $\rightarrow 5$
$2 \rightarrow$ $\rightarrow 3$
$1 \rightarrow$ $\rightarrow 1$

(ii)
$0 \rightarrow$ [multiply by 3] $\rightarrow$ [?] $\rightarrow 1$
$1 \rightarrow$ $\rightarrow 4$
$5 \rightarrow$ $\rightarrow 16$

(iii)
$4 \rightarrow$ [multiply by 3] $\rightarrow$ [?] $\rightarrow 10$
$1 \rightarrow$ $\rightarrow 1$
$6 \rightarrow$ $\rightarrow 16$

(iv)
$1 \rightarrow$ [?] $\rightarrow$ [?] $\rightarrow 3$
$2 \rightarrow$ $\rightarrow 5$
$3 \rightarrow$ $\rightarrow 7$

9. What numbers went into each of these function machines?

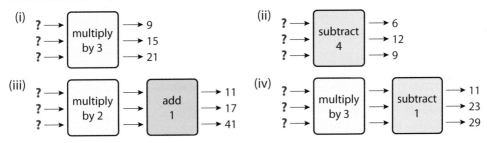

(i)
$? \rightarrow$ [multiply by 3] $\rightarrow 9$
$? \rightarrow$ $\rightarrow 15$
$? \rightarrow$ $\rightarrow 21$

(ii)
$? \rightarrow$ [subtract 4] $\rightarrow 6$
$? \rightarrow$ $\rightarrow 12$
$? \rightarrow$ $\rightarrow 9$

(iii)
$? \rightarrow$ [multiply by 2] $\rightarrow$ [add 1] $\rightarrow 11$
$? \rightarrow$ $\rightarrow 17$
$? \rightarrow$ $\rightarrow 41$

(iv)
$? \rightarrow$ [multiply by 3] $\rightarrow$ [subtract 1] $\rightarrow 11$
$? \rightarrow$ $\rightarrow 23$
$? \rightarrow$ $\rightarrow 29$

Section 19.2 Mapping diagrams

Consider this function machine: $\dots \rightarrow$ [multiply by 3] $\rightarrow$ [subtract 4] $\rightarrow \dots$

We will input all the numbers from the set $\{1, 3, 5, 7, 9\}$.

The output numbers are: $\{-1, 5, 11, 17, 23\}$.

The set of input numbers is called the **domain**.

The set of output numbers is called the **range**.

The input numbers and output numbers can be represented by a special type of diagram called a **mapping diagram**.

Each input number is mapped onto its output number.

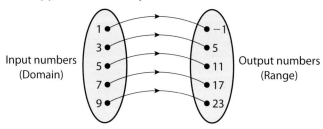

In the mapping diagram above, notice that there is one and only **one output number for each input number**.

> In mathematics, we use the word **function** for any rule that produces one output value only for each input value.

Notation for a function

Consider this rule for a function: "Double the number and add 4".

If we input x, the output will be $2x + 4$.

The rule for this function may be written in any one of these three ways:

    (i) $f(x) = 2x + 4$

   (ii) $f: x \rightarrow 2x + 4$

  (iii) $y = 2x + 4$.

These three notations tell us that if the input is 3, the output $(2x + 4)$ is $[(2 \times 3) + 4]$, i.e. 10. This can be written as $f(3) = 10$.

The codomain

Take the two sets $A = \{1, 2, 3\}$ and $B = \{1, 3, 5, 7, 9, 11\}$.

If we are asked to list the couples of the function $f: x \rightarrow 2x - 1$, where the input numbers come from set A and the output numbers come from set B, we could set up a mapping diagram as follows:

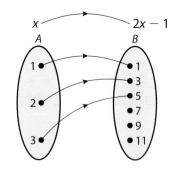

The couples are (1, 1), (2, 3) and (3, 5).

The set A is the **domain**, i.e. $\{1, 2, 3\}$.

The **range** is $\{1, 3, 5\}$.

The set B is called the **codomain**, that is, the set of allowable outputs.

∴ the codomain $= \{1, 3, 5, 7, 9, 11\}$.

> The set of inputs is called the **domain**.
>
> The set of outputs is called the **range**.
>
> The set of possible outputs is called the **codomain**.

Example 1

A function *f* is defined as $f: x \rightarrow 3x - 2$.
The domain of *f* is {0, 1, 2, 3, 4}.
Represent *f* on a mapping diagram and write out the couples generated.
What is the range of *f*?

x	3x − 2	f(x)
0	0 − 2	−2
1	3 − 2	1
2	6 − 2	4
3	9 − 2	7
4	12 − 2	10

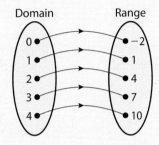

The couples are: {(0, −2), (1, 1), (2, 4), (3, 7), (4, 10)}.

The range is {−2, 1, 4, 7, 10}.

Identifying functions

When a function is represented by a mapping diagram, each element of the domain maps onto **one and only one** element of the range.

Consider these two mapping diagrams:

 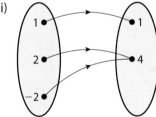

Diagram (i) is not a function since the element *b* is paired with 2 elements in the range.
Diagram (ii) is a function since each element in the domain is mapped onto one and only one element in the range.

Couples

We have already seen that a function can be written as a set of **couples** or **ordered pairs**, i.e. (input, output).
When a function is written as a set of couples, no two distinct couples will have the same input.

❯ {(1, 4), (2, 5), (3, 6), (4, 7)} is a function as no two couples have the same input.

❯ {(2, 7), (3, 8), (3, 9), (4, 12)} is **not** a function as the input 3 has two different outputs.

Exercise 19.2

1. Use the given mapping diagram to write down
   (i)   the domain
   (ii) the range
   (iii) the set of couples formed
   (iv) the rule that gives the outputs.

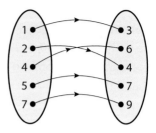

2. Copy and complete the mapping diagrams below.
   Write down the domain and range of each function.

   (i)

   Rule: Add 5

   (ii)

   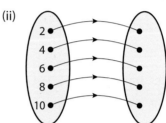

   Rule: $x \rightarrow 2x + 1$

3. State whether each of the following mapping diagrams is a function.
   Give a reason for your answer in each case:

   (i)

   (ii)

   (iii)

   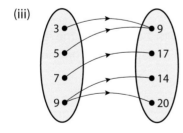

   (iv)

4. Say why the following set of couples is a function:
   {(1, 4), (2, 5), (3, 6), (4, 7)}.

5. Say why the following set of couples is not a function:
   {(2, 5), (3, 6), (5, 8), (2, 10)}.

6. Investigate if each of these sets of couples represents a function.
   If it is not a function, state the reason why.

   (i) {(0, 0), (1, 1), (2, 4), (3, 9), (4, 16)}
   (ii) {(−2, 1), (−1, 3), (−2, 5), (1, 6), (2, 9)}
   (iii) {(−3, 4), (0, 7), (2, 9), (4, 11)}

7. The diagram $x \longrightarrow$ [add 3] $\longrightarrow$ [multiply by 2] $\longrightarrow y$ shows how to find the output (y)

   for any input (x).

   Express this in the form $y = \ldots\ldots$.

   Use this function to find the values
   of the outputs in the given table.

Input (x)	Output (y)
1	
2	
3	
4	
5	

8. For each of the mapping diagrams below, write down

   (i) the domain
   (ii) the range
   (iii) the codomain.

   (a)   (b)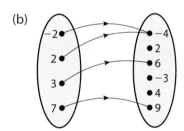

9. The rule for a function is: 'Multiply by 2 and add 3'.
   If the domain of the function is {0, 1, 3, 5}, write down

   (i) the range
   (ii) the couples generated.

10. A function f is defined as $f : x \rightarrow 3x - 1$.
    The domain of the function is {1, 2, 4, 6}.
    Write down the range of the function.

11. A function f is defined as $f(x) = 4x - 5$.
    The domain of the function is {−2, 0, 2, 4}.

    (i) What is the range of f?
    (ii) Write f as a set of couples.

12. Make a copy of this table.
Fill it in for the function machine shown below.

x	1	2	3	4	5
y					

$x \longrightarrow$ multiply by 2 $\longrightarrow$ add 7 $\longrightarrow y$

Write the function in the form $y = \ldots\ldots$.

13. This is a function machine:

$x \longrightarrow$ multiply by 4 $\longrightarrow$ add 10 $\longrightarrow y$

Write the function in the form $y = \ldots\ldots$.
If the input is 5, what is the output?
Use the function rule to find the input when the output is 22.

14. $x \longrightarrow$ multiply by 2 $\longrightarrow$ add 4 $\longrightarrow y$ describes a function.

Copy the table on the right and fill in
the missing input and output numbers.

Input	Output
3	
-2	
	14
	-8

15. In the three tables below, some input and output numbers are given.
By 'trial and error' or guessing, find the rule for each function in the form $y = \ldots\ldots$.

(i)
Input	Output
3	2
7	10
5	6
11	18

(ii)
Input	Output
1	5
3	11
5	17
10	32

(iii)
Input	Output
1	4
3	10
6	19
8	25

16. $f : x \rightarrow 6x - 2$ defines a function.
If the couples $(2, a)$, $(-4, b)$, $(c, 16)$ and $(d, -14)$ are all couples of f, work out the values
of a, b, c and d.

Section 19.3 Notation for functions

We have already seen that a function can be written in any of these ways:

(i) $f(x) = 3x - 2$ 　　　　(ii) $f : x \rightarrow 3x - 2$ 　　　　(iii) $y = 3x - 2$

In each case, the output is $(3x - 2)$ when the input is x.

The notation **f(3)** is used to represent the output number when 3 is the input number.
If $f(x) = 3x - 2$, then $f(3) = 3(3) - 2 = 9 - 2 = 7$.
Thus, $f(3) = 7$.

While $f(x)$ is generally used to describe a function, other letters such as $g(x)$ and $h(x)$ are used
when we are dealing with more than one function.

Example 1

The functions f and g are defined on R such that
$$f: x \rightarrow x + 5 \quad \text{and} \quad g: x \rightarrow x^2 - 1.$$
Find   (i) $f(3)$ (ii) $g(-3)$ (iii) $f(2k)$ (iv) $f(k+1)$ (v) $g(3k)$ (vi) $g(k+1)$

(i) $f(x) = x + 5$
$f(3) = 3 + 5$
$\quad = 8$

(ii) $g(x) = x^2 - 1$
$g(-3) = (-3)^2 - 1$
$\quad = 9 - 1 = 8$

(iii) $f(x) = x + 5$
$f(2k) = 2k + 5$

(iv) $f(x) = x + 5$
$f(k+1) = (k+1) + 5$
$\quad = k + 6$

(v) $g(x) = x^2 - 1$
$g(3k) = (3k)^2 - 1$
$\quad = 9k^2 - 1$

(vi) $g(x) = x^2 - 1$
$g(k+1) = (k+1)^2 - 1$
$\quad = k^2 + 2k + 1 - 1$
$\quad = k^2 + 2k$

Example 2

A function is defined by $f: x \rightarrow 4x - 5$.
  (i) Find $f(3)$
  (ii) Find the value of k for which $kf(3) = f(10)$.

(i) $f(x) = 4x - 5$
$f(3) = 4(3) - 5$
$\quad = 12 - 5$
$\quad = 7$

(ii) $f(3) = 7$ … from (i)
$kf(3) = 7k$
$f(10) = 4(10) - 5 = 40 - 5 = 35$
$kf(3) = f(10)$
$\Rightarrow \quad 7k = 35$
$\quad k = 5$

Exercise 19.3

1. If $f(x) = 2x - 3$, find
   (i) $f(1)$ (ii) $f(0)$ (iii) $f(2)$ (iv) $f(-1)$ (v) $f(-3)$.

2. If $f(x) = 4x - 5$, find
   (i) $f(2)$ (ii) $f(0)$ (iii) $f(-3)$ (iv) $f\left(\frac{1}{2}\right)$ (v) $f\left(\frac{1}{4}\right)$.

3. If $f(x) = x^2 - 3$, find
   (i) $f(0)$ (ii) $f(1)$ (iii) $f(2)$ (iv) $f(-2)$ (v) $f(-4)$.

4. If $f(x) = 5 - 2x$, find

    (i) $f(0)$ (ii) $f(2)$ (iii) $f(-3)$ (iv) $f\left(-\frac{1}{2}\right)$ (v) $f(k)$.

5. If $f(x) = 5x - 2$, solve the following equations:

    (i) $f(x) = 8$ (ii) $f(x) = 3$ (iii) $f(k) = -12$.

6. If $f(x) = 3x - 2$ and $g(x) = 2 - 4x$, solve these equations:

    (i) $f(x) = 4$ (ii) $g(x) = -10$ (iii) $g(x) = f(4)$.

7. Given $f(x) = 5x - 1$, find

    (i) $f(-3)$ (ii) $f\left(\frac{1}{5}\right)$ (iii) $f(k)$ (iv) $f(2k)$ (v) $f(2k - 1)$.

8. The function f is defined as $f: x \rightarrow 2 - 3x$.

    Find the value of the number k if $kf(3) = 7f(2)$.

9. If $f(x) = 2x - 3$ and $g(x) = 3 - 5x$, solve these equations:

    (i) $f(x) = 7$ (ii) $g(x) = -7$ (iii) $f(x) = g(-3)$.

10. A function is defined by $f: x \rightarrow 5x - 7$.

    (i) Find $f(4)$.   (ii) Find the value of k for which $f(-3) = kf(3)$.

11. The function f is defined by $f: x \rightarrow 3x - 4$.

    For what value of k is $f(k) + f(2k) = 0$?

12. $f: x \rightarrow 4x$ and $g: x \rightarrow x + 1$ define two functions.

    If $g(3) + k[f(3)] = 8$, find the value of k.

13. $f: x = 2x^2 - 1$ and $g(x) = x + 2$ define two functions.

    Solve these equations:

    (i) $f(x) = 3$ (ii) $g(x) = f(3)$ (iii) $f(x) = g(x)$.

14. $h: x \rightarrow 2x + a$ and $k: x \rightarrow b - 5x$ are two functions where a and b are real numbers.

    If $h(1) = -5$ and $k(-1) = 4$, find the value of a and the value of b.

15. A function $f(x)$ is defined by $f(x) = 1 + \dfrac{2}{x}$.

    (i) Evaluate $f(-4)$ and $f\left(\frac{1}{5}\right)$.

    (ii) Find the value of x for which $f(x) = 2$.

    (iii) Find the value of k if $kf(2) = f\left(\frac{1}{2}\right)$.

16. $g(x) = 1 - 4x$ defines a function.

    (i) Find $g(k + 1)$.

    (ii) Solve the equation $g(k + 1) = g(-3)$.

17. Given that $f(x) = 2^x$, find

    (i) $f(4)$ (ii) $f(-2)$ (iii) the value of x for which $f(x) = \dfrac{\sqrt{2}}{2}$.

Section 19.4 Finding coefficients of functions

In a later chapter we will learn how to draw the graphs of functions such as $f(x) = 2x + 4$ or $f(x) = x^2 + 2x - 4$.

The function $f(x) = 2x + 4$ represents a straight line.

The function $f(x) = x^2 + 2x - 4$ represents a shape like that shown on the right.
This smooth curve is called a **parabola**.

Consider the function $f(x) = ax + b$.
If we are told that (2, 4) is on this line, this is another way of saying that $f(2) = 4$.
Similarly, if (3, 0) is on the line, then $f(3) = 0$.

The following example illustrates how to find unknown coefficients of a function when given some couples of the function.

Example 1

The given diagram shows part of the graph of the function
$y = ax + b$.
Find the values of a and b.

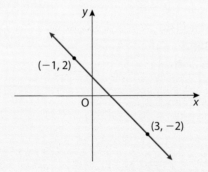

$(3, -2) \in y = ax + b$
$\Rightarrow \quad -2 = 3a + b$ i.e. $3a + b = -2$ ...①
$(-1, 2) \in y = ax + b$ i.e. $-a + b = 2$ ...②
$\Rightarrow \quad 2 = -a + b$ subtracting : $4a \quad\quad = -4$
                                  $\Rightarrow \quad\quad a = -1$

From ① : $3(-1) + b = -2$
$\Rightarrow \quad -3 + b = -2 \Rightarrow b = 1$
$\therefore \quad a = -1 \quad$ and $\quad b = 1$

Quadratic functions

A function such as $f(x) = x^2 - 3x + 2$ which contains a term in x^2 is called a **quadratic function**.

The diagram on the right shows a curve crossing the x-axis at the points where $x = -3$ and $x = 2$.

These numbers are the roots of the equation

$$(x + 3)(x - 2) = 0$$
i.e. $x^2 + x - 6 = 0$

Thus, the equation of the curve is

$$f(x) = x^2 + x - 6$$

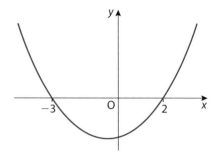

Example 2

The graph of the quadratic function
$f(x) = x^2 + bx + c$ is shown.
Find the values of b and c.
Hence write down the coordinates of p and q.

$(-1, 0) \in$ the curve $\Rightarrow f(-1) = 0$
$f(-1) = 1 - b + c \Rightarrow 1 - b + c = 0$
$\qquad \Rightarrow -b + c = -1 ...①$
$(4, 5) \in$ the curve $\Rightarrow f(4) = 5$
$f(4) = 16 + 4b + c \Rightarrow 16 + 4b + c = 5$
$\qquad \Rightarrow 4b + c = -11 ...②$
We now solve equations ① and ②
①: $-b + c = -1$
②: $\underline{4b + c = -11}$
$\quad -5b \quad = \quad 10 \Rightarrow b = -2$
From ①: $2 + c = -1 \Rightarrow c = -3$
$\quad \therefore \quad b = -2$ and $c = -3$ i.e. $f(x) = x^2 - 2x - 3$.

To find the coordinates of p, we solve the equation $f(x) = 0$.
$f(x) = 0 \Rightarrow x^2 - 2x - 3 = 0$
$\qquad \Rightarrow (x - 3)(x + 1) = 0$
$\qquad \Rightarrow x = 3$ or $x = -1$
$\quad \therefore$ the coordinates of p are $(3, 0)$

To find the coordinates of the point where a curve crosses the y-axis, we let $x = 0$.
$x = 0 \Rightarrow f(x) = 0 - 0 - 3$ i.e. $f(x) = -3 \Rightarrow y = -3$
$\quad \therefore$ the coordinates of q are $(0, -3)$

Exercise 19.4

1. $f(x) = 3x + k$ is a function.

   If $f(4) = 10$, find the value of k.

2. If $(1, 5)$ is a couple of the function $f(x) = kx + 4$, find the value of k.

3. $f(x) = ax - 6$ is a function.

   If $f(2) = -2$, find the value of a.

4. $f: x \rightarrow x^2 - 2x + k$ is a function.

   If $(1, 2)$ is a couple of the function, find the value of k.

5. $(-3, 2)$ is a point on the line $y = ax + 11$. Find the value of a.

6. $f(x) = kx^2 + 3$ is a function.

   If $(-1, -1)$ is a couple of this function, find the value of k.

7. The graph of the linear function

   $f(x) = ax + b$ is shown.

   Find the values of a and b.

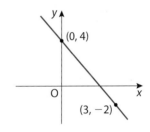

8. A function f is defined as $f: x \rightarrow 2x - 1$.

   If the mapping diagram on the right represents f, find the values of a, b and c.

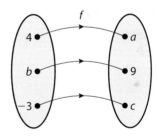

9. $g: x \rightarrow ax^2 + bx + 1$ defines a function.

   If $g(1) = 0$ and $g(2) = 3$, write down two equations in a and b.
   Solve these equations to find the values of a and b.

10. A function is defined by $f: x \rightarrow ax^2 + bx + 1$.

    If $f(1) = 0$ and $f(-1) = 0$, find the value of a and the value of b.

11. $f: x \rightarrow x^2 + px + q$ defines a function.

    Given that $f(3) = 4$ and $f(-1) = 4$, find the values of p and q.
    Using these values for p and q, solve the equation $x^2 + px + q = 0$.

12. The function $f(x) = x^2 + bx + c$ is graphed on the right.

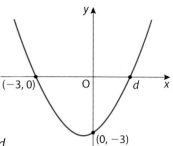

   (i) Use $f(0)$ to find the value of c.

   (ii) Use the graph to find another equation in b and c. Use this equation and the value for c found in (i) to find the value of b.

   (iii) Using these values for b and c, solve the equation $x^2 + bx + c = 0$ to find the coordinates of the point d.

13. Functions f and g are defined as follows:

$f: x \rightarrow x^2 + 1$ and $g: x \rightarrow ax + b$, where a and b are constants.
If $f(0) = g(0)$ and $g(2) = 15$, find the values of a and b.

14. The diagram shows part of the graph of the function

$$f: x \rightarrow x^2 + bx + c.$$

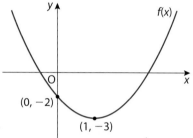

The named couples are elements of the function.

   (i) Find the values of b and c.

   (ii) If $(2, y)$ is a point on the graph, find the value of y.

15. The curve on the right is the graph of the function

$$y = x^2 + 2x - 3.$$

Find the coordinates of the points a, b and c.

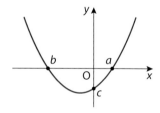

16. $f(x) = 2x^2$ and $g(x) = 3x - 1$ are two functions.

Find   (i) $f(3)$ (ii) $g(1)$ (iii) $g\left(\frac{1}{3}\right)$.

If $f(3) = kg(1)$, find k.

17. Given that $f(x) = 3^x$, find

   (i) $f(4)$ (ii) $f(-2)$ (iii) $f\left(\frac{1}{2}\right)$ (iv) the value of x for which $f(x) = \dfrac{\sqrt{3}}{3}$.

Test yourself 19

1. (a) Complete the ordered pairs below and hence draw a graph of the line $y = 2x - 4$.
   $(-2, \ldots), (0, \ldots), (2, \ldots)$.

   (b) A function f is defined by $f: x \rightarrow 5x - 1$.
   If the domain of $f = \{0, 1, 2, 3\}$, find the range of f.

   (c) The curve on the right is the graph of the function
   $$f(x) = 8 - 2x - x^2.$$
   Find the coordinates of the points marked a, b and c.

   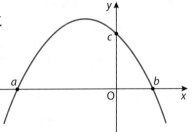

2. (a) State whether each of these mapping diagrams represents a function, giving a reason for your answers:

   (i)   (ii)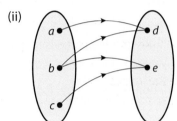

   (b) The function f is defined by $f(x) = 7 - 3x$. If $f(24) = kf(-2)$, find the value of k.

   (c) $f(x) = 2x - 1$ and $g(x) = 1 - 3x$ are two functions.
   (i) For what value of k is $f(k) + f(2k) = 4$?
   (ii) For what value of t is $tf(3) = g(t)$?

3. (a) State why the set of couples $\{(1, 3), (2, 7), (3, 10), (1, 12)\}$ is not a function.

   (b) The function f is defined by $f: x \rightarrow 3x - 4$.
   For what value of k is $f(k) + f(2k) = 1$?

   (c) The curve on the right is the graph of the function
   $$f(x) = 10 - 3x - x^2.$$
   Find the coordinates of the points marked a, b and c.

   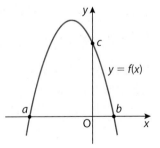

4. (a) A function f is defined by $f: x \rightarrow 5x - 3$.
   Copy and complete these three couples of f:
   $$(1, *), (3, *), (0, *).$$
   Hence draw a graph of the function $f: x \rightarrow 5x - 3$.

(b) The function f is defined on R such that $f: x \rightarrow 3x - 1$.

Find (i) $f(2)$ (ii) $f\left(\frac{1}{2}\right)$.

Find the value of $k \in N$ such that $f(2) = kf\left(\frac{1}{2}\right)$.

Investigate if $f(h) = kf\left(\frac{1}{h}\right)$.

(c) The graph shown is defined by the function $f(x) = -x^2 + kx + \ell$.

(i) What is $f(0)$?

Hence write down the value of ℓ.

(ii) Use another point on the curve to find the value of k.

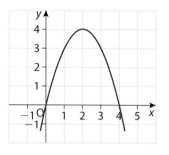

5. (a) (i) What operation does the question mark stand for in the given function machine?

(ii) $f(x) = 3x - 4$ defines a function. If the domain of $f(x)$ is $\{-3, -2, -1, 0\}$, what is the range of $f(x)$?

(b) A function is defined by $f(x) = ax^2 + bx + 1$.

If $f(-1) = 6$ and $f(1) = 2$, write down two equations in a and b.

Solve these equations to find the values of a and b.

(c) A function is defined by $f(x) = \sqrt{x^2 + 8}$.

(i) Evaluate $f(2)$ and $f(8)$.

(ii) Given that $f(2) \times f(8) = k\sqrt{6}$, find k, where $k \in N$.

6. (a) $y = 3x - 2$ defines a function.

Copy and complete the given table for this function and hence draw its graph.

x	-1	0	1	2
y				

(b) A function is defined as $f(x) = \sqrt{\dfrac{12}{x}}$, where $x > 0$.

(i) Express $f(27)$ as a fraction in its simplest form.

(ii) If $f(x) = 4\sqrt{3}$, find the value of x.

(c) The function $f(x) = x^2 + bx + c$ is graphed on the right. The curve crosses the x-axis at $(-1, 0)$ and it contains the point $(3, -4)$.

(i) Write down two equations in b and c.

(ii) Solve these equations to find the values of b and c.

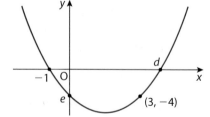

(iii) Use these values for b and c to write down the function $f(x)$.

(iv) Use this function to find the coordinates of d and e.

Drawing and interpreting real-life graphs

chapter 20

Key words

distance–time graphs   average speed   steepness   directly proportional
real-life graphs   interpret   constant rate

Section 20.1 Distance–time graphs

> A distance–time graph (or travel graph) is a special type of line graph used to describe a journey.

> The vertical axis represents the distance from a certain point, while the horizontal axis represents time.

The distance–time graph below shows the journey of a cyclist who set out from town A.

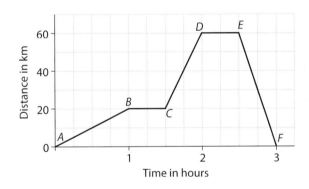

(i)   From A to B he cycled a distance of 20 km in 1 hour.

(ii) At B he stopped for half an hour which is represented by [BC].

(iii) At C he took a lift on a lorry and travelled to D, a distance of 40 km. This part of the journey took half an hour.

(iv) He then rested for half an hour. This is represented by [DE].

(v)   He then took a train back to the town he originally left and completed the 60 km return journey in half an hour. This is represented by [EF].

[Note that both A and F represent town A.]

Distance–time graphs

> A change in speed represents a change in steepness.
> The steeper the line, the faster the speed.
> The flatter the line, the slower the speed.
> A horizontal line indicates that the person or object is stopped.

The formulae that connect distance (D), time (T) and average speed (S) are given below:

$$D = S \times T \qquad S = \frac{D}{T} \qquad T = \frac{D}{S}$$

Exercise 20.1

1. This travel graph gives the distance of a boy from home.

   (i) When did the boy leave home? When did he return?

   (ii) How far was he from home at 1.00 p.m.?

   (iii) At what times was he 15 km from home?

   (iv) At what times did he rest?

   (v) When was he travelling most quickly?

2. The distance–time graph given shows Olivia's 3-hour journey.

   (i) How far did she travel in the first hour?

   (ii) For how long was she stopped?

   (iii) How far did she travel in the third hour?

   (iv) What was the total length of the journey?

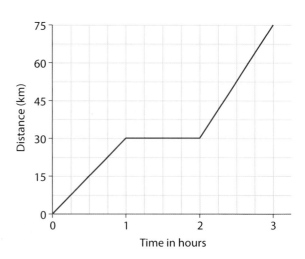

3. The travel graph shows the distance of a cyclist from his home between the times of 10. a.m. and 4.30 p.m.

   (i) How far does the cyclist travel in the first 2 hours?

   (ii) How far from home is he when he stops to rest?

   (iii) At what time does he commence the return journey?

   (iv) At 3.00 p.m. his speed changes. Does it increase or decrease? How can you tell without calculating the actual speeds?

   (v) How far does he travel?

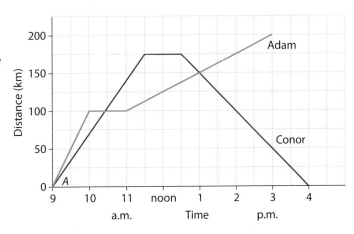

4. The graph shows the journeys of two motorists, Conor and Adam. They are travelling on the same road and in the same direction, leaving town A at 9.00 a.m.

   (i) Who travels faster in the first hour?

   (ii) How many times do they pass each other?

   (iii) At what time do they pass the second time?

   (iv) How far apart are they at 3.00 p.m.?

   (v) How far does each man travel altogether?

5. The given graph indicates the distance a cyclist must travel to work.

Use the graph to determine:

   (i) the distance to work
  (ii) the time taken to get to work
 (iii) the distance travelled after
      (a) 10 minutes
      (b) 17 minutes
  (iv) the time taken to travel
      (a) 6 km
      (b) 11 km
   (v) the average speed for the whole distance. (Exclude the two minute stop.)

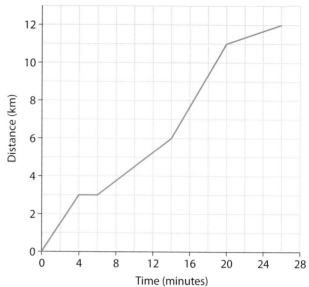

6. The graph shows the journeys of two motorists and gives their distances from their home town.

   (i) How far is David from the town when Darren starts his journey?
  (ii) At approximately what times do their paths cross?
 (iii) At what time does David begin his return journey?
  (iv) How far is Darren from town when David begins his return journey?
   (v) Who returns to town first? What time elapses before the other motorist arrives?

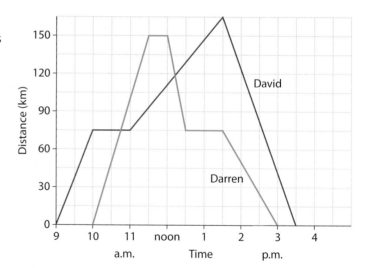

7. The travel graph shows Mr McLoone's journey by car from home to work.

At *A*, he stops to buy a newspaper.
At *B*, he stops to buy petrol.
At *D*, he arrives at work.

(i) How long does the journey take?

(ii) For how long does Mr McLoone stop to buy petrol?

(iii) What is the car's average speed from *C* to *D*?

(iv) Excluding the two stops, what was the car's average speed for the whole journey?

8. Two aircraft were flying the air route from *A* to *B* but in opposite directions. The distance from *A* is shown on the graph alongside. Use the graph to determine:

(i) the distance from *A* to *B*

(ii) in which direction the flight was completed more rapidly, and by how much

(iii) how long into the flight the planes were when they crossed

(iv) the average speed of the flight in each direction.

9. The given distance–time graph describes the journey of a family travelling from a French ferry-port to their campside for a holiday. The distance is 590 km.

Describe which line segment or point is appropriate for these statements:

(i) "We will have lunch now."
(ii) "This is the fastest section."
(iii) "At last we have arrived."
(iv) "We are only stopping for petrol."
(v) "This is the slowest section."
(vi) "This is the longest section."

Estimate the average speed for the whole journey, excluding stops.

10. Noel cycled to his friend's place. He started at 8.00 a.m. and covered 15 km in the first hour. After resting for half an hour, he then covered the next 20 km to his friend's place in two hours.
  (i) At what time did he reach his friend's place?
  (ii) How far was it from his home to his friend's place?
  (iii) Using a scale 1 cm : 5 km on the distance axis and 1 cm : $\frac{1}{2}$ hr on the time axis, make a travel graph for Noel's trip.

11. Sam and Bob travel between Dublin and Sligo.

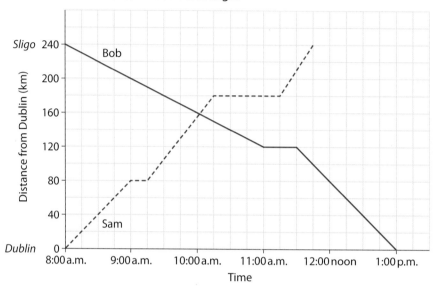

  (i) How far is it between the two towns?
  (ii) At what time do Brian and Sam pass each other?
      How far are they from Dublin when they pass?
  (iii) Who has the faster means of transport, Bob or Sam?
  (iv) At what times is Sam stationary (not moving)?
  (v) Find the average speed of each person excluding stops.

12. Abdul is going to college, 1.25 km from his home.
  He walks 250 metres to the bus stop. This takes him 4 minutes.
  A bus arrives after 5 minutes and the journey takes 6 minutes.
  (i) Draw a distance–time graph for his journey.
  (ii) Work out the speed of the bus in
      (a) metres/minute   (b) km/hour.

Section 20.2 Directly proportional graphs

Lucy is paid for the hours that she works at the rate of €12 per hour.
If she works 2 hours, she is paid €12 × 2 = €24.
If she works 5 hours, she is paid €12 × 5 = €60.

The hours worked and the pay received are said to be **directly proportional**.

When two quantities are in direct proportion, a graph is particularly useful for illustrating how one quantity increases (or decreases) relative to the second quantity.

Directly proportional graphs are always straight lines through the origin.

Example 1

The graph below shows the relationship between kilograms and pounds.

Use the graph to approximately convert
   (i)   20 pounds to kilograms (kg)
   (ii) 14 pounds to kilograms
   (iii) 4 kg to pounds
   (iv) 7.5 kg to pounds.

From the graph,
   (i)   20 pounds = 9.1 kg
   (ii) 14 pounds = 6.4 kg
   (iii) 4 kg = 8.8 pounds
   (iv) 7.5 kg = 16.5 pounds

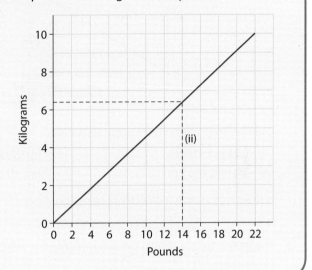

Exercise 20.2

1. In which of these graphs is h directly proportional to t?

(i) h

(ii) h

(iii) h

(iv) h
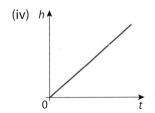

Explain your answer.

2. The graph below shows the relationship between kilometres and miles.

Use the graph to convert approximately

   (i) 60 km to miles   (ii) 80 km to miles

  (iii) 30 miles to km   (iv) 15 miles to km.

Is the given graph a directly proportional one?

3. The graph below shows the relationship between degrees Celsius (°C) and degrees Fahrenheit (°F).

Is this a directly proportional graph? Explain your answer.

Use the graph to convert approximately

   (i) 35°C to Fahrenheit   (ii) 15°C to Fahrenheit

  (iii) 50°F to Celsius   (iv) 100°F to Celsius.

If the temperature in a city on a particular day ranges between 55°F and 90°F, express this range in °C.

4. Television repair charges depend on the length of time taken for the repair, as shown on the graph.

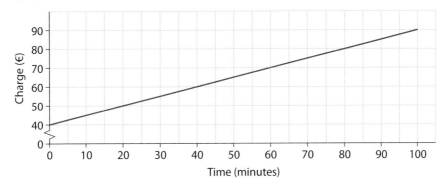

- (i) What is the charge for a repair that took 60 minutes?
- (ii) What is the charge for a repair that took 30 minutes?
- (iii) If the charge was €80, how long did the repair take?
- (iv) If the charge was €60, how long did the repair take?

The standing charge is the basic charge before the time charge is added.

- (v) What is this standing charge?

5. In which of these graphs is Q directly proportional to P? Give reasons.

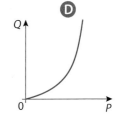

6. The given diagram shows that the length of the shadow cast by a tree at midday is directly proportional to the height of the tree.

- (i) What is the length of the shadow when the tree is 8 m in height?
- (ii) By using two points on the line, find the equation of the line in terms of s and h.
- (iii) Use the equation you have found to write down the length of the shadow when the tree is 15 metres in height.

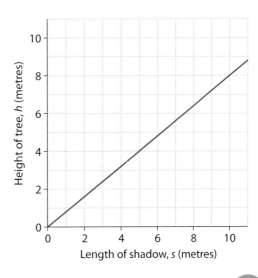

7. Is each of these statements true or false?

  (i)   The cost of petrol is directly proportional to the quantity purchased.
  (ii) The height of a person is directly proportional to their age.
  (iii) The area of a square is directly proportional to the length of the side.
  (iv) The distance travelled in a certain time by a car travelling at constant speed is directly proportional to the speed of the car.
  (v)   The time taken for a journey is directly proportional to the speed of travel.

8. The graph below shows the cost of using broadband internet for one month on three different tariffs.

The three tariffs are:

Tariff 1: Rental €30 + 10c/GB
Tariff 2: No rental but 30c/GB
Tariff 3: Rental €37.50 + 5c/GB
        with the first 60GB free

  (i)   Match each tariff with the letter of its graph.

Carol downloads more than 140 Gigabytes of data each month.

  (ii) Explain which tariff would be the cheapest for her to use.

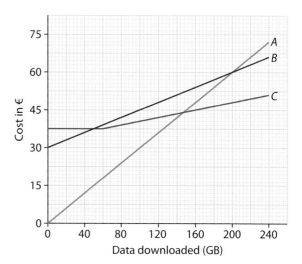

9. This graph shows how much petrol two cars use.

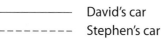 David's car
- - - - - - - - Stephen's car

  (i)   David's car travelled 80 km. How much petrol did it use?
  (ii) Stephen's car used 9 litres of petrol one day. How far did it go?
  (iii) How much more petrol does Stephen's car use than David's car when each car travels 60 km?
  (iv) Is each line graph directly proportional? Explain your answer.
  (v)   Find the equation of the broken red line in the form $y = mx$.
        Now use this equation to find the number of litres used when the car travels 300 km.

Section 20.3 Real-life graphs

When water is poured into the vessel below **at a steady rate**, the water will rise in the vessel also at a steady rate.
The graph of the water's height as time passes is shown on the right below.

 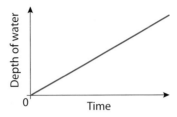

The graph is a straight line because the water rises at a **constant rate**.

Containers with sides that bulge out have a curved line graph. They may start steep, get less steep and then get steep again.
The graph of the water's height for the given container is shown on the right.
The top part of the graph is a straight line because the top part rises at a constant rate.

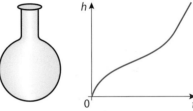

Example 1

Match these containers to their graphs when they are filled with liquid at a constant rate.

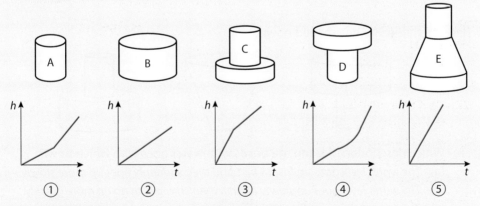

A is matched to ⑤ since A has straight sides and is thin.
B is matched to ② since B has straight sides but is wider than A.
C is matched to ① since C is initially wide with straight sides and then narrow with straight sides – hence two line segments.
D is matched to ③ since D is initially narrow with straight sides and then wide with straight sides.
E is matched to ④ since E has three sections which can be identified on the graph.

Exercise 20.3

1. Water is poured at the same rate into each of these containers.
Match these containers with their graphs showing the rate at which the water is rising.

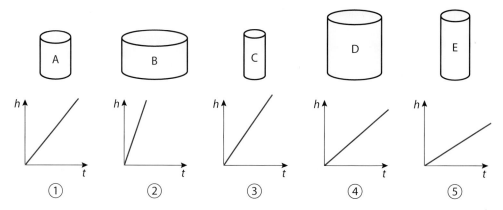

2. Water is added to the tank shown at a steady rate.
Which graph best represents the increase in the water level *h*?

3. Here are three different-shaped bowls.

   (i) Which description of filling the bowls with water goes with which bowl?
     (a) *The water level goes up fast at first and then suddenly goes up more slowly.*
     (b) *The water level goes up slowly at first, then changes to go up more quickly.*
     (c) *The water level starts by going up quickly, but gets slower and slower.*
   (ii) Which graph goes with which bowl?

4. Match the graph to the story.

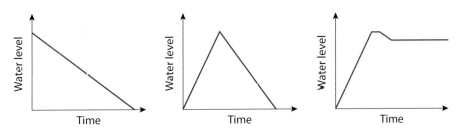

(i)   I fill a bucket with water. After a few minutes, my dog drinks some of the water.
      I decide to leave the water in the bucket in case he wants a drink later.

(ii) I quickly fill a bucket with water but the bucket is spilt and the water
      runs out.

(iii) I start with a full bucket of water and pour the water slowly over my seedlings
      until the bucket is empty.

5. Liquid is poured at a constant rate into these five containers.
The height, h cm, of the liquid in the containers is plotted against time, t seconds.
Match these containers with their graphs.

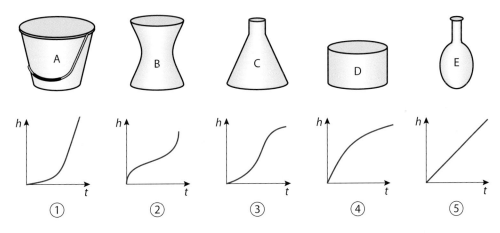

6. Liquid is poured into each of these containers at a constant rate.
Draw, for each container and on the same graph, the height of the liquid h against the
time t in seconds.

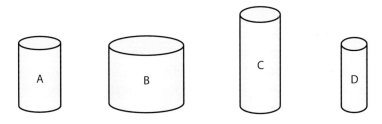

7. Here are three containers.

For each one, sketch a graph showing how it fills up with water.

8. Liquid is poured into each of these receptacles at a constant rate.

Draw, on the same graph, the height of the liquid h, against time t, in seconds.

9. The graph shows the temperature inside a new fridge.
The temperature was taken every minute over a two-hour period.

The fridge has a motor which cools down the inside.
The motor is switched on and off by a thermostat.

    (i)   What happens to the temperature in the fridge when the motor is running?
   (ii)   At what temperature does the thermostat switch the motor on?
  (iii) What happens to the temperature when the motor is not running?
  (iv) At what temperature does the thermostat switch the motor off?
   (v) For about how long does the motor run each time it is switched on?

10. A point *A* is on the circumference of a wheel.
The wheel completes one revolution where the
starting position of *A* can be at any of the points
1, 2, 3 or 4 marked in the diagram on the right.

Which one of the graphs below best represents the
height of *A* above the ground when *A* starts at:

(i) position 1   (ii) position 3   (iii) position 2 ?

Note: You will need to know that the wheel is rolled
from left to right.

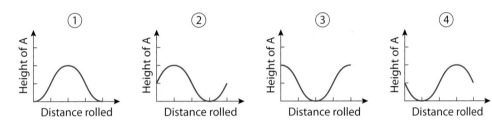

11. Each of the four containers pictured is filled with water at a steady rate.
When the level of water in each container was plotted, the graphs ① to ④ were
obtained.
Match each container to its graph.

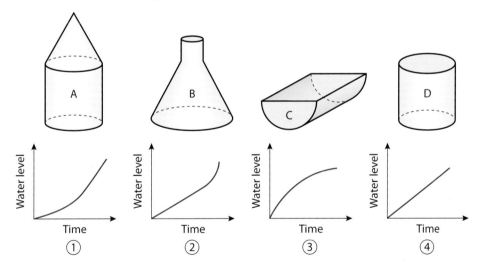

12. Each of these containers is filled with water at a steady rate.
If the graphs represent the rise in the level of the water, match each container to its graph.

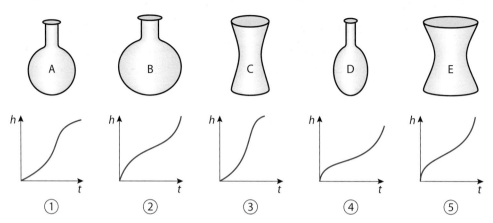

13. A stone is thrown in the air.
This graph illustrates its flight.
Use the graph to roughly find

   (i) the height of the stone after
      (a) 1.5 seconds (b) 7.5 seconds

  (ii) the time taken for the stone to
      reach
      (a) 80 metres on the way up
      (b) 80 metres on the way down.

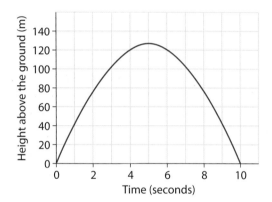

Algebraic Fractions – Formulae

Key words

algebraic fractions   simplifying terms   LCM (lowest common multiple)

mathematical sentence   algebraic division   rearranging formulae

changing the subject of a formula   writing formulae

Section 21.1 Adding algebraic fractions

To add $\frac{3}{4} + \frac{4}{5}$, we find the LCM of 4 and 5, i.e. 20.

We now express each fraction with 20 as denominator.

$$\therefore \quad \frac{3}{4} + \frac{4}{5} = \frac{5(3)}{20} + \frac{4(4)}{20} = \frac{15}{20} + \frac{16}{20} = \frac{15 + 16}{20} = \frac{31}{20}$$

Similarly, $\dfrac{6}{7} - \dfrac{2}{3} = \dfrac{3(6) - 7(2)}{21} = \dfrac{18 - 14}{21} = \dfrac{4}{21}$

Algebraic fractions can be added or subtracted in the same way as numerical fractions.

Example 1

Express as a single fraction: $\dfrac{5x - 3}{2} - \dfrac{2x + 1}{3}$

The LCM of 2 and 3 is 6.

$$\frac{5x - 3}{2} - \frac{2x + 1}{3} = \frac{3(5x - 3) - 2(2x + 1)}{6}$$

$$= \frac{15x - 9 - 4x - 2}{6} = \frac{11x - 11}{6}$$

Simplifying algebraic terms

The fraction $\frac{8}{12}$ can be simplified by dividing the numerator and denominator by 4, as shown.

$$\frac{^{2}\cancel{8}}{_{3}\cancel{12}} = \frac{2}{3}$$

Similarly, the algebraic fraction $\dfrac{4ab}{2b}$ can be simplified by dividing the numerator and denominator by any common factors.

Thus, $\dfrac{4ab}{2b} = \dfrac{^{2}\cancel{4} \times a \times \cancel{b}^{1}}{_{1}\cancel{2} \times \cancel{b}_{1}} = 2 \times a = 2a$

Example 2

Simplify each of the following:

(i) $\dfrac{9x^2y}{3x}$ (ii) $\dfrac{12a^3b}{ab^2}$

(i) $\dfrac{9x^2y}{3x} = \dfrac{^3\cancel{9} \times \cancel{x}^1 \times x \times y}{_1\cancel{3} \times \cancel{x}_1}$

$= 3xy$

(ii) $\dfrac{12a^3b}{ab^2} = \dfrac{12 \times a \times a \times \cancel{a}^1 \times \cancel{b}^1}{_1\cancel{a} \times b \times \cancel{b}_1}$

$= \dfrac{12a^2}{b}$

Exercise 21.1

1. Simplify each of the following expressions:

(i) $\dfrac{10ab}{2b}$ (ii) $\dfrac{8xy}{4x}$ (iii) $\dfrac{15cd}{5d}$ (iv) $\dfrac{18ab}{6a}$

(v) $\dfrac{8x^2y}{4xy}$ (vi) $\dfrac{16b^2c}{2c}$ (vii) $\dfrac{14x^3y}{2x^2y}$ (viii) $\dfrac{28ab^2}{7ab}$

2. Simplify these expressions:

(i) $\dfrac{3}{x} \times \dfrac{4x}{9}$ (ii) $\dfrac{km}{4n} \times \dfrac{2n}{m}$ (iii) $\dfrac{ab}{3} \times \dfrac{6b}{a}$ (iv) $\dfrac{2ab \times 6a}{3a}$

(v) $\dfrac{x}{3} \div \dfrac{x}{6}$ (vi) $\dfrac{3}{2x} \div \dfrac{1}{3x}$ (vii) $\dfrac{3ab^2}{2} \div \dfrac{ab}{6}$ (viii) $\dfrac{8a \times 3ak}{2a \times 6k}$

3.

A	E	G	L	M	N	O	P	R
$2b$	$4bc$	bc^2	$4d$	cd	$2b^2$	$3bd$	$3c$	$2b^2d$

Simplify each expression below as far as you can.
Use the code above to find a letter for each expression.

Rearrange each set of letters to spell a fruit.

(i) $\dfrac{8cd}{2c}$ $\qquad$ $\dfrac{12bc}{3}$ $\qquad$ $\dfrac{15cd}{5d}$ $\qquad$ $\dfrac{4bc}{2c}$ $\qquad$ $\dfrac{9c^2b}{3cb}$

(ii) $\dfrac{18b^2d}{6b}$ $\qquad$ $\dfrac{10ab^2}{5a}$ $\qquad$ $\dfrac{20b^2c^2}{5bc}$ $\qquad$ $\dfrac{12cd^5}{3cd^4}$ $\qquad$ $\dfrac{5c^2d}{5c}$

4. Express each of the following as a single fraction:

(i) $\dfrac{1}{2} + \dfrac{2}{3}$ (ii) $\dfrac{3}{4} + \dfrac{3}{5}$ (iii) $\dfrac{5}{12} + \dfrac{2}{12} + \dfrac{1}{12}$

(iv) $\dfrac{7}{8} - \dfrac{3}{4}$ (v) $\dfrac{x}{2} + \dfrac{x}{3}$ (vi) $\dfrac{x}{5} + \dfrac{x}{3}$

Express each of these as a single fraction.

5. $\dfrac{3x}{4} + \dfrac{5x}{2}$

6. $\dfrac{3x}{5} + \dfrac{2x}{3}$

7. $\dfrac{x}{4} - \dfrac{x}{6}$

8. $\dfrac{x}{2} - \dfrac{x}{5}$

9. $\dfrac{7x}{5} - \dfrac{x}{2}$

10. $\dfrac{3x}{4} - \dfrac{2x}{5}$

11. $\dfrac{x+1}{2} + \dfrac{x}{2}$

12. $\dfrac{x+1}{2} + \dfrac{x+4}{2}$

13. $\dfrac{x+4}{3} + \dfrac{2x+1}{3}$

14. $\dfrac{3x-4}{5} + \dfrac{5x-2}{5}$

15. $\dfrac{3x-2}{4} + \dfrac{5x+6}{4}$

16. $\dfrac{2x+1}{3} + \dfrac{2x-3}{3}$

17. $\dfrac{2x+1}{3} + \dfrac{x+4}{2}$

18. $\dfrac{2x-1}{3} + \dfrac{x+2}{4}$

19. $\dfrac{2x-1}{6} + \dfrac{x-3}{4}$

20. $\dfrac{5x-1}{4} - \dfrac{2x-4}{5}$

21. $\dfrac{2x-3}{2} + \dfrac{x-1}{4} - \dfrac{5}{6}$

22. $\dfrac{x-6}{3} + \dfrac{3}{4} - \dfrac{3x-4}{2}$

23. $\dfrac{3x-1}{4} - \dfrac{x}{10} - \dfrac{4x+2}{5}$

24. $\dfrac{3x+5}{6} - \dfrac{1}{12} - \dfrac{2x+3}{4}$

25. $\dfrac{3}{5} - \dfrac{2x-1}{10} + \dfrac{3x-2}{4}$

26. Express in its simplest form the perimeter of the given triangle.

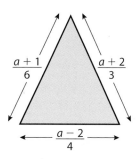

Section 21.2 Solving equations involving fractions

Consider the equation $\dfrac{x-1}{5} = 4$.

To get rid of the fraction, we multiply both sides by 5.

$$\therefore \ \frac{{}^{1}\cancel{5}(x-1)}{\cancel{5}_{1}} = 4 \times 5$$

$$x - 1 = 20$$

$$x - 1 + 1 = 20 + 1$$

$$x = 21$$

> If an equation contains more than one fraction, we multiply each part by the lowest common multiple (LCM) of the denominators.

Example 1

Solve each of these equations:

(i) $\dfrac{3x}{4} - \dfrac{x}{2} = 3$

(ii) $\dfrac{2x - 5}{3} = \dfrac{x - 2}{2}$

(i) The LCM of 4 and 2 is 4.
Multiply each term by 4.

$$\dfrac{4(3x)}{4} - \dfrac{4(x)}{2} = 3 \times 4$$
$$3x - 2x = 12$$
$$x = 12$$

(ii) The LCM of 3 and 2 is 6.
Multiply each term by 6.

$$\dfrac{6(2x - 5)}{3} = \dfrac{6(x - 2)}{2}$$
$$2(2x - 5) = 3(x - 2)$$
$$4x - 10 = 3x - 6$$
$$4x - 3x - 10 = 3x - 6 - 3x$$
$$x - 10 = -6$$
$$x - 10 + 10 = -6 + 10$$
$$x = 4$$

Example 2

Solve the equation: $\dfrac{3x - 1}{6} - \dfrac{x - 3}{4} = \dfrac{4}{3}$

The LCM of 6, 4 and 3 is 12.
We now multiply each term by 12.

$$\dfrac{12(3x - 1)}{6} - \dfrac{12(x - 3)}{4} = \dfrac{12(4)}{3}$$
$$2(3x - 1) - 3(x - 3) = 4(4)$$
$$6x - 2 - 3x + 9 = 16$$
$$3x + 7 = 16$$
$$3x + 7 - 7 = 16 - 7$$
$$3x = 9$$
$$x = 3$$

Exercise 21.2

Solve the following equations:

1. $\dfrac{2x}{3} = 6$

2. $\dfrac{3x}{5} = 3$

3. $\dfrac{x}{2} = \dfrac{6}{4}$

4. $\dfrac{3x}{4} = \dfrac{9}{2}$

5. $\dfrac{5x}{3} = 10$

6. $\dfrac{x - 3}{2} = 4$

7. $\dfrac{3x - 1}{4} = 2$

8. $\dfrac{3x - 1}{4} = 8$

9. $\dfrac{2x + 1}{3} = \dfrac{1}{2}$

10. $\dfrac{2x - 5}{3} = \dfrac{x - 2}{3}$

11. $\dfrac{x - 3}{4} = \dfrac{x - 2}{5}$

12. $\dfrac{x + 2}{6} = \dfrac{2x - 5}{3}$

13. $\dfrac{2x}{5} + \dfrac{x}{2} = \dfrac{9}{2}$

14. $\dfrac{2x}{3} - \dfrac{x}{4} = \dfrac{5}{6}$

15. $\dfrac{3x}{4} - \dfrac{5x}{8} = \dfrac{1}{2}$

16. $\dfrac{2x}{3} - \dfrac{x}{4} = \dfrac{5}{2}$

17. $\dfrac{2x - 1}{3} + \dfrac{x}{4} = \dfrac{6}{4}$

18. $\dfrac{x - 3}{6} = \dfrac{x}{5} - \dfrac{3}{2}$

19. $\dfrac{x + 2}{4} + \dfrac{x - 3}{2} = \dfrac{1}{2}$

20. $\dfrac{x + 2}{4} - \dfrac{x - 3}{3} = \dfrac{1}{2}$

21. $\dfrac{3x - 1}{6} - \dfrac{x - 3}{4} = \dfrac{4}{3}$

22. $\dfrac{x - 2}{5} + \dfrac{2x - 3}{10} = \dfrac{1}{2}$

23. $\dfrac{2x - 3}{5} + \dfrac{1}{20} = \dfrac{x - 1}{4}$

24. $\dfrac{3x - 1}{2} - \dfrac{2x - 5}{3} = 2$

25. $\dfrac{x - 2}{3} + \dfrac{x - 3}{4} = \dfrac{x - 1}{2}$

26. $\dfrac{2x - 1}{4} - \dfrac{x - 1}{5} = 1$

27. $\dfrac{3x - 2}{6} - \dfrac{3x + 1}{4} = \dfrac{2}{3}$

28. $\dfrac{3(x - 4)}{5} + 3 = \dfrac{3(x - 5)}{2}$

29. $\dfrac{4x + 5}{5} + \dfrac{2x + 7}{2} = \dfrac{3x}{10}$

30. The diagram shows an isosceles triangle ABC.

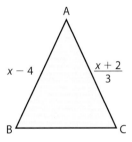

If $|AB| = |AC|$,

   (i) write down an equation in terms of x.

   (ii) work out the length of [AB].

Section 21.3 Solving problems involving fractions ———

The ability to change a problem expressed in words into a mathematical sentence is very important in mathematics.

You will already have changed statements like that shown on the right into mathematical sentences.

> I think of a number.
> I take off 5.
> I multiply the result by 3.
> My answer is 21.
> What is my number?

Discuss which of these equations you would use to solve this puzzle.

$3x - 5 = 21$ $3(x - 5) = 21$ $x - 5 \times 3 = 21$

In this section we will deal with some simple problems that involve the use of fractions.

Example 1

If the sum of a quarter of a number and a fifth of the same number is 18, find the number.

Let x be the number.

$\frac{1}{4}$ of the number $= \frac{x}{4}$ $\qquad$ $\frac{1}{5}$ of the number $= \frac{x}{5}$

The equation is: $\frac{x}{4} + \frac{x}{5} = 18$

Multiply each term by 20, the LCM of 4 and 5.

$$\frac{20(x)}{4} + \frac{20(x)}{5} = \frac{20(18)}{1}$$

$$5x + 4x = 360$$
$$9x = 360$$
$$x = 40$$

The required number is 40.

Example 2

One number is 4 bigger than another number.
One quarter of the smaller number and one third of the larger sum to 6.
Find the numbers.

Let x and $(x + 4)$ be the numbers.

$\frac{1}{4}$ of the smaller number $= \frac{x}{4}$ $\qquad$ $\frac{1}{3}$ of the larger number $= \frac{x + 4}{3}$

Equation: $\frac{x}{4} + \frac{x + 4}{3} = \frac{6}{1}$

Multiply each term by 12, the LCM of 4, 3 and 1.

$$\frac{12(x)}{4} + \frac{12(x + 4)}{3} = 12(6)$$

$$3x + 4(x + 4) = 72$$
$$3x + 4x + 16 = 72$$
$$7x + 16 = 72$$
$$7x + 16 - 16 = 72 - 16$$
$$7x = 56$$
$$x = 8$$

The two numbers x and $(x + 4)$ are 8 and 12.

Exercise 21.3

1. The sum of a number and half the number is 12. Find the number.

2. If the sum of half a number and a third of the same number is 15, find the number.

3. The sum of half and three quarters of a certain number is 20. Find the number.

4. When half a certain number is taken from three quarters of the number, the result is 5. Find the number.

5. One number is 5 bigger than another number. When one third of the smaller number is added to half the bigger number, the answer is 10. Find the smaller number.

6. When 5 is added to a number and the result is divided by 4, the answer is 3. Find the number.

7. When 3 is taken from four times a certain number and the result is divided by 7, the answer is 3. Find the number.

8. I think of a number x. I add 8 to the number and then divide the total by 3. The result is the same as half the number I thought of. Find the value of x.

9. One number is 3 greater than another number. When one sixth of the bigger number is taken from one third of the smaller one, the result is 2. Find the two numbers.

10. x and $x + 1$ are two consecutive natural numbers. When one fifth of the smaller number is added to one quarter of the larger one, the result is 7. Find the value of x.

11. A father is 30 years older than his son. When one fifth of the father's age is added to one third of the son's age, the result is 14 years. Find the son's age.

12. The length of a rectangle is $(2x + 3)$ cm.
The width of the rectangle is $\frac{1}{2}(x + 3)$ cm.
If the perimeter of the rectangle is 49 cm, find the value of x.

Section 21.4 Algebraic division

We have already learned how to multiply two algebraic expressions such as $(x + 4)(x + 3)$.

In this section, we will learn how to divide an expression such as $x^2 + x - 12$ by $(x + 4)$ by using a method very similar to long division in arithmetic.
The work is laid out as follows:

$$
\begin{array}{r}
x - 3 \\
x + 4 \overline{\smash{)}\, x^2 + x - 12} \\
\underline{x^2 + 4x} \\
-3x - 12 \\
\underline{-3x - 12}
\end{array}
$$

... Divide x into x^2

... Multiply $(x + 4)$ by x

... Subtract and then divide x into $-3x$

... Multiply $(x + 4)$ by -3 and then subtract

The answer is $x - 3$.

Example 1

Divide $2x^3 + x^2 - 8x + 3$ by $(2x - 3)$.

$$\begin{array}{r} x^2 + 2x - 1 \\ 2x - 3\overline{)2x^3 + x^2 - 8x + 3} \\ 2x^3 - 3x^2 \\ 4x^2 - 8x \\ 4x^2 - 6x \\ -2x + 3 \\ -2x + 3 \end{array}$$

... Divide $2x^3$ by $2x$ to get x^2

... Multiply $(2x - 3)$ by x^2

... Subtract and then divide $4x^2$ by $2x$ to get $2x$

... Multiply $(2x - 3)$ by $2x$ and then subtract

... Subtract

The answer is $x^2 + 2x - 1$.

Take the expression $x^3 + 11x - 30$. Here there is no term in x^2.

If we are asked to divide $x^3 + 11x - 30$ by $(x - 2)$, we rewrite the first expression as $x^3 + 0x^2 + 11x - 30$, and then divide by $(x - 2)$.

Example 2

Divide $4x^3 - 13x - 6$ by $x - 2$.

Rewrite $4x^3 - 13x - 6$ as $4x^3 + 0x^2 - 13x - 6$.

$$\begin{array}{r} 4x^2 + 8x + 3 \\ x - 2\overline{)4x^3 + 0x^2 - 13x - 6} \\ 4x^3 - 8x^2 \\ 8x^2 - 13x \\ 8x^2 - 16x \\ 3x - 6 \\ 3x - 6 \end{array}$$

... Divide $4x^3$ by x to get $4x^2$

... Multiply $(x - 2)$ by $4x^2$

... Subtract

... Divide $8x^2$ by x

$\therefore$ $4x^3 - 13x - 6 \div x - 2$ is $4x^2 + 8x + 3$

Exercise 21.4

Divide each of the following:

1. $x^2 + 5x + 6 \div x + 3$

2. $x^2 + 8x + 15 \div x + 5$

3. $x^2 + 9x + 14 \div x + 2$

4. $2x^2 + 9x + 4 \div x + 4$

5. $6x^2 + 5x + 1 \div 2x + 1$

6. $2x^2 + x - 10 \div 2x + 5$

7. $6x^2 - 10x - 4 \div 3x + 1$

8. $2x^2 - 7x - 4 \div x - 4$

9. $3x^2 - 22x + 7 \div 3x - 1$

10. $6x^2 + 11x - 35 \div 2x + 7$

11. $10x^2 - 7x - 12 \div 2x - 3$

12. $15x^2 - 26x + 8 \div 5x - 2$

13. $x^3 + 3x^2 + 5x + 3 \div x + 1$

14. $x^3 + 5x^2 + 11x + 10 \div x + 2$

15. $x^3 + 3x^2 - 10x - 24 \div x - 3$

16. $3x^3 - 2x^2 - 19x - 6 \div 3x + 1$

17. $2x^3 - x^2 - 7x + 6 \div 2x - 3$

18. $2x^3 - 3x^2 - 12x + 20 \div 2x + 5$

19. $2x^3 + 9x^2 - 55x + 50 \div 2x - 5$

20. $2x^3 + 3x^2 - 8x - 12 \div 2x + 3$

21. $x^3 - 19x - 30 \div x - 5$

22. $4x^3 - 11x + 3 \div 2x - 3$

23. $6x^3 - 13x^2 + 4 \div 2x + 1$

24. $3x^3 + 9x^2 + 48 \div x + 4$

25. If the area of a rectangle is found by multiplying the length by the breadth, find the missing side in each of these rectangles.

(i)

Area $= 6x^2 - x - 12$ **?**

$3x + 4$

(ii)

Area $= 10x^2 + x - 2$ $2x + 1$

?

Section 21.5 Rearranging formulae

Examine the box on the right to see how the letters in the formula $a = 6b + 5$ have been changed around.

We have changed the formula from

$a = 6b + 5$ to $b = \dfrac{a - 5}{6}$.

$$a = 6b + 5$$
$$a - 5 = 6b + 5 - 5$$
$$a - 5 = 6b$$
$$\frac{a - 5}{6} = b \text{ or } b = \frac{a - 5}{6}$$

In the formula $b = \dfrac{a - 5}{6}$, we have expressed b in terms of a.

This is known as **rearranging the formula** to make b the **subject of the formula**.

The process of changing the subject of a formula is very similar to the steps we use when solving an equation.

> An equation remains unchanged if the same operation is performed on both sides.

The following examples will illustrate the basic rules for changing the subject of a formula.

Example 1

If $bc - d = a$, make c the subject of the formula.

$$bc - d = a$$
$$\therefore \quad bc = a + d \quad \text{... add } d \text{ to both sides}$$
$$\therefore \quad c = \frac{a + d}{b} \quad \text{... divide both sides by } b$$

Example 2

If $a = \dfrac{b}{c} - d$, make b the subject of the formula.

$$a = \frac{b}{c} - d$$
$$ac = b - cd \quad \text{... multiply each term by } c$$
$$ac + cd = b$$
$$b = ac + cd$$

Example 3

If $y = \dfrac{c - ax}{b}$, make x the subject of the formula.

$$y = \frac{c - ax}{b}$$
$$by = c - ax \quad \text{... multiply each term by } b$$
$$by + ax = c$$
$$ax = c - by$$
$$x = \frac{c - by}{a}$$

Exercise 21.5

1. Change the following equations to the form $y = \ldots$

    (i) $2x + y - 4 = 0$ (ii) $2x + y = -7$ (iii) $3x + y - 7 = 0$

2. Make the underlined letter the subject of the formula in each of the following:

    (i) $2\underline{x} - 4 = y$ (ii) $a = 8\underline{b} - 6$ (iii) $c = 4\underline{d} - 1$ (iv) $h = 2\underline{k} - 2$

3. Rearrange each of these formulas to make the underlined letter the subject:

    (i) $a = 3\underline{b} - 5$ (ii) $b = 4\underline{w} + 2$ (iii) $d = 6\underline{e} - 12$ (iv) $g = 18 - 5\underline{h}$

4. Which of the following are correct rearrangements of $a = 2b - 10$?

A $b = \dfrac{a - 10}{2}$ **B** $b = \dfrac{a}{2} + 5$ **C** $b = \dfrac{a + 10}{2}$ **D** $b = \dfrac{a + 2}{10}$ **E** $b = \dfrac{a - 2}{10}$ **F** $b = \dfrac{10 + a}{2}$

5. Copy and complete each of the following:

(i) $v = u + at$

$v - \square = at$

$t = \ldots$

(ii) $ap + bq = k$

$ap = k - \square$

$p = \dfrac{k - \square}{\square}$

(iii) $p = \dfrac{g}{5} + 3h$

$p - \square = \dfrac{g}{5}$

$\square \, (p - \square) = g$

$g = \ldots$

6. Make x the subject of the formula in each of these:

(i) $x - y = 2z$ (ii) $3x - b = 4c$ (iii) $6y + 3x = 7$ (iv) $\dfrac{x}{3} - 2y = 8$

7. Make a the subject of the formula in each of these:

(i) $2a - b = \frac{1}{2}$ (ii) $ab - 3a = 5$ (iii) $7(a - 3) = 4b$

8. Make the letter in brackets the subject of the formula in each of the following:

(i) $c = \dfrac{a}{2} - 4b \ldots (a)$ (ii) $2(a - 2b) = 3c \ldots (a)$ (iii) $2x - \dfrac{1}{3} = \dfrac{y}{3} \ldots (x)$

(iv) $5(b - 3) = \dfrac{a}{2} \ldots (b)$ (v) $x = \dfrac{y - 2z}{3} \ldots (z)$ (vi) $a = \dfrac{b}{2} - \dfrac{3c}{4} \ldots (b)$

9. Make x the subject of the formula in each of these:

(i) $xa + xb = 3c$ (ii) $ax - 3x = 5$ (iii) $y + \dfrac{2}{3} = \dfrac{x - 1}{3}$

10. If $k = s(a - b)$, make b the subject of the formula.

11. The formula $h = \dfrac{a}{k} + j$ gives h in terms of a, k and j.

Which of the following are correct rearrangements of the formula?

A $a = hk - j$ **B** $a = k(h - j)$ **C** $a = jk - kh$ **D** $a = \dfrac{k}{h - j}$ **E** $a = hk - jk$

12. Make the letter in brackets the subject of the formula in each of the following:

(i) $x = \dfrac{2y - 3z}{4} \ldots (z)$ (ii) $\dfrac{b}{3} + \dfrac{3c}{4} = 2a \ldots (b)$ (iii) $\dfrac{3x}{4} = 5(y + z) \ldots (y)$

(iv) $\dfrac{ab}{3} = \dfrac{b}{2} + c \ldots (b)$ (v) $t = \dfrac{x - 2y}{z} \ldots (y)$ (vi) $\dfrac{p}{q} = \dfrac{q}{t} + 1 \ldots (t)$

(vii) $y = \dfrac{3x + 4}{x - 1} \ldots (x)$ (viii) $p = \dfrac{qr}{q - r} \ldots (r)$

13. Given that $z = \dfrac{3y + 2}{y - 1}$, express y in terms of z.

Hence find the value of y when $z = \frac{1}{2}$.

423

14. The area A of a trapezium can be written $A = \dfrac{(a + b)h}{2}$.

    (i) Rearrange this formula to make h the subject.

   (ii) Work out the height of a trapezium whose area is 100 cm²
and whose parallel sides are 6.5 cm and 7.8 cm.
Give your answer to the nearest whole number.

Section 21.6 Evaluating and writing formulae

A **formula** describes the relationship between two or more variables.
For example, the formula for the area of a rectangle is
$$A = \ell \times b$$
If $\ell = 6$ and $b = 4$, then $A = 6 \times 4 = 24$.
For different values of ℓ and b, you get the corresponding value for A.

Example 1

If $V = \pi r^2 h$, find V when $r = 3$ and $h = 8$.

$V = \pi r^2 h$
$V = \pi \times 3^2 \times 8$
$V = 226.19$ ... use the π key on your calculator

Writing formulae

It is important to be able to **derive a formula** from information that you are given. Here is an example:

If the cost (€C) of hiring a car consists of a fixed daily charge of €F and €k for each kilometre travelled, then the cost of hiring a car for 12 days, having travelled 800 km, is given by the formula
$$€C = 12F + 800k.$$

Example 2

The number of children at a party is four times the number of adults.
Three teenagers are helping with the party.
If a represents the number of adults at the party, find a formula for N, the number of people at the party.

If there are a adults at the party, there are $4a$ children.
The number of people at the party is adults + children + teenagers
    ∴ $N = a + 4a + 3$ ... for every 1 adult, there are 4 children
        $N = 5a + 3$

Exercise 21.6

1. (i) If $V = \dfrac{AH}{3}$, find V when $A = 12$ and $H = 4$.

   (ii) If $s = ut + \frac{1}{2}at^2$, find s when $u = 10$, $t = 5$ and $a = 8$.

   (iii) If $A = \dfrac{h}{2}(a + b)$, find A when $h = 12$, $a = 10$ and $b = 9$.

   (iv) If $A = \frac{1}{2}h(x + y)$, find A when $h = 12$, $x = 6$ and $y = 3$.

2. The formula $C = \frac{5}{9}(F - 32)$ changes degrees Celsius into degrees Fahrenheit.
   Find C when
   (i) $F = 212°$ (ii) $F = 32°$ (iii) $F = -40°$ (iv) $F = 14°$ (v) $F = -13°$.

3. If $v = u + at$, find
   (i) v when $u = 5$, $a = 4$ and $t = 6$
   (ii) u when $v = 25$, $a = 3$ and $t = 5$
   (iii) a when $v = 15$, $u = 5$ and $t = 3$.

4. If $V = \sqrt{u^2 - 2as}$, find V when $u = 0$, $a = -10$ and $s = 5$.

5. The general equation of a straight line is $y = mx + c$.
   (i) Find the value of y when $m = \frac{1}{2}$, $x = 4$ and $c = -2$.

   Rearrange the formula to make m the subject.
   (ii) Now find the value of m when $x = 3$, $y = 5$ and $c = -4$.

6. Write down a formula for P, the perimeter of each of these figures:

   (i)   (ii)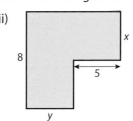

7. Given that $T = \dfrac{ab}{6} + C$, find the value of T when $a = 4$, $b = 12$ and $C = 5$.
   Rearrange the formula to make b the subject.
   Now find the value of b when $T = 15$, $a = 5$ and $C = 4$.

8. The cost of hiring a taxi from the airport is $C = 3 + 1.5k$, where C is the cost in euro and k is the number of kilometres driven.
   (i) Find the cost of a journey of 12 km.
   (ii) Joe hired a taxi from the airport to his house. The cost was €33. How far from the airport does Joe live?

9. The time taken T, in minutes, to complete my homework consists of 15 minutes to get my books organised and then 40 minutes to do each assignment, a.
   Write down a formula, making T the subject.

10. The members of the school social committee calculate that the profit, in euro, made on the school disco is given by

   $P = 5T - 900$,

where T represents the number of tickets sold. Find:

   (i) the profit made when 195 tickets are sold
   (ii) the number of tickets sold if the profit is €870
   (iii) the number of tickets that must be sold in order to break even (i.e., no profit made).

11. The cost of hiring a minibus is given by the formula $C = 20 + 12d + 2k$, where C is the cost in euro, d is the number of days the minibus is hired for, and k is the number of kilometres the minibus travels.

   (i) The minibus is hired for 8 days and travels 300 km.
   Calculate the total cost of hiring the minibus.
   (ii) Margaret hires the bus for 6 days and the total bill comes to €452.
   How many kilometres did she travel?

12. On each long side of a table at a restaurant, the number of seats is equal to the length of the table (in metres) multiplied by 2.
Two more people can sit at each end of the table.

   (i) Write a formula that gives the number of people at a table of length ℓ metres.
   (ii) Find the number of people who can sit at a table 6 m long.
   (iii) What length of table would have 32 seats?

13. The diagram shows a trapezium.

   (i) Show that the area, A, of the trapezium is given by $A = 2x^2$.
   (ii) Rearrange this formula to make x the subject.
   (iii) Find the value of x for a trapezium of area 20 cm².

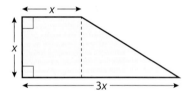

14. $C = 180R + 2000$ is the formula which gives the capacity, C litres, of the tank needed to supply water to R hotel rooms.

   (i) If $R = 5$, work out the value of C.
   (ii) If $C = 3440$, work out the value of R.
   (iii) A water tank has a capacity of 3800 litres.
   Work out the greatest number of hotel rooms it could supply.

15. A taxi driver charges a fare (F) of €4 added to €1.50 per kilometre (k) added to €2 per passenger (p).

   (i) Write a formula that relates the fare to the number of kilometres travelled and the number of passengers.
   (ii) Find the fare for 4 passengers if the journey was 18 km in length.
   (iii) If 3 passengers paid a total of €28, how long was the journey?

Test yourself 21

1. (a) Simplify each of these as much as possible:

   (i) $\dfrac{8x^3}{2x}$ (ii) $\dfrac{12xy^2}{3xy}$ (iii) $\dfrac{10x^2}{7} \times \dfrac{14y^2}{5xy}$

   (b) (i) If $y = \dfrac{2x - 6}{3x - 4}$, express x in terms of y.

        (ii) Divide $x^3 + 5x^2 - 2x - 24$ by $(x + 3)$.

   (c) Solve the equation $\dfrac{x}{3} + \dfrac{2x - 2}{5} = 4$

2. (a) Evaluate $\dfrac{ab}{a - b}$ when $a = \frac{1}{2}$ and $b = \frac{1}{3}$.

   (b) If $7a - \dfrac{ab}{c} = c$, express b in terms of a and c.
   Hence find the value of b when $a = -1$ and $c = -3$.

   (c) The given figure consists of a square
   and a rectangle.

        (i) If the perimeter of the figure is P cm,
   express P in terms of x, y and z.
        (ii) If $x = 2y$, $y = 2z$ and $P = 55$,
   find the value of x.

3. (a) Divide $x^3 - x^2 - 14x + 24$ by $(x - 2)$.

   (b) The number of hours (H) of sleep that children need depends on their age (A) in
   years and is given by the formula $H = 17 - \dfrac{A}{2}$.

        (i) Find the number of hours of sleep needed when a child is 14 years old.
        (ii) Find how old the child is who needs 8 hours sleep.

   (c) Solve the equation $\dfrac{x + 1}{4} - \dfrac{x}{3} = \dfrac{1}{12}$

4. (a) Evaluate $\dfrac{2}{x + 2} + \dfrac{3}{2x + 1}$ when $x = \frac{1}{2}$

   (b) (i) If $\dfrac{b}{2x} = b - a$, express x in terms of a and b.

        (ii) Simplify as far as possible:
   $$\dfrac{3a^2b}{5c} \div \dfrac{9ab}{10}$$

   (c) In the given triangle, the two equal
   sides are marked.
   If the perimeter of the triangle is 26 cm,
   write an equation in x and solve it to find
   its value.

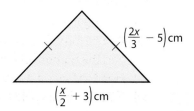

5. (a) Express $\dfrac{3x - 1}{3} + \dfrac{x + 5}{4}$ as a single fraction in its simplest form.

(b) The charge C, in euro, for hiring a hall for an event is $C = 150 + 2N$, where N stands for the number of people at the event.
   (i) Find the charge when 250 people are present.
   (ii) Find the number of people at the event when the charge is €790.

(c) If $\dfrac{3a - 2b}{3} = \dfrac{1}{2}$, express a in terms of b.

Use your result to show that $6a - 4b$ can be expressed as a single number k, where $k \in N$ and write down this number.

6. (a) If $\dfrac{1}{x} = \dfrac{1}{y} + \dfrac{2}{z}$, find the value of x when $y = \dfrac{1}{3}$ and $z = 4$.

(b) Solve the equation $\dfrac{x - 2}{3} - \dfrac{x + 1}{6} = \dfrac{x - 1}{10}$.

(c) To convert temperatures between Celsius and Fahrenheit, you can use one of these formulas.

$$C = \frac{5(F - 32)}{9} \qquad F = \frac{9C}{5} + 32$$

C stands for the temperature in °C, F stands for the temperature in °F.

   (i) The freezing point of water is 0°C. What is it in Fahrenheit?
   (ii) The boiling point of water is 100°C. What is it in Fahrenheit?
   (iii) A comfortable room temperature is about 72°F. What is it in Celsius?
   (iv) The temperature in a domestic fridge should be about 36°F. What is this in Celsius?

7. (a) If $\dfrac{ap}{3} = \dfrac{p}{2} + c$, express p in terms of a and c.

Hence, find the value of p when $a = -1\tfrac{1}{2}$ and $c = 3$.

(b) Divide $2x^3 - 9x^2 + 7x + 6$ by $(x - 3)$.

(c) These two rectangles have equal perimeters.
Form an equation and solve it to find x.

$(2x + 1)\,\text{cm}$

$(x - 3)\,\text{cm}$

$\left(\dfrac{2}{3}x + 2\right)\text{cm}$

$(x + 3)\,\text{cm}$

Trigonometry

Key words

The Theorem of Pythagoras   right-angled triangle   ratio   sine
cosine   tangent   opposite side   adjacent side   hypotenuse
degrees, minutes, seconds   angle of elevation   angle of depression
clinometer   surds

Section 22.1 The Theorem of Pythagoras

As you begin the study of trigonometry, you will hear a lot about
Pythagoras and his great discovery regarding right-angled
triangles. The theorem that carries his name, **Pythagoras'
Theorem**, is perhaps the best-known theorem in mathematics.

The diagram below illustrates his theorem.

Theorem of Pythagoras
In a right-angled triangle,
the area of the square
drawn on the hypotenuse
is equal to the sum of the
squares drawn on the
other two sides.

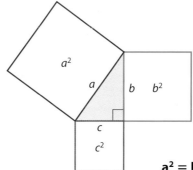

$$a^2 = b^2 + c^2$$

Example 1

Find the length of the side marked x in the
given right-angled triangle.

$$x^2 - 8^2 + 6^2$$
$$x^2 = 64 + 36$$
$$x^2 = 100$$
$$x = \sqrt{100}$$
$$x = 10$$

Exercise 22.1

1. Find the missing areas of the squares on these right-angled triangles.

(i)

(ii)

(iii)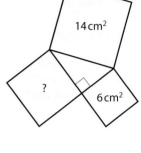

2. What is the area of the square drawn here?

3. Work out the missing area or length in each of these.

(i)

(ii)

(iii)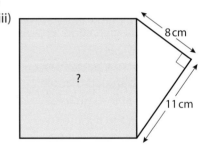

4. Use Pythagoras' theorem to find the length of the side [AC].

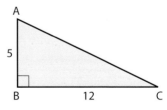

5. Calculate the length of the side marked with a letter in each of the following triangles. You may leave your answer in $\sqrt{}$ form, where necessary.

(i)

(ii)

(iii)

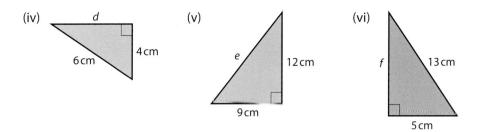

(iv) d, 4 cm, 6 cm

(v) e, 12 cm, 9 cm

(vi) f, 13 cm, 5 cm

6. Find the length of the side marked *x* in each of these triangles.
Give each answer correct to 1 decimal place.

(i) 14 cm, *x*, 20 cm

(ii) 12 cm, *x*, 16 cm

(iii) *x*, 5 cm, 11 cm

7. A rectangle is 10 cm long and 8 cm wide.
Calculate the length of the diagonal.
Give your answer in centimetres, correct to
one decimal place.

8 cm

10 cm

8. Use the given grid to write down the lengths
of [PR] and [QR].
Hence find the length of [PQ], correct to one
decimal place.

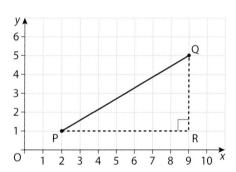

9. The diagram shows a ladder leaning against a vertical wall.
The foot of the ladder is on horizontal ground, 3.6 m from
the wall. The length of the ladder is 5 m.
Work out how far up the wall the ladder reaches.
Give your answer in metres, correct to 1 decimal place.

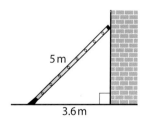

5 m

3.6 m

10. In the given figure, |AB| = 10 cm, |AD| = 5 cm
and |DC| = 6 cm.
The angles at A and D are right angles.
Find the length of [BC], correct to one
decimal place.

D, 6 cm, C, 5 cm, A, 10 cm, B

11. The diagram shows a right-angled triangle ABC.
   (i)   Find the length of [BD].
   (ii) Find the length [AD] in centimetres,
         correct to one decimal place.

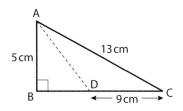

12. Use the grid and the Theorem of
Pythagoras to work out the
lengths of the sides of the
given figure.
Give your answer correct to
one decimal place.

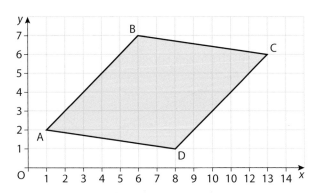

13. Calculate the lengths of the sides marked x and y in
the given right-angled triangles.

14. In the given figure, the two right angles
are marked.
Find the lengths of c and d.

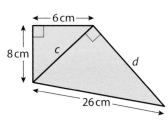

15. The diagram shows a horizontal shelf [AB].
The shelf is fixed to a vertical wall at A.
The support [CD] is fixed to the wall at C and to
the shelf at D.
$|AB| = 23$ cm, $|AC| = 20$ cm and $|BD| = 8$ cm.
Calculate the length of [CD].

16. The area of a square drawn on the hypotenuse of a right-angled, isosceles triangle is 24 cm².
Work out the area of the square drawn on each of the other two sides.

17. The given television has a rectangular screen with a diagonal of length 74 cm.
The sides of the screen are in the ratio 5 : 3.
Work out the lengths of these sides, in centimetres, correct to 1 decimal place.

18. Explain why a triangle of sides 12 cm, 13 cm and 18 cm is not right-angled.

Section 22.2 Sine, Cosine and Tangent ratios

One of the most common uses of trigonometry is in working out lengths and angles in right-angled triangles. Three very special ratios connecting angles and sides are given below.

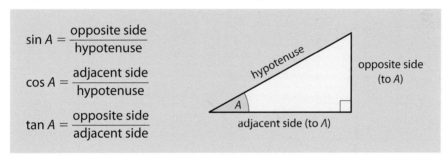

$$\sin A = \frac{\text{opposite side}}{\text{hypotenuse}}$$

$$\cos A = \frac{\text{adjacent side}}{\text{hypotenuse}}$$

$$\tan A = \frac{\text{opposite side}}{\text{adjacent side}}$$

In the given triangle,

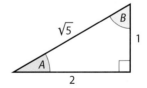

$$\sin A = \frac{1}{\sqrt{5}} \qquad \sin B = \frac{2}{\sqrt{5}}$$

$$\cos A = \frac{2}{\sqrt{5}} \qquad \cos B = \frac{1}{\sqrt{5}}$$

$$\tan A = \frac{1}{2} \qquad \tan B = \frac{2}{1} = 2$$

If we are given $\cos A = \frac{3}{4}$, we can draw a sketch
of a right-angled triangle in which the side
adjacent to A is 3 and the hypotenuse is 4.

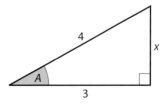

We now find the third side by using the
Theorem of Pythagoras.

Let the third side $= x$.
$$x^2 + 3^2 = 4^2$$
$$x^2 + 9 = 16$$
$$x^2 = 7$$
$$x = \sqrt{7}$$

433

Example 1

If $\tan B = \dfrac{\sqrt{5}}{2}$, find the value of sin B and cos B.

$\tan B = \dfrac{\sqrt{5}}{2} \Rightarrow$ opposite side to B is $\sqrt{5}$ and adjacent side is 2.

Now draw a rough sketch of a right-angled triangle.
Let x be the length of the hypotenuse.

$$x^2 = 2^2 + (\sqrt{5})^2$$
$$x^2 = 4 + 5 \ldots \; (\sqrt{5})^2 = 5$$
$$x^2 = 9 \Rightarrow x = 3$$

From the triangle: $\sin B = \dfrac{\sqrt{5}}{3}$ and $\cos B = \dfrac{2}{3}$.

Exercise 22.2

1. Find the sin, cos and tan of the angle marked with a capital letter in each of the following triangles:

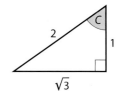

2. In the given triangle, state which of the ratios sine, cosine or tangent

    (i)   connects 3, 4 and the angle A

    (ii) connects 4, 5 and the angle A

    (iii) connects 3, 5 and the angle A.

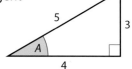

3. Write down what should be inserted into each of the following coloured boxes:

    (i) $\sin \square = \dfrac{5}{13}$ (ii) $\tan \square = \dfrac{12}{5}$

    (iii) $\cos \square = \dfrac{5}{13}$ (iv) $\square\, A = \dfrac{12}{13}$

    (v) $\square\, B = \dfrac{5}{13}$ (vi) $\square\, A = \dfrac{5}{12}$

4. Find the length of the side marked x in the given right-angled triangle. Hence write down the value of

    (i) $\sin A$ (ii) $\cos A$ (iii) $\tan A$.

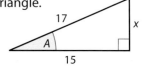

5. Find the value of a in the given right-angled triangle.
Hence write down the value of

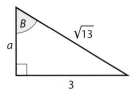

    (i) sin B (ii) cos B (iii) tan B.

6. The angle θ and three sides of a right-angled triangle are shown in the given diagram.
State whether each of these ratios represents sin θ, cos θ or tan θ.

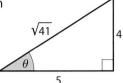

    (i) $\dfrac{4}{5}$ (ii) $\dfrac{4}{\sqrt{41}}$ (iii) $\dfrac{5}{\sqrt{41}}$

7. Given that $\cos B = \frac{5}{13}$, draw a rough sketch of a right-angled triangle and use it to write down the ratios sin B and tan B.

8.   (i) If $\tan A = \frac{1}{2}$, find sin A.   (ii) If $\cos B = \frac{2}{5}$, find tan B.

9. If $\tan C = \dfrac{1}{\sqrt{3}}$, find the values of sin C and cos C.

10. From the given triangle, write down the value of
    (i) $\sin^2 A + \cos^2 A$ (ii) $\sin^2 B + \cos^2 B$.

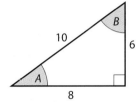

If you have done your calculations correctly, you will have verified a very important fact about any angle, i.e.,

$$\sin^2 A + \cos^2 A = 1.$$

Section 22.3 Using a calculator to find ratios and angles —

Angles are generally measured in degrees.
A right angle, which is a quarter of a
full rotation, measures 90°.

We can find the value of the sine, cosine or tangent of any angle by using the [sin], [cos] and
[tan] keys on an electronic calculator.

To find sin 35°, key in [sin] 35 [=].

The result is 0.573576 … = 0.5736, correct to 4 decimal places.

To find tan 37.4°, key in [tan] 37.4 [=].

The result is 0.7646.

Angles measured in degrees, minutes and seconds (DMS)

A degree can be divided into 60 parts.

Each part is called **1 minute**, written **1'**.

$$1° = 60'$$

Each minute can also be divided into 60 parts.

Each of these small parts is called **1 second**, written **1"**.

When angles are written in DMS form, the angle is generally given to the nearest minute.

When using a calculator to change 38.6° to DMS form, either of these two methods may be used:

1. Key in 38.6 [SHIFT] [D°M'S]

The result is 38°36'0.

> [D°M'S] is represented by
> [°'''] on CASIO calculators.

2. $0.6° = 0.6 \times 60' = 36'$ ... $1° = 60'$
Thus 38.6° = 38°36'.

Example 1

(i)   Convert 76.7° to DMS form.
(ii) Convert 35°54' to decimal form.

(i)   Key in 76.7 [D°M'S] [=]
The result is 76°42'0" = 76°42'

(ii) Key in 35 [D°M'S] 54 [D°M'S] [=] [SHIFT] [D°M'S]
The result is 35.9°.

Using the [sin⁻¹] [cos⁻¹] and [tan⁻¹] keys

If we are given that sin A = 0.8661, we can find the angle A by using the [sin⁻¹] key.

The [sin⁻¹] key is got by keying in [SHIFT] [sin].

Thus if sin A = 0.8661, we find A by keying in [SHIFT] [sin] 0.8661 [=].

The result is 60.008° = 60°.

Similarly, if tan B = 1.2734, we find the angle B by keying in [SHIFT] [tan] 1.2734 [=].

The result is 51.86°... correct to 2 decimal places.

Example 2

(i) Find cos 72°18′, correct to 4 decimal places.

(ii) If sin A = 0.5216, find A correct to the nearest degree.

(i) To find cos 72°18′, key in $\boxed{\text{cos}}$ 72 $\boxed{\text{D°M′S}}$ 18 $\boxed{\text{D°M′S}}$ $\boxed{=}$

> Notice that the $\boxed{\text{D°M′S}}$ key is used twice.

The result is 0.3040.

$$\text{Or } 18′ = \frac{18°}{60} = 0.3° \Rightarrow 72°18′ = 72.3°$$

Thus to find 72.3°, key in $\boxed{\text{cos}}$ 72.3 $\boxed{=}$

(ii) If sin A = 0.5216, we find A by keying in

$\boxed{\text{SHIFT}}$ $\boxed{\text{sin}}$ 0.5216 $\boxed{=}$

The result is 31.44°.   ⇒ A = 31°, to the nearest degree.

Note: If you are given sin $A = \frac{4}{7}$, you can find the angle A by keying in

$\boxed{\text{SHIFT}}$ $\boxed{\text{sin}}$ 4 $\boxed{÷}$ 7 $\boxed{=}$

The result is 34.8°.

Example 3

(i) Express the sum of 28°14′ and 45°52′ in DMS form.

(ii) Find 84°28′ − 16°36′ in decimal form.

(i) Key in 28 $\boxed{\text{D°M′S}}$ 14 $\boxed{\text{D°M′S}}$ + 45 $\boxed{\text{D°M′S}}$ 52 $\boxed{\text{D°M′S}}$ $\boxed{=}$

The result is 74°6′0″ = 74°6′.

(ii) Key in 84 $\boxed{\text{D°M′S}}$ 28 $\boxed{\text{D°M′S}}$ − 16 $\boxed{\text{D°M′S}}$ 36 $\boxed{\text{D°M′S}}$ $\boxed{=}$

The result is 67°52′0″ = 67°52′.

To change 67°52′ to decimal form, key in

67 $\boxed{\text{D°M′S}}$ 52 $\boxed{\text{D°M′S}}$ $\boxed{=}$ $\boxed{\text{SHIFT}}$ $\boxed{\text{D°M′S}}$

The result is 67.866° = 67.9°.

Exercise 22.3

1. Change each of the following angles to degrees and minutes:

(i) 28.5°   (ii) 31.4°   (iii) 62.8°

(iv) 74.6°   (v) 16.25°   (vi) 44.75°

(vii) 0.5°   (viii) 27.65°

2. Convert each of the following angles to decimal form.
   Give each answer correct to 1 decimal place.
   (i)   24°30′
   (ii) 46°36′
   (iii) 72°42′
   (iv) 21°48′
   (v)   65°26′
   (vi) 13°28′
   (vii) 29°35′
   (viii) 68°15′

3. Express each of the following as a single angle in DMS form:
   (i)   12°15′ + 28°34′
   (ii) 29°14′ + 36°54′
   (iii) 37°14′ + 46°38′
   (iv) 74°12′ − 57°38′
   (v)   38°16′ − 31°48′
   (vi) 124°17′ − 68°40′

4. Find the measure of the angle A in the given triangle.

Give your answer in degrees and minutes.

5. Use your calculator to evaluate each of the following, correct to 4 decimal places:
   (i)   sin 48°
   (ii) cos 74°
   (iii) tan 15°
   (iv) sin 72°
   (v)   cos 28.5°

6. Using your calculator, evaluate each of the following correct to 4 decimal places:
   (i)   cos 28°18′
   (ii) sin 36°42′
   (iii) tan 74°54′
   (iv) sin 17°52′

7. Use your calculator to find the measure of each of these angles, correct to the nearest degree:
   (i) $\sin A = 0.7453$
   (ii) $\cos B = 0.3521$
   (iii) $\tan C = 1.4538$
   (iv) $\cos A = 0.2154$
   (v) $\tan B = 0.8923$
   (vi) $\sin C = 0.2132$

8. Find the value of A in each of the following.
   Give your answer in degrees, correct to one decimal place.
   (i) $\sin A = 0.6$
   (ii) $\cos A = 0.7534$
   (iii) $\tan A = 3.84$
   (iv) $\cos A = 0.2715$

9. Find the measure of the angle θ, correct to the nearest degree, in each of the following:
   (i) $\sin \theta = \frac{2}{3}$
   (ii) $\cos \theta = \frac{3}{5}$
   (iii) $\tan \theta = \frac{7}{8}$
   (iv) $\sin \theta = \frac{2}{5}$
   (v) $\tan \theta = \frac{6}{11}$
   (vi) $\sin \theta = \frac{1}{5}$
   (vii) $\cos \theta = \frac{9}{11}$
   (viii) $\tan \theta = 1\frac{3}{5}$

10. If $\cos A = 0.5484$ and $A < 90°$, find A and hence find the value of sin A, correct to 2 decimal places.

11. If $\tan A = 1.3462$, find A in degrees and minutes, correct to the nearest minute.

12. Write down which trigonometric ratio is needed to calculate the angle θ in each of these triangles:

(i)

(ii)

(iii)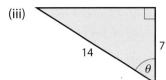

13. Find, correct to the nearest degree, the sizes of the angles marked A, B and C in the triangles below:

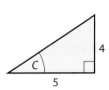

14. In the given triangles, all of the lengths are in cm.
Calculate the value of each angle marked with a letter, correct to the nearest degree.

15. By using the appropriate ratio, work out the measure of each of the marked angles in degrees, correct to one decimal place:

16. Find the value of the angle θ in each of these:
   (i) $2 \sin \theta = 1$ (ii) $5 \cos \theta = 2$ (iii) $2 \tan \theta = 1$
Give each angle correct to the nearest degree.

17. The diagram shows a vertical mast of height 12 metres.
The length of the mast's shadow on horizontal ground is 30 metres.
Calculate the measure of the angle marked x, correct to the nearest degree.

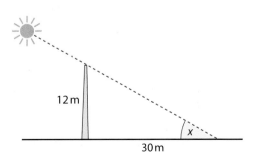

18. During a trigonometry lesson, a group of students write down some statements about what they expected to happen when they look at the values of the trigonometric functions of some angles. They then find the Sin, Cos and Tan of some angles, correct to three decimal places, to test their ideas. Here are some of the things they wrote down.

(a) The value from any of these trigonometric functions will **always** be less than 1.

(b) If the size of the angle is doubled, then the value from the trigonometric functions will not double.

(c) The value from all of the trigonometric functions will increase if the size of the angle is increased.

    (i) Do you think that (a) is correct?
       Give an example to justify your answer.

    (ii) Do you think that (b) is correct?
       Give an example to justify your answer.

    (iii) Do you think that (c) is correct?
       Give an example to justify your answer.

Section 22.4 Solving right-angled triangles

In this section we will use the sine, cosine and tangent ratios to find an unknown side or an unknown angle in a right-angled triangle.

When using your calculator to find the sine, cosine or tangent of an angle, write the value correct to 4 decimal places.

Example 1

Find the lengths of the sides marked x and y in the given triangle.

Give your answers correct to 1 decimal place.

$$\frac{x}{12} = \cos 35°$$

$$\frac{x}{12} = 0.8192$$

$$x = 12(0.8192)$$

$$x = 9.8304$$

$$x = 9.8$$

$$\frac{y}{12} = \sin 35°$$

$$\frac{y}{12} = 0.5736$$

$$y = 12(0.5736)$$

$$y = 6.8832$$

$$y = 6.9$$

Example 2

In the given triangle, $|AB| = 9$ and $|BC| = 13$.

Find $|\angle ACB|$, correct to the nearest degree.

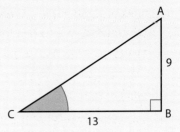

$\tan \angle ACB = \frac{9}{13}$

$\quad |\angle ACB| = \tan^{-1} \frac{9}{13}$

$\quad |\angle ACB| = 34.695°$ Key in [SHIFT][tan] 9 [÷] 13 [=]

$\qquad = 35°$, correct to the nearest degree.

Exercise 22.4

1. Write down which trigonometric ratio is needed to calculate the length of the side marked x in each of these triangles:

(i)

(ii)

(iii)

2. In each of the following triangles, work out the length of the side marked with a letter. Give each answer correct to 1 decimal place.

(i)

(ii)

(iii)

3. Find the length of the side marked x in these triangles. Give your answers correct to one decimal place.

(i)

(ii)

(iii)

4. Find the size of the angle marked *A* in each of these triangles.
Give your answers correct to the nearest degree.

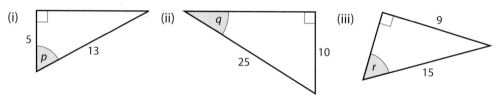

(i)   (ii)   (iii)

5. Find the measure of the angles marked *p*, *q* and *r* in each of these triangles.
Give each answer correct to the nearest degree.

(i)   (ii)   (iii)

6. Copy and complete the following to find the length of the side marked *x*.

$$\frac{8}{x} = \cos 32°$$

$$x \times \cos 32° = 8$$

$$x = \frac{8}{\cos 32°}$$

Give your answer correct to 1 decimal place.

7. Find the length of the hypotenuse marked *x* in each of these triangles:

(i)   (ii)   (iii)

Give each answer correct to 1 decimal place.

8. Find the values of *x* and *y*, correct to the nearest whole number, in the given triangle.

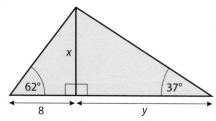

9. Work out the length of the side marked with a letter in each of the following triangles. Give each answer correct to 1 decimal place.

10. In the given triangle, find

(i) x, correct to 1 decimal place

(ii) the angle A, correct to the nearest degree.

11. ABCD is a rectangle as shown.
If $|DC| = 11$ cm and $|\angle BDC| = 28°$, find the length of the diagonal [DB].
Give your answer in centimetres, correct to one decimal place.

12. The diagram represents the frame, PQRS, of a roof.

$|PQ| = 7.5$ m, $|QR| = 4$ m and $|SQ| = 3.2$ m.

(i) Calculate the length of [PS].

(ii) Find $|\angle SRQ|$, correct to the nearest degree.

13. In the given diagram, $|AD| = 6$ cm,
$|DB| = 9$ cm, $|\angle CAD| = 35°$ and $CD \perp AB$.

Find (i) $|CD|$, correct to 1 decimal place 4.2

(ii) $|\angle CBD|$, correct to the nearest 25°
degree.

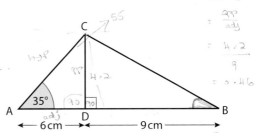

$Tan\ B$
$\frac{opp}{adj}$
$\frac{4.2}{9}$
$= 0.46$

$Tan\ B = 0.46$

$Tan\ 35° = \frac{opp}{adj} = \frac{|CD|}{6}$

$\frac{0.07}{1} = \frac{|CD|}{6}$ $CD = 4.2$

$B = 24.7°$
$= 25°$

443

Section 22.5 Using trigonometry to solve problems

The terms **angle of elevation** and **angle of depression** will occur frequently when dealing with trigonometric problems.

The diagrams below illustrate what these terms mean.

A **clinometer** is generally used to measure angles of elevation and depression.

Example 1

Alan stands at A, directly under the end of a crane. From A, he walks 10 m to B. At B, he measures the angle of elevation of the end of the crane as 73°.

How high is the end of the crane?

We will use the tangent of 73° to find h.

$$\frac{h}{10} = \tan 73°$$

$$h = 10 \times \tan 73°$$

$$h = 10\,(3.2709)$$

$$h = 32.709 \text{ m}$$

∴ the height of the end of the crane is 32.7 m.

Exercise 22.5

1. A ladder makes an angle of 70° with the ground.
   The foot of the ladder is 1.2 m from the wall.
   How long is this ladder?

   Give your answer correct to 1 decimal place.

2. From a point on the ground 20 m from the base of a tree, the angle of elevation to the top of the tree is 47°. Calculate the height of the tree, correct to the nearest metre.

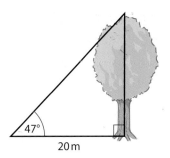

47°
20 m

3. The diagram shows a lighthouse, 30 m in height, standing on horizontal ground.

Work out the angle of elevation of the top of the lighthouse from the point A on the ground, correct to the nearest degree.

30 m
A
20 m

4. Two yachts sail into a harbour at R. Their positions are shown in the given diagram where PQ is perpendicular to PR.
   (i) Find the distance from Q to R.
   (ii) Find the measure of the angle PRQ.
Give each answer correct to the nearest whole number.

P
112 km
R
54 km
Q

5. Paula stands at point P on the bank of a river. Vertically across from her on the other bank is a tree, T.
She walks 25 metres along the bank to a point Q. She measures the angle between QT and QP and finds that it is 38°.
Find the width of the river, correct to the nearest metre.

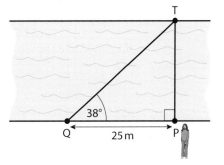

T
38°
Q
25 m
P

6. The diagram shows the cross-section of a swimming pool.
θ is the angle the sloping part makes with the horizontal.
Find θ, correct to the nearest degree.

50 m
2.5 m
14 m
θ

7. From the top of a 25 m high cliff, the angle of depression of a canoe is 28°. How far is this canoe from the foot of the cliff? Give your answer correct to the nearest metre.

8. Andy stood 5 m from the foot of a tree. He measured the angle of elevation of the top of the tree as 59° and the angle of depression of the foot of the tree as 20°.
   (i)   What is the length of [GH]?
   (ii) Work out the length of [TH], correct to 1 decimal place.
   (iii) What other calculations need to be made to find the height of the tree?
   (iv) What is the height of the tree, in metres, correct to 1 decimal place?

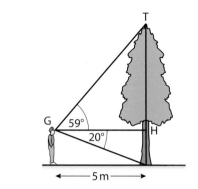

9. At the edge of a beach, which is 8 m wide, there is a 2.1 m high wall. From the top of this wall, Susan measures the angle of depression of a swimmer as 6°.
How far out to sea is the swimmer?
Give your answer to the nearest metre.

10. The diagram shows a vertical building standing on horizontal ground.
The points A, B and C are in a straight line on the ground.
The point T is at the top of the building so that TC is vertical.
The angle of elevation of T from A is 40°, as shown in the diagram.

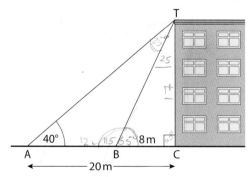

   (i)   Work out the height, |TC|, of the building.
   (ii) Work out the size of the angle of elevation of T from B.
   (iii) Work out the size of angle ATB.
   Give all answers correct to the nearest whole number.

11. Drainage pipes were being laid along the diagonal of a rectangular paddock, as shown in this diagram.
At what angle, to the shorter sides of this paddock, were the pipes laid?
Give your answer correct to the nearest degree.

12. A flagpole is on the top of a government building.
From the point D, 4 m from the base of the building, Joanne measures the angles of elevation of the top, A, and the bottom, B, of the flagpole.
Her measurements are shown on the diagram.

  (i) Find the length [AC].
 (ii) Find the length [BC] and the height, h, of the flagpole.
Give all answers correct to 1 decimal place.

13.

Is it possible to turn a 2.3 m by 1.6 m desk in a room that is 4 m by 2.75 m?
Explain your answer.

14. The guidelines for preventing occupational overuse syndrome say that you should sit with your eyes 55 cm from the centre of the screen and at an angle of depression of 15°.

  (i) What height should your eyes be above the centre of the screen?
 (ii) What horizontal distance should you sit from the screen?
Give each answer in centimetres, correct to 1 decimal place.

15. Marguerite finds the distance between two boats,
P and R, on the other side of the river, as follows.
She begins at A, opposite boat P.
From A she walks to B, a distance of 54 m.
She measures the angle ABP as 43° and angle
CBR as 47°.
From these measurements she is able to find the
distance |PR|, between the two boats.

    (i) Calculate w, the width of the river, using the
triangle APB.

    (ii) Using triangle CBR, calculate the distance |BC|.
Hence find the distance between the boats.

Give each answer in metres, correct to 1 decimal place.

16. The diagram shows a vertical cliff face, PZ,
standing on a horizontal beach, XYZ.
The angle of elevation of P from a rock on
the beach at X is 44°, as shown in the diagram.

    (i) Work out the height, PZ, of the cliff face.

    (ii) Work out the angle of elevation of
P, from the point Y on the beach, to
the nearest degree.

    (iii) Work out the size of angle XPY to
the nearest degree.

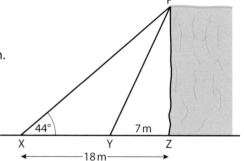

17. Harry wants to refelt the roof of his lean-to shed.
Felt is sold in 5 m rolls that are 1 m wide.
They cost €40 each.

    (i) How many rolls will he need to buy?

The felt is stuck on with an adhesive which
costs €18 for a 2.5 litre tin. It will cover 6 m².

    (ii) How much will Harry have to pay for the
materials to do the job?

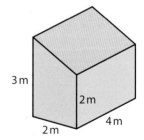

18. The diagram shows the cross-section of a roof
with sides 7.5 m in length.
Both sides are inclined at an angle of 32° to
the horizontal.

    (i) Find the height marked h.

    (ii) Find the width, w, of the roof support.

Give each answer in metres, correct to 1 decimal place.

Section 22.6 The angles 30°, 45° and 60°

The angles 30°, 45° and 60° are used very frequently and we will use triangles to express the sine, cosine and tangent ratios of these angles as fractions or surds.

The 45° angle

The triangle on the right is isosceles where the equal sides are 1 unit in length.

The hypotenuse is $\sqrt{2}$ units in length.

The sine, cosine and tangent ratios can be read from the triangle.

$$\sin 45° = \frac{1}{\sqrt{2}} \qquad \cos 45° = \frac{1}{\sqrt{2}} \qquad \tan 45° = 1$$

The angles 30° and 60°

The given right-angled triangle has angles of 60° and 30°.

We can use this triangle to write down the trigonometric ratios of these two angles.

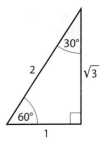

$$\sin 60° = \frac{\sqrt{3}}{2} \qquad \cos 60° = \frac{1}{2} \qquad \tan 60° = \sqrt{3}$$

$$\sin 30° = \frac{1}{2} \qquad \cos 30° = \frac{\sqrt{3}}{2} \qquad \tan 30° = \frac{1}{\sqrt{3}}$$

Note: The sine, cosine and tangent ratios for 30°, 45° and 60° are given on page 13 of *Formulae and Tables*.

> **Example 1**
>
> Without using a calculator, find the values of x and y in the given right-angled triangle.
>
>
>
> $$\frac{x}{4} = \tan 60° \qquad\qquad \frac{4}{y} = \cos 60°$$
>
> $$\Rightarrow \quad \frac{x}{4} = \frac{\sqrt{3}}{1} \qquad\qquad \Rightarrow \quad \frac{4}{y} = \frac{1}{2}$$
>
> $$\Rightarrow \quad x = 4\sqrt{3} \qquad\qquad \Rightarrow \quad y = 8$$

Note: $\sin^2 60° = (\sin 60°)^2 = \left(\frac{\sqrt{3}}{2}\right)^2 = \frac{3}{4}$

Exercise 22.6

Without using a calculator, write the value of each of the following as a simple fraction or as a surd:

1. $\cos 60°$ 2. $\tan 45°$ 3. $\sin 30°$ 4. $\cos 45°$ 5. $\sin^2 30°$

6. $\cos 30°$ 7. $\sin 60°$ 8. $\cos^2 45°$ 9. $\sin^2 60°$ 10. $\tan^2 30°$

11. Show that   (i) $1 - \sin^2 30° = \cos^2 30°$ (ii) $\sin 60° = 2 \sin 30° \cos 30°$

12. Without using a calculator, find the values of x and y in the given triangle.

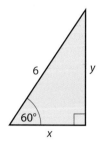

13. Find the values of x and y in the given triangle, without using a calculator.

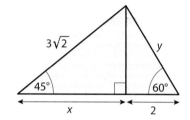

14. Find the values of x, y and z in the given diagram, without using a calculator.

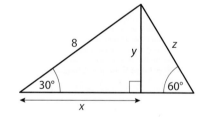

15. Without using a calculator, find the value of the angle marked A in the given triangle.

16. A field is in the shape of an equilateral triangle, as shown.
    Each side is 40 m in length.
    Suggest two methods of finding the area of this field without using a calculator.
    Find the area using each of these methods.
    Give your answer in surd form.

Test yourself 22

1. Find the length of the side marked x in the given triangle.
   Hence write down as fractions
      (i) tan A (ii) sin A (iii) cos A.
   Now find the measure of the angle A,
   correct to the nearest degree.

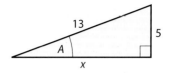

2. In the given triangle, $|\angle ACB| = 34°$, $|\angle ABC| = 90°$ and
   $|AB| = 12$ cm.

   Find $|BC|$, in cm, correct to one decimal place.

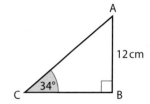

3. Find the missing area in each of the following figures:

   (i)

   (ii)

   (iii)

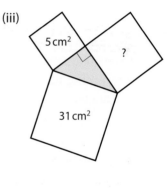

4. In the given triangle, $|AB| = 12$ cm, $|CD| = 20$ cm,
   $|\angle ABC| = 43°$ and $|\angle ACD| = 90°$.

      (i) Find $|AC|$, correct to the nearest cm.
     (ii) Find $|\angle ADC|$, correct to the nearest
         degree.

5. A plane, which took off from Shannon Airport, had gained an altitude of 2.1 km after it
   had travelled 8 km.

   At what angle was this plane climbing?
   Give your answer to the nearest degree.

6. In the given diagram, $|AD| = 6\,cm$, $|DB| = 9\,cm$, $|\angle CAD| = 35°$ and CD is perpendicular to AB.

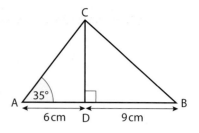

(i) Find $|CD|$, in cm, correct to one decimal place.
(ii) Find $|\angle CBD|$, correct to the nearest degree.

7 (i) Express $28.75°$ in degrees and minutes.
(ii) Express $37°06'$ in degrees.
(iii) Use the triangle on the right to write the value of
$\sin^2 60° + \cos^2 30°$ in the form $\dfrac{a}{b}$, where $a, b \in \mathbb{N}$.

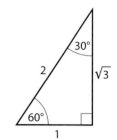

8. The diagram shows the design for a logo that is to be hung outside a company's headquarters.
It comprises triangles ABC and ADE.
The angles ACB and ADE are both 90°.

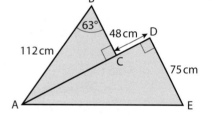

(i) Work out the length of [AC], correct to the nearest whole number.
(ii) Find $|\angle DAE|$, correct to the nearest degree.

9. The dimensions for the side of a bird box are shown in the diagram on the right.
Calculate the length of the side [PS].
Give your answer in cm, correct to 1 decimal place.

10. Find the missing length in each of the following figures:

(i)

(ii)

(iii)
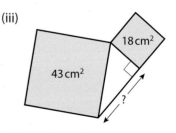

11. By how many degrees is the angle *x* bigger than the angle *y*?

Give your answer correct to the nearest degree.

12. (i) In the given right-angled triangle, one of the acute angles is four times as large as the other acute angle.
Find the measures of the two acute angles.

(ii) The triangle in part (i) is placed on a coordinate diagram. The base is parallel to the *x*-axis, as shown.
Find the slope of the line ℓ that contains the hypotenuse of the triangle.
Give your answer correct to two decimal places.

13. The given triangle ABC is right-angled at B.
(i) Calculate the area of triangle ABC.

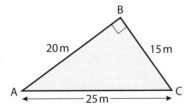

(ii) |BD|, the height of triangle ABC, is drawn as shown.

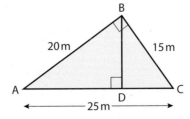

Use your answer to part (i) to calculate the height |BD|.

453

14. A group of students wish to calculate the height of the
Millennium Spire in Dublin. The Spire stands on flat, level
ground. Maria, who is 1.72 m tall, looks up at the top of
the Spire using a clinometer and records an angle of
elevation of 60°. Her feet are 70 m from the base of the
Spire. Ultan measures the circumference of the base of
the Spire as 7.07 m.

    (i) Explain how Ultan's measurement will be used in
the calculation of the height of the Spire.

   (ii) Draw a suitable diagram and calculate the height
of the Spire, to the nearest metre, using the
measurements obtained by the students.

15. Mary is thinking of buying a new television. The television is advertised as having a "40
inch" screen. This refers to the diagonal measurement of the screen. The *aspect ratio* of a
television screen is the ratio of its width to its height. For this television, the aspect ratio
is 16 : 9 (sixteen units wide for every nine units in height).

    (i) Convert 40 inches to centimetres if

$$1 \text{ inch } = 2.54 \text{ cm.}$$

   (ii) Find the width and height of the
screen in cm.
Give your answers correct to the
nearest cm.

  (iii) A different 40-inch television screen
has an aspect ratio of 4 : 3.
Which of the two television screens
has the greater area, and by how much?

16. Find the values of *a* and *b* in the given diagram,
where the right angles are indicated.
Give each answer as a surd.

Graphing functions

Section 23.1 Graphing linear functions

Consider the function $f(x) = x + 3$.
This function can be written as a set of couples by taking different values for x.

$$f(1) = 1 + 3 = 4 \Rightarrow (1, 4) \text{ is one couple.}$$
$$f(2) = 2 + 3 = 5 \Rightarrow (2, 5) \text{ is another couple.}$$

Other couples are $(0, 3), (-3, 0), \ldots$
When these couples are plotted and joined,
they will form a line, as shown.

Since the graph of $f(x) = x + 3$ is a line,
we say $f(x)$ is a **linear function**.

A line is the most straightforward function to
graph as we need only two points to plot it.

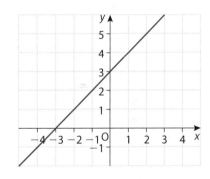

Usually we are given the domain in which to draw any function.
The domain $x = -2$ to $x = 3$, both included, is written as $-2 \leqslant x \leqslant 3$.

When plotting a line, two points are sufficient to plot but we generally take three points in
case any errors are made.

Example 1

Graph the function $f(x) = 2x - 4$ in the domain $-1 \leqslant x \leqslant 4$.
Use your graph to find
(i) $f(3)$ (ii) the value of x for which $f(x) = -2$.

To find three points, we select the smallest and largest x-values in the given domain and one value for x in between those two.

x	$2x - 4$	y
-1	$-2 - 4$	-6
0	$0 - 4$	-4
4	$8 - 4$	4

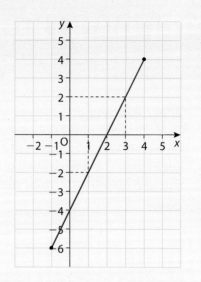

The three points are $(-1, -6)$, $(0, -4)$ and $(4, 4)$.
Join these points to give a line.

(i) $f(3)$ represents the y-value when $x = 3$.
From the graph, this is 2, i.e., $f(3) = 2$.

(ii) $f(x) = -2 \Rightarrow y = -2$
The value of x in the graph when $y = -2$ is $x = 1$.

The intercept method for drawing a line

If the equation of a line is in a form such as $3x - 4y = 12$, it is more convenient to find the two points where the line intersects the x-axis and y-axis.

$$3x - 4y = 12$$

$x = 0 \Rightarrow 0 - 4y = 12 \Rightarrow y = -3$

$\therefore$ $(0, -3)$ is one point on the line.

$y = 0 \Rightarrow 3x = 12 \Rightarrow x = 4$

$\therefore$ $(4, 0)$ is a second point on the line.

These points are joined to give the required line.

This method is generally called the **intercept method**.

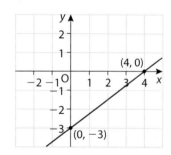

Exercise 23.1

1. Copy and complete the table on the right and use the table to draw a graph of the line $y = 2x - 3$ in the domain $-1 \leqslant x \leqslant 4$.

x	$2x - 3$	y
-1		
0		
1		
2		
3		
4		

2. Draw the graph of $f(x) = 2x - 5$ in the domain $0 \leqslant x \leqslant 5$.

3. Copy and complete the table on the right
and hence draw a graph of the function
$f(x) = 3x - 4$ in the domain $-1 \leqslant x \leqslant 3$.

x	3x − 4	y
−1		
0		
3		

4. Draw the graph of the function $f(x) = 6 - x$ in the domain $0 \leqslant x \leqslant 6$ by finding only
three points on the line.

5. Draw the graph of the function $f(x) = 2x - 2$ in the domain $-2 \leqslant x \leqslant 3$.

6. Drawn on the right is the graph of a
function $y = f(x)$.

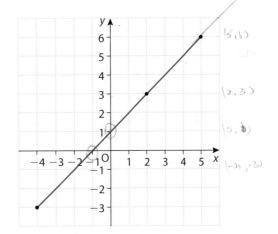

Use this graph to write down

  (i) $f(3)$ (ii) $f(0)$ (iii) $f(-4)$

  (iv) the value of x when $f(x) = -2$

  (v) the value of x when $f(x) = 6$.

7. The given diagram shows the graphs of
two lines,

$$f(x) = x + 1 \text{ and } g(x) = 2x - 2.$$

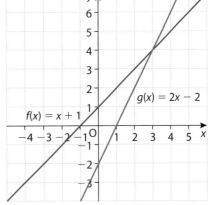

  (i) Write down the point of intersection
of the two lines.

  (ii) What is the meaning of the equation
$f(x) = g(x)$ in this situation?

  (iii) Solve the equation $x + 1 = 2x - 2$.
Is there any connection between
the value you found for x and the
point of intersection of the two lines?

  (iv) Is there another way of finding the
point of intersection of two lines besides drawing their graphs?

  (v) If $f(k)$ has the same value as $g(k)$, write down the value of k.

8. On the same diagram, draw the lines $y = 5 - x$ and $y = 2x - 4$, in the
domain $0 \leqslant x \leqslant 4$.
Use your graph to write down the point of intersection of the two lines.

9. By finding the couples (∗, 0) and (0, ∗), draw a graph of the line $y = 4 - 2x$.

10. Use the intercept method to draw the graph of the line $3x + 2y = 6$.

11. Use the intercept method to draw the following two lines on the same graph:

$2x + y = 4$ and $x - y = 2$.

Where do the two lines intersect?

12. The lines $y = x + 2$, $y = -x + 2$ and $y = 2x + 2$ have been graphed on the same axes on the right.

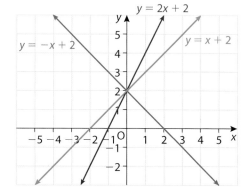

   (i) How are the lines similar?

  (ii) How are the linear equations similar?

 (iii) How are the lines different?

 (iv) How are the linear equations different?

13. Write down the next three points of the pattern started below:

$(1, 8), (0, 6), (-1, 4) \ldots$

Now plot these points to show that they lie on a straight line.

14. Penguins survive in freezing climates. The temperature $T°C$ at a penguin colony, t hours after midnight, is given by the rule $T = -0.5t - 1$.

t	0	1	2	3	4	5	6
T							

   (i) Complete the table, which gives the temperatures up to 6 a.m.

  (ii) Plot the points whose coordinates are given by the values in the table on a set of axes of your own.

 (iii) Join the plotted points with a straight line. Do not extend the line.

 (iv) From your graph, read off the temperature at 5.30 a.m..

  (v) Use the rule that relates T to t to find the exact temperature at 5.30 a.m..

15. Ian and Liz decide to walk to the local swimming pool which is half a kilometre away.

Liz begins to walk at a speed of 40 metres per minute.

Ian starts 2 minutes later and walks at a speed of 50 metres per minute.

   (i) Copy and complete the following table which shows how many metres Liz has walked after various minutes:

t (min)	0	1	2	3	4	5	6	7	8	9	10
d (metres)	0	40	80								

(ii) On a set of axes of your own, plot the points given in this table.
Set out *t* values along the horizontal axis and *d* values up the vertical axis.
Join the plots with a straight line.
Label and scale your axes clearly.

(iii) Copy and complete this table which shows how many metres Ian has walked after various minutes:

t (min)	0	1	2	3	4	5	6	7	8	9	10
d (metres)	0	0	0	50							

(iv) Using a different colour, plot these values on the same set of axes.
Join the plotted points to form a straight line.

(v) From the two graphs, find out when Ian meets up with Liz.
How far has each walked when they meet?

Section 23.2 Graphs of quadratic functions

The curve on the right is called a **parabola**.
The name parabola comes from the Greek word for throw, because when a ball, for example, is thrown high in the air, its path makes a parabolic shape.

Ground

Suspension bridges, such as the Golden Gate bridge in San Francisco, form parabolic curves.

The simplest quadratic function is $y = x^2$.
Its graph can be drawn from a table of values from $x = -3$ to $x = 3$.

x	−3	−2	−1	0	1	2	3
y	9	4	1	0	1	4	9

The points shown on this curve are:
$(-3, 9), (-2, 4), (-1, 1), (0, 0), (1, 1), (2, 4), (3, 9)$

When these points are joined, a smooth curve called a parabola is formed.
Notice that the curve is symmetrical about the *y*-axis.
Hence the *y*-axis is called **the axis of symmetry**.

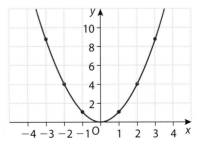

The function shown above may be written in one of these ways:

(i) $y = x^2$ (ii) $f(x) = x^2$ (iii) $f : x \rightarrow x^2$

A function in the form $f(x) = ax^2 + bx + c$, where a, b and c are constants and $a \neq 0$, is called a **quadratic function**.
It is called a quadratic function because it contains a term in x^2.

To draw the **graph of a quadratic function**, we take a given number of x values and find the corresponding $f(x)$ values (or y-values) and plot the resulting points.

When asked to draw the graph of a function, we are usually given the x-values we are to use. The values of x from -2 to 3 inclusive are written as $-2 \leqslant x \leqslant 3$.

The steps used in drawing a quadratic graph are given in the following example.

Example 1

Draw the graph of the function $f(x) = x^2 - 2x - 3$ in the domain $-2 \leqslant x \leqslant 4$.

We set out a table of ordered pairs as follows:

x	$x^2 - 2x - 3$	y
-2	$4 + 4 - 3$	5
-1	$1 + 2 - 3$	0
0	$0 + 0 - 3$	-3
1	$1 - 2 - 3$	-4
2	$4 - 4 - 3$	-3
3	$9 - 6 - 3$	0
4	$16 - 8 - 3$	5

Plotting these ordered pairs, we get the following curve:

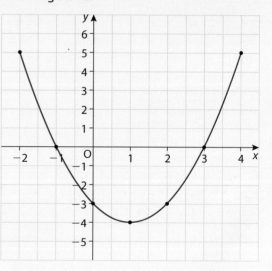

The ordered pairs found are:
$(-2, 5), (-1, 0), (0, -3), (1, -4),$
$(2, -3), (3, 0), (4, 5)$.

Graphing functions when the coefficient of x^2 is negative

If the coefficient of x^2 is negative in a quadratic function, e.g., $f(x) = -3x^2 + 4$, then the graph of the function will take the shape shown on the right.

x^2 negative

Example 2

Draw the graph of the function $f(x) = -x^2 + 3x + 4$ in the domain $-2 \leqslant x \leqslant 5$.

The table of values is set out below:

x	$-x^2 + 3x + 4$	y
−2	$-4 - 6 + 4$	−6
−1	$-1 - 3 + 4$	0
0	$0 + 0 + 4$	4
1	$-1 + 3 + 4$	6
2	$-4 + 6 + 4$	6
3	$-9 + 9 + 4$	4
4	$-16 + 12 + 4$	0
5	$-25 + 15 + 4$	−6

The required points are:
$(-2, -6)$, $(-1, 0)$, $(0, 4)$, $(1, 6)$, $(2, 6)$, $(3, 4)$, $(4, 0)$, $(5, -6)$.
The graph of the function is shown below:

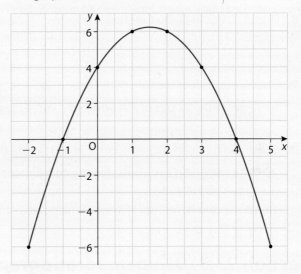

Exercise 23.2

1. Complete the table on the right and hence draw a graph of the function $f(x) = x^2 - 4$ in the domain $-3 \leqslant x \leqslant 3$.

x	$x^2 - 4$	y
−3		
−2		
−1		
0		
1		
2		
3		

2. Draw the graph of the function $f: x \to x^2 - 4x$ in the domain $-1 \leqslant x \leqslant 4$.

3. Draw the graph of the function $f(x) = x^2 + x - 2$ in the domain $-3 \leqslant x \leqslant 3$.

4. Draw the graph of the function $f(x) = 2x^2 - x - 3$ in the domain $-2 \leqslant x \leqslant 3$.

5. Draw the graph of the function $f(x) = 2x^2 + 3x - 4$ in the domain $-3 \leqslant x \leqslant 2$.

6. Draw the graph of the function $f(x) = 2x^2 - 5x - 3$ in the domain $-2 \leqslant x \leqslant 4$.
Use your graph to write down the coordinates of the points at which the graph crosses the x-axis.
Now write down the coordinates of the point where the graph crosses the y-axis.

7. Draw the graph of the function $y = -x^2$ in the domain $-2 \leqslant x \leqslant 2$.

8. Draw the graph of the function $f : x \rightarrow -x^2 + 2x + 3$ in the domain $-2 \leqslant x \leqslant 4$.
Use your graph to find the coordinates of the points where the graph crosses the x-axis.

9. Draw the graph of the function $f : x \rightarrow -2x^2 + x + 3$ in the domain $-2 \leqslant x \leqslant 3$.
Write down the values of x at which the curve crosses the x-axis.

10. Graph the function $f(x) = -2x^2 + 7x - 3$ in the domain $-1 \leqslant x \leqslant 4$.
    (i) Use the graph to write down the coordinates of the points at which the graph intersects the x-axis.
    (ii) Write down the coordinates of the point at which the graph crosses the y-axis.

Section 23.3 Using quadratic graphs

1. Solving the equation $f(x) = 0$

The graph on the right shows the curve
$f(x) = x^2 - 2x - 3$ intersecting the x-axis
at a and b.

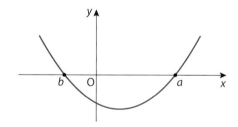

The x-values of these points are the roots
of the associated quadratic equation
$x^2 - 2x - 3 = 0$.
Why is this?

$f(x) = x^2 - 2x - 3$ may be also written as $y = x^2 - 2x - 3$.
When $y = 0$, then $x^2 - 2x - 3 = 0$.
$y = 0$ is another name for the x-axis.

Thus, the solution of the equation $x^2 - 2x - 3 = 0$ gives the x-values of the points at
which the curve crosses the x-axis.

The curve on the right is the graph of the function

$$f(x) = x^2 + 2x - 5$$

The roots of the equation $x^2 + 2x - 5 = 0$ are found by reading from the graph the x-values of the points at which the graph intersects the x-axis.

These values are

$$x = -3.5 \text{ and } x = 1.5$$

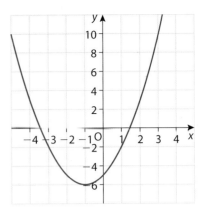

2. Solving the equation $f(x) = k$, where $k \in R$

The graph of the function $f(x) = x^2 - 3x$ is drawn below.

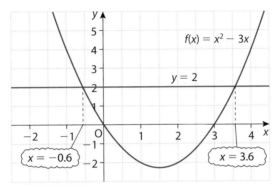

This graph can be used to solve the equation $f(x) = 2$ or $y = 2$ by drawing the line $y = 2$ and then reading from the graph the x-values of the points where the line $y = 2$ intersects the curve.

These values are $x = -0.6$ or $x = 3.6$.

3. When is a function negative?

On the right is a graph of the function $f(x) = x^2 + x - 2$.

The function is said to be **negative** when the curve is **below** the x-axis. It is negative because the $f(x)$ values (or y-values) are negative.

Thus, the function is negative for $-2 < x < 1$.

The function is **positive** when $x > 1$ or $x < -2$.

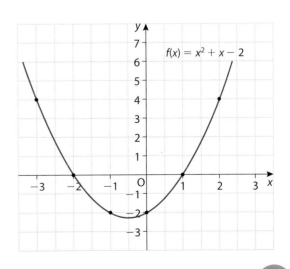

4. Intersecting graphs

Graphed below are the functions,

$$f(x) = x^2 \text{ (i.e. } y = x^2) \text{ and } g(x) = x + 2 \text{ (i.e. } y = x + 2)$$

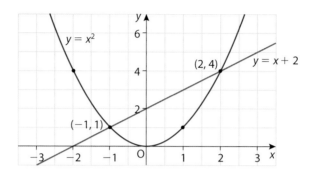

Notice that the curve $f(x)$ and the line $g(x)$ intersect at the points $(-1, 1)$ and $(2, 4)$.

We will now solve the equation $x^2 = x + 2$.

$$x^2 = x + 2 \Rightarrow x^2 - x - 2 = 0$$
$$\Rightarrow (x + 1)(x - 2) = 0$$
$$\Rightarrow x + 1 = 0 \text{ or } x - 2 = 0 \text{ i.e. } x = -1 \text{ or } x = 2.$$

Notice that these are the x-values of the points where the two graphs intersect.

Remember	If $f(x)$ and $g(x)$ are two functions, then the equation $f(x) = g(x)$ can be solved by drawing the graphs of the functions, using the same axes and same scales, and then writing down the x-values of the points of intersection of the graphs.

We can also use the curve above to solve the inequality **$f(x) < g(x)$**.

$f(x) < g(x)$ represents that part of the graph where the curve $f(x)$ is below the line $g(x)$.

From the graph, the curve is below the line from $x = -1$ to $x = 2$.

Thus, $f(x) < g(x)$ for $-1 < x < 2$.

5. Maximum and minimum values

On the right is a graph of the function

$$y = x^2 - 2x - 3$$

The point marked A is called the **minimum point** or **minimum turning point** of the curve.
This point is (1, −4).

The y-value of this point is called the **minimum value**.
In this graph, the minimum value is −4.

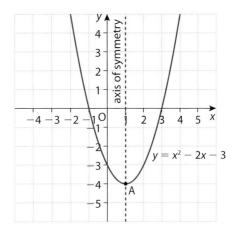

The broken red line is called the **axis of symmetry** of the curve.

The equation of this axis of symmetry is $x = 1$.

A quadratic curve with a shape like the one shown will have a **maximum turning point**.

Maximum point

6. Finding $f(k)$ from a graph

The graph of the function $f(x) = x^2 + 5x - 1$ is shown.

$f(-4)$ is the value of y when $x = -4$.
To find $f(-4)$, we draw the line $x = -4$ and then read the y-value of the point where this line intersects the curve.

This y-value is −5.

Thus, $f(-4) = -5$.

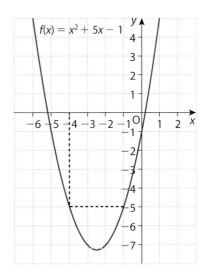

465

7. When is a function increasing or decreasing?

The given graph shows that the function is
decreasing (i.e. the y-value is decreasing)
from $x = -5$ to $x = -1$.

The function is **increasing** from
$x = -1$ to $x = 3$.

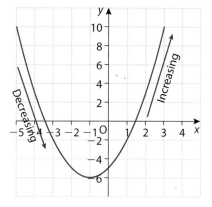

Exercise 23.3

1. The curve on the right is the graph of the function

$$y = x^2 - 4x + 3.$$

From the graph, write down

(i) the coordinates of the points where the curve
crosses the x-axis

(ii) the value of y when $x = 2$

(iii) the values of x when $y = 8$

(iv) the minimum point of the curve.

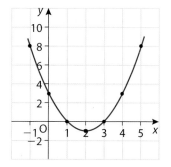

2. The curve on the right is the graph of the
function

$$f(x) = x^2 - 1$$

Use the graph to find

(i) the value of $f(x)$ when $x = 2$

(ii) the value of $f(x)$ when $x = -2$

(iii) the minimum point of the curve

(iv) the values of x when $f(x) = 0$

(v) the values of x when $f(x) = 3$.

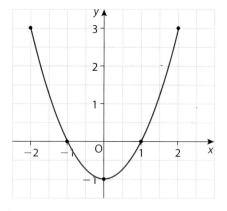

3. Shown below is the graph of the function

    $f(x) = x^2 - 3x - 4$ in the domain $-2 \leqslant x \leqslant 5$.

Use the graph shown to write down

  (i) the values of x for which
      $f(x) = 0$

  (ii) the values of x for which
      $f(x) = 6$

  (iii) the values of x for which
      $f(x) = -4$

  (iv) the value of $f(2)$

  (v) the value of $f\left(\frac{1}{2}\right)$

  (vi) the coordinates of the
      minimum point of the curve

  (vii) the minimum value of $f(x)$.

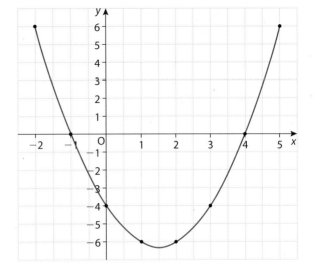

4. The graph of $f(x) = x^2 - 2x - 5$ is given on
the right.

Use this graph to write down

  (i) $f(-3)$ and $f(1)$

  (ii) the values of x for which $f(x) = 0$

  (iii) the values of x for which $f(x) = 6$

  (iv) the minimum point of the curve

  (v) the minimum value of $f(x)$.

  (vi) the range of values of x for which $f(x)$
      is negative.

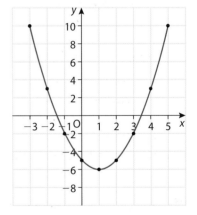

5. Drawn below is a graph of the function:

    $f: x \rightarrow 3 + 2x - x^2$, for $-2 \leqslant x \leqslant 4, x \in R$.

Use the graph to write down

  (i) the roots of the equation $f(x) = 0$

  (ii) the values of x for which $f(x) = 3$

  (iii) the value of $f\left(2\frac{1}{2}\right)$

  (iv) the maximum value of $f(x)$

  (v) the coordinates of the maximum
      point of $f(x)$

  (vi) the range of values of x for which
      $f(x)$ is increasing

  (vii) the range of values of x for which
      $f(x)$ is positive

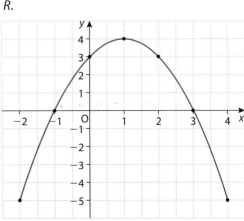

  (viii) the equation of the axis of symmetry of the curve.

6. Draw the graph for the function $f(x) = 2x^2 - x - 3$ in the domain $-2 \leqslant x \leqslant 3$.
Use your graph to find

   (i) the values of x for which $f(x) = 0$

   (ii) the values of x for which $f(x) = 6$

   (iii) the coordinates of the minimum point of the curve

   (iv) the values of x for which $f(x) < 0$.

7. The graphs of the functions $f(x) = x^2$ and $g(x) = 2x + 3$ are shown below.

   (i) Write down the coordinates of the points where the curve and line meet.

   (ii) Solve the equation $x^2 = 2x + 3$.

   (iii) What is the connection between the answers in (i) and (ii) above?

   (iv) Explain the meaning of the equation $f(x) = g(x)$.

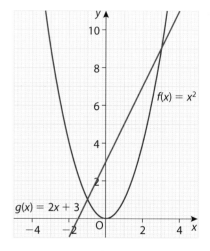

8. Drawn below are the graphs $f(x) = x^2 + x - 6$ and $g(x) = 3x - 3$.

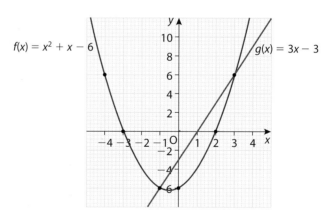

Use the graph to estimate

   (i) $f(-2)$ and $g(3)$

   (ii) the roots of the equation $f(x) = 0$

   (iii) the roots of the equation $f(x) = 4$

   (iv) the roots of the equation $f(x) = g(x)$

   (v) the range of values of x for which $f(x) \leqslant g(x)$

   (vi) the range of values of x for which $f(x) \leqslant 0$.

9. Here are two graphs:

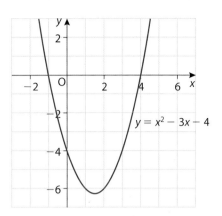

Use the graphs to solve these equations:

(i) $3x - x^2 = 0$

(ii) $x^2 - 3x - 4 = 0$

(iii) $3x - x^2 = -3$

(iv) $x^2 - 3x - 4 = -2.$

10. This is the graph of $y = 3x^2 - 5$.

Use the graph to solve these equations:

(i) $3x^2 - 5 = 0$

(ii) $3x^2 - 5 = 20.$

For what values of x is $3x^2 - 5 < 20$?

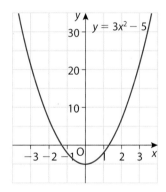

11. Drawn below are the graphs of $f(x) = x^2 - 2x$ and $g(x) = x - 1$ in the domain $-1 \leq x \leq 3$.

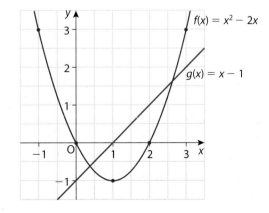

Use the graph to write down
   (i) the roots of the equation $f(x) = 0$
  (ii) the roots of the equation $f(x) = 3$
 (iii) the roots of the equation $f(x) = g(x)$
 (iv) the range of values of x for which $f(x) < 0$
  (v) the range of values of x for which $g(x) < f(x)$.

Explain how the graph could be used to solve the equation
     $x^2 - 2x - 2 = 0$.

12. Using the same axes and the same scales, graph the functions,
        $f: x \rightarrow x^2 + 3x - 3$ and $g: x \rightarrow x - 2$ in the domain $-4 \leqslant x \leqslant 2, x \in R$.

Use the graph to estimate
   (i) the roots of the equation $x^2 + 3x - 3 = 0$
  (ii) the roots of the equation $x^2 + 3x - 3 = -2$
 (iii) the roots of the equation $f(x) = g(x)$
 (iv) the minimum value of $f(x)$.

What is the meaning of $f(x) < g(x)$?
Now use your graph to find the range of values of x for which $f(x) < g(x)$.

13. The equation of the given curve is $y = (x + 2)^2$.
   (i) Solve the equation $(x + 2)^2 = 0$.
  (ii) Did you get one or two values for x?
 (iii) If you got one value only, the value for x that you found
       is called a **repeated root**.
       Explain how the graph shows this repeated root.

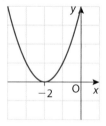

14. The diagram below shows the graphs of
        $f(x) = x^2 - 6x + 9$ $g(x) = x^2 - 3x + 3$.

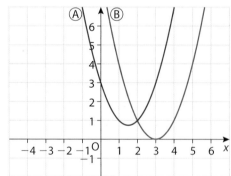

   (i) By substituting $x = 0$ (or any other value of x) into each equation, work out which
       graph corresponds to which equation.
  (ii) Use the graph to find one value of x for which $f(x) = g(x)$.
 (iii) Why has the equation $f(x) = 0$ only one root?

Section 23.4 Quadratic graphs and real-life problems

Many real-life situations such as the flight of a golf ball or maximising the area of a rectangle with a given perimeter can be modelled by quadratic equations.

The graph on the right shows the height of a ball as it is thrown through the air.
From the graph, it can be seen that

 (i) the ball reaches a height of 12 m
(ii) the ball lands 50 m away from the position from which it was thrown.

Example 1

Graphed on the right is the function

$$f(x) = 7 + 5x - 2x^2$$

in the domain $-1 \leqslant x \leqslant 4$.

Use your graph to solve

$$7 + 5x - 2x^2 = 0.$$

$f(x)$ is the height, in metres, reached by a particle fired from level ground at the point where $x = -1$, the x-axis representing level ground. From the time of firing until it hits the ground again, the particle was in flight for exactly 4.5 seconds.

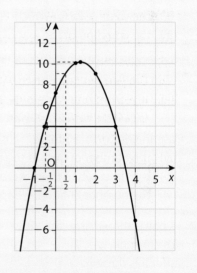

Use your graph to estimate
  (i) the maximum height reached by the particle
 (ii) the height reached by the particle after 1.5 seconds of flight
(iii) the number of seconds the particle is 4 m or more above the ground.

From the graph, the roots of the equation $7 + 5x - 2x^2 = 0$ are

$$\Rightarrow x = -1 \quad \text{or} \quad x = 3.5$$

(i) The maximum height reached by the particle is 10.3 m.

(ii) The height reached after 1.5 seconds is found by drawing a vertical line from $x = \frac{1}{2}$ until it meets the curve.
The corresponding y-value (i.e. the height) is 9 metres.

(iii) To find the number of seconds the particle is 4 m or more above the ground, draw the line $y = 4$ and then read the x-values of the points where it intersects the curve.
These x-values are -0.5 and 3.
∴ the number of seconds is 3.5.

Exercise 23.4

1. On the right is the graph of the function
$f(x) = -x^2 + 4x + 12$.
Use the graph to write down
   (i) $f(1)$
   (ii) the values of x for which $f(x) = 12$
   (iii) the equation of the axis of symmetry.

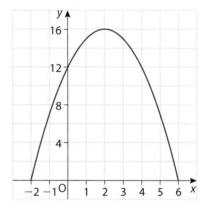

$f(x)$ represents the number of taxis at a taxi-rank from 6 a.m. ($x = -2$) to 10 p.m. ($x = 6$).
Each unit on the x-axis represents 2 hours and each unit on the y-axis represents one taxi.

Use the graph to estimate
   (iv) the number of taxis at the rank at 12 noon
   (v) the times when there were 14 taxis at the rank
   (vi) the number of hours when there were 10 taxis or more at the rank.

2. A ball is thrown into the air.
The formula $y = 20x - 4x^2$ shows its height, y metres above the ground, x seconds after it is thrown.
   (i) Copy and complete the table of values to show the height of the ball during its first five seconds.
   (ii) Use the table to plot a graph to show the ball's height against time.
   (iii) Use your graph to find
       (a) the maximum height reached by the ball and the time at which it reaches this height
       (b) two times when the ball is 12 metres above the ground
       (c) the interval of time when the ball is above 15 metres.

x	$20x - 4x^2$	y
0	$0 - 0$	0
1	$20 - 4$	16
2		
3		
4		
5		

3. Given that $f(x) = 4 - 3x - x^2$, $x \in R$,
copy and complete the given table.

Draw the graph of $f(x)$ in the domain
$-5 \leqslant x \leqslant 2$.

If the graph represents the temperature, in °C,
taken every two hours between 6 a.m. ($x = -5$)
and 8 p.m. ($x = 2$) in a certain city, use the
graph to estimate
   (i) the temperature at 11 a.m.
  (ii) the time when the temperature was highest
 (iii) the times when the temperature was 3°C
 (iv) the number of hours the temperature was at or above freezing point.

x	$4 - 3x - x^2$	y
-5	$4 + 15 - 25$	-6
-4		
-3		
-2		
-1		
0		
1	$4 - 3 - 1$	0
2		

4. A farmer has 16 metres of fencing with which to make a rectangular enclosure for sheep.
If one side of the enclosure is x metres long, show that the area A is given by $A(x) = 8x - x^2$.

Draw the graph of $A(x)$ in the domain $0 \leqslant x \leqslant 8$.

Use your graph to estimate
   (i) the area of the enclosure when $x = 2.5$.
  (ii) the maximum possible area and the value of x when this occurs
 (iii) the two values of x for which the area is 12 m².

5. Draw the graph of the function $f: x \rightarrow 6x - x^2$ in the domain $0 \leqslant x \leqslant 6$.

$f(x)$ represents the height, in metres, reached by a golf ball from the time it was hit
($x = 0$) to the time it hit the ground ($x = 6$).

If each unit on the x-axis represents 1 second and each unit on the y-axis represents
5 metres, use your graph to estimate

   (i) the greatest height reached by the golf ball
  (ii) the height of the golf ball after $1\frac{1}{2}$ seconds
 (iii) after how many seconds the ball was 10 metres above ground
 (iv) after how many seconds the ball reached its maximum height.

6. The area of a circle is given roughly by the formula $A = 3r^2$.
   (i) Copy and complete the table given on the right
       and draw a graph of the function for $0 \leqslant r \leqslant 3$.
  (ii) Use your graph to find an estimate for the area
       of a circle of radius 2.5 m.
 (iii) If a circle has an area of 10 m², use the graph to
       estimate the length of its radius.
 (iv) Check your answers to parts (ii) and (iii) using the
       accurate version of the formula for the area of a circle.

r	$3r^2$	A
0		
1	$3(1)$	3
2		
3		

7. A farmer has 20 metres of fencing.
He wishes to use it to form a rectangular
enclosure in the corner of a field, as in the diagram.

(i) Write down an expression for the area,
A m², enclosed by the fencing.

(ii) Plot the graph of A for values of x between
0 and 20.

(iii) For what values of x is the area 40 m²?

(iv) What values of x give an enclosed area greater than 90 m²?

(v) What is the maximum area the farmer can enclose?
What are the lengths of the fencing for this maximum area?

Section 23.5 Graphs of exponential functions

$f(x) = 2^x$ is a function.
Notice that the power is the variable x.

A function of x in which x appears as a power is called an **exponential function**.
$f(x) = 3^x$ and $g(x) = 4.3^x$ are other exponential functions.

To draw the graph of $f(x) = 2^x$, we set out a table of inputs and outputs from $x = -2$ to
$x = 3$, for example.

x	2^x	y
-2	$2^{-2} = \frac{1}{4}$	$\frac{1}{4}$
-1	$2^{-1} = \frac{1}{2}$	$\frac{1}{2}$
0	$2^0 = 1$	1
1	$2^1 = 2$	2
2	$2^2 = 4$	4
3	$2^3 = 8$	8

The graph of $f(x) = 2^x$ is shown below.

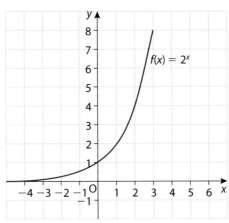

Any number to the
power of zero is 1.

Draw a graph of the function $f(x) = 2.3^x$ in the domain $-2 \leqslant x \leqslant 3$.
 (i) Use your graph to find an estimate for $f(2.5)$.
 (ii) Use your graph also to estimate the value of x for which $f(x) = 7$.

We set out a table of values for $f(x) = 2.3^x$, $-2 \leqslant x \leqslant 3$.

x	2.3^x	y
-2	2.3^{-2}	$\frac{2}{9}$
-1	2.3^{-1}	$\frac{2}{3}$
0	2.3^0	2
1	2.3^1	6
2	2.3^2	18
3	2.3^3	54

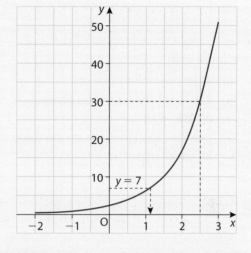

The graph is shown on the right.

 (i) To find $f(2.5)$, draw a vertical
    line from $x = 2.5$ until it
    meets the curve.
    The y-value of the point of intersection is 30.
    $\therefore f(2.5) = 30$

 (ii) To find the value of x for which $f(x) = 7$, draw the line $y = 7$ and read the
    x-value of the point of intersection of this line and the curve.
    This value is $x = 1.1$.

Exercise 23.5

1. This is the graph of $f(x) = 2^x$.

Use the graph to write down
 (i) $f(0)$ (ii) $f(1)$ (iii) $f(1.5)$.

$f(3)$ is not shown on the graph.

 (iv) What is $f(3)$?
 (v) For what value of x is $f(x) = 5$?

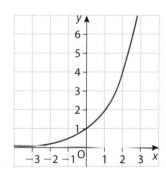

2. Copy and complete the table below and then draw the graph of the function $f(x) = 3^x$.

x	−2	−1	0	1	2	3
3^x		$\frac{1}{3}$				

Use your graph to write down
  (i) $f(1.5)$
  (ii) the value of x for which $f(x) = 4$.

3. On the right is the graph of $f(x) = k \cdot 2^x$,
  where $k \in N$.

  (i) Write down the value of k.
  (ii) $f(2)$ is not shown on the graph.
     What is $f(2)$?
  (iii) Use the graph to estimate the value of x
     for which $f(x) = 1$.

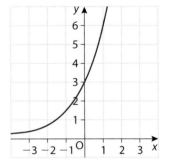

4. Copy and complete the table below:

x	−2	−1	0	1	2
2^x	$\frac{1}{4}$				
4.2^x	1				

Use the table to draw a sketch of the function $f(x) = 4.2^x$ in the domain $-2 \leqslant x \leqslant 2$.
Use your graph to find an estimate for $f(0.5)$.

5. Three graphs – Ⓐ, Ⓑ and Ⓒ – are sketched on the right.

  Associate each graph with one of the functions
  given below:

  | $f(x) = 2^x$ | | $f(x) = 3^x$ | | $f(x) = 3.3^x$ |

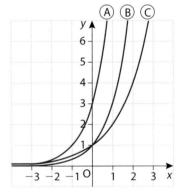

6. The diagram shows a sketch of the curve $y = 3^x$.
  (i) Write down the coordinates of the point
     where the curve cuts the y-axis.
  (ii) Copy the diagram and add sketches of the curves
     (a) 2×3^x (b) 5×3^x.

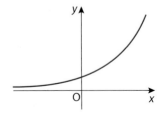

7. Niamh is told that the given curve is the graph of either

(a) $f(x) = k \cdot 2^x$ or (b) $f(x) = k \cdot 3^x$.

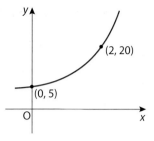

(i) Find the value of k.

(ii) Write down which of the two functions the curve represents.

8. Draw the graph of the function $f(x) = 2^x$ in the domain $-2 \leqslant x \leqslant 3$. $g(x)$ is another function where $g(x) = x + 3$.

Draw a sketch of $g(x)$ on the same axes and using the same scales.

Use your graph to estimate the positive solution of the equation $2^x = x + 3$.

Test yourself 23

1. (a) The graph of the function $f(x) = 2x + 5$ is shown.

Use the graph to write down

(i) $f(0)$ (ii) $f(1)$ (iii) $f(-1)$

(iv) the value of x for which $y = 3$

(v) the value of y when $x = -2.5$.

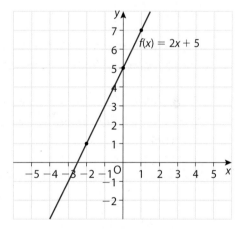

(b) On the right is the graph of the function $f(x) = x^2 - 4x$.

Use the curve to write down

(i) $f(3.5)$

(ii) the values of x for which $f(x) = -3$

(iii) the minimum value of $f(x)$.

(iv) the equation of the axis of symmetry of the curve.

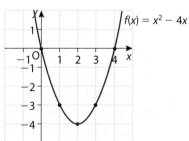

(c) Match each of the graphs below with one of the equations given.
In each equation, k is a positive number.
(One of the equations is not needed.)

$$y = kx$$

$$y = x^2 - k$$

$$y = k - x^2$$

$$y = k - x$$

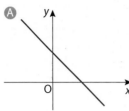

2. (a) Draw the graph of the function $f(x) = 3x - 1$ in the domain $-2 \leqslant x \leqslant 3$.
Use your graph to estimate
  (i) $f(-1.5)$ (ii) the value of x when $y = 3.5$.

(b) The curve on the right is the graph of the function

$$f(x) = x^2 + 2x - 3.$$

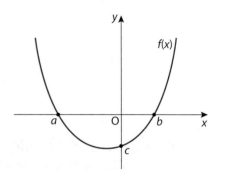

  (i) Find the coordinates of a, b and c.
  (ii) Write down the values of x for which $f(x) \leqslant 0$.
  (iii) If $f(k) = -3$, find two values for k.

(c) Copy and complete the following table.

x	−3	−2	−1	0	1	2	3	4	5
2ˣ	0.125			1		4			

  (i) Use the values in your table to draw the graph of $y = 2^x$ using a scale of 1 cm for 1 unit on the x-axis and 1 cm for 5 units on the y-axis.
  (ii) Use your graph to solve the equation $2^x = 6$.

3. (a) Draw the graph of the function

$$f : x \rightarrow 2x^2 - x - 6 \text{ for } -3 \leqslant x \leqslant 4, x \in R.$$

Use the graph to estimate
  (i) the values of x for which $f(x) = 0$
  (ii) the minimum value of $f(x)$
  (iii) the value of $f(2.5)$
  (iv) the range of values of x for which $f(x)$ is less than zero.

(b) Three times one number plus twice another is 9.
Twice the first number less the second number is 13.
If x is one number and y is the other, form two equations in x and y.
By drawing a sketch of the two equations, find the two numbers.

4. (a) The graph of $y = x^2 - 2x$ has been drawn on the given grid.

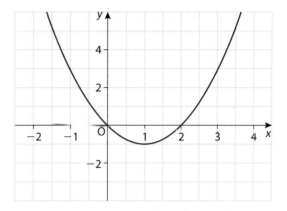

Use the graph to find estimates for the solution of these equations:

(i) $x^2 - 2x - 0$

(ii) $x^2 - 2x = 3$.

Write down the equation of the axis of symmetry of the curve.

(b) Which sketch graph fits which equation? Give reasons for your answers.

Ⓐ   Ⓑ   Ⓒ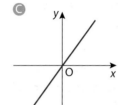

$y = 2x$

$y = x^2 - 2$

$y = 2 - x^2$

$y = x^2 + 2$

(c) A gardener has 18 metres of timber fencing to enclose a rectangular vegetable patch using a straight stone wall as one of the sides as shown. The width is x metres.

Show that the area of the enclosure is given by the function

$A(x) = 18x - 2x^2$.

Draw the graph of the function $y = A(x)$ in the domain $0 \leqslant x \leqslant 9$.

(i) Find the area of the enclosure when $x = 3$.

(ii) Find the two values of x for which the area is $30 \, \text{m}^2$.

(iii) Find the length and breadth of the enclosure of maximum area.

(iv) What is the maximum area?

5. (a) The following table gives the cost of hiring a surfboard for a number of days:

Days t	3	4	5	6
Cost €C	50	60	70	80

(i) By using any two couples, write down the equation of the line that relates the cost €C to the number of days t.

(ii) Use the equation to find the cost of hiring a surfboard for two weeks.

(b) Two functions, f and g, are defined as follows:

$$f: x \rightarrow 2^x, \quad g: x \rightarrow 9x - 3x^2 - 1.$$

Complete the table below and use it to draw the graphs of f and g for $0 \leqslant x \leqslant 3$.

x	0	0.5	1	1.5	2	2.5	3
$f(x)$							
$g(x)$							

(i) Use your graph to estimate the value(s) of x for which $2^x = 9x - 3x^2 - 1$.

(ii) If $2^k = 6$, use your graph to estimate the value of k.

Key words

> transformation   object   image   translation   axial symmetry
> central symmetry   symmetrical   axis of symmetry   centre of symmetry
> construction   perpendicular bisector   ray   hypotenuse

Section 24.1 Transformation geometry

The figure marked A in the diagram below has been moved to different positions. All the figures have the same shape and size. Some are upside-down and some are back-to-front.

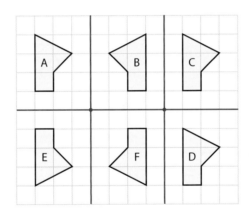

Each of the figures B, C, D, E and F is an **image** of the figure A under a **transformation**.
The original figure A is called the **object**.
The new position is called the **image**.
In this section we consider three transformations.
These are **translations**, **axial symmetry** and **central symmetry**.

1. Translations

A translation is movement in a straight line.
It may also be described as a 'sliding movement'.

The shape A on the left has been moved in the direction PQ and by a distance equal to |PQ|.
The translation PQ is written $\overrightarrow{\mathbf{PQ}}$.

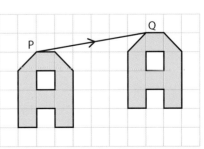

The image of the given figure is found by moving 4 units to the right and 3 units up. Notice that the size and shape of the figure is unchanged.

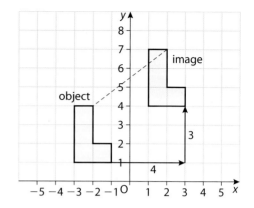

Here is the image of a line segment [AB] under the translation $\vec{t}$.

The image is labelled A′B′.

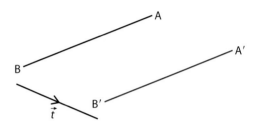

The image of the triangle ABC under the translation $\overrightarrow{BC}$ is shown on the right.

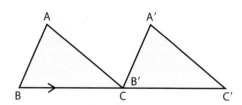

Exercise 24.1

1. Describe the translation that maps the blue shape onto the red shape in each of the following. Use words such as right, left, up and down.

2.

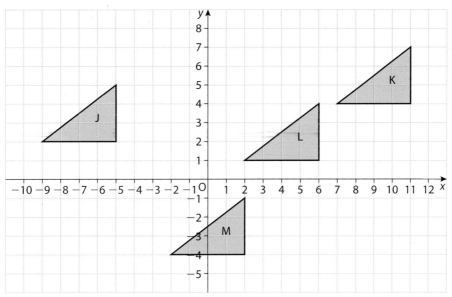

Describe fully the translation that maps
   (i)   shape L onto shape K
  (ii)   shape J onto shape L
 (iii)   shape M onto shape L
 (iv)   shape J onto shape M
  (v)   shape L onto shape M.

3. Construct the image of the letter T
under the given translation $\overrightarrow{AB}$.

4. Draw the triangle ABC twice and
construct its image under
   (i) $\overrightarrow{BC}$ (ii) $\overrightarrow{AC}$.

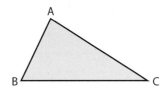

5. ABCD is a square, as shown.
Copy the diagram and draw a rough
sketch of the image of ABCD
   (i) under $\overrightarrow{AB}$ (ii) under $\overrightarrow{DB}$.

6. ABCD is a rectangle with the diagonals
intersecting at the point O.
Find each of the following:

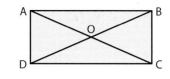

  (i) the image of A under $\overrightarrow{DC}$

  (ii) the image of [AB] under $\overrightarrow{BC}$

  (iii) the image of D under $\overrightarrow{OB}$

  (iv) the image of [DC] under $\overrightarrow{DA}$.

7. ABCD and ABEC are parallelograms.
Under the translation $\overrightarrow{CE}$, write down
the image of

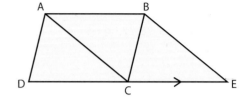

  (i) the point A

  (ii) [AD]

  (iii) △ADC

  (iv) [AC].

8. In the given figure, ABCD is a square
and BECD is a parallelogram.

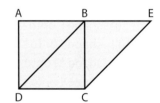

  (i) What is the image of [BD] under $\overrightarrow{DC}$?

  (ii) What is the image of C under $\overrightarrow{DB}$?

  (iii) What is the image of △ABD under $\overrightarrow{BE}$?

  (iv) Of what point is B the image under $\overrightarrow{CE}$?

  (v) Of what line segment is [BC] its image under $\overrightarrow{DC}$?

  (vi) Of what triangle is ABD the image under $\overrightarrow{CD}$?

9.

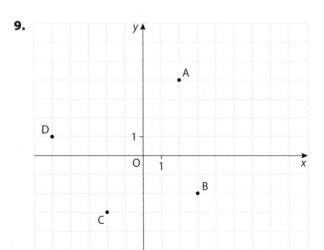

  (i) Write down the coordinates of A, B, C and D.

  (ii) Each point is translated 5 units to the right and 2 units up.
What are the coordinates of the image points A′, B′, C′ and D′?

Section 24.2 Symmetries

1. Symmetrical shapes

Each of the figures below is **symmetrical**.

The broken line in each figure is called an **axis of symmetry**.

A figure will have an axis of symmetry if it can be reflected in that line so that each half of the figure is reflected exactly onto the other half of the figure.

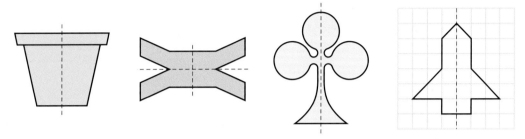

Here are some well-known geometrical figures and their axes of symmetry.

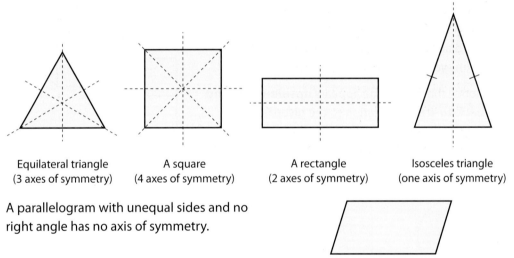

Equilateral triangle	A square	A rectangle	Isosceles triangle
(3 axes of symmetry)	(4 axes of symmetry)	(2 axes of symmetry)	(one axis of symmetry)

A parallelogram with unequal sides and no right angle has no axis of symmetry.

2. Axial symmetry

In the given diagram, the blue figure is the image of the green figure under reflection in the broken line ℓ.

We name the image figure A'B'C'D'.

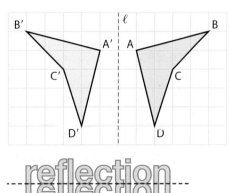

Here is another reflection in the horizontal broken red line.

485

The word MAM has line symmetry.
Can you think of any other words
that have line symmetry?

The diagram on the right illustrates how
the image of a figure is constructed under
reflection in a line.

3. Central symmetry

In the diagram on the right, the
point A is joined to the point X
and produced to A′ such that
$$|XA'| = |AX|.$$
We say that the point A′ is the image of A under
reflection in the point X or **central symmetry** in X.

The diagram on the right shows the letter F and
its image under central symmetry in the point X.

Notice that the image appears **upside-down and
back-to-front** in relation to the given figure.

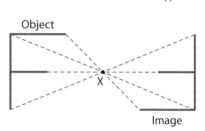

4. Centre of symmetry

All the figures below are mapped onto themselves under central symmetry in the point X.

In each case, the point X is the centre of symmetry.

Exercise 24.2

1. Use a set square and ruler to construct the image of the point X under reflection in the
line ℓ in each of the following:

  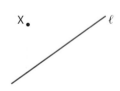

2. Use a set square and ruler to draw a rough sketch of the images of these triangles under reflection in the line *m*.

  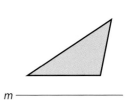

3. The rectangle DCFE is the image of the rectangle ABCD under axial symmetry in the line *k*.

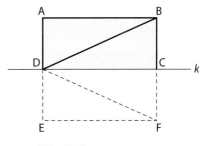

Write down the image of each of the following under reflection in the line *k*.

  (i) the point B   (ii) [AB]   (iii) [DB]

 (iv) △DCB   (v) △ABD   (vi) [CB]

4. Which of the following transformations represent reflection in a line?

  (i)   (ii)   (iii)   (iv)

5. Which of the letters in the word below have an axis of symmetry?

6. Sketch the image of the triangle ABC under central symmetry in the point C in each of the following.

 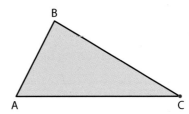

7. ABCD is a rectangle with the diagonals intersecting at the point O.

Find the image of each of the following under central symmetry in the point O.

(i) D   (ii) C   (iii) [BC]   (iv) △AOB

(v) [AO]   (vi) △ADB   (vii) [OC]   (viii) ABCD.

8. Which of the four faces shown below could be the image of the face shown on the right under a central symmetry?

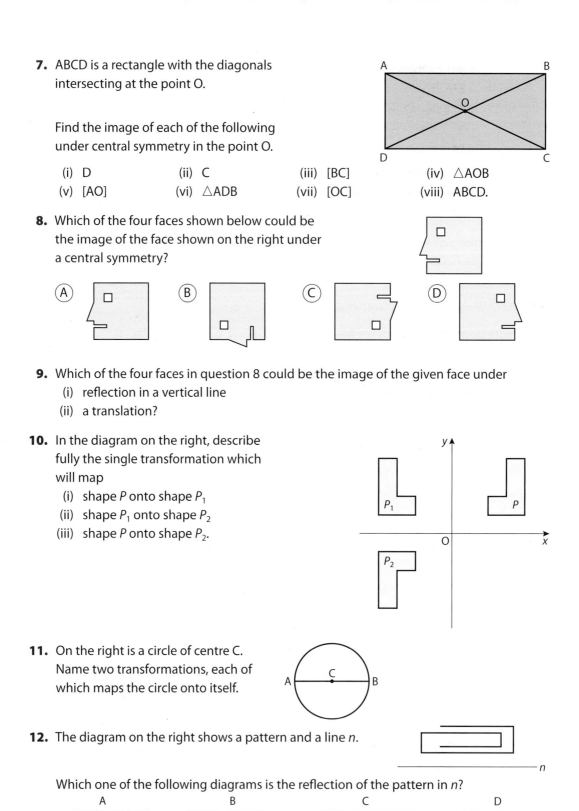

(A)   (B)   (C)   (D)

9. Which of the four faces in question 8 could be the image of the given face under
(i) reflection in a vertical line
(ii) a translation?

10. In the diagram on the right, describe fully the single transformation which will map
(i) shape P onto shape P_1
(ii) shape P_1 onto shape P_2
(iii) shape P onto shape P_2.

11. On the right is a circle of centre C. Name two transformations, each of which maps the circle onto itself.

12. The diagram on the right shows a pattern and a line n.

Which one of the following diagrams is the reflection of the pattern in n?

A   B   C   D

13. The diagram on the right shows the triangle ABC.

The image of ABC under reflection in the y-axis is A'B'C'.

   (i) Find the coordinates of A', B' and C'.

A", B" and C" are the images of A, B and C under reflection in the x-axis.

   (ii) Find the coordinates of A", B" and C".

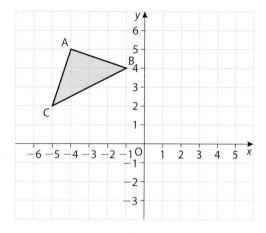

14. How many axes of symmetry has each of the following figures?

  (i)   (ii)   (iii)   (iv)

15. Which of the figures in question 14 have a centre of symmetry?

16.

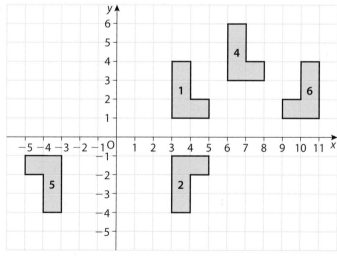

Which of the transformations – axial symmetry, central symmetry or translation – will map

   (i) L_1 onto L_2

  (ii) L_1 onto L_4

 (iii) L_5 onto L_2

 (iv) L_1 onto L_6

  (v) L_1 onto L_5?

17. Each of the four diagrams – A, B, C and D – shows the object in Figure 1 and its image under a transformation. For each of A, B, C and D, state one transformation (translation, axial symmetry or central symmetry) that will map the object onto that image.

Figure 1

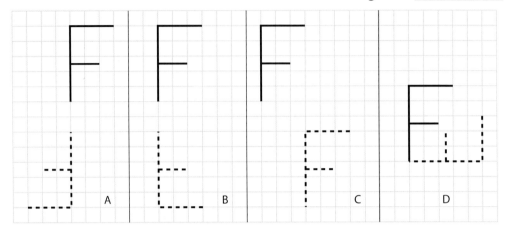

A   B   C   D

18. For these triangles, describe fully the single transformation that maps

   (i)   A onto B

  (ii) B onto D

 (iii) B onto C.

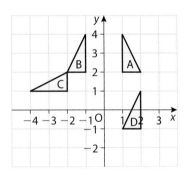

19.   (i) Draw a shape which has exactly three axes of symmetry. Show the axes on the diagram.

     (ii) Draw a shape which has exactly four axes of symmetry. Show the axes on the diagram.

20. ABCD is a rectangle with the diagonals intersecting at the point O.
ℓ is a line that contains O and ℓ is perpendicular to DC.
Find the image of each of the following under the indicated transformation.

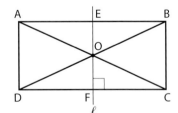

    (i) the image of △AOD under central symmetry in O

   (ii) the image of △AOB under central symmetry in O

  (iii) the image of △BOC under axial symmetry in ℓ

  (iv) the image of △DOF under axial symmetry in ℓ

   (v) the image of [AD] under the translation $\overrightarrow{DF}$.

Section 24.3 Constructions 1 ────────────────

1. Bisector of a given angle using only compass and straightedge

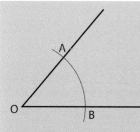

To bisect the given angle, place the point of the compass at O and draw an arc to cut both arms of the angle at A and B.

With the point of the compass at A and with the same radius, draw an arc between the arms of the angle. Repeat at B, cutting the first arc at C.

Join the point O to C. OC is the bisector of the angle AOB.

2. How to construct the perpendicular bisector of a line segment

Set your compass to over half the length of [AB]. With A as centre, draw an arc above and below the line.

Keep your compass with the same radius. With B as centre, draw two more arcs. These arcs intersect the first two arcs at P and Q.

Join P and Q. PQ is the perpendicular bisector of [AB]. M is the midpoint of [AB].

3. Line perpendicular to a given line ℓ, passing through a given point on ℓ

(i) Using a set square and straightedge

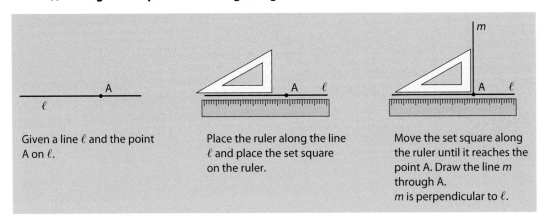

Given a line ℓ and the point A on ℓ.

Place the ruler along the line ℓ and place the set square on the ruler.

Move the set square along the ruler until it reaches the point A. Draw the line m through A.
m is perpendicular to ℓ.

(ii) Using a compass and straightedge

With the point of the compass at A and with a suitable radius, draw two arcs cutting the line ℓ at P and Q.

With the point of the compass at P, draw an arc above A.
Keeping the same radius, repeat at Q.
The arcs meet at the point X.

Using a straightedge, draw a line through X and the point A. The line XA is perpendicular to ℓ and contains A.

4. Line perpendicular to a given line ℓ, passing through a given point not on ℓ

(i) Using a straightedge and set square

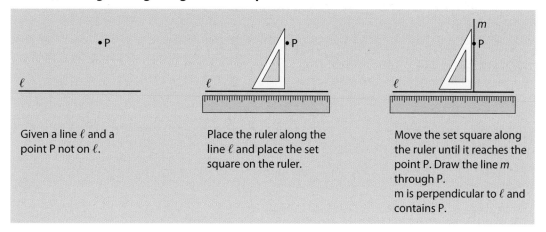

Given a line ℓ and a point P not on ℓ.

Place the ruler along the line ℓ and place the set square on the ruler.

Move the set square along the ruler until it reaches the point P. Draw the line m through P.
m is perpendicular to ℓ and contains P.

(ii) Using only a compass and straightedge

Given a line ℓ and a point P not on ℓ.
Place the point of the compass at P and draw two arcs cutting the line ℓ at A and B.

With A as the centre and with the same radius, draw an arc below the line ℓ.
With B as centre and with the same radius, draw a second arc intersecting the first arc at Q.

Join the points P and Q to form the line m.
m is perpendicular to ℓ and contains P.

5. How to draw a line parallel to a given line, through a given point

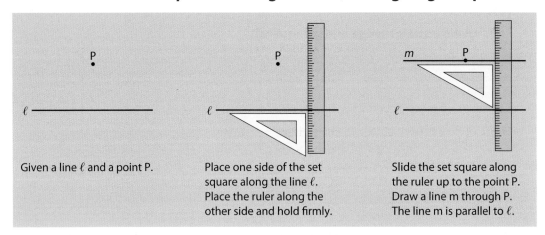

Given a line ℓ and a point P.

Place one side of the set square along the line ℓ. Place the ruler along the other side and hold firmly.

Slide the set square along the ruler up to the point P. Draw a line m through P. The line m is parallel to ℓ.

6. Division of a line segment into three equal parts

Draw a line segment [XY]. Draw a line through X making an acute angle with [XY].

Use a compass with X as centre and draw an arc crossing the line at A. With A as centre and with the same radius, draw another arc crossing the line. Mark this point B. Repeat the process at point B and mark the new point C.

Join C to Y. Using a set square and ruler, draw lines through B and A parallel to CY. These lines meet [XY] at the points V and U, respectively. U and V divide [XY] into three equal parts.

7. Division of a line segment into any number of equal segments, without measuring it

The method shown in 6 above can be used to divide a line segment into any number of equal parts.

In the given figure, the line XE is divided into 5 equal parts.
Join EY.
Using a set square and straightedge, draw lines through D, C, B and A parallel to EY.
The line segment [XY] is divided into 5 equal parts.

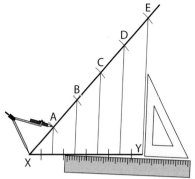

8. Line segment of a given length on a given ray

We use a compass, ruler and straightedge to draw a line segment of a given length on a given ray.

To draw a line segment of 5 cm, we use a compass and ruler to get a radius of 5 cm.
We now place the compass at the point A and without changing the radius, draw an arc intersecting the line at B.
[AB] is 5 cm in length.

9. Angle of a given number of degrees with a given ray as one arm

We use a protractor to measure angles and draw angles of given sizes. The diagrams below show how to draw an angle of 74°.

Draw a line.
Mark the vertex of the angle.

Position the protractor as if you were measuring an angle.
Mark a dot at 74°.

Draw a line from the vertex through the dot.

Exercise 24.3

1. Using only a compass and straightedge, construct the bisector of each of the angles shown below:

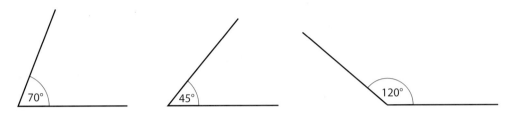

2. Use your set square to draw a right angle.
   Now use your compass and straightedge to divide the angle into two equal parts.
   Use your protractor to verify that each part is 45°.

3. Draw a line segment 6 cm in length.
   Use your compass and straightedge to construct the perpendicular bisector of this line segment.
   Verify that each half is 3 cm in length.

4. Draw a line segment 7 cm in length.
   Bisect the line and verify that both halves are equal in length.

5. Draw a line segment [AB], 8 cm in length.
   Use a compass and straightedge to construct the perpendicular bisector of this line segment.
   Pick any point on the perpendicular bisector and verify that it is the same distance from A and B.

6. Using a set square and straightedge, construct a line perpendicular to the given line through the given point for each of the lines shown below:

7. Using diagrams similar to those in question 6 above, construct a line perpendicular to the given line through the given point using only a compass and straightedge.

8. In each of the following, construct a line perpendicular to the given line and through the given point, using
   (i) a set square and straightedge only
   (ii) a compass and straightedge only.

• A   • B   • C

q

p ———————————

r

9. Using a set square and straightedge, draw a
line through the point P parallel to the line ℓ.

P•

ℓ ———————————

10. Draw any other line segment and plot a point P not on the line.
Now, using a set square and straightedge, draw a line through P parallel to the line
segment you have drawn.

11. The diagram on the right shows a line segment [AB]
and a line AY in which $|AX| = |XY|$.
Use your set square and ruler to draw XM parallel to YB.
Verify that M is the midpoint of [AB].

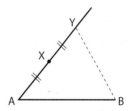

12. Draw a line segment 9 cm in length.
Now use your compass, ruler and set square to divide the line into 3 equal parts.
Use your ruler to verify that each part is 3 cm in length.

13. Draw a line segment 10 cm in length.
Now use your compass, ruler and set square to divide the line into 4 equal parts.

14. Use your protractor to draw an angle of 65° (∠BAC).
Now use a compass and straightedge to construct
the bisector of this angle.
If X is any point on the bisector of the angle BAC and
XB ⊥ AB and XC ⊥ AC, use congruent triangles to
show that $|XB| = |XC|$.

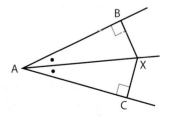

15. Copy the given diagram and then construct the shortest line segment from P to the line *m*.

16. Construct a right-angled triangle with the same dimensions as the given triangle. Verify that |AB| = 5 cm.

Now construct the perpendicular bisectors of [AC] and [AB].
If your constructions are accurate, the two bisectors should meet on [AB].

17. The given parallelogram has these dimensions:
|DC| = 8 cm, |AD| = 3 cm and |DB| = 10 cm.

Using a compass and ruler only, construct this parallelogram.

Section 24.4 Constructing triangles and rectangles

1. Triangle given lengths of the three sides

Make an accurate drawing of triangle ABC with |AB| = 6 cm, |BC| = 5 cm and |CA| = 4 cm.

Make a rough sketch first, to get an idea of what your finished drawing should be like.

Start with the longest side. Using a ruler, draw a line segment 6 cm long and label its ends A and B.

Set your compass to a radius of 5 cm. Put the point at B and draw an arc.

Set your compass to 4 cm. Put the point at A and draw a second arc. Point C is where the two arcs cross.

Join C to A and B to complete the triangle.

2. Triangle given side, angle and side measurements

Construct a triangle ABC with [BC] as base,
where |BC| = 4 cm, |AB| = 3 cm and |∠ABC| = 60°.
Measure the side [AC].

A rough sketch is shown on the right.

B   4 cm   C

Draw a horizontal line and use your compass to mark off 4 cm. This gives the base [BC] = 4 cm.

Use your protractor to measure ∠CBA = 60° and draw the line BA. Place the point of your compass at B and draw an arc using a radius of 3 cm. The point where the arc cuts the line BA gives us the required point A.

Join A to C. ABC is the required triangle. If we measure |AC|, we get 3.6 cm.

3. Triangle given angle, side, angle measures

Construct a triangle ABC with |BC| = 5 cm, |∠ABC| = 40° and |∠ACB| = 50°.

A rough sketch is shown.

B   C

Draw a line segment [BC], 5 cm in length.

Use a protractor to make
    |∠ABC| = 40° and |∠BCA| = 50°
The lines meet at the point A.
ABC is the required triangle.

4. Right-angled triangle, given the length of the hypotenuse and one other side

Construct the triangle ABC so that $|\angle ABC| = 90°$, $|BC| = 5$ cm and $|AC| = 6$ cm.

A rough sketch of the triangle is shown.

Draw a line segment [BC], 5 cm in length.

Use a protractor to make an angle of 90° at B.
Draw a vertical line BA.
Set your compass to a radius of 6 cm.
With C as centre, draw an arc cutting the vertical line.
Mark this point A and join AC.
ABC is the required triangle.

5. Right-angled triangle, given one side and one of the acute angles

Construct the triangle ABC so that the base [BC] = 5 cm, $|\angle ABC| = 90°$ and $|\angle ACB| = 40°$.

A rough sketch is shown.

Draw a line segment [BC], 5 cm in length.

Use a protractor to make an angle of 90° at B.
Draw a vertical line BA.
Now use your protractor to make an angle of 40° at C.
Mark the point A where the arm of the angle meets the vertical line.
ABC is the required triangle.

6. Constructing rectangles

Construct a rectangle of sides 5 cm and 3 cm in length.

Draw a horizontal line and mark a point A on it.
Use a set square or protractor to draw a line perpendicular to given line at A.

Use a compass to measure 5 cm on the horizontal line and 3 cm on the vertical line.
Mark the points D and B, respectively.

Draw a line through B parallel to AD.
Draw a line through D parallel to AB.
These lines meet at the point C.
ABCD is the required rectangle.

Exercise 24.4

1. Draw an accurate construction of each of the following triangles.
All construction lines must be shown.

2. Draw a rough sketch of each of the following triangles.
Use [BC] as base in each case.
Now draw an accurate construction of each triangle.

   (i) $\triangle$ABC in which $|BC| = 6$ cm, $|AB| = 5$ cm and $|AC| = 4$ cm.
  (ii) $\triangle$ABC in which $|BC| = 8$ cm, $|AB| = 5.5$ cm and $|AC| = 6$ cm.

3. Draw a triangle of sides 3 cm, 5 cm and 6 cm.
Measure the three angles and verify that
   (i) the smallest angle is opposite the shortest side
  (ii) the largest angle is opposite the longest side.

4. Construct the following triangles based on the dimensions shown in the rough sketches below.

Measure |AC| Measure |DE| Measure |XZ|

5. Construct a triangle ABC, with [BC] as base, in each of the following cases.
(First draw a rough sketch.)
Measure the third side in each triangle.

    (i) |BC| = 4 cm, |AB| = 3 cm and |∠ABC| = 50°.
   (ii) |BC| = 6 cm, |∠BCA| = 60° and |AC| = 4.5 cm.

6. Draw accurate diagrams of the sketches shown below:

Measure |AC| Measure |DF| Measure |XZ|

7. Draw an accurate construction of each of the following right-angled triangles:

8. Construct the triangle DEF, with base [EF], in which |DE| = 5 cm, |EF| = 6.5 cm and |∠DEF| = 90°.

9. Construct the triangle ABC, with [BC] as base, in which |BC| = 7 cm, |∠ABC| = 90° and |∠ACB| = 50°.
Measure |AC|.

10. Draw a rectangle of sides 6 cm and 4 cm in length.
Verify that both diagonals are equal in length.

11. Draw a rectangle of sides 7 cm and 4.5 cm in length.
Measure the length of the diagonal.

12. Construct the rectangle ABCD with base [AB] = 7 cm in length if the area of the
rectangle is 28 cm².

13. Draw a triangle ABC having the same measurements as those
shown on the right.
Use your compass to perpendicularly bisect the three sides of
the triangle.
If your drawing is accurate, the three lines should intersect at
the same point.
Now use this point as the centre to draw a circle through A, B and C.
This circle is called the **circumcircle** of the triangle.

14. Draw a triangle with base 7 cm and other sides of length 5 cm and 6 cm.
Bisect the three angles using a compass and ruler.
The three bisectors should meet at the one point.
Using this point as centre, draw a circle which touches the three sides of the triangle.
This circle is called the **incircle** of the triangle.

Test yourself 24

1. (a) How many axes of symmetry has each of the following letters?

(i) T (ii) E (iii) A (iv) M

(b) Copy the diagram on the right
and then use a ruler and set
square to draw a line through
P perpendicular to ℓ.

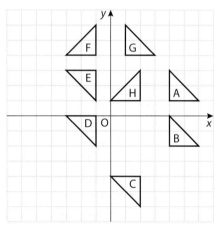

(c) Describe in full the transformation that
maps each of these:

    (i)   F onto G   (ii)   D onto F

    (iii) A onto B   (iv) A onto H

    (v)   E onto B   (vi) E onto C.

2. (a) Construct the triangle based on
the dimensions shown in the
rough sketch on the right.

(b) Which of the four fish in the boxes below could be
the image of the fish shown on the right under

    (i) a translation   (ii) an axial symmetry   (iii) a central symmetry?

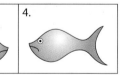

(c) A′B′C′D′ is the image of the figure ABCD
under reflection in the *y*-axis.

Write down the coordinates of A′, B′, C′ and D′.

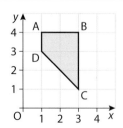

3. **(a)** Use your protractor to draw an angle of 70°.
Now use your compass and straightedge only to construct the bisector of this angle.

(b) Copy these diagrams onto squared paper.
Shade **two more squares** in each diagram to make the dashed line an axis of symmetry.

(i)   (ii)   (iii)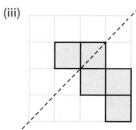

(c) ABCD is a parallelogram with the diagonals intersecting at the point O.

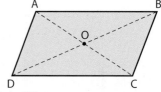

  (i) What is the image of D under $\overrightarrow{AB}$?
 (ii) What is the image of [AD] under central symmetry in O?
(iii) What is the image of △AOB under central symmetry in O?
(iv) What is the image of [DC] under $\overrightarrow{CB}$?
 (v) Is the triangle DCB the image of the triangle DAB under reflection in the line DB?

4. **(a)** Use a compass and ruler only to construct a line through P perpendicular to the line *k*.

(b) Describe the transformation that will map

 (i) shape T onto shape S
(ii) shape P onto shape Q
(iii) shape A onto shape B.

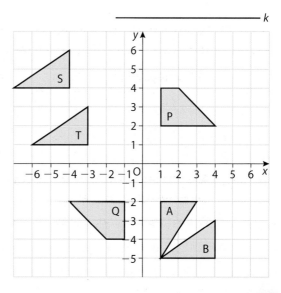

Answers

Chapter 1: Algebra 1

Exercise 1.1

1. $5x$
2. $11a + 9$
3. $3x + 5y$
4. $3a - 2b$
5. $15a + 6b$
6. $7x + 5y + 4$
7. $7x + 4$
8. $4x + 3$
9. $8a + 3b + 2$
10. $6x + 1$
11. $5a + 4b$
12. $5ab + 2$
13. $3p - q + r$
14. $2k + 5$
15. $7ab - 3c$
16. $4xy + 11z$
17. $5ab + 5cd$
18. $11x - 8xy$
19. $-x^2 + 2x + 1$
20. $4x^2 - 11x + 7$
21. $7a^2 - 8a - 3$
22. $-2y^2 - 6y - 3$
23. $3x^2 - 2x - 5$
24. $2a^2 - a + 6$
25. (i) 4   (ii) 4   (iii) 2   (iv) 8
26. (i) $7p + 8q$ (ii) $6a + 4b + 13$ (iii) $4a + 4b + 4c$
27. (i) $4p + 2$ (ii) 3   (iii) $2x$ (iv) $5x + 4$

Exercise 1.2

1. (i) $12a$ (ii) $15a^2$ (iii) $2ab$ (iv) $12xy$ (v) $-6a^2$ (vi) $8ab^2$ (vii) $2a^3b^2$ (viii) $24a^3$
2. $11x + 7$
3. $8x + 7$
4. $13x - 8$
5. $x + 2$
6. $18x - 20$
7. $3x - 14$
8. $a - 1$
9. $a - 5$
10. $4x^2 - 4x - 6$
11. $x^2 + x - 24$
12. $2x^2 + 10x + 12$
13. $6x^2 + 16x + 8$
14. $6x^2 - 10x - 4$
15. $10x^2 + 11x - 6$
16. $2x^2 - 13x + 15$
17. $15x^2 - 12x - 3$
18. $3x^3 + 7x^2 + 5x + 1$
19. $4x^3 + 6x^2 - 10x - 12$
20. $5x^3 - 7x^2 + 22x - 8$
21. $6x^3 - 13x^2 + 27x - 14$
22. $4x^3 - 17x^2 + 28x - 6$
23. $8x^3 - 18x^2 + 17x - 6$
24. $6a^3 - 17a^2 + 18a - 8$
25. $2y^3 - y^2 - 19y - 7$
26. (i) $2xy$ (ii) $2km + nm$ (iii) $15a^2 + ac$
27. (i) $\boxed{d + 5}$ (ii) $\boxed{n - 4}$ (iii) $\boxed{5 - p}$ (iv) $\boxed{4 + k}$

28. (i) $2q$ (ii) $3m$ (iii) $3b$ (iv) $5x^2$ (v) $5c^2$ (vi) $4v^2w$

Exercise 1.3

1. (i) 12   (ii) 14   (iii) 3   (iv) 19   (v) 33
2. (i) 4   (ii) 3   (iii) 22   (iv) -10
3. (i) 4   (ii) 3   (iii) 33   (iv) 10   (v) 12   (vi) 26   (vii) 5   (viii) 2   (ix) 2
4. (i) 7   (ii) 5   (iii) 1   (iv) 6
5. (i) 19   (ii) 1   (iii) 30   (iv) 24
6. 7
7. (i) -11 (ii) 34   (iii) 180
8. (i) 30   (ii) 15   (iii) 1   (iv) $\frac{9}{2}$ (v) 180
9. (i) 24   (ii) 36   (iii) 25
10. (i) $125 \, \text{cm}^2$ (ii) $96 \, \text{cm}^2$
11. (i) $125 \, \text{cm}^2$ (ii) $242 \, \text{cm}^2$
12. A and F, B and G, C and E, D and H
13. $1\frac{1}{2}$

Exercise 1.4

1. (i) 7   (ii) 4   (iii) 10   (iv) 4   (v) 3   (vi) 6
2. (i) $x = 4$ (ii) $x = 9$ (iii) $x = 7$ (iv) $x = 7$ (v) $x = 7$
3. $x = 3$
4. $x = 6$
5. $x = 6$
6. $x = 4$
7. $x = 1$
8. $x = 4$
9. $x = 6$
10. $x = 5$
11. $x = 3$
12. $x = 8$
13. $x = 6$
14. $x = 7$
15. $x = 7$
16. $x = 5$
17. $x = 9$
18. $x = 2$
19. $x = 5$
20. $x = 1$
21. $x = 10$
22. $x = 4$
23. $x = 5$
24. $x = 5$
25. $x = 2$
26. $x = 2$
27. $x = -6$
28. $x = 3$
29. $x = 2$
30. $x = 4$
31. $x = 2$
32. (i) $x = 2$ (ii) $x = 2$
33. $x = 2\frac{3}{11}, f = 3\frac{3}{8}$

Exercise 1.5

1. 5
2. 2
3. 6 and 11
4. 14 yrs old
5. (i) $6x + 1$ (ii) 9
6. 7
7. 12
8. 51
9. (i) 15   (ii) $9\frac{1}{2}$ (iii) 10
10. $\frac{7}{12}$

11. (i) 8   (ii) 5

12. (i) As $20 - x + x = 20$

(ii) $15 - x$ (iii) 8

13. $(7x - 4)$ cm^2; 6

14. (i) $(x - 6)$ yrs   (ii) $(x + 12)$ yrs

(iii) 15 yrs

15. 48

16. Air – 2 hours, Sea – 5 hours 20 min,
Train – 3 hours 20 min

Exercise 1.6

1. (i) T (ii) T (iii) F (iv) T

   (v) F (vi) F (vii) T (viii) T

2. (i) $>$ (ii) $<$ (iii) $>$ (iv) $<$

3. (i) $x < 4$ (ii) $2 > -3$

(iii) $S \leqslant 40$ km/hr   (iv) $b \leqslant -5$

(v) $A \geqslant 18$ (vi) $A \leqslant 60$

4. (i) 1, 2, 3   (ii) 1, 2, 3, 4, 5

(iii) 1, 2, 3, 4, 5, 6   (iv) 3, 4, 5, 6

(v) 1, 2, 3, 4   (vi) 2, 3, 4, 5, 6, 7

5. (i) $-2, -1, 0, 1$ (ii) 0, 1, 2, 3, 4

(iii) $-3, -2, -1, 0$ (iv) $-4, -3, -2, -1, 0$

(v) $-4, -3, -2, -1, 0, 1$

(vi) $-2, -1, 0, 1, 2, 3$

7. (i) $x > 3$ (ii) $x < 3$

(iii) $x = 3$ (iv) $x \leqslant 3$

8. (i) $x \geqslant 1$ (ii) $x \leqslant -1$ (iii) $x < 4$

(iv) $x > -6$ (v) $x > 6$ (vi) $x < 2$

10. (i) 3, 4, 5, 6   (ii) 1, 2, 3

(iii) $-2, -1, 0, 1, 2, 3, 4, 5$

(iv) $-2, -1, 0, 1, 2, 3$

11. (i) $x \geqslant 1, x \in N$ (ii) $x \geqslant -1, x \in Z$

(iii) $x \geqslant -3, x \in Z$ (iv) $-3 \leqslant x \leqslant 9, x \in R$

(v) $-4 \leqslant x \leqslant 4, x \in R$

(vi) $-5 \leqslant x < 15, x \in R$

12. $\sqrt{9}, \sqrt{20}$ **13.** 12, 16, 20, 24

14. 9, −4, 0

15. (i) $n \geqslant 6$ (ii) $n \leqslant 5°C$

(iii) $n \leqslant 10$ kg   (iv) $n > 5$

(v) $20 \leqslant n \leqslant 30$ (vi) $5n - 12 > -7$

Exercise 1.7

1. A, B, D, E **2.** A, C, D, E **3.** $x \leqslant 5$

4. $x \leqslant 4$ **5.** $x \leqslant 4$ **6.** $x \leqslant 3$

7. $x \leqslant -2$ **8.** $x \leqslant 4$ **9.** $x < -3$

10. $x \leqslant 2$ **11.** $x \leqslant 4$ **12.** $x \leqslant 3$

13. $x < 2$ **14.** $x \geqslant -1$ **15.** $x \leqslant 6$

16. $x < 3$ **17.** $\{-1, 0, 1, 2, 3, 4, 5\}$

18. ●—+—+—+—○   **19.** $-2 \leqslant x < 2$
     0 1 2 3 4

20. $-5 < x \leqslant 3$ **21.** $-3 \leqslant x < 1$

22. $-3 < x \leqslant 2$ **23.** $-\frac{1}{2} \leqslant x < \frac{3}{4}$

24. $-2 < x \leqslant 2$ **25.** $2 \leqslant x \leqslant 7$

---

26. $-2 \leqslant x < 5$ **27.** 7

28. $\{3, 4, 5\}$ **29.** (iii)

30. $-4, -3, -2, -1, 0, 1, 2, 3, 4$

31. (i) $350 < c < 500$

(iii) $120 \leqslant c \leqslant 200$

(v) $12 \leqslant c \leqslant 20$

Test yourself 1

1. (a) (i) $6x^2 + x - 3$ (ii) $x = 3$

(b) $2 \leqslant x \leqslant 4$

(c) $16x - 12; x = 3$

2. (a) (i) $10(x + 3)$ (ii) $2 - 4x^2$

(b) (i) $(x + 3)$ cm   (ii) $(x - 1)$ cm

(iii) $(3x + 2)$ cm

(iv) $3x + 2 = 44$; $|AB| = 14$ cm,

$|BC| = 17$ cm, $|CA| = 13$ cm

3. (a) (i) $x = 3$ (ii) 7 units

(b) $-1 \leqslant x \leqslant 4$

(c) (i) $p = 4x + 2y + 2z$

(ii) $x = 10$

4. (a) $x = 11$

(b) (i) $6x^3 - x^2 + 7x - 6$ (ii) 1

(c) 7, 11

5. (a) (i) 35   (ii) 41

(b) (i) $6x + 17$ (ii) 21

(c) (i) $10x + 11$ (ii) 3.9

(iii) $1\frac{1}{2}$

6. (a) $a = 2\frac{5}{8}$

(b) (i) A, D, F   (ii) C, D, E (1)

(c) (i) $6x^2 + 11x + 3$ (ii) $11x + 3$

(iii) 5

Chapter 2: Factors

Exercise 2.1

1. (i) 3   (ii) 6

(iii) 7   (iv) 7

2. (i) $4x$ (ii) $3n$

(iii) $5x$ (iv) $3a$

(v) $3x$ (vi) $2ab$

3. (i) $(x + 2y)$ (ii) $(2a + 3b)$

(iii) $(a + c)$ (iv) $(a + 2)$

(v) $(x - 3y)$ (vi) $(2x - 3z)$

(vii) $(3x + 2y)$ (viii) $(3a - 4b + 2)$

4. $6(x + 3y)$ **5.** $3b(a + c)$

6. $6a(x - 2y)$ **7.** $6a(a - 2)$

8. $7x(x - 4)$ **9.** $5x(3x + 5y)$

10. $3x^2(1 - 2y)$ **11.** $3ab(b - 2)$

12. $3p(p - 2q)$ **13.** $2x^2(y - 3z)$

14. $2y^2(3z + 5)$ **15.** $5pq(2p + q)$

16. $2a(a^2 - 2a + 4)$ **17.** $2x(2x - 3y + 4z)$

18. $5xy(y - 4x)$ **19.** $4xy(xy - 2)$
20. $5x(x^2 - 2x + 3)$ **21.** $2ab(a - 2b + 6c)$
22. (i) PARROT (ii) THRUSH
  (iii) GROUSE (iv) STARLING

Exercise 2.2

1. $(2a + 3)(x + y)$ **2.** $(3x - 4)(2a - b)$
3. $(3a - 4)(2b - c)$ **4.** $(2x + b)(5y - z)$
5. $(2a - 1)(x - 2y)$ **6.** $(a + c)(a + b)$
7. $(x + 3)(x - a)$ **8.** $(a - 5)(b + c)$
9. $(a + 5)(b + 3)$ **10.** $(3x + 4y)(x - z)$
11. $(c - 2d)(2c + 1)$ **12.** $(2a - 3)(x - 3y)$
13. $(2a + b)(c - 2d)$ **14.** $(3xy + 2z)(1 - z)$
15. $(4a - 3b)(2x + y)$ **16.** $(3a - 4)(2x^2 + 3)$
17. $(2y - z)(x - 1)$ **18.** $(n - 5)(a + b)$
19. $(2x - 3)(xy - z)$ **20.** $(7y + 2a)(y - 3b)$
21. $(2a + b)(2ab - 3)$ **22.** $(3a - 2b)(4a + 3c)$
23. $(2b - c)(5a - d)$ **24.** $(2x - a)(2x - 3y)$
25. $(2a - 3x)(3a - 5y)$ **26.** $(3y - 4z)(2x - 3y)$
27. $(ax - y)(3bx - 5y)$ **28.** $(3a + 2c)(3a^2 - 2b)$
29. $(x - 2a)(x + b)$ **30.** $(2x - 3y)(3x - 2a)$

Exercise 2.3

1. $(x + y)(x - y)$ **2.** $(a + b)(a - b)$
3. $(x + 2y)(x - 2y)$ **4.** $(x + 4y)(x - 4y)$
5. $(2x + y)(2x - y)$ **6.** $(3x + 4y)(3x - 4y)$
7. $(2a + 5b)(2a - 5b)$ **8.** $(6x + 7y)(6x - 7y)$
9. $(8x + 3y)(8x - 3y)$ **10.** $(4x + 5)(4x - 5)$
11. $(5x + 1)(5x - 1)$ **12.** $(6x + 5)(6x - 5)$
13. $(5x + 8y)(5x - 8y)$ **14.** $(1 + 6x)(1 - 6x)$
15. $(1 + 9y)(1 - 9y)$ **16.** $(6 + 11y)(6 - 11y)$
17. $(7a + 2b)(7a - 2b)$ **18.** $(xy + 2)(xy - 2)$
19. $(ab + 5)(ab - 5)$ **20.** $(xy + 4)(xy - 4)$
21. $(ab + 7)(ab - 7)$ **22.** $(5xy + 6)(5xy - 6)$
23. $(4ab + 5)(4ab - 5)$ **24.** $(3xy + 1)(3xy - 1)$
25. $(2ab + 7cd)(2ab - 7cd)$
26. $(11a + 8bc)(11a - 8bc)$
27. $(9hk + 5pq)(9hk - 5pq)$
28. (i) $3(x + 3y)(x - 3y)$ (ii) $3(2x + y)(2x - y)$
  (iii) $3(3x + y)(3x - y)$ (iv) $5(3 + x)(3 - x)$
  (v) $5(3k + 2)(3k - 2)$
  (vi) $4(ax + 3y)(ax - 3y)$
29. $(a^2 + b^2)(a + b)(a - b)$
30. (i) 9200 (ii) 240 (iii) 88
31. $2(9x^2 - 4y^2)$; $2(3x + 2y)(3x - 2y)$
32. $(3x + y)(3x - y)$

Exercise 2.4

1. $(x + 2)(x + 3)$ **2.** $(x + 2)(x + 6)$
3. $(x + 7)(x + 2)$ **4.** $(x + 3)(x + 8)$
5. $(x + 2)(x + 10)$ **6.** $(x + 3)(x + 9)$
7. $(x + 5)(x + 6)$ **8.** $(x + 4)(x + 11)$
9. $(x + 2)(x + 18)$ **10.** $(2x + 1)(x + 2)$

11. $(2x + 7)(x + 2)$ **12.** $(5x + 1)(x + 4)$
13. $(x - 3)(x - 4)$ **14.** $(x - 3)(x - 6)$
15. $(x - 4)(x - 5)$ **16.** $(x - 2)(x - 12)$
17. $(x - 3)(x - 9)$ **18.** $(x - 4)(x - 9)$
19. $(2x - 1)(x - 3)$ **20.** $(3x - 2)(x - 5)$
21. $(5x - 2)(x - 3)$ **22.** $(3x - 5)(x - 4)$
23. $(5x - 3)(x + 6)$ **24.** $(3x - 5)(x - 3)$
25. $(x + 2)(x - 6)$ **26.** $(x + 2)(x - 5)$
27. $(x - 2)(x + 9)$ **28.** $(x - 3)(x + 10)$
29. $(x + 2)(x - 15)$ **30.** $(x + 2)(x - 20)$
31. $(2x + 3)(x - 5)$ **32.** $(3x - 4)(x + 5)$
33. $(5x + 3)(x - 3)$ **34.** $(x + 6)(x - 12)$
35. $(4x - 1)(2x + 3)$ **36.** $(2x - 1)(x - 9)$
37. $(4x - 5)(3x + 1)$ **38.** $(3x + 5)(2x - 3)$
39. $(4x - 1)(2x - 3)$ **40.** $(3x - 2)(x + 5)$
41. $(3x + 4)(3x + 4)$ **42.** $(5x - 1)(x - 6)$
43. $(3x - 7)(x + 2)$ **44.** $(3x - 1)(2x - 3)$
45. $(4x - 5)(3x - 2)$ **46.** $(9x - 2)(x + 3)$
47. $(6x - 11)(x + 2)$ **48.** $(9x - 10)(x + 1)$
49. $(4x - 3)(x - 2)$ **50.** $(5x + 4)(2x - 5)$
51. $(9x - 4)(4x + 1)$ **52.** $(4x - 3)(3x - 2)$
53. $(3x - 4)(5x + 2)$ **54.** $(6x + 5)(4x - 3)$

Exercise 2.5

1. (i) $\frac{2}{5}$ (ii) $\frac{x}{2}$ (iii) $3x$ (iv) $4p$ (v) $3x$
2. (i) $x + y$ (ii) 4 (iii) $\frac{3}{x}$ (iv) $\frac{4}{3}$
3. $x - 1$ **4.** $2(y + 3)$ **5.** $x + 7$
6. $\frac{1}{x - 2}$ **7.** $\frac{1}{x + 7}$ **8.** $\frac{3}{x - 1}$
9. $\frac{2}{x + 4}$ **10.** $x + 6$ **11.** $\frac{a}{3}$
12. $x + 3$ **13.** $\frac{a + 4}{3}$ **14.** $\frac{1}{n + 9}$
15. $\frac{4}{x + 2}$ **16.** $x + 3$ **17.** $x + 3$
18. a **19.** -1 **20.** $\frac{3}{a + 1}$

Test yourself 2

1. (a) (i) $(x - 3y)$ (ii) $(x - 4)(x - 6)$
  (b) (i) $(a + b)(7 + x)$ (ii) $(5a + 9)(5a - 9)$
  (c) $\frac{4x + 1}{4x}$

2. (a) (i) $(3x - 2)(2x + 1)$
  (ii) $(3a + b)(2a + c)$
  (b) (i) $3ax(2a + x - 3)$
  (ii) $3(x + 4)(x - 4)$
  (c) $\frac{3x + 2}{2x + 5}$

3. (a) (i) $2ab(4a + b)$ (ii) $(3x - 7)(x - 3)$
  (b) (i) $2(x + 2y)(x - 2y)$
  (ii) $(x - 1)(2y - z)$
  (c) $12(x + a)(x - a)$

4. (a) (i) $3c(5b - c)$ (ii) $(8x + 3)(3x - 1)$
   (b) (i) $2(2x + y)(2x - y)$
      (ii) $(a - b)(x - 2y)$
   (c) $\dfrac{5x - 2}{2x + 5}$

5. (a) (i) $(3x - 4)(x + 2)$
      (ii) $(a - 2)(a + b)$
   (b) (i) $5(a + 5b)(a - 5b)$
      (ii) $(2x + 3)(x + y)(x - y)$
   (c) $\dfrac{2x - 3}{x(x + 6)}$

Chapter 3: Sets

Exercise 3.1

1. (i) {1, 3, 4, 5, 6, 7}
   (ii) {1, 7, 8, 9, 10, 11}
   (iii) {1, 7}
   (iv) {1, 3, 4, 5, 6, 7, 8, 9, 10, 11}
2. (i) {1, 3, 5, 7, 8}   (ii) {3, 7}
   (iii) {2, 4, 9, 10}   (iv) {1, 2, 5, 8, 10}
   (v) {2, 10}   (vi) {4, 9}
3. (i) 7   (ii) 7   (iii) 14
   (iv) 11   (v) 3   (vi) 3
4. 22
6. (i) 33   (ii) 24   (iii) 9
8. (i) 5   (ii) 30   (iii) 11   (iv) 7
9. (i) 6   (ii) 10
10. 10
11. $32 = 24 + 18 - x; x = 10$
12. (i) 6   (ii) 18   (iii) 11
13. (i) 16   (ii) 46   (iii) 30

Exercise 3.2

1. (i) {1, 2, 4, 5, 7, 8}   (ii) {3, 9, 10}
   (iii) {1, 3, 5, 7}   (iv) { } (or ∅)
2. (i) {a, c, e}   (ii) {f, g, h}
   (iii) {f, g, h, i, j}   (iv) {a, c, e, f, g, h, i, j}
3. (i) T   (ii) F   (iii) T   (iv) F
   (v) T   (vi) T   (vii) T   (viii) F
4. (i) {2, 4, 8, 10}
   (ii) {3, 9, 15}; No; Set diff. not commutative
5. (i) 3   (ii) 4   (iii) 2   (iv) 7
7. (i) All the people who live in Newtown
      excluding car owners
   (ii) All the people who live in Newtown
      excluding retired people
   (iii) Car owners who live in Newtown that are
      not retired
   (iv) Retired people who live in Newtown that
      do not own a car
   (v) Car-owning, retired people who live in
      Newtown

Exercise 3.3

1. (i) {1, 3, 4, 5, 9, 12}   (ii) {4, 6, 7, 8, 9, 10, 12}
   (iii) {4, 9, 12}   (iv) {9}
   (v) {1, 3, 5}   (vi) {8, 10}
2. (i) {2, 8}   (ii) {1, 2, 8}
   (iii) {3, 7}   (iv) {1}
   (v) {12, 13}   (vi) {14, 15}
3. (i) 15   (ii) 17   (iii) 7   (iv) 3   (v) 2
4. (i) T   (ii) T   (iii) F   (iv) T
   (v) F   (vi) F   (vii) T   (viii) F
5. (i) 21   (ii) 3   (iii) 17
6. (i) $A \cup B \cup C$ (ii) $A \cap B \cap C$
   (iii) $A \cap C$
8. (i) T   (ii) T
   (iii) Not true; $3 \div 4 \neq 4 \div 3$
   (iv) Not true; $2 - 3 \neq 3 - 2$
   (v) Not true; $(11 - 12) - 13 \neq 11 - (12 - 13)$
   (vi) Not true; $4 \div (6 \div 8) \neq (4 \div 6) \div 8$
9. (i) Addition is commutative
   (ii) Multiplication is associative
   (iii) Subtraction is not commutative
   (iv) Multiplication is distributive over addition
   (v) Subtraction is not associative
   (vi) Division is not associative
10. Union of sets is distributive over intersection
11. Set difference is not associative
12. (i) Union of sets is commutative
   (ii) Intersection of sets is associative
   (iii) Union of sets is associative
   (iv) Intersection of sets is distributive over
      union
   (v) Union of sets is distributive over
      intersection
   (vi) Set difference is not associative

Exercise 3.4

1. (i) 28   (ii) 9   (iii) 4   (iv) 10
   (v) 22   (vi) 18   (vii) 14; 100
2. (i) 139   (ii) 113   (iii) 13
3. (i) 1   (ii) 7   (iii) 2   (iv) 81
4. (i) 6   (ii) 26   (iii) 4
5. (i) 16   (ii) 14   (iii) 8   (iv) 21
6. $x = 2$
7. (i) 4   (ii) 37
8. (i) 15   (ii) 17   (iii) 40
9. $x = 4, y = 7$
10. (i) 12   (ii) 7   (iii) 4
11. $x = 12, y = 9$

Test yourself 3

1. (a) (i) {5, 7}   (ii) {2, 4, 6, 10}
   (c) (i) 19   (ii) 9
      (iii) 7   (iv) 22

2. (a) (i) {2, 3, 4, 5, 7}   (ii) {3, 5, 7}
      (iii) {1, 6, 9, 10,11}   (iv) {1, 9}
   (b) (i) 34   (ii) 3   (iii) 6
3. (a) (i) 27   (ii) 11   (iii) 4   (iv) 30
   (b) $x = 2, y = 16$
   (c) (i) 56   (ii) 38   (iii) 12
4. (a) Intersection of sets is distributive over union
   (b) From left: 55, 5, 10, 30
   (c) (i) 40   (ii) 10   (iii) 30   (iv) 14
5. (a) (i) $u = a + b - c + d$
      (ii) $d = u - a - b + c$
      (iii) $B \subset A$
      (iv) a
   (b) 9
6. (a) (iv) is true
   (b) (i) 4   (ii) 26   (iii) 8   (iv) 34
   (c) 9

Chapter 4: Applied Arithmetic

Exercise 4.1

1. (i) 0.07   (ii) 0.035   (iii) 0.12   (iv) 0.15
   (v) 0.165   (vi) 1.04   (vii) 1.1   (viii) 1.14
   (ix) 1.25   (x) 0.875
2. (i) 132   (ii) 159   (iii) 570   (iv) 717.5
3. (i) €29.12   (ii) €35
4. €25   **5.** €639.60   **6.** €800
7. €180   **8.** €1600
9. (i) €245   (ii) €240
10. (i) €320   (ii) 17%
11. €1104   **12.** 20%   **13.** $21\frac{1}{3}$%
14. Store C; €6.15 cheaper than Store A
15. $16\frac{2}{3}$%   **16.** Equates to a $57\frac{1}{2}$% reduction

Exercise 4.2

1. €356.72
2. Maher – €161.27; O'Gorman – €223.71
3. 480   **4.** €232.24   **5.** €106.13
6. (i) €900   (ii) 2275 km
7. (i) 8   (ii) €640   (iii) 5
8. (i) 30c   (ii) 75c   (iii) €1.20
9. (i) €12.60   (ii) €31.52   (iii) 152
10. (i) €77.50   (ii) 234 km
11. Tariff 3

Exercise 4.3

1. €730   **2.** €29 729   **3.** €115.50
4. €424   **5.** €136.80   **6.** €5640
7. (i) €174   (ii) €876
8. (i) €13 160   (ii) €9960
9. (i) €275.20   (ii) €231.20
10. €8080

11. (i) €3308.80   (ii) €53.40
     (iii) €3728.80   (iv) €70.90
12. 22   **13.** €1000
14. €4950   **15.** €35 000
16. €46 000
17. (i) €173.60   (ii) €49.90
     (iii) €36   (iv) €640.50
18. (i) €10 460   (ii) €3098.80
     (iii) €2160   (iv) €38 281.20
     (v) 71%
19. (i) €520   (ii) €67.20
     (iii) €23.30   (iv) €26
     (v) €403.50
20. (i) €11 200   (ii) €5600
     (iii) €5600   (iv) €14 000
     (v) €42 000

Exercise 4.4

1. (i) $585   (ii) €615.38
2. (i) 108 000 yen   (ii) €75
3. (i) £960   (ii) €750
4. €400
5. (i) C$4900   (ii) €4000
6. (i) 6900 kr   (ii) €163.04
7. €2970   **8.** 41 600 baht
9. €57.89   **10.** €1625
11. 2%   **12.** €29 931; €3975 gain

Exercise 4.5

1. €49.44   **2.** €133.12
3. €92.25   **4.** €188.10
5. €57.12   **6.** €178.50
7. €126.10   **8.** €485.91
9. €257.34   **10.** €224.76
11. (i) €661.50   (ii) €2138.58
     (iii) €4348.04   (iv) €8648.00
12. €423.20   **13.** €1606.80
14. €9235.20
15. (i) 1.08   (ii) 1.08
16. €6400   **17.** 4.5%
18. €800   **19.** €8200
20. €8904; 4%   **21.** $11\frac{1}{2}$%
22. (i) 1.05   (ii) 1.04; €8500
23. €11 475; 4%   **24.** €10 837.50
25. (i) €11 776   (ii) €18 000
26. 16%

Test yourself 4

1. (a) €225.49   (b) €7806   (c) €6675.20
2. (a) €651.60   (b) 2.5%
   (c) (i) €420   (ii) $31\frac{1}{4}$%
3. (a) €2.10   (b) 64 g
   (c) (i) €5040   (ii) 5%

4. (a) 7 (b) €4650 (c) €6000
5. (a) €445.48 (b) 2% (c) €23 000
6. (a) Offer A (b) 4500 (c) €45 000

Chapter 5: Statistics 1 – Collecting Data

Exercise 5.1
1. (i) N (ii) C (iii) C (iv) N
    (v) N (vi) C (vii) C (viii) N
2. (i) D (ii) C (iii) D (iv) C (v) D (vi) C
3. (i) Categorical
    (ii) Continuous
    (iii) 4 legs – D
        4 years old – C
        4 *munchies* – D
4. (i) N (ii) O (iii) O (iv) N
    (v) N (vi) O (vii) O
5. Eight candidates – Numerical data (discrete)
    Order from 1 to 8 – Categorical data (ordinal)
6. (i) Continuous
    (ii) Days (Mon, Tue, Wed ... etc) – Categorical data (nominal)
        Dates (1st, 2nd, 3rd ... etc) – Categorical data (ordinal)
        Month (July) – Categorical data (nominal)
    (iii) Categorical (ordinal)
7. 24 first-team players – 24 is discrete numerical data, 'first-team' is ordinal categorical data
    Average age 26 years – Continuous numerical data
    Country of birth – Nominal categorical data
    Premier League – ordinal categorical data

Exercise 5.2
1. (i) P (ii) P (iii) S (iv) S
3. (i) Overlap between 'not very often' and 'sometimes'; Not specific enough; no time-frame provided
4. Q(i) is the one to use as Q(ii) is a leading question.
5. (i) Too personal
    (ii) May cause embarrassment
    (iii) Biased
    (iv) Leading question
    (v) Too personal/embarrassing/shaming
    (vi) Too personal
    (vii) Leading question
6. (i) Too personal, first name would suffice
    (ii) 'Often' and 'sometimes' are too vague
7. (i) Question is too personal and response boxes aren't specific enough/are too subjective

9. QA – Too subjective/potentially embarrassing
    QB – Biased question which encourages a positive response
10. (i) A (ii) A (iii) C (iv) B
12. (ii) 10 (iii) 2 (iv) 8

Exercise 5.3
1. (i) 820 (ii) 40
2. (i) • People already at a cinema are much more likely to be regular "cinema-goers"
       • No men surveyed
3. These people are likely to be "sporty", i.e. not representative
4. B
5. B; this sample best represents the community at large.
6. Method 2

Test yourself 5
1. (i) C (ii) N (iii) N (iv) C (v) C (vi) N
2. (i) D (ii) C (iii) C (iv) D (v) C
3. (i) P (ii) S (iii) S (iv) S
5. (a) (ii) is better
    (b) Too restricted, 'rush-hour' not included
6. (b) Ordinal categorical data
7. (a) Sample 4 is a good sample
    (b) (i) only positive options
        (ii) too limited, no scope for answer under €6
        (iii) Too vague

Chapter 6: Perimeter – Area – Volume

Exercise 6.1
1. (i) 46 cm (ii) 42 cm (iii) 55 cm
2. (i) 126 cm^2 (ii) 104 cm^2 (iii) 178.5 cm^2
3. (i) 7 cm (ii) 16 cm (iii) 22 cm
4. (i) 58 cm (ii) 54 cm (iii) 58 cm
5. (i) 5 cm (ii) 12 m (iii) 25 cm
6. (i) 56 cm^2 (ii) 120 cm^2 (iii) 120 cm^2
7. (i) 31.5 cm^2 (ii) 60 cm^2 (iii) 240 cm^2
8. (i) 10 cm (ii) 14 cm (iii) 12 cm
9. (i) 121 cm^2 (ii) 182 cm^2 (iii) 420 cm^2
10. (i) 12 cm^2 (ii) 24 cm^2 (iii) 8 cm
11. 20 m^2; 25 m^2 **12.** 440 cm^2
13. $x = 4, y = 16, z = 3$
14. 11.5 cm^2
15. (i) etc. (P = 160 cm)
    (ii) (P = 120 cm)

Exercise 6.2

1. (i) 240 cm²   (ii) 63 cm²   (iii) 165 cm²
2. (i) 60 cm²   (ii) 52.5 cm²   (iii) 30 cm²
3. (i) 6 cm   (ii) 7 cm   (iii) 4.5 cm
4. 308 cm²; $x = 17\frac{1}{9}$
5. (i) 10 cm²   (ii) 5 cm²   (iii) 2:1
6. (i) 5 cm   (ii) 6.5 cm   (iii) 12 cm
7. (i) 1.5 cm   (ii) 1.6 cm   (iii) 4 cm
8. 20 cm²; $1\frac{2}{3}$ cm
9. (i) 784 m²   (ii) 440 m²
10. 154 cm²

Exercise 6.3

1. (i) radius   (ii) chord
   (iii) diameter   (iv) arc
   (v) semicircle   (vi) sector
   (vii) segment   (viii) tangent
2. (i) 62.8 cm   (ii) 25.12 cm
   (iii) 75.36 cm   (iv) 56.52 cm
3. (i) 88 cm   (ii) 132 cm
   (iii) 220 cm   (iv) 44 cm
4. (i) 616 cm²   (ii) 1386 cm²
   (iii) 3850 cm²   (iv) 154 cm²
5. (i) (a) 201.1 cm²   (b) 50.3 cm
   (ii) (a) 1385.4 cm²   (b) 131.9 cm
   (iii) (a) 380.1 cm²   (b) 69.1 cm
   (iv) (a) 254.5 cm²   (b) 56.5 cm
6. (i) 81.64 cm   (ii) 94.2 cm   (iii) 251.2 cm
7. (i) $\frac{1}{4}$ (ii) $\frac{1}{3}$ (iii) $\frac{1}{6}$ (iv) $\frac{1}{8}$
8. (i) 33 cm   (ii) 11 cm   (iii) $58\frac{2}{3}$ cm
9. (i) 346.5 cm²   (ii) 77 cm²   (iii) $821\frac{1}{3}$ cm²
10. (i) 72 cm   (ii) $42\frac{2}{3}$ cm   (iii) 47 cm
11. (i) 190.0 cm²   (ii) 150.8 cm²   (iii) 244.5 cm²
12. 400 m; 25
13. (i) 91.4 cm   (ii) 301.6 cm²
14. (i) 5 cm   (ii) 11 cm   (iii) 13 cm
15. (i) 7 cm   (ii) 44 cm
16. (i) 2500 m   (ii) 796
17. Both the same length
18. 42 cm²
19. (i) 98 cm²   (ii) 56 cm²
20. (i) 2 m   (ii) 75.4 m²   (iii) 79%
21. 63%
22. Alan; 25 m

Exercise 6.4

1. (i) 12 cm³   (ii) 30 cm³   (iii) 63 cm³
2. (i) 32 cm²   (ii) 62 cm²   (iii) 102 cm²
3. (i) (a) 2304 cm³   (b) 1120 cm²
   (ii) (a) 7680 cm³   (b) 2368 cm²
   (iii) (a) 360 m³   (b) 372 m²
4. 84

5. (iv) 88 cm²
6. (i) 900 cm³   (ii) 368 cm³   (iii) 532 cm³
7. €652.80
8. (i) 405 cm³   (ii) 414 cm²
9. $a = 5$ cm, $b = 7$ m, $c = 20$ cm
10. (i) 5 cm   (ii) 125 cm³
11. (i) 6   (ii) 168
12. (i) 4 cm   (ii) 96 cm²
13. (i) 124 cm²   (ii) 72 cm³
14. (i) open   (ii) 1936 cm³   (iii) 836 cm²
15. (i) 8 cm   (ii) 1.5   (iii) 157 cm²
16. (i) F   (ii) [CB]   (iii) [KL]
17. (i) 7 cm   (ii) closed
    (iii) 672 cm³   (iv) 472 cm²
18. A – 5, B – 3, C – 6
19. $x^3 = 6x^2$; 6 cm
20. (i) 6 ℓ   (ii) 1.6 ℓ   (iii) 6.75 ℓ
21. (i) 4800 cm³   (ii) 8 cm

Exercise 6.5

1. (i) 2112 cm³   (ii) 1116 cm³   (iii) 156 cm³
2. (i) 28 cm²   (ii) 252 cm³
3. 54 cm³
4. (i) 450 m³   (ii) 1440 cm³   (iii) 48 cm³
   (iv) 48 cm³   (v) 264 mm³   (vi) 1512 m³
5. (i) 5   (ii) 2   (iii) 84 cm²
6. (i) 152 cm²   (ii) 300 sq. units
   (iii) 241 cm²
7. (i) 780 cm²   (ii) 120 mm²   (iii) 200 cm²
8. (i) (a) 480 m³   (b) 432 m²
   (ii) (a) 270 m³   (b) 330 m²
   (iii) (a) 337.5 m³   (b) 335 m²
9. (i) $x = 5$; 84 cm²   (ii) $x = 12$; 480 cm²
10. (i) 32.31 m²   (ii) €650
11. (i) 410.4 cm³   (ii) 441.6 cm²
13. • Star opposite yellow circle with red border
    • Square with green border opposite square
      with circle in it
    • Triangle opposite red and green square
14. E, I
15. (i) triangular prism   (ii) 6

Exercise 6.6

1. (i) 1:40   (ii) 1:100   (iii) 1:60 000
   (iv) 1:2000   (v) 1:10 000   (vi) 1:10 000
2. Kangaroo – 1.2 m, giraffe – 3.6 m,
   horse – 1.35 m
3. (i) 5 m   (ii) 11 m   (iii) 8.5 m
   (iv) 14.8 m
4. (i) 6 m   (ii) 20 m   (iii) 40 m
   (iv) 3.6 m   (v) 28.8 m   (vi) 14.375 m
5. 6.2 m; 2.7 m

6. (i) (a) 500 m   (b) 1.25 km
     (c) 2.125 km   (d) $1687\frac{1}{2}$ m
     (ii) (a) 40 cm   (b) 16 cm
     (c) 26 cm   (d) 51 cm
7. (i) 17 km   (ii) 4.4 cm
8. (i) (a) 12 cm   (b) 8.5 cm
9. 1 : 40 000; 75 cm
10. (i) $|CB| = 5$ cm; 1 : 200   (ii) 6 m
     (iii) 30 m^2

Test yourself 6

1. (a) 44 cm^2 (b) 5.5 cm
     (c) (i) 96 cm^3 (ii) 144 cm^2
2. (a) 37.68 cm^2 (b) 7.2
     (c) (i) 324 cm^3 (ii) 342 cm^2
3. (a) (i) 89.1 cm^2 (ii) 36.6 cm
     (b) (i) 50 cm   (ii) 1 : 25
     (c) (i) both 18 m^3
     (ii) Not the same   (iii) €1323
4. (a) 56 cm^2
     (b) 375 cm^2
     (c) 11.60 cm
5. (a) 125 cm
     (b) (i) 1 km   (ii) 14 cm
     (c) 14
6. (a) Yes (€90 000 > €88 128)
     (b) A triangular prism;
        (i) 6.8 cm^3 (ii) 27.4 cm^2
     (c) 64.5 cm^2

Chapter 7: Statistics 2 – Averages and Spread

Exercise 7.1

1. (i) 12   (ii) 45   (iii) 5.7
     (iv) 7   (v) bus   (vi) $\frac{1}{4}$
2. 5
3. 3, 3, 5, 7, 7, 7, 8, 8, 9, 11, 12;
     (i) 7   (ii) 7
4. (i) 2, 3, 5, 6, 7, 8, 9; 6
     (ii) 6, 7, 8, 9, 10, 12, 14, 18; 9.5
5. (i) 14   (ii) 14
6. (i) 9   (ii) 9
7. (i) 9   (ii) 9
8. 6
9. €12.80
10. $a = 2, 4$
11. (i) 32   (ii) Size 6   (iii) No
     (iv) No; In general, boys wear larger shoes.

Exercise 7.2

1. (i) 5   (ii) 14   (iii) 7   (iv) 19.75
2. 61   **3.** 26   **4.** 84

5. (i) 36   (ii) 5
6. 13 cm   **7.** 12   **8.** 25
9. (i) 18   (ii) 12   (iii) 0
10. €1.73
11. 6; 10; Mean also increased by 4; 30;
     Mean increases by same factor (5)
12. 4 4 5 8 9 etc.
13. (i) 13.2 m   (ii) $165\frac{1}{3}$ cm
14. 19
15. (i) 2   (ii) 17
16. (i) 195   (ii) 19
17. 4, 6
18. (i) A – 16.4, B – 25.3
     (ii) The final value
     (iii) The outlier (91) has a big effect on mean
19. (i) 44   (ii) 44   (iii) 40
     (iv) Increase; $40\frac{1}{6}$ points
20. 7, 9
21. 40

Exercise 7.3

1. (i) 2   (ii) 1
     (iii) As 6 of the 8 values are well below the
        mean (6.9) due to the two outliers
2. Mean – 17, Median – 3; Median
3. (i) 25   (ii) 15; Median
4. (i) $30\frac{4}{7}$ °C
     (ii) The data is tightly grouped with no
        outliers
5. (i) 27
     (ii) The mode (37) is the highest data value
6. (i) Denim
     (ii) As the data is categorical it is the only
        average that can be used
7. (i) Mean   (ii) Mode
     (iii) Median/mean (use median if there is an
        outlier)
     (iv) Mode   (v) Median
8. Mean – 3.3, Mode – 0, Median – 2.5; Median
9. Mean (65) as it is the highest of the three
     averages.
10. (i) 28   (ii) 38   (iii) 63.9   (iv) Mean

Exercise 7.4

1. (i) 4   (ii) 3   (iii) 2; 6 marks
2. (i) 1   (ii) 4   (iii) 2
     (iv) 150   (v) 3
3. (i) 8   (ii) 2   (iii) 180   (iv) 3
4. (i) 3   (ii) 1   (iii) 25%   (iv) 26
5. 3.6
6. (i) 30   (ii) 7   (iii) 13   (iv) 13
7. (i) 19   (ii) (41–60)   (iii) (61–80)
     (iv) Exact mean cannot be found from table

8. (i) (4–6) (ii) 6.5
9. 12
10. 18.6
11. (i) (0–4) (ii) 9 (iii) 45 (iv) 7
12. (i) 250 cm (ii) 240 cm
(iii) 100 cm (iv) 251 cm

Exercise 7.5

1. (i) 11 (ii) 21
2. (i) has bigger range
3. (i) Saskia – 44, John – 20; John far more consistent
(ii) Saskia
4. (i) Emer – 82, Anna – 83
(ii) Emer – 20, Anna – 12
(iii) Anna; Marginally inferior mean score but more consistent
5. 5, 9
6. (i) 6 (ii) 8; boys did better
7. (i) ☐3☐ ☐4☐ ☐6☐ ☐6☐ ☐7☐ etc.
(ii) ☐4☐ ☐6☐ ☐6☐ ☐7☐
8. (i) 62 min
(ii) Q_1 – 50 min, Q_3 – 70 min
(iii) 20 min
9. (i) 33 (ii) 29
(iii) (a) 18.5 (b) 34 (c) 15.5
10. (i) 13 min (ii) 8 min (iii) 15 min (iv) 7 min
11. 8, 9, 13, 15, 25
12. (i) 105 g (ii) 19 g
(iii) The mean weight of a South African apple is higher but the variability of the apples is the same.
13. (i) 11 kg (ii) 7 kg
14. (i) 25% (ii) 25%
(iii) Greater spread of weights for variety A but variety B are, on average, heavier.

Test yourself 7

1. (a) 12
(b) (i) 8.1
(ii) 6; Median as it has the same number of values above and below it.
(c) (i) 8 (ii) 9 (iii) 5
2. (a) 1.73 m
(b) (i) 5
(ii) 14.5
(iii) The boys had a higher mean score and were more consistent.
3. (a) 6, 15, 18
(b) (i) 2
(ii) $Q_3 = 9$, $Q_1 = 1$
(iii) 8

4. (a) Mean – 27.1; The mode is not representative of the other values
(b) 14.8
(c) (i) 8.17; 22.87 (ii) 6.67; 21.33
5. (a) (i) €376.67 (ii) €245
(iii) No two data values (wages) the same; Median
(b) 45, 2
(c) 12
6. (a) 37
(b) (a) False (b) Could be true
(c) False (d) Could be true

Chapter 8: Quadratic Equations

Exercise 8.1

1. $x = 2, 4$ 2. $x = -2, 4$ 3. $x = -4, 6$
4. $\frac{3}{2}, 4$ 5. $-3, \frac{3}{2}$ 6. $-4, \frac{1}{2}$
7. 0, 3 8. $-5, 0$ 9. $-3, 0$
10. $-5, -2$ 11. $-7, -5$ 12. $-8, -6$
13. 2, 3 14. 3, 5 15. 3, 7
16. $-3, 4$ 17. $-2, 5$ 18. $-7, 4$
19. $\frac{1}{2}, 2$ 20. $\frac{-1}{2}, 2$ 21. $\frac{-3}{2}, 2$
22. $-2, -\frac{1}{2}$ 23. $\frac{1}{3}, 2$ 24. $-2, \frac{5}{3}$
25. $-4, \frac{2}{3}$ 26. $\frac{-2}{3}, 5$ 27. $-7, \frac{2}{3}$
28. $\frac{1}{2}, \frac{5}{2}$ 29. $\frac{-2}{5}, 3$ 30. $\frac{3}{5}, 2$
31. 0, 6 32. $0, \frac{5}{2}$ 33. $0, \frac{4}{3}$
34. $0, \frac{1}{4}$ 35. $0, \frac{6}{5}$ 36. $0, \frac{7}{3}$
37. ± 3 38. ± 5 39. $\pm \frac{1}{2}$
40. $\pm \frac{5}{2}$ 41. $\pm \frac{4}{3}$ 42. $\pm \frac{7}{2}$
43. $\frac{-5}{2}, 6$ 44. $-2, 7$ 45. $\frac{-1}{2}, 5$
46. ± 4
47. $-3, 1$
48. (i) $-5, 4$ (ii) $-4, -2$
(iii) 5, 6
49. (i) $x = 3, 5$ (ii) $x = -4, -2$
(iii) $x = -1, 2$
50. (i) one ($x = -2$) (ii) B

Exercise 8.2

1. $x = -3.41, -0.59$ 2. $x = -5.24, -0.76$
3. $-3.45, 1.45$ 4. $-1.83, 3.83$
5. $-0.81, 0.31$ 6. $-0.43, 0.77$
7. 0.42, 1.58 8. $-2.91, 0.57$
9. $-0.35, 1.15$ 10. $-2.39, -0.28$
11. $-0.36, 1.86$ 12. $-2.59, 0.26$
13. $-1.55, 0.80$ 14. 0.72, 2.78
15. $-2.14, 0.47$

Exercise 8.3

1. $x^2 + x = 72; -9, 8$ **2.** 10
3. 8, 11   **4.** 10
5. 4, 7   **6.** 4
7. length – 11 cm, breadth – 7 cm
8. 9
9. length – 7 cm, breadth – 4 cm
10. 6 years old
11. (II) 4, 5 or $-5, -4$
12. 7 m   **13.** 5
14. (i) When 0 or 20 cakes an hour are baked
    (ii) When 6 or 14 cakes are baked
15. (i) 0 sec or 6 sec   (ii) 2 sec or 4 sec
16. (ii) 4
17. 10 months
18. $x^2 + 10x - 144 = 0; x = 8$

Exercise 8.4

1. $x^2 - 6x + 8 = 0$ **2.** $x^2 - 6x + 5 = 0$
3. $x^2 - 5x + 6 = 0$ **4.** $x^2 - 2x - 3 = 0$
5. $x^2 - 2x - 8 = 0$ **6.** $x^2 + 7x + 12 = 0$
7. $x^2 - 4x - 12 = 0$ **8.** $x^2 - 5x = 0$
9. $2x^2 + 3x - 2 = 0$ **10.** $x^2 + 9x + 20 = 0$
11. $2x^2 - 7x - 4 = 0$ **12.** $4x^2 - 33x + 8 = 0$
13. $x^2 + 4x = 0$ **14.** $4x^2 - 1 = 0$
15. $x^2 - 9 = 0$ **16.** $4x^2 - x = 0$
17. $a = -1, b = -2$ **18.** $y = x^2 + 3x - 4$

Test yourself 8

1. (a) $x = -5, 7$ (b) ± 4
    (c) $x^2 + x - 90 = 0; x = 9$
2. (a) $x = -4, \frac{2}{3}$ (b) $x = 0.72, 2.78$
    (c) length – 12 cm, breadth – 8 cm
3. (a) -2 (b) $x^2 - x - 6 = 0$
    (c) (ii) $x = 3$; Perimeter $= 30$ cm
4. (a) (i) $x = 0, \frac{7}{2}$ (ii) $x = \pm 6$
    (b) Ⓑ
    (c) (i) $A = (10 + 2x)(8 + 2x)$
       (ii) $x = 2$
5. (a) $x = -6, 3$ (b) 11   (c) 2 sec
6. (a) $x = \frac{-1}{2}, \frac{5}{6}$
    (b) $x^2 + 3x - 10 = 0$
    (c) $2x^2 + 8x + 8 = 72; x = 4$
    (d) Either 5 or 20 hurleys

Chapter 9: Geometry 1 – Triangles and Quadrilaterals

Exercise 9.1

1. (i) Line segment [AB]   (ii) Line AB
    (iii) Ray [BA

2. $A = 117°, B = 85°, C = 45°, D = 140°, E = 70°,$
    $F = 23°$
3. $A = 70°, B = 110°, C = 150°, D = 30°,$
    $E = 140°, F = 40°, G = 62°, H = 118°, I = 62°,$
    $J = 128°, K = 52°, L = 128°, P = 147°,$
    $Q = 33°, R = 147°$
4. (i) 4   (ii) 7   (iii) 4
5. $a = 110°, b = 70°, c = 46°, d = 134°, e = 60°,$
    $f = 120°$
6. $a = 48°, b = 132°, c = 132°, d = 132°,$
    $e = 160°, f = 20°, g = 20°, x = 132°, y = 132°,$
    $z = 132°$
7. $p = 80°, q = 80°, r = 75°, s = 105°$
8. $a = 96°, b = 96°, c = 84°, d = 72°, e = 68°,$
    $f = 112°, g = 68°$
9. (i) 15°   (ii) 29°   (iii) 19°

Exercise 9.2

1. $a = 50°, b = 86°, c = 111°, d = 50°, e = 60°,$
    $f = 43°, g = 85°, h = 95°, i = 37°, j = 143°,$
    $k = 79°$
2. $a = 70°, b = 70°, c = 71°, d = 71°, e = 62°,$
    $f = 56°$
3. $a = 65°, b = 40°, c = 52.5°, d = 60°, e = 30°$
4. $p = 106°, q = 37°, r = 37°, d = 25°, e = 130°,$
    $f = 50°, v = 59°, w = 31°, x = 59°, y = 121°$
5. $a = 50°, b = 58°, c = 25°$
6. $a = 62°, b = 110°, c = 55°, d = 34°$
7. (i) $x = 55°$; $\angle CAB$ and $\angle EBD$ are
       corresponding angles
    (ii) $y = 45°$; angles in a $\triangle$ sum to 180°
8. $x = 82°, y = 16°, a = 48°, b = 114°$
10. $d = 35°, e = 35°, f = 110°$
11. $a = 95°, b = 115°, c = 39°, d = 85°$
13. As $|\angle BCA| = 49°$

Exercise 9.3

1. $A = 78°, B = 102°, C = 60°, D = 120°, E = 60°,$
    $F = 120°$
2. $A = 66°, B = 72°, C = 80°, D = 45°, E = 75°,$
    $F = 55°, G = 55°$
3. $A = 42°, B = 100°, C = 35°, D = 65°, E = 28°,$
    $F = 112°, G = 52°$
4. $x = 70°, y = 40°, z = 40°, r = 70°$
5. (i) 8   (ii) 11   (iii) 10   (iv) 7
6. $x = 55°, y = 55°, z = 70°$
7. $g = 67.5°, h = 45°$
8. $a = 121°, b = 89°, c = 129°, d = 53°$
9. (i) $x = 80°$ (ii) $x = 77°$ (iii) $x = 55°$
10. (i) $y = 86°$ (ii) $y = 64°$

Exercise 9.4

1. SAS

2. (i) SSS   (ii) SAS   (iii) SAS
     (iv) ASA   (v) RHS   (vi) ASA

3. A and D; SSS

4. (i) Yes; ASA
     (ii) No; not the same size (sides don't correspond)

5. Yes; SSS

6. SAS ($|\angle AOB| = |\angle COD|$ ... vertically opposite)

7. ASA;   (i) [EF]   (ii) [AB]   (iii) 35°

8. $x = 70°, y = 10\,cm$

9. Corresponding angles, both opposite [AC].

Exercise 9.5

1. (i) 5   (ii) 10   (iii) 17

2. $a = 7, b = 12, c = 21$

3. (i) 3   (ii) 5   (iii) 8

4. P = 44 cm², Q = 46 cm², R = 50 cm²

5. (i) $2\sqrt{19}$ (ii) $4\sqrt{2}$ (iii) $2\sqrt{11}$

6. 6; 13.5 sq. units

7. (i) $x = 13\,cm, y = \sqrt{394}\,cm$
     (ii) $x = 6\,cm, y = \sqrt{145}\,cm$
     (iii) $x = 9\,cm, y = \sqrt{2581}\,cm$

8. $x = 5, y = 12$

9. 74 cm

10. $x = 10, y = 8$

11. (i) 2.47 m   (ii) 10.17 m   (iii) 6.21 m²

12. No; the diagonal is 100 cm, i.e. less than 105 cm.

13. (i) No   (ii) Yes

14. As $|AD|^2 = |CD|^2 + |AC|^2$

15. (i) 13 cm   (ii) 15.3 cm

16. Yes, equal

Test yourself 9

1. (a) $a = 110°, b = 70°, c = 140°, d = 55°,$
       $e = 125°$
    (b) A = 50°, B = 70°, C = 73°

2. (a) $a = 63°, b = 30°$
    (b) A = 35°, B = 67°, C = 40°, D = 65°,
       E = 33°, F = 107°, G = 45°

3. (a) $a = 74°, b = 53°, c = 142°, d = 68°,$
       $e = 38°, f = 74°$
    (b) $x = 56$; isosceles △
    (c) $a = 23.5°, b = 83.5°, c = 23.5°$

4. (a) $a = 55°, b = 50°$
    (b) 1 and 4; SAS
    (c) (ii) No; As $|\angle ABC| \neq |\angle ACB| \Rightarrow |\angle DAE| \neq |\angle CAE|$

5. (a) (i) 124°   (ii) 63°   (iii) 32°
    (b) 0.9 m

6. (a) (i) $x = 140°, y = 100°$
        (ii) $x = 20°, y = 140°$
        (iii) $x = 69°, y = 37°$
    (b) (i) 6.4 m   (ii) 7 m

Chapter 10: Probability

Exercise 10.1

1. 12

2. HH, HT, TH, TT

3. (i) 18   (ii) 6   (iii) 3

4. 36   **5.** 24   **6.** 27

7. (i) 36   (ii) 12

8. 12

9. (i) 4   (ii) 128

Exercise 10.2

1. (i) E.C.   (ii) Certain   (iii) Impossible
    (iv) Unlikely   (v) Likely   (vi) E.C.
    (vii) Likely   (viii) Unlikely   (ix) E.C.
    (x) Likely

2. (i) Event 1: Unlikely   (ii) Event 1: Likely
       Event 2: E.C.   Event 2: Certain
       Event 3: E.C.   Event 3: Impossible
       Event 4: Impossible   Event 4: Unlikely
       Event 5: Certain   Event 5: Likely

3. (i) B   (ii) C   (iii) C   (iv) A   (v) B   (vi) C

4. (i) (b), (a), (c)   (ii) (c), (a), (b)

5. Green − (a), Red − (b), Blue − (c)

6. (i) 6   (ii) 8   (iii) 2

Exercise 10.3

1. (i) (a) Red, blue
       (b) Red, blue, yellow, green
       (c) Red, blue
    (ii) (a) $\frac{1}{2}$ (b) $\frac{1}{4}$ (c) $\frac{1}{2}$

2. (i) $\frac{1}{4}$ (ii) $\frac{1}{2}$ (iii) $\frac{1}{4}, \frac{3}{4}$

3. (i) $\frac{1}{6}$ (ii) $\frac{1}{3}$ (iii) $\frac{1}{2}$ (iv) $\frac{1}{2}$ (v) $\frac{1}{3}$ (vi) $\frac{1}{2}$

4. (i) $\frac{3}{10}$ (ii) $\frac{2}{5}$ (iii) $\frac{7}{10}$ (iv) $\frac{3}{5}$ (v) $\frac{3}{10}$ (vi) $\frac{3}{10}$

5. (i) $\frac{1}{11}$ (ii) $\frac{2}{11}$ (iii) $\frac{2}{11}$ (iv) $\frac{4}{11}$ (v) $\frac{4}{11}$

6. (i) $\frac{1}{6}$ (ii) $\frac{3}{8}$ (iii) $\frac{2}{5}$

7. (i) $\frac{1}{4}$ (ii) $\frac{1}{9}$ (iii) $\frac{4}{9}$ (iv) $\frac{1}{36}$ (v) $\frac{1}{18}$ (vi) $\frac{1}{6}$

8. (i) $\frac{1}{13}$ (ii) $\frac{1}{13}$ (iii) $\frac{3}{13}$ (iv) 1   (v) 0   (vi) $\frac{2}{13}$

9. (i) $\frac{1}{4}$ (ii) $\frac{1}{2}$ (iii) $\frac{1}{2}$ (iv) $\frac{1}{13}$ (v) $\frac{3}{13}$ (vi) $\frac{2}{13}$

10. (i) $\frac{10}{13}$ (ii) $\frac{7}{13}$ (iii) $\frac{7}{13}$ (iv) 0

11. (i) Red and any colour other than red or black
    (ii) Red and any colour other than red or blue

12. (i) $\frac{1}{6}$ (ii) $\frac{3}{8}$ (iii) $\frac{1}{6}$ (iv) $\frac{1}{12}$

14. (i) $\frac{1}{7}$ (ii) $\frac{2}{7}$ (iii) $\frac{1}{6}$

15. (i) $\frac{5}{12}$ (ii) $\frac{1}{6}$ (iii) $\frac{1}{12}$ (iv) $\frac{1}{12}$ (v) $\frac{5}{12}$
    (vi) $\frac{7}{12}$; Every disc is either even or odd, i.e. every outcome covered

16. (i) $\frac{3}{10}$ (ii) $\frac{7}{20}$ (iii) $\frac{13}{20}$ (iv) $\frac{7}{20}$

17. (i) $\frac{2}{5}$ (ii) $\frac{3}{10}$ (iii) $\frac{11}{25}; \frac{1}{6}$

18. (i) $\frac{1}{100}$ (ii) $\frac{1}{10}$ (iii) $\frac{1}{20}$ (iv) $\frac{21}{25}$
    (v) 30   (vi) 20   (vii) 25   (viii) 100

19. $\frac{3}{7}$

20. (i) $\frac{4}{13}$ (ii) $\frac{4}{13}$ (iii) $\frac{5}{13}$ (iv) $\frac{9}{13}$

21. (i) 30   (ii) (a) $\frac{3}{10}$ (b) $\frac{1}{2}$ (iii) $\frac{1}{5}$

22. (i) $\frac{1}{4}$ (ii) $\frac{3}{4}$

Exercise 10.4

1. (i) $\frac{1}{4}$ (ii) $\frac{1}{4}$ (iii) $\frac{1}{2}$

2. (i) $\frac{3}{16}$ (ii) $\frac{1}{2}$ (iii) $\frac{3}{16}$ (iv) $\frac{3}{16}$

3. (i) $\frac{1}{18}$ (ii) $\frac{1}{9}$ (iii) $\frac{1}{6}$ (iv) $\frac{1}{3}$ (v) $\frac{2}{9}$ (vi) $\frac{5}{18}$

4. (ii) (a) $\frac{3}{16}$ (b) $\frac{1}{2}$ (c) $\frac{5}{8}$

5. (i) $\frac{1}{16}$ (ii) 1   (iii) $\frac{3}{8}$ (iv) $\frac{1}{4}$ (v) $\frac{7}{16}$ (vi) $\frac{9}{16}$

6. HHH, HHT, HTH, THH, TTT, TTH, THT, HTT;
    (i) $\frac{1}{8}$ (ii) $\frac{3}{8}$ (iii) $\frac{1}{8}$ (iv) $\frac{7}{8}$

7. (i) $\frac{1}{9}$ (ii) $\frac{1}{12}$ (iii) $\frac{1}{12}$ (iv) $\frac{5}{36}$

8. (i) AR, AL, AD, ER, EL, ED, IR, IL, ID
    (ii) $\frac{1}{9}$ (iii) $\frac{1}{9}$ (iv) $\frac{2}{9}$

Exercise 10.5

1. 50

2. (i) 10   (ii) 10   (iii) 30

3. (i) 160   (ii) 240

4. $\frac{3}{10}$

5. (i) $\frac{1}{2}$ (ii) $\frac{3}{4}$
    (iii) Nicky's result as it involved a greater
      number of trials

6. (i) $\frac{3}{8}$ (ii) $\frac{27}{32}$

7. (ii) 0.6   (iii) 180

8. (i) $\frac{1}{6}$ (ii) $\frac{1}{2}$ (iii) $\frac{1}{2}$

9. (i) 4 (relative frequency of 0.525)
    (ii) 2 (relative frequency of 0.23)

10. Ben's (relatively even spread of outcomes as
     between the 6 faces); Joe's (relative frequency
     of a "6" was $\frac{1}{72}$)

11. Red – 1, White – 2, Blue – 3

12. (i) $\frac{12}{25}$ (ii) 48

13. (i) Red – $\frac{7}{50}$, Green – $\frac{12}{25}$
     (ii) Red – one side, Green – three sides;
      $\frac{7}{50} \simeq \frac{1}{6}, \frac{12}{25} \simeq \frac{1}{2}$

14. 100

15. (i) 10 sectors with 5 coloured red, 3 white
     and 2 blue

16. (i) $\frac{3}{10}$ (ii) $\frac{14}{25}$

Exercise 10.6

1. (i) $\frac{13}{41}$ (ii) $\frac{6}{41}$ (iii) $\frac{13}{41}$ (iv) $\frac{26}{41}$ (v) $\frac{15}{41}$

2. (i) 30   (ii) 7   (iii) $\frac{1}{10}$
    (iv) $\frac{11}{30}$ (v) $\frac{2}{15}$ (vi) $\frac{8}{15}$

3. (i) 12   (ii) $\frac{3}{5}$ (iii) $\frac{1}{10}$ (iv) $\frac{21}{25}$ (v) $\frac{37}{50}$

4. (i)

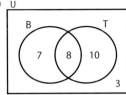

    (ii) $\frac{5}{14}$ (iii) $\frac{3}{28}$

5. (i) 24
    (ii) They liked both chocolate and ice-cream
    (iii) $\frac{3}{20}$ (iv) $\frac{3}{4}$

6. (i) 100   (ii) $\frac{7}{25}$ (iii) $\frac{9}{100}$ (iv) $\frac{1}{25}$
    (v) $\frac{1}{10}$ (vi) $\frac{9}{50}$ (vii) $\frac{7}{50}$

7. (i) $\frac{12}{25}$ (ii) $\frac{11}{100}$ (iii) $\frac{29}{50}$ (iv) $\frac{21}{100}$ (v) $\frac{7}{100}$

8. (i)

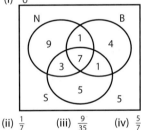

    (ii) $\frac{1}{7}$ (iii) $\frac{9}{35}$ (iv) $\frac{5}{7}$ (v) $\frac{2}{5}$

Exercise 10.7

1. (i) $\frac{1}{4}$ (ii) $\frac{1}{2}$

2. (i) $\frac{8}{15}$ (ii) $\frac{7}{15}$

3. (i) $\frac{13}{18}$ (ii) $\frac{5}{36}$

4. (ii) (a) $\frac{2}{9}$ (b) $\frac{4}{9}$ (c) $\frac{5}{9}$

5. (ii) $\frac{12}{25}$

6. (ii) $\frac{12}{25}$

7. (ii) (a) $\frac{1}{36}$ (b) $\frac{5}{18}$

8. (i) $\frac{1}{4}$ (ii) $\frac{3}{8}$

9. (i) $\frac{4}{9}$ (ii) $\frac{4}{9}$ (iii) $\frac{8}{9}$

Test yourself 10

1. (a) (i) B   (ii) C   (iii) A
    (b) (i) $\frac{7}{10}$ (ii) $\frac{1}{10}$ (iii) $\frac{1}{20}$
       (iv) $\frac{3}{10}$ (v) $\frac{3}{20}$
    (c) (ii) $\frac{1}{5}$ (iii) $\frac{4}{15}$ (iv) $\frac{7}{15}$ (v) $\frac{8}{15}$

2. (a) (i) $\frac{2}{5}$ (ii) $\frac{6}{25}$ (iii) $\frac{16}{25}$

    (b) Spinner A; Experimental probabilities v. close to true probabilities

    (c) (i) (3, 2), (3, 4), (3, 7), (6, 2), (6, 4), (6, 7), (8, 2), (8, 4), (8, 7)

      (ii) $\frac{4}{9}$ (iii) $\frac{4}{9}$

3. (a) $\frac{7}{10}$ (b) 10

    (c) (i) $\frac{19}{30}$ (ii) $\frac{3}{10}$ (iii) $\frac{9}{10}$

      (iv) $\frac{1}{15}$ (v) $\frac{1}{10}$ (vi) $\frac{14}{15}$

4. (a) (i) Event cannot happen

      (ii) Event has a '50-50 chance' of happening

      (iii) Event will occur three times out of four, i.e., it's likely to occur

      (iv) Event will definitely happen

    (b) (i) $\frac{2}{5}$ (ii) $\frac{4}{5}$ (iii) $\frac{3}{5}$

    (c) (i) 0.2   (ii) 0.4

5. (a) (i) $\frac{1}{2}$ (ii) $\frac{1}{52}$ (iii) $\frac{5}{13}$

      (iv) $\frac{3}{26}$ (v) $\frac{1}{13}$ (vi) $\frac{7}{13}$

    (b) (i) (a) $\frac{1}{10}$ (b) $\frac{13}{30}$ (c) $\frac{1}{3}$

      (ii) Similar results – yes, identical results – no.

    (c)

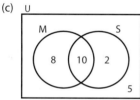

    (i) $\frac{8}{25}$ (ii) $\frac{2}{25}$ (iii) $\frac{4}{5}$ (iv) $\frac{2}{5}$

6. (a) 80

    (b) Highly unlikely to be fair; Relative frequency of rolling a 2 (0.44) is far higher than a fair dice (0.25)

    (c) Graph C

    (d) (ii) $\frac{4}{15}$

Chapter 11: Coordinate Geometry – The Line

Exercise 11.1

1. A(2, 3), B(4, 2), C(2, 1), D(−3, 3), E(−2, 2), F(−4, 1), G(−3, 0), H(−4, −2), I(−2, −3), J(0, −3), K(2, −3), L(3, −2), M(5, −3)

3. (i) First   (ii) Third   (iii) Fourth

    (iv) Second   (v) Fourth   (vi) Third

4. (i) x-axis   (ii) x-axis   (iii) y-axis

    (iv) y-axis   (v) both

5. (i) $\sqrt{34}$ (ii) $\sqrt{50}$ (iii) $\sqrt{53}$; No

6. (i) $\sqrt{10}$ (ii) $\sqrt{5}$ (iii) $\sqrt{13}$

    (iv) $\sqrt{89}$ (v) $\sqrt{53}$ (vi) 5

8. $\sqrt{53}$

9. (i) $\sqrt{18}$ (ii) $\sqrt{34}$; No

10. (i) $|FE| = 6$, $|ED| = 3$ (ii) $\sqrt{45}$

11. (i) (4, 3)   (ii) (1, 3)   (iii) (3, 1)

     (iv) (1, 1)   (v) (1, −2)   (vi) (−2, 0)

12. $(0, \frac{11}{2})$; y-axis   **13.** (2, 4)

14. $(1, \frac{1}{2})$ **15.** (−1, −1)

16. (5, 8)   **17.** (−1, 6)

Exercise 11.2

1. (i) b, c   (ii) a, d

2. a: $\frac{3}{2}$, b: 1, c: $\frac{1}{3}$, d: −1

3. (i) b   (ii) $\frac{2}{3}$ (iii) 2

4. The line is falling (from left to right); $-\frac{3}{2}$

5. (i) 1   (ii) $-\frac{3}{2}$ (iii) 8

    (iv) 1   (v) 1   (vi) $\frac{2}{3}$

6. Parallel lines

7. Yes, parallel

9. a: $\frac{1}{2}$, b: 1, c: 2

10. (i) $\frac{3}{4}$ (ii) $-\frac{4}{3}$

11. (i) $-\frac{3}{2}$ (ii) $-\frac{5}{4}$ (iii) $\frac{4}{3}$ (iv) $\frac{5}{2}$ (v) 2

12. (i) −1   (ii) 1

13. (i) 1   (ii) −1

14. 5

15. $\frac{-8}{3}$

16. (i) $\frac{1}{2}$ (ii) $\frac{2}{k-1}$ (iii) 5

17. Ramps A and C are suitable

18. −8

Exercise 11.3

1. (i) $2x - y - 2 = 0$ (ii) $4x - y + 1 = 0$

    (iii) $5x - y + 13 = 0$ (iv) $3x + y + 6 = 0$

    (v) $5x + y + 17 = 0$ (vi) $2x - 3y - 9 = 0$

2. (i) $3x - 4y - 19 = 0$ (ii) $3x - 5y + 22 = 0$

3. (i) $4x - y + 11 = 0$ (ii) $2x + y + 1 = 0$

    (iii) $3x - 4y + 18 = 0$ (iv) $2x + 3y - 5 = 0$

4. $3x + y = 0$

5. (i) $3x - y = 0$ (ii) $5x + y = 0$

    (iii) $x - 3y = 0$

    (iv) $3x + 2y = 0$; no constant number

6. −3; $3x + y - 5 = 0$

7. (i) $3x - 2y = 0$ (ii) $2x + y = 0$

    (iii) $x + 6y - 1 = 0$ (iv) $4x + 5y - 7 = 0$

    (v) $x - y + 5 = 0$ (vi) $2x - y + 1 = 0$

8. $5x + 4y - 2 = 0$

9. (i) 3, $3x - y - 6 = 0$

    (ii) $\frac{1}{3}$, $x - 3y + 6 = 0$

10. $x - 2y + 4 = 0$

Exercise 11.4

1. (i) 3   (ii) 2   (iii) $\frac{1}{2}$
2. (i) (0, 5)   (ii) (0, −3)   (iii) (0, 4)
3. (i) $y = -x + 4$; −1   (ii) $y = -3x + 5$; −3
   (iii) $y = -\frac{2}{3}x + \frac{7}{3}$, $-\frac{2}{3}$ (iv) $y = \frac{5}{2}x + \frac{3}{2}$, $\frac{5}{2}$
   (v) $y = -\frac{3}{4}x + \frac{1}{2}$, $-\frac{3}{4}$ (vi) $y = \frac{3}{4}x + \frac{3}{2}$, $\frac{3}{4}$
4. $y = -\frac{2}{3}x + \frac{7}{3}$; (i) $-\frac{2}{3}$ (ii) $-\frac{2}{3}$ (iii) $\frac{3}{2}$
5. −2
7. (i) $y = 3x + c$ (ii) $y = -\frac{1}{3}x + c$
8. Yes, parallel
9. (i) A & E, B & F, C & I, D & G
   (ii) H
10. (i) $\frac{2}{3}$ (ii) $y = \frac{2}{3}x + 1$
11. $r -$ ☐ $y = 2x + 5$ ☐ $p -$ ☐ $y = x + 5$ ☐
    $q -$ ☐ $y = x - 2$ ☐
12. $y = \frac{1}{2}x + 1$
13. (i) a & f   (ii) e & f   (iii) e   (iv) a
14. 4
15. 2
16. (i) $y = 2x + 3$ (ii) $y = x + 2$
    (iii) $y = 3x - 3$
17. A & C

Exercise 11.5

1. −2; $2x + y - 8 = 0$
2. $3x - y - 9 = 0$
3. $\frac{2}{3}$; $-\frac{3}{2}$; $3x + 2y - 10 = 0$
4. $2x - 3y + 7 = 0$
5. $3x - y + 12 = 0$
6. (i) Slope a: 2, Slope b: $-\frac{1}{2}$
   (ii) Yes, perpendicular
   (iii) $2x - y - 8 = 0$
7. $2x + y - 5 = 0$
8. C
9. (2, 4); $5x - y - 6 = 0$
10. (i) Slope: 2, P(0, 5)   (ii) $x + 2y - 10 = 0$
11. $\frac{1}{3}$; $y = \frac{1}{3}x + 2$; P(3, 3); $y = -3x + 12$
12. (i) $\frac{5}{3}$ (ii) (b) $3x + 5y = 2$

Exercise 11.6

1. a: $y = 1$, b: $y = 3$, c: $x = 3$, d: $x = -1$
3. (i) 3   (ii) (0, 6)   (iii) 4
   (iv) 2   (v) 9 sq. units
4. (i) (0, 5)   (ii) (5, 0)
5. (i) (0, 6)   (ii) (2, 0)
6. (6, 0), (0, −3)
7. (5, 0), (0, $-2\frac{1}{2}$)
8. Same slope, i.e. all parallel to each other

9. 9 sq. units
10. (i) a (ii) b
    (iii) Not perpendicular (iv) $\frac{15}{2}$ sq. units
11. (i) A(0, 2), B(−4, 0)   (ii) $\frac{1}{2}$
13. (i) d (ii) c (iii) a (iv) b
14. (iv) Not on this line
16. −6
17. 3
18. (i) 2   (ii) 5

Exercise 11.7

1. (4, 1)   2. (1, 3)   3. (1, 4)
4. (2, 3)   5. (3, 1)   6. (−2, 1)
7. (−3, 1)   8. (−2, 3)   9. (−3, −1)
10. (−1, −2)   11. (3, −4)   12. (−2, 5)
14. P(0, 6), Q(−7, 0)

Exercise 11.8

1. (i) (a) 10 ℓ/min   (b) 3 ℓ/min
   (ii) 10, 3
   (iii) Slope = rate of flow
2. (i) (a) $\frac{7}{4}$ ℓ/sec   (b) 2 ℓ/sec
   (ii) $\frac{7}{4}$, 2
   (iii) Both the same value
3. (i) $\frac{1}{2}$ (ii) C is true
4. (i) (a) 2.25 ℓ (b) 2 ℓ (c) 4.4 pints
   (ii) $\frac{4}{7}$
   (iii) $4x - 7y = 0$ (or $4p - 7\ell = 0$)
   (iv) $6\frac{6}{7}$ litres
5. (i) −8
   (ii) Goes from forty gallons to zero gallons
   (iii) 8 gallons/min
   (iv) Slope means that the rate of flow is
       −8 gallons per minute
6. (i) (a) 9.1 kg   (b) 8.8 lb
   (ii) $\frac{5}{11}$
   (iii) Slope means that 5 kg = 11 lb
        2.2 lb = 1 kg (rate of change)
   (iv) $5y - 11x = 0$ (or $5k - 11\ell = 0$)
   (v) 44 lb
7. (i) (a) €182   (b) €125
   (ii) (a) 24 days   (b) 47 days
   (iii) $\frac{19}{5}$
   (iv) Value of slope = daily hire charge (€3.80)
   (v) €30
8. (i) ℓ_1: 11, ℓ_2: $\frac{17}{2}$
   (ii) That the fuel consumptions are 11 km/ℓ
        and 8.5 km/ℓ respectively.
   (iii) €7.76

Test yourself 11

1. (i) 2   (ii) (0, −4) (iii) (2, 0)   (iv) $-\frac{1}{2}$
2. (i) $\frac{1}{2}$; $y = \frac{1}{2}x + 1$ (ii) B
3. (i) (0, 5); y-axis   (ii) $\frac{4}{3}$
   (iii) $-\frac{3}{4}$ (iv) $3x + 4y = 0$
4. (i) (a) A: $2x - y + 3 = 0$, B: $2x - y - 2 = 0$
   (b) $2x - y + c = 0$
   (ii) (2, 2)
5. (i) 2   (ii) A(3, 0), B(0, 2); 3 sq. units
6. $a = \frac{-3}{5}, b = 3$
7. (i) b & c (ii) 2   (iii) D & a, E & b, F & c
8. (i) $3x - y - 1 = 0$
   (ii) (a) 0.675
   (b) Yes as the slope is 0.675, i.e. under 0.7
9. (ii) $-\frac{1}{2}$
10. (i) $2x - y + 1 = 0$
    (ii) By checking whether the product of their slopes is −1 (which it isn't)
11. (i) 7070 m   (ii) 3 km
    (iii) $3x - 4y + 31 = 0$
    (iv) $4x + 3y - 92 = 0$
    (v) (11, 16)
    (vi) Up North St. to Tangent St. and then follow Tangent St. directly to the museum; 21.5 km

Chapter 12: Ratio – Time – Speed

Exercise 12.1

1. (i) 1 : 3   (ii) 5 : 9   (iii) 2 : 7
   (iv) 1 : 4   (v) 1 : 3   (vi) 1 : 8
   (vii) 1 : 7   (viii) 2 : 9
2. (i) 2 : 1   (ii) 3 : 1   (iii) 2 : 3
   (iv) 4 : 3   (v) 4 : 5   (vi) 6 : 7
   (vii) 7 : 3   (viii) 1 : 3
3. Ann – €180, David – €108
4. €1600, €800, €400
5. €390, €910
6. €225
7. (i) B and C, A and E
   (ii) One quarter of the class are girls OR The ratio of boys to girls is 3 : 1
8. 210
9. €5508
10. (i) 10 kg   (ii) 15 kg
11. 250
12. (i) 15 apples, 125 g br. sugar, 1 kg flour, 250 g c. sugar, 5 tbsp water
    (ii) 20 ppl
13. 3 : 7
14. $16\frac{1}{5}$ c

15. (i) 50 cm   (ii) 16 m
16. €10
17. (i) Butter – 400 g, Flour – 600 g
    (ii) 500 g   (iii) 1875 g
18. 10 days
19. (i) 9 days   (ii) 18
20. 1 : 2
21. 13 : 47
22. 3 : 2
23. 2 : 1

Exercise 12.2

1. (i) 8 hr 24 min   (ii) 2 hr 36 min
   (iii) 4 hr 58 min   (iv) 1 hr 41 min
2. (i) 204 min   (ii) 336 min
   (iii) 474 min
3. (i) 1.25 am   (ii) 10.30 pm
   (iii) 6.50 am   (iv) 4.45 pm
4. (i) 11.40 am   (ii) 3.35 pm
   (iii) 12.20 pm   (iv) 12.30 am
   (v) 10.15 pm
5. (i) 06.00   (ii) 10.45
   (iii) 16.00   (iv) 22.12
   (v) 12.00
6. (i) 4 hr 30 min   (ii) 7 hr 5 min
   (iii) 8 hr 15 min   (iv) 8 hr 28 min
7. (i) 4 hr 10 min   (ii) 3 hr 32 min
   (iii) 8 hr 9 min
8. A and (i), B and (iv), C and (ii), D and (iii)
9. 36 hr 15 min   10. 10.55 pm
11. 3 hr 48 min   12. 14.26
13. (i) 3 hr 35 min   (ii) 19 min
    (iii) 1 hr 53 min   (iv) Train 2
    (v) 2 hr 55 min   (vi) 2 min
    (vii) 38 min   (viii) Train 2
14. €27.23

Exercise 12.3

1. (i) 225 km   (ii) 198 km
2. (i) 2 hr 30 min   (ii) $\frac{3}{4}$ hr
3. (i) 60 km/hr   (ii) 60 km/hr
   (iii) 50 km/hr   (iv) 135 km/hr
4. 180 km/hr   5. 70 km/hr
6. $4\frac{1}{2}$ hours   7. 72 km/hr
8. 5 hr 12 min   9. $53\frac{1}{3}$ km/hr
10. 12 m/sec   11. 42 km/hr
12. 72 km/hr
13. (i) 86 km/hr   (ii) 67 ℓ
14. 8 km/hr
15. Cheetah is faster; 469.4 m/min
16. 8.35 am
17. Cheetah, Antelope, Racehorse, Deer

18. 125 km/hr

19. 1418 hours

Test yourself 12

1. (a) (i) 4:5   (ii) 1:5
    (iii) 1:12   (iv) 1:5
  (b) (i) 2.5 hr   (ii) 88 km/hr
  (c) 3:11

2. (a) 6   (b) 9 ℓ (c) 192 cm

3. (a) (i) 5:7:10:3   (ii) 0.8 kg
  (b) 40 min each   (c) 1625

4. (a) (i) 240 km   (ii) 3 hours
    (iii) 80 km/hr
  (b) 81 kg
  (c) (i) 19.17   (ii) 23.49

5. (a) €2080   (b) 12.24 pm   (c) 7:23

6. (a) $\frac{1}{4}$ (b) 56
  (c) (i) 3 hr   (ii) 8 km/hr
  (d) 25.2 m

Chapter 13: Statistics 3 – Presenting Data

Exercise 13.1

1. (i) 15   (ii) 1
  (iii) 0 to 5 (i.e. 5)   (iv) 20%

2. (i) 18°C   (ii) 28°C   (iii) 3
  (iv) $53\frac{1}{3}$%   (v) $\frac{4}{15}$

3. (i) 42   (ii) 3   (iii) 10
  (iv) 29.2%   (v) $\frac{1}{13}$

4. (i) 25   (ii) 10
  (iii) 3   (iv) 5–10 (i.e. 5)
  (v) 9

5. (i) 7   (ii) 12   (iii) 13   (iv) 4
  (v) 30   (vi) $16\frac{2}{3}$%   (vii) $\frac{1}{10}$

6. (i) 6   (ii) 3   (iii) 4   (iv) $\frac{1}{5}$

7. (i) 6   (ii) 16   (iii) 8   (iv) 5

8. (i) 60   (ii) 115   (iii) 1.9

9. (iii) 3   (iv) $22\frac{1}{2}$%   (v) 70%

10. (i) 4   (ii) 5
   (iii) 3   (iv) 0.225

Exercise 13.2

1. (i) 105°   (ii) 120°   (iii) 125°

2. (i) 300   (ii) 150   (iii) 100   (iv) 30°

3. (i) 45°   (ii) 40   (iii) Spain
  (iv) France   (v) Spain and Portugal

4. (i) 90°   (ii) 45°   (iii) 165°

5. (i) Bus – 120°, Car – 90°, Train – 72°,
    Walk – 48°, Bicycle – 30°

6. (i) €1800   (ii) (a) 120°   (b) €600

7. Pie chart Ⓒ

8. (i) $\frac{1}{10}$ (ii) 100

9. (i) 150
  (ii) Slightly larger % of cards at *Cardworld* are
     c'ions cards but there are 3 times as many
     cards (in total) at *Card Den*.

10. 90

11. (i) 20%   (ii) $x = 126°$, $y = 79°$

Exercise 13.3

1. (i) 20   (ii) 16
  (iii) (6–9) km   (iv) 62

2. (i) 7.30 am
  (ii) 45
  (iii) Breakfast
  (iv) 10.30 am–11.30 am
  (v) Elevenses

3. (ii) 28   (iii) 12

4. (i) 32   (ii) (30–40) sec
  (iii) 25%   (iv) 23   (v) $\frac{9}{32}$

5. (ii) 12   (iii) (20–40) km
  (iv) (20–40) km   (v) 38 km

6. (i) 2   (ii) (€20 000–€30 000)
  (iii) 7   (iv) 20   (v) $\frac{3}{20}$

7. (i) 12   (ii) 60   (iii) (50–60) yrs
  (iv) $\frac{1}{10}$ (v) 21   (vi) $43\frac{1}{2}$ yrs

8. (i) Ⓑ   (ii) Ⓒ   (iii) Ⓐ

Exercise 13.4

1. (i) 4   (ii) 27 yrs   (iii) 8   (iv) 36 yrs

2. (i) 20   (ii) 5   (iii) 43   (iv) 76

3. (i) 50   (ii) $75\frac{1}{2}$ (iii) $65\frac{1}{2}$
  (iv) $88\frac{1}{2}$ (v) 23

4. (ii) 8   (iii) 16   (iv) 15

5. (i) 62   (ii) 47   (iii) 67   (iv) 20

6. (ii) 16.5 km/hr   (iii) 40 km/hr
  (iv) 23.5 km/hr

7. (i) 19   (ii) 66   (iii) 64   (iv) 26

8. (i) Before – 48, After – 45
  (ii) Before – 66, After – 79
  (iii) The pulse rates were consistently higher
      after PE

9. (i) 23
  (ii) Dynamo – 37 hours, Energy Plus – 29
     hours
  (iii) Dynamo better as it has a much higher
     median though is less predictable (much
     larger range)

10. (ii) Male median – 53 yrs
Female median – 56 yrs
Male range – 32 yrs
Female range – 36 yrs

11. (i) 10   (ii) 5   (iii) 2   (iv) 6   (v) 3

Exercise 13.5

1. (i) 2   (ii) 4   (iii) 8
(iv) 3   (v) 9   (vi) 27

2. Graph only shows part of the scale

3. (i) Area of column for "fish 2" increased dramatically by larger width
(ii) Increased width and depth (and by extension, volume) of carton B creates illusion of greater production despite the actual productions being the same.
(iii) Scale doesn't start at 0
(iv) "Creative" cubes (area and volume) mislead

4. Vertical axis unlabelled; cylinders of varying radii used

5. (i) Graph shows only part of the vertical scale

6. (i) Graph A   (ii) No   (iii) No, untrue

Test yourself 13

1. (a) (i) 45°   (ii) 60   (iii) $12\frac{1}{2}$%
(b) (i) 36   (ii) 28
(iii) $Q_1 = 18$, $Q_3 = 36$; 1

2. (a) (i) As the continuous data is grouped
(ii) 7   (iii) 8   (iv) 16
(b) (ii) Mode – 3.7 kg, Median – 4.15 kg
(c) No; Greendale has >60, Nevin has <50

3. (a) (i) 60°   (ii) 84°
(b) (i) No vertical scale
(ii) Increased width of mobile phone on right distorts the actual increase
(c) (i) 49 kg   (ii) 30 kg
(iii) 54 kg   (iv) 24 kg

4. (a) (i) €1133.33   (ii) €400
(iii) €666.67   (iv) €200
(b) (i) S – $92\frac{1}{2}$, D – $99\frac{1}{2}$
(ii) S – 49, D – 23
(iii) Dynamos; much smaller range
(iv) While they did achieve 3 v. high scores, they also got the 4 lowest scores (Erratic scoring)

5. (ii) 24
(iii) 1st Test – 33   2nd Test – 29
(iv) Yes; higher mean, higher median, higher starting point (27 → 33)
(v) Slightly better-than-average improvement (3 compared to 2.83)

Chapter 14: Simultaneous Equations

Exercise 14.1

1. $x = 2, y = 4$ **2.** $x = 4, y = 2$
3. 1, 4   **4.** 3, 5
5. 2, 3   **6.** 4, 2
7. 3, 4   **8.** 6, 3
9. 2, 3   **10.** 4, −2
11. 1, 2   **12.** 5, −2
13. 6, 3   **14.** 7, 2
15. 2, 2   **16.** 3, −4
17. 7, −2   **18.** 3, −5
19. 1, 5   **20.** $1\frac{1}{2}$, 2
21. 3, 4   **22.** 6, −4
23. 15, 12   **24.** −3, 8
25. 9, 4   **26.** 6, 1
27. 2, 10   **28.** 4, 10
29. 3, 5   **30.** 6, $1\frac{1}{2}$

Exercise 14.2

1. (i) (2, 1)   (ii) $x = 2, y = 1$
(iii) Same

2. (2, 3)

3. (i) −2, −3   (ii) 3, 5
4. (i) 4, 2   (ii) 2, 1
5. (i) 3, 7   (ii) 1, 3   (iii) 11, −1
6. (i) (a) 0, 4   (b) 1, 3
(ii) Parallel lines, therefore no point of intersection

7. 12, −3   **8.** 10, 3   **9.** 10, 7

10. $x = 5, y = 2$

11. 14 g

12. (i) Ⓒ   (ii) $b = 55$ g, $e = 75$ g

13. Twenty 5c coins and fourteen 10c coins

14. Small mug – 196 g, large mug – 366 g

15. $x = 6\frac{1}{2}$ cm, $y = 3\frac{1}{2}$ cm

16. (i) $2x + 3y = 33$ (ii) $4x + 2y = 46$
(iii) $x = 9, y = 5$ (iv) 39 cm

17. (i) $2a + b = 8$, $4a − 3b = 1$
(ii) $a = 2\frac{1}{2}$, $b = 3$

18. €50, 40 c

19. 40, 12

20. 42, 36

21. □ = 4, ♡ = 20, ◇ = 2

22. $2x − y = 3$, $x + 2y = −6$

Test yourself 14

1. (a) 7, 3
(b) (i) $4b + 3r = 58$, $5b + 6r = 86$
(ii) blue – 10 g, red – 6 g
(iii) 66 g

2. (a) 1, −2
   (b) (i) $\frac{1}{2}$, $2\frac{1}{2}$ (ii) $6\frac{1}{2}$ cm
3. (a) 4, 3
   (b) (i) −2, 7
     (ii) $2x - y = 4$, $x + y = 5$
   (c) $x = 18$, $y = 24$
4. (a) 15, 12
   (b) $a = €45$, $b = €75$; €1170
   (c) $(2, −1)$
5. (a) 10, 4
   (b) $x = 3$, $y = 1$
   (c) Mother – 45, son – 13

Chapter 15: Indices – Scientific Notation – Surds

Exercise 15.1

1. (i) 49   (ii) 64   (iii) 16
   (iv) 25   (v) 36
2. (i) 2^3 (ii) 2^4 (iii) 4^5
   (iv) 5^6 (v) a^6 (vi) $6x^3$
   (vii) $8x^5$ (viii) a^3
3. (i) 3^2 (ii) 5^2 (iii) 3^3
   (iv) 2^5 (v) 10^3 (vi) 20^2
4. (i) 5^2 (ii) 3^4 (iii) 7^2
   (iv) 3^4 (v) 5^7 (vi) 4^4
5. (i) F   (ii) T   (iii) F   (iv) F
6. (i) 8   (ii) 16   (iii) 9   (iv) 343
   (v) 9
7. (i) $\frac{1}{9}$ (ii) 8   (iii) 12   (iv) $\frac{1}{12}$
   (v) 1
8. (i) 8   (ii) 3   (iii) 4   (iv) 8
9. A − 27 (3^3); B − $\frac{1}{9}$ (3^{-2}); C − $\frac{1}{64}$ (2^{-6});
   D − $\frac{1}{216}$ (6^{-3}); E − 1 (7^0); F − $\frac{1}{4}$ (2^{-2}); G − 9 (3^2);
   H − 3125 (5^5)
10. (i) 36   (ii) $\frac{1}{8}$ (iii) $\frac{4}{9}$
   (iv) $a^3 b^3$ (v) $\frac{4a^2}{9b^2}$
11. (i) $3^8 \times 5^7$ (ii) $2^6 \times 9^5$
   (iii) 3^8, 4^8 (iv) $11^3 \times 3^1$
12. C
13. (i) 4^6 (ii) $(2^4)^3$
   (iii) 2^{4n} (iv) $(5^x)^4$
14. (i) 3^2 (ii) 3^4
   (iii) 3^9 (iv) 3^8
   (v) 3^{2n}
15. A and I; B and H; C and G; D and F
16. (i) $\frac{1}{a}$ (ii) 1
   (iii) $6a^2$ (iv) a^4
17. (i) 3^8 (ii) 4^4 (iii) a^{-1}

Exercise 15.2

1. (i) 5   (ii) 12   (iii) 3
   (iv) 4   (v) 4   (vi) 5
2. (i) 5   (ii) 4   (iii) 6
   (iv) $\frac{2}{3}$ (v) $\frac{4}{5}$ (vi) $\frac{2}{3}$
3. (i) $x^{\frac{1}{2}}$ (ii) $x^{\frac{1}{3}}$ (iii) $a^{\frac{1}{4}}$
   (iv) $a^{\frac{2}{3}}$ (v) $a^{\frac{3}{2}}$ (vi) $a^{\frac{3}{4}}$
4. (i) $\frac{1}{2}$ (ii) $\frac{1}{3}$ (iii) $\frac{1}{4}$
   (iv) 3   (v) $\frac{1}{10}$ (vi) 0.1
5. (i) $\sqrt{a}$ (ii) $\sqrt[4]{a}$ (iii) $\sqrt[3]{a^2}$
   (iv) $\sqrt{a^5}$ (v) $\sqrt[4]{a^3}$ (vi) $\sqrt{\frac{a}{x}}$ or $\frac{\sqrt{a}}{\sqrt{x}}$
6. (i) 9   (ii) 4   (iii) 8
   (iv) 8   (v) 9   (vi) 64
   (vii) 16   (viii) 1000   (ix) 27
   (x) 25
7. (i) $\frac{1}{3}$ (ii) $\frac{1}{16}$ (iii) $\frac{1}{2}$
   (iv) 2   (v) $\frac{1}{4}$
8. (i) $\frac{1}{4}$ (ii) 4   (iii) $\frac{1}{8}$
   (iv) $\frac{1}{1000}$ (v) $\frac{1}{8}$
9. (i) $\frac{9}{4}$ (ii) 16   (iii) $\frac{25}{9}$
   (iv) $\frac{3}{2}$ (v) $\frac{5}{3}$
10. (i) $\frac{1}{343}$ (ii) $\frac{125}{27}$ (iii) $\frac{27}{8}$
   (iv) $\frac{25}{9}$ (v) 5
11. $a = 16$, $b = \frac{1}{9}$; 12
12. (i) $\frac{4}{9}$ (ii) $\frac{1}{125}$
13. 5   **14.** 4^{-2} **16.** 3^{-2}

Exercise 15.3

1. (i) 2^3 (ii) 2^4 (iii) 2^{-2}
   (iv) 2^{-3} (v) 2^{-5}
2. (i) 3^2 (ii) 3^3 (iii) 3^4
   (iv) 3^{-3} (v) 3^{-4}
3. (i) $2^{\frac{3}{2}}$ (ii) $2^{\frac{7}{2}}$ (iii) $2^{\frac{3}{2}}$
   (iv) $2^{\frac{7}{2}}$ (v) $2^{\frac{-5}{2}}$
4. (i) $x = 3$ (ii) $x = 3$ (iii) $x = \frac{3}{2}$
   (iv) $x = \frac{5}{3}$ (v) $x = \frac{5}{2}$ (vi) $x = \frac{3}{2}$
   (vii) $x = \frac{3}{2}$ (viii) $x = \frac{5}{4}$
5. (i) $x = -2$ (ii) $x = -3$ (iii) $x = \frac{-3}{2}$
   (iv) $x = 3$
6. (i) $x = \frac{4}{3}$ (ii) $x = -3$ (iii) $x = \frac{-5}{2}$
   (iv) $x = 3$
7. (i) $x = 6$ (ii) $x = 3$ (iii) $x = -\frac{3}{2}$
   (iv) $x = \frac{-1}{2}$

8. (i) $5^{\frac{1}{2}}$ (ii) $5^{\frac{3}{2}}$ (iii) $5^{\frac{3}{2}}$

     (iv) $5^{\frac{7}{2}}$ (v) $5^{\frac{-5}{2}}$

9. (i) $\frac{-1}{2}$ (ii) $\frac{-1}{2}$ (iii) $\frac{5}{2}$

     (iv) $\frac{-3}{2}$

10. $3^{\frac{7}{2}}$; $x = \frac{3}{4}$

11. $3^{\frac{5}{2}}$; $x = \frac{13}{4}$ **12.** $2^{\frac{5}{2}}$; $x = \frac{9}{4}$

13. $3^{\frac{-5}{2}}$; $x = \frac{17}{4}$

14. (i) 2^4 (ii) $2^{\frac{3}{2}}$; $x = \frac{7}{4}$

Exercise 15.4

1. (i), (ii), (iv), (vi) all rational
2. (i), (iii), (v), (vi) all irrational
3. (i) 5   (ii) 20   (iii) 12
    (iv) 5   (v) 29   (vi) 10
4. (i) $\sqrt{10}$ (or π) (ii) $\sqrt{17}$ (iii) $\sqrt{109}$
    (iv) $\sqrt{0.8}$
5. (i) $\sqrt{10}$ (ii) $\sqrt{21}$ (iii) $\sqrt{24}$
    (iv) $\sqrt{55}$
6. (i) 5   (ii) 6   (iii) 12
    (iv) 4   (v) 4
7. (i) $2\sqrt{2}$ (ii) $2\sqrt{3}$ (iii) $3\sqrt{2}$
    (iv) $3\sqrt{3}$ (v) $3\sqrt{5}$
8. (i) $5\sqrt{3}$ (ii) $5\sqrt{5}$ (iii) $4\sqrt{2}$
    (v) $12\sqrt{3}$ (v) $8\sqrt{3}$
9. A and K, F and G, B and H, E and J, C and I; D
10. (i) $8\sqrt{3}$ (ii) $5\sqrt{2}$ (iii) $5\sqrt{2}$
    (iv) $7\sqrt{2}$ (v) $7\sqrt{3}$ (vi) $3\sqrt{3}$
11. 4 times
12. (i) 10   (ii) 18   (iii) 60
    (iv) 21
13. (i) $5 - 2\sqrt{5}$
    (ii) $6 - 4\sqrt{3}$ $\left[$or $2(3 - 2\sqrt{3})\right]$
    (iii) $6 - \sqrt{6}$
14. (i) $2(\sqrt{10} - 5)$ (ii) 1   (iii) 22
    (iv) -9 (v) -11 (vi) -3
15. (i) 2   (ii) $-7 - 13\sqrt{2}$
    (iii) 1
16. $24 - 8\sqrt{5}$
17. $4\sqrt{15}$
18. 6
19. (i) (a) $2\sqrt{3}$ (b) Irrational
    (ii) (a) 1   (b) Rational

Exercise 15.5

1. (i), (iv)
2. (i) 600   (ii) 450
    (iii) 6800   (iv) 51 000
    (v) 67 000   (vi) 516
    (vii) 7050   (viii) 18 600

3. (i) 4×10^2 (ii) 2.8×10^2
    (iii) 8.4×10^2 (iv) 6.2×10^3
    (v) 8.6×10^3 (vi) 1.27×10^2
    (vii) 8.27×10^2 (viii) 7.6×10^4
    (ix) 1.468×10^2 (x) 7.24×10^4
4. (i) 4×10^3 (ii) 3.2×10^5
    (iii) 9×10^2 (iv) 9.43×10^3
5. (i) 2080   (ii) 660.6
    (iii) 8230   (iv) 570
6. (i) 5.4×10^5 (ii) 1.702×10^2
    (iii) 3.276×10^3 (iv) 1.44×10^2
7. (i) 0.25   (ii) 0.06
    (iii) 0.0048   (iv) 0.00092
8. (i) 4×10^{-2} (ii) 6.2×10^{-2}
    (iii) 7×10^{-3} (iv) 6.5×10^{-3}
9. (i) 8×10^{-3} (ii) 7.9×10^{-3}
    (iii) 6×10^{-4} (iv) 5.3×10^{-4}
10. (i) 7×10^3 (ii) 6×10^2
    (iii) 5.6×10^3 (iv) 7×10^{-5}
11. (i) 1.62×10^8 (ii) 5×10^{-3}
    (iii) 8×10^{-4} (iv) 2×10
    (v) 5×10^{-1} (vi) 1.6×10^{-5}
12. (i) 2.8×10^3 (ii) 8×10^2
13. 2.4×10^4
14. 0.3779
15. (i) 19.625   (ii) 78.4
16. (i) Earth
    (ii) 5900 km (5.9×10^3)
    (iii) (1.95×10^4) km

Exercise 15.6

1. (i) 80   (ii) 350   (iii) 1790
    (iv) 7320   (v) 1610
2. (i) 100   (ii) 100   (iii) 1800
    (iv) 2500   (v) 9800
3. (i) 46.3   (ii) 8.8   (iii) 0.4
    (iv) 0.5   (v) 0.1
4. (i) 1   (ii) 2   (iii) 3
    (iv) 3   (v) 4
5. (i) 3200   (ii) 650   (iii) 2900
    (iv) 29 000   (v) 41 000
6. (i) 7140   (ii) 45 300   (iii) 3610
    (iv) 160 000   (v) 701 000
7. (i) 0.47   (ii) 0.063   (iii) 2.4
    (iv) 0.67   (v) 55
8. (i) 0.738   (ii) 8.37   (iii) 0.0284
    (iv) 1.08   (v) 12.3
9. (i) 72 700   (ii) 73 000   (iii) 70 000
10. (i) 40   (ii) 2   (iii) 125
11. (i) 10   (ii) 0.3   (iii) 8
12. (i) 3   (ii) 3   (iii) $2\frac{2}{3}$
13. (i) 5   (ii) 360   (iii) 9
14. (i) 40   (ii) 120   (iii) 60

15. $\dfrac{40 \times 60}{300}$

Exercise 15.7

1. (i) $\frac{1}{6}$ (ii) 2   (iii) $\frac{4}{3}$
    (iv) $-\frac{3}{2}$ (v) $\frac{4}{5}$

2. (i) 0.38   (ii) 0.18   (iii) -0.36
    (iv) 1.47   (v) -1.25

4. (i) 7.91   (ii) 9.09   (iii) 12.47

5. (i) 5.52   (ii) 18.65   (iii) 10.38
    (iv) 15.21   (v) 267.00

6. (i) 0.16   (ii) 1.27   (iii) 4.22
    (iv) 44.28   (v) 2.50

7. (i) 22.16   (ii) 98.01   (iii) 9.56
    (iv) 4.13

8. (i) 0.47   (ii) 7.53   (iii) 38.27

9. 41.23

10. 2.47   **11.** 14.96   **12.** 15.08

Test yourself 15

1. (a) (i) 12   (ii) $x = \frac{-1}{3}$
    (b) (i) $5\sqrt{2}$ (ii) $\sqrt{37}$
    (c) 12; 11.43

2. (a) (i) $4^{\frac{1}{2}}$ and $16^{\frac{1}{4}}$ (ii) 5.3×10^3
    (b) (i) $3\sqrt{3}$ (ii) $0.2\ (2 \times 10^{-1})$
    (c) (i) $x = 0$ (ii) $y = -2$
       (iii) $z = \frac{1}{5}$ (iv) $b = -4$

3. (a) (i) 4^{-1} and 2^{-2} (ii) $x = 2\ (8, 18\ldots)$
    (b) (i) $4x^2$ (ii) 3×10^5
    (c) (i) 125   (ii) $x = \frac{-3}{4}$

4. (a) (i) 32   (ii) $\frac{1}{9}$ (iii) 2   (iv) 1   (v) 3
    (b) (i) 4×10^{-2} (ii) $x = \frac{3}{2}$
    (c) (i) $F(0^2 = 0)$ (ii) $F[(-8)^2 = 64]$
       (iii) $F(1 < 2)$ (iv) T
       (v) $F\left(2^{-4} = \frac{1}{16} \text{ and } \frac{1}{16} > 0\right)$

5. (a) (i) 16   (ii) $\frac{1}{2}$ (iii) 5   (iv) 2
    (b) (i) $10\sqrt{2}$ (ii) $\frac{1}{4}$
    (c) 2.5×10^3

6. (a) (i) $5\frac{1}{2}$ (ii) $-\frac{1}{2}$
    (b) (i) 3   (ii) $\frac{5}{7}$
    (c) $5\frac{3}{2}; \frac{1}{4}$

Chapter 16: Geometry 2: Similar Triangles – Circles – Theorems

Exercise 16.1

1. (i) [SR]   (ii) [LM]   (iii) 8
    (iv) 16.4   (v) 7.5

2. (i) $1 : 2$ (ii) 14.4   (iii) 4

3. $x = 13.5, y = 18$

4. (i) $p = 6, q = 13.5$ (ii) $x = 9, y = 1$

5. (i) $1\frac{1}{2}$ (ii) $x = 6, y = 4.5$

6. As they have equal angles and corresponding sides of different lengths (i.e. not congruent $\triangle$s); $x = 21$ cm, $y = 15$ cm

7. (i) [RQ]   (ii) [RP]   (iii) [QP]; 9

8. (i) [KL]   (ii) [EF]   (iii) 15

9. (ii) [DF]   (iii) $x = 13\frac{5}{7}$ cm, $y = 9\frac{1}{7}$ cm

10. (i) [XY]; opposite equal angles
    (ii) $d = 9, e = 13.5$

11. (i), (iv), (v)

12. 11.2 cm

13. (i) Same angles (corresponding angles, e.g. $|\angle ABC| = |\angle ADE|$)
    (ii) 14

14. (i) $|\angle BDC| = |\angle ABD|$
    (iii) [CD]   (iv) [AD]   (v) 9.6 cm

15. $x = 16\frac{2}{3}, y = 10$

16. $x = 13.5, y = 27$

17. 2 m

18. 40 cm

19. (i) $|\angle JKM| = |\angle KML|$ … alternate angles
    (ii) 4.9 cm

20. $13\frac{1}{3}$ m

21. (i) Use similar $\triangle$s, namely $\triangle ABE$ and $\triangle ACD$
    (ii) 180 m

Exercise 16.2

1. (i) 10   (ii) 12   (iii) 14

2. (i) $x = 10, y = 12$ (ii) $x = 2.5, y = 6$
    (iii) $x = 5, y = 15$ (iv) $x = 4, y = 22$

3. $a = 0.3$ cm

4. $x = 5, y = 14$

5. (i) 8 cm   (ii) 7 cm

6. (i) $2\frac{1}{2}$ (ii) 9   (iii) $6\frac{2}{3}$

7. (i) $6\frac{2}{5}$ (ii) $5\frac{5}{6}$ (iii) $2\frac{4}{7}$

8. $x = 10, y = 10\frac{4}{5}, z = 11\frac{3}{7}$

9. 6

10. 7 cm

11. 10.5 cm

12. (i) $20\frac{5}{8}$ (ii) $2\frac{2}{3}$

13. $14\frac{2}{5}$ cm

14. (i) 21   (ii) $16\frac{1}{3}$

15. (i) $|AC|$, $|BC|$ (ii) $x = 9\frac{3}{5}, y = 2\frac{2}{5}$

16. (i) A, B, C must be collinear and the same for A, E, D with BE $\parallel$ CD
    (ii) 36 m
    (iii) 50 m

Exercise 16.3

1. (i) Angle in semicircle   (ii) 45°
   (iii) Right-angled, isosceles
2. (i) 90°   (ii) 30°   (iii) 40°
3. A = 90°, B = 90°, C = 20°, D = 90°, E = 45°,
   F = 53°
4. (i) both radii   (ii) 90°   (iii) 35°
   (iv) 55°   (v) As |OB| = |OC| = radius
5. (i) 70°   (ii) 60°   (iii) 35°
6. $a = 63°$, $b = 46°$, $c = 118°$, $d = 32°$, $e = 78°$,
   $f = 103°$, $g = 21°$, $h = 47°$, $i = 62°$, $j = 75°$,
   $k = 25°$
7. $d = 135°$, $e = 76°$, $g = 143°$, $h = 100°$,
   $i = 124°$, $j = 54°$, $m = 125°$, $n = 250°$,
   $p = 94°$, $q = 43°$
8. $a = 116°$, $b = 64°$, $c = 90°$, $d = 135°$,
   $e = 110°$, $f = 35°$
9. (i) 70°   (ii) 30°   (iii) 40°   (iv) 40°
10. (i) $x = 50°$, $y = 20°$
    (ii) $x = 60°$, $y = 120°$
    (iii) $x = 36°$, $y = 54°$
11. 20°
12. (i) 40°   (ii) 43.5°   (iii) 60°
13. (i) ∠RSQ   (ii) 100°
14. △SPQ is isosceles (each base angle = 33°)
15. △AXB and △DXC are similar ⇒ |∠XAB| =
    |∠XCD|;
    As these are alternate angles ⇒ AB ∥ DC
16. $2|△| + 2|△| = 180° ⇒ |△| + |△| = 90° ⇒$
    |∠QPS| = 90° (angles in △ sum to 180°)
17. |∠AXB| = |∠DXC| (vertically opposite),
    |∠BAX| = |∠CDX| and |∠ABX| = |∠DCX|
18. (i) |∠ACP| = |∠BDA| (angles standing on
    same arc) ⇒ △s similar
    (ii) Corresponding sides are proportional
19. Isosceles triangle, $x + y$ = Angle in semicircle,
    i.e. 90°

Test yourself 16

1. (a) (i) ∠ADC and ∠ABC
       (ii) 45°   (iii) 70°
   (b) (ii) $x = 9$, $y = 10.5$
   (c) $a = 2$, $b = 9\frac{1}{3}$
2. (a) $a = 35°$, $b = 95°$, $c = 70°$, $d = 65°$
   (b) $a = 7.5$ cm, $b = 9.6$ cm
   (c) $x = 9$, $y = 18$
3. (a) (i) 5   (ii) 6
   (b) (i) 96°   (ii) 120°   (iii) 84°
   (c) 1.6 m
4. (a) (i) $x = 40°$, $y = 140°$
       (ii) $x = 28°$, $y = 62°$
   (b) (i) 6 cm   (ii) 5 cm   (iii) 15 cm
   (c) 15.5 m

5. (a) $3\frac{3}{8}$ (b) 17 m
   (c) (ii) 16.8 cm
6. (a) (i) $x = 95°$, $y = 85°$
       (ii) $x = 64°$, $y = 116°$
   (b) 8.2 m
   (c) |∠ADE| = 60° and |∠AEC| = 120° ⇒
       |∠AED| = 60° ⇒ |∠DAE| = 60°
7. (a) 3 cm   (b) $116\frac{2}{3}$ m   (c) 652 m

Chapter 17: Cylinder – Sphere – Cone

Exercise 17.1

1. (i) 1848 cm³   (ii) 2816 cm³
   (iii) 18 480 cm³
2. (i) 836 cm²   (ii) $1106\frac{2}{7}$ cm²
   (iii) 3872 cm²
3. (i) 54 259 cm³   (ii) 402 cm³
   (iii) 1413 cm³
4. 24 640 cm³; 25 ℓ
5. 707 cm³
6. (i) $V = \pi r^2 h$ (ii) $350\pi = \pi r^2 14$
   (iii) 5 cm
7. 6 cm   8. 10 cm   9. 3.5 cm
10. 5 cm   11. 7 cm   12. 4938 cm³
13. (i) 1570 cm³   (ii) 14.13 kg
14. 176 cm³; 1792 cm³
15. 16 cm
16. (i) 209 m²   (ii) 298 m³
17. (i) 3542 cm³   (ii) 1366 cm²

Exercise 17.2

1. (i) 3052.1 cm³   (ii) 5572.5 cm³
   (iii) 718.0 cm³
2. (i) 1018 cm²   (ii) 1521 cm²
   (iii) 462 cm²
3. (i) $\frac{250\pi}{3}$ cm³   (ii) 75π cm²
4. (i) 6 cm   (ii) 144π cm²
5. (i) 7 cm   (ii) $1437\frac{1}{3}$ cm³
6. 36π cm³   7. 396 cm³   8. 8 cm
9. 3 cm   10. 52%   11. $4\frac{1}{2}$
12. (i) 36π cm³   (ii) 162π cm³   (iii) 54π cm³
13. 1.5 cm   14. 10 cm
15. $\frac{128\pi}{3}$ cm³; 14 cm   16. $4\frac{1}{2}$ cm
17. (i) 126π cm³   (ii) 8 cm

Exercise 17.3

1. (i) 301.6 cm³   (ii) 10 cm   (iii) 302 cm²
2. 1474 cm³
3. (i) 12 cm   (ii) 204.2 cm²
   (iii) 282.7 cm²   (iv) 314.2 cm³

4. 8 cm   **5.** 10 cm
6. (i) 6 cm   (ii) 234.6 cm^3
7. 30 cm   **8.** 3 cm
9. 192π cm^3; 36
10. 144π cm^3; $h = 2.25$ cm
11. 99π cm^3 **12.** 8 cm
13. (i) 12$h\pi$ cm^3 (ii) 6 cm
14. 4
15. 7.91 cm
16. (i) 72   (ii) 6912 cm^3
17. 12.7 cm
18. (i) 800π cm^3 (ii) 32 cm   (iii) 20 cm

Test yourself 17

1. (a) (i) 113040 m^3 (ii) 7536 m^2
     (b) (i) 720π cm^3 (ii) 15 cm
2. (a) (i) 2592π cm^3 (ii) 144π cm^3
       (iii) 18
     (b) 118 m^2
3. (a) (i) 54π cm^3 (ii) 12π cm^3
       (iii) 207 cm^3
     (b) $\dfrac{4\pi r^3}{3}$
4. (a) (i) 3 cm   (ii) 4 cm
     (b) 44 cm^3
5. (a) 24 cm   (b) 63
6. (a) (i) 20 000π cm^3 (ii) 160π cm^3
       (iii) 125
     (b) 10 mins
7. (a) (i) 1018 cm^3
       (ii) Yes; 1018 cm^3 > 1000 cm^3
       (iii) 2   (iv) 4
     (b) (i) 509 mm^3 (ii) 5064 mm^3
     (c) 88 cm^3; 75 mins

Chapter 18: Patterns & Sequences
Exercise 18.1

1. (i) 13, 15, 17, 19   (ii) 17, 20, 23, 26
     (iii) 24, 28, 32, 36   (iv) 12, 10, 8, 6
     (v) 30, 25, 20, 15   (vi) 0, -4, -8, -12
2. (i) 3, 3.5, 4   (ii) -2, 0, 2
     (iii) 162, 486, 1458   (iv) $5\frac{1}{2}$, 7, $8\frac{1}{2}$
     (v) -5, -2.5, -1.25 (vi) -3, -6, -9
3. (i) 2, 6, 10, 14   (ii) 5, 8, 11, 14
     (iii) 3, 8, 13, 18   (iv) 30, 26, 22, 18
     (v) 10, -7, -4, -1
4. (i) Start with 3 and count forwards in steps of 3
     (ii) Start with 0 and increase in steps of 4
     (iii) Start with 10 and increase in steps of 5
     (iv) Start with 16 and count backwards in steps of 2

(v) Start with -6 and count forwards in steps of 3
(vi) Start with $-2\frac{1}{2}$ and count forwards in steps of $\frac{1}{2}$

5. (i) 'add 4'   (ii) 'add 3'   (iii) 'add 4'
     (iv) 'subtract 2'   (v) 'add a $\frac{1}{4}$'   (vi) 'add 3'

6.

1st term	Term-to-term rule	2nd, 3rd, 4th and 5th terms
8	$+5$	13, 18, 23, 28
5	$+4$	9, 13, 17, 21
9	$+3$	12, 15, 18, 21
0	-3	-3, -6, -9, -12
-12	$+5$	-7, -2, 3, 8
0	$+\frac{1}{7}$	$\frac{1}{7}$, $\frac{2}{7}$, $\frac{3}{7}$, $\frac{4}{7}$
$5\frac{1}{4}$	$-\frac{1}{4}$	5, $4\frac{3}{4}$, $4\frac{1}{2}$, $4\frac{1}{4}$

7. (i) 8   (ii) 20
8. (i) 14   (ii) 26
9. (i) 7   (ii) 1, 5   (iii) 1, 4
11. 3, 7, 11, 15, 19 and 21, 18, 15, 12, 9
12. 1, 2, 4, 8, 16, 32
13. (i) 4, 6, 8, 10, 12, 14, …
     (ii) 25, 22, 19, 16, 13, 10, …
     (iii) 1, 6, 11, 16, 21, 26, …
     (iv) 7, 10, 13, 16, 19, 22, …
14. (i) 33333 × 11 = 366663
     (ii) 9 × 12345 = 111105
     (iii) 66667 × 66667 = 4444488889

Exercise 18.2

1. (i) □, ○   (ii) 2, 6, 10; Yes
     (iii) △   (iv) □   (v) □   (vi) ○
2. (i) green   (ii) blue
     (iii) red   (iv) blue
     (v) 5, 10, 15, 20 …   (vi) 30th
3. (i) 8, 4   (ii) 4   (iii) 6   (iv) 23rd
4. 8, 16, 24, 32, 40, 48, 56, 64, 72, 80;
     (i) |8, 6, 4, 2, 0|, |8, 6, 4, 2, 0|, …
     (ii) 5   (iii) 0

Exercise 18.3

1. (i) 2, 4, 6, 8   (ii) 4, 7, 10, 13
     (iii) 1, 5, 9, 13   (iv) 7, 9, 11, 13
     (v) 1, 6, 11, 16   (vi) 5, 3, 1, -1
2. (i) -2, -5, -8 (ii) 2, 5, 10
     (iii) $\frac{1}{2}$, $\frac{3}{4}$, 1
3. (i) 5, 7, 9, 11, 13   (ii) 43, 203
5. As the difference between the terms is a constant

6. (i) Yes (ii) No
(iii) No (iv) Yes

7. (i) A – 5, 12, 19, 26
B – 9, 8, 7, 6
C – $-2\frac{1}{2}, -2, -1\frac{1}{2}, -1$
D – 2, 5, 10, 17
E – 60, 30, 20, 15
F – 2, 4, 8, 16
(ii) A – 138
B – -10
C – 7
D – 401
E – 3
F – 1048576
(iii) A, B, C are linear

8. (i) 5, 8, 11, 14, 17, 20 (ii) 302

Exercise 18.4

1. (i) $+4$ (ii) 4
(iii) $4n + 1$ (iv) 81
2. (i) $2n + 3$ (ii) $3n + 1$
(iii) $4n + 2$
3. $4n + 3$; 43, 83
4. (i) Subtract 2 (ii) -2
(iii) $-2n + 14$ (iv) -6
(v) T_{14}
5. (i) $3n - 6$ (ii) $-5n + 25$
6. $-3n + 11$; 15

Exercise 18.5

1. (ii) 6, 11, 16, 21, 26, 31
(iv) 101 (v) 10th
2. (ii) 15 (iii) $2n + 1$ (iv) Diagram 16
3. (i) 19 (ii) $3n + 1$ (iii) 151
4. (i) 13 (ii) $2n + 3$ (iii) Pattern 24
5. (i) 21 (ii) Add 5 (iii) $5n + 1$
(iv) 13 (v) No
6. (iii) Start at 5 and add 4 (iv) $T_n = 4n + 1$
(v) Shape 20
(vi) Yes; Shape 22
7. (iii) $3n + 1$ (iv) 121 (v) 30

Exercise 18.6

1. (i) 5, 8, 13, 20 (ii) -1, 2, 7, 14
(iii) 1, 7, 17, 31 (iv) -1, 8, 23, 44
2. (i) 18, 24 (ii) 38, 51
(iii) 47, 62
3. (i), (iii), (iv)
4. 116
5. (ii) The coefficient of n^2 in the nth term is the 2nd diff. $\div 2$
(iii) 6
6. $a = 1$; $T_n = n^2 + 3$

7. (i) $T_n = n^2 + 6$ (ii) $T_n = n^2 + 2n - 1$
(iii) $T_n = 2n^2$
9. (i) 30
(ii) As the term-to-term rule does not involve adding or subtracting a constant
(iii) Yes; 2nd differences all the same
(iv) $T_n = n^2 + n$ (v) 420
10. (i) 24 (ii) 35
(iv) $T_n = n^2 + 2n$ (v) 120

Exercise 18.7

1. Constant difference between outputs
2. 3, 5, 7, 9, 11
3. (i) €30 (ii) €105
(iii) 5 (iv) Yes
(v) €21 (vi) Yes, both 21
(vii) €240
4. (i) Yes (ii) €120
(iii) $y = 10x$ (or $a = 10w$) (iv) €200
5. (ii) $T_n = 4n + 2$
6. (ii) 14 (iii) 29 (iv) 2
(v) 2 cm per day
(vi) The slope of the line equals the rate of growth of the plant
7. (i) 26 (iii) $T_n = 5n + 1$
(v) $E = 5n + 1$ (vi) 5
(vii) The increase in the number of edges from one pattern to the next
8. (ii) 2
(iv) The graph is curved (parabola)
9. (i) 81, 243, 729
(ii) It is not
(iii) 2nd differences are not all the same
(iv) The curve rises very steeply
10. A and 1, B and 2, C and 3

Test yourself 18

1. (a) (i) The sequence begins at 3 and goes up in steps of 4
(ii) The sequence begins at -1 and goes down in steps of 2
(iii) The sequence begins at 3 and after that, each term is double the previous term
(b) (i) 4, 7, 10 (ii) -1, -3, -5 (iii) 1, 7, 17
(c) (ii) 15 (iii) $T_n = 3n$ (iv) 21st
2. (a) (i) -5, -8, -11 (ii) 5, $\frac{5}{2}, \frac{5}{4}$
(iii) 16, 22, 29
(b) (i) Yellow, green (ii) 3, 8, 13, 18 ...
(iii) 48th (iv) blue
(c) (i) 4, 10, 20
(ii) 2; 2nd differences are all the same or 2nd difference is constant (2)

3. (a) (iii)
  (b) (ii) 29   (iii) $T_n = 4n + 1$
    (iv) Shape 25
4. (a) (i) -2 (ii) 4   (iii) 9   (iv) 15
  (b) (ii) $T_n = 3n + 1$ (iii) $T_{40} = 121$
  (c) 12, 15, 20, 27, 36, 47
5. (a) (i) 7, 15, 31   (ii) 11, 43, 171
    (iii) 4, 7, 11
  (b) (I) 13   (iii) $T_n - 3n + 1$
    (iv) Pattern 8
  (c) (i) 2   (ii) $T_n = n^2 + n$
6. (a) (i) 19, 25
    (ii) The sequence starts at 2 and each term
      after that is treble the previous term
  (b) (i) 15, 21, 27   (ii) 17, 27, 39
    (iii) 27, 81, 243
    (iv) The exponential one
    (v) As any number of 2nd differences are
      possible
  (c) (i) 32   (ii) $T_n = 2^{n-1}$

Chapter 19: Functions

Exercise 19.1

1. (i) 2 (ii) 16 (iii) 11 (iv) 5 (v) 6 (vi) 15
3. (i) 2, 10, 12   (ii) 12, 10, 8

4.

x	1	2	3	4	5
y	9	12	15	18	21

5. (i) $y = 2x + 6$ (ii) $y = 8x - 9$
  (iii) $y = \frac{x}{4} - 3$ (iv) $y = 4(x + 3)$
6. (i) $x \to 3x + 2$ (ii) $x \to 5x - 2$
  (iii) $x \to \frac{x}{3} + 2$ (iv) $x \to 7(x + 2)$
7. (i) 'Multiply by 5'   (ii) 'Add 4'
  (iii) 'Divide by 4'
8. (i) 'Subtract 1'   (ii) 'Add 1'
  (iii) 'Subtract 2'
  (iv) 'Multiply by 2', 'Add 1'
9. (i) 3, 5, 7   (ii) 10, 16, 13
  (iii) 5, 8, 20   (iv) 4, 8, 10

Exercise 19.2

1. (i) {1, 2, 4, 5, 7}   (ii) {3, 4, 6, 7, 9}
  (iii) {(1, 3), (2, 4), (4, 6), (5, 7), (7, 9)}
  (iv) 'Add 2' [or $f: x \to x + 2$]
2. (i) {1, 2, 3, 4}; {6, 7, 8, 9}
  (ii) {2, 4, 6, 8, 10}; {5, 9, 13, 17, 21}
3. (i) Yes   (ii) No   (iii) No   (iv) Yes
4. As no two couples have the same input.
5. The input 2 has two different outputs
6. (i) Yes   (ii) No   (iii) Yes

7. $y = 2(x + 3)$;

Input (x)	Output (y)
1	8
2	10
3	12
4	14
5	16

8. (a) (i) {0, 1, 3, 5}   (II) {3, 4, 5, 8}
    (iii) {3, 4, 5, 6, 8}
  (b) (i) {−2, 2, 3, 7}   (ii) {−4, 6, 9}
    (iii) {−4, −3, 2, 4, 6, 9}
9. (i) {3, 5, 9, 13}
  (ii) {(0, 3), (1, 5), (3, 9), (5, 13)}
10. {2, 5, 11, 17}
11. (i) {−13, −5, 3, 11}
  (ii) {(−2, −13), (0, −5), (2, 3), (4, 11)}

12.

x	1	2	3	4	5
y	9	11	13	15	17

; $y = 2x + 7$

13. $y = 4x + 10$; 30; 3

14.

Input	Output
3	10
−2	0
5	14
−6	−8

15. (i) $y = 2x - 4$ (ii) $y = 3x + 2$
  (iii) $y = 3x + 1$
16. 10, −26, 3, −2

Exercise 19.3

1. (i) −1 (ii) −3 (iii) 1   (iv) −5 (v) −9
2. (i) 3   (ii) −5 (iii) −17 (iv) −3 (v) −4
3. (i) −3 (ii) −2 (iii) 1   (iv) 1   (v) 13
4. (i) 5   (ii) 1   (iii) 11
  (iv) 6   (v) $5 - 2k$
5. (i) $x = 2$ (ii) $x = 1$ (iii) $k = -2$
6. (i) $x = 2$ (ii) $x = 3$ (iii) $x = -2$
7. (i) −16   (ii) 0   (iii) $5k - 1$
  (iv) $10k - 1$ (v) $10k - 6$
8. $k = 4$
9. (i) $x = 5$ (ii) $x = 2$ (iii) $x = \frac{21}{2}$
10. (i) 13   (ii) $k = \frac{-11}{4}$
11. $k = \frac{8}{9}$ **12.** $k = \frac{1}{3}$
13. (i) $x - \pm\sqrt{2}$ (ii) $x = 15$
  (iii) $x = -1, \frac{3}{2}$
14. $a = -7$, $b = -1$
15. (i) $\frac{1}{2}$, 11   (ii) 2   (iii) $\frac{5}{2}$
16. (i) $-4k - 3$ (ii) $k = -4$
17. (i) 16   (ii) $\frac{1}{4}$ (iii) $-\frac{1}{2}$

Exercise 19.4

1. -2 **2.** 1 **3.** 2
4. 3 **5.** 3 **6.** -4
7. $a = -2, b = 4$
8. $a = 7, b = 5, c = -7$
9. $a + b = -1, 2a + b = 1; a = 2, b = -3$
10. $a = -1, b = 0$
11. $p = -2, q = 1; x = 1$
12. (i) $c = -3$ (ii) $b = 2$ (iii) $(1, 0)$
13. $a = 7, b = 1$
14. (i) $b = -2, c = -2$ (ii) $y = -2$
15. $a(1, 0), b(-3, 0), c(0, -3)$
16. (i) 18 (ii) 2 (iii) $0; k = 9$
17. (i) 81 (ii) $\frac{1}{9}$ (iii) $\sqrt{3}$ (iv) $-\frac{1}{2}$

Test yourself 19

1. (a) $(-2, -8), (0, -4), (2, 0)$
  (b) $\{-1, 4, 9, 14\}$
  (c) $a(-4, 0), b(2, 0), c(0, 8)$
2. (a) (i) Yes (ii) No
  (b) -5
  (c) (i) $k = 1$ (ii) $t = \frac{1}{8}$
3. (a) As the input 1 has two different outputs
  (b) $k = 1$
  (c) $a = (-5, 0), b = (2, 0), c = (0, 10)$
4. (a) $(1, 2), (3, 12), (0, -3)$
  (b) (i) 5 (ii) $\frac{1}{2}; k = 10$; No
  (c) (i) $0; \ell = 0$ (ii) $k = 4$
5. (a) (i) 'add 3'
    (ii) $\{-13, -10, -7, -4\}$
  (b) $a = 3, b = -2$
  (c) (i) $\sqrt{12} \ (2\sqrt{3}), \sqrt{72} \ (6\sqrt{2})$ (ii) $k = 12$
6. (a)

x	−1	0	1	2
y	−5	−2	1	4

  (b) (i) $\frac{2}{3}$ (ii) $\frac{1}{4}$
  (c) (i) $-b + c = -1, 3b + c = -13$
    (ii) $b = -3, c = -4$
    (iii) $f(x) = x^2 - 3x - 4$
    (iv) $d(4, 0), e(0, -4)$

Chapter 20: Drawing and interpreting Real-life Graphs

Exercise 20.1

1. (i) 9 am; 3 pm
  (ii) 30 km
  (iii) 9.45 am, 2 pm
  (iv) 10 am–10.30 am, Noon–1 pm
  (v) From 9 am to 10 am (20 km/hr)
2. (i) 30 km (ii) 1 hour (iii) 45 km (iv) 75 km

3. (i) 20 km (ii) 20 km (iii) 1 pm
  (iv) Increase; The steepness of the line
  (v) 40 km
4. (i) Adam (ii) twice (iii) 1 pm
  (iv) 150 km
  (v) Adam – 200 km Conor – 350 km
5. (i) 12 km (ii) 26 min
  (iii) (a) $4\frac{1}{2}$ km (b) $8\frac{1}{2}$ km
  (iv) (a) 3 min (b) 20 min
  (v) 30 km/hr
6. (i) 75 km
  (ii) 10.45 am and 12.12 pm
  (iii) 1.30 pm
  (iv) 75 km
  (v) Darren; 30 min
7. (i) 55 min (ii) 10 min
  (iii) 30 km/hr (iv) 24 km/hr
8. (i) 6000 km (ii) B → A; 1 hour
  (iii) 3 hr
  (iv) A → B : 857 km/hr B → A : 1000 km/hr
9. (i) [EF] (ii) [HJ] (iii) J (iv) [GH]
  (v) [AB] (vi) [DE]; 87 km/hr
10. (i) 11.30 am (ii) 35 km
11. (i) 240 km (ii) 10.02 am; 158 km
  (iii) Sam
  (iv) 9.00 am to 9.15 am, 10.15 am to 11.15 am
  (v) Sam – 96 km/hr Bob – $53\frac{1}{3}$ km/hr
12. (ii) (a) $166\frac{2}{3}$ m/min (b) 10 km/hr

Exercise 20.2

1. (iv); straight line graph through the origin
2. (i) $37\frac{1}{2}$ miles (ii) 50 miles
  (iii) 48 km (iv) 24 km; Yes
3. No; it doesn't go through the origin;
  (i) 95°F (ii) 59°F (iii) 10°C
  (iv) 38°C; 13°C to 32°C
4. (i) €70 (ii) €55 (iii) 80 min
  (iv) 40 min (v) €40
5. Graph C; only graph where the line is both straight and through the origin.
6. (i) 10 m (ii) $4s - 5h = 0$
  (iii) 18.75 m
7. (i) T (ii) F (iii) F (iv) T (v) F
8. (i) T1 and B, T2 and A, T3 and C
  (ii) Tariff A
9. (i) 8ℓ (ii) 60 km (iii) 3ℓ
  (iv) Yes (v) $\ell = \frac{3}{20}k; 45\ell$

Exercise 20.3

1. ① and A, ② and C, ③ and E, ④ and D, ⑤ and B
2. Graph Ⓐ

3. (i) (a) and A, (b) and C, (c) and B
(ii) 1st graph – B
2nd graph – C
3rd graph – A
4. (i) and 3rd graph, (ii) and 2nd, (iii) and 1st
5. A and ④, B and ③, C and ①, D and ⑤,
E and ②
9. (i) It drops (ii) 5°C (iii) It rises
(iv) −12°C (v) 8 min
10. (i) ③ (ii) ① (iii) ④
11. A and ②, B and ①, C and ③, D and ④
12. A and ⑤, B and ④, C and ③, D and ②,
E and ①
13. (i) (a) 60 m (b) 90 m
(ii) (a) 2 sec (b) 8 sec

Chapter 21: Algebraic Fractions – Formulae

Exercise 21.1
1. (i) $5a$ (ii) $2y$ (iii) $3c$ (iv) $3b$
(v) $2x$ (vi) $8b^2$ (vii) $7x$ (viii) $4b$
2. (i) $1\frac{1}{3}$ (ii) $\frac{k}{2}$ (iii) $2b^2$ (iv) $4ab$
(v) 2 (vi) $4\frac{1}{2}$ (vii) $9b$ (viii) $2a$
3. (i) APPLE (ii) LEMON or (MELON)
4. (i) $\frac{7}{6}$ (ii) $\frac{27}{20}$ (iii) $\frac{2}{3}$
(iv) $\frac{1}{8}$ (v) $\frac{5x}{6}$ (vi) $\frac{8x}{15}$
5. $\frac{13x}{4}$ **6.** $\frac{19x}{15}$ **7.** $\frac{x}{12}$ **8.** $\frac{3x}{10}$
9. $\frac{9x}{10}$ **10.** $\frac{7x}{20}$ **11.** $\frac{2x+1}{2}$ **12.** $\frac{2x+5}{2}$
13. $\frac{3x+5}{3}$ **14.** $\frac{8x-6}{5}$ **15.** $\frac{8x+4}{4}$
16. $\frac{4x-2}{3}$ **17.** $\frac{7x+14}{6}$
18. $\frac{11x+2}{12}$ **19.** $\frac{7x-11}{12}$
20. $\frac{17x+11}{20}$ **21.** $\frac{15x-31}{12}$
22. $\frac{9-14x}{12}$ **23.** $\frac{-3x-13}{20}$
24. 0 **25.** $\frac{11x+4}{20}$ **26.** $\frac{9a+4}{12}$

Exercise 21.2
1. $x = 9$ **2.** $x = 5$ **3.** $x = 3$
4. 6 **5.** 6 **6.** 11 **7.** 3 **8.** 11
9. $\frac{1}{4}$ **10.** 3 **11.** 7 **12.** 4 **13.** 5
14. 2 **15.** 4 **16.** 6 **17.** 2 **18.** 30
19. 2 **20.** 12 **21.** 3 **22.** 3 **23.** 2
24. 1 **25.** 11 **26.** $3\frac{1}{2}$ **27.** −5 **28.** 9
29. −3 **30.** (i) $x - 4 = \frac{x+2}{3}$ (ii) $|AB| = 3$

Exercise 21.3
1. 8 **2.** 18 **3.** 16 **4.** 20
5. 9 **6.** 7 **7.** 6 **8.** 16
9. 15, 18 **10.** 15
11. 15 years old **12.** 8

Exercise 21.4
1. $x + 2$ **2.** $x + 3$
3. $x + 7$ **4.** $2x + 1$
5. $3x + 1$ **6.** $x - 2$
7. $2x - 4$ **8.** $2x + 1$
9. $x - 7$ **10.** $3x - 5$
11. $5x + 4$ **12.** $3x - 4$
13. $x^2 + 2x + 3$ **14.** $x^2 + 3x + 5$
15. $x^2 + 6x + 8$ **16.** $x^2 - x - 6$
17. $x^2 + x - 2$ **18.** $x^2 - 4x + 4$
19. $x^2 + 7x - 10$ **20.** $x^2 - 4$
21. $x^2 + 5x + 6$ **22.** $2x^2 + 3x - 1$
23. $3x^2 - 8x + 4$ **24.** $3x^2 - 3x + 12$
25. (i) $2x - 3$ (ii) $5x - 2$

Exercise 21.5
1. (i) $y = 4 - 2x$ (ii) $y = -2x - 7$
(iii) $y = 7 - 3x$
2. (i) $x = \frac{y+4}{2}$ (ii) $b = \frac{a+6}{8}$
(iii) $d = \frac{c+1}{4}$ (iv) $k = \frac{h+2}{2}$
3. (i) $b = \frac{a+5}{3}$ (ii) $w = \frac{b-2}{4}$
(iii) $e = \frac{d+12}{6}$ (iv) $h = \frac{18-g}{5}$
4. B, C, F
5. (i) u, $\frac{v-u}{a}$ (ii) bq, bq, a
(iii) $3h$, 5, $3h$, $5(p - 3h)$
6. (i) $x = y + 2z$ (ii) $x = \frac{b+4c}{3}$
(iii) $x = \frac{7-6y}{3}$ (iv) $x = 3(2y + 8)$
7. (i) $a = \frac{2b+1}{4}$ (ii) $a = \frac{5}{b-3}$
(iii) $a = \frac{4b+21}{7}$
8. (i) $a = 2(4b + c)$ (ii) $a = \frac{4b+3c}{2}$
(iii) $x = \frac{y+1}{6}$ (iv) $b = \frac{a+30}{10}$
(v) $z = \frac{y-3x}{2}$ (vi) $b = \frac{4a+3c}{2}$
9. (i) $x = \frac{3c}{a+b}$ (ii) $x = \frac{5}{a-3}$
(iii) $x = 3y + 3$
10. $b = \frac{as-k}{s} \left(= a - \frac{k}{s} \right)$ **11.** B, E

12. (i) $z = \dfrac{2y - 4x}{3}$ (ii) $b = \dfrac{24a - 9c}{4}$

    (iii) $y = \dfrac{3x - 20z}{20}$ (iv) $b = \dfrac{6c}{2a - 3}$

    (v) $y = \dfrac{x - tz}{2}$ (vi) $t = \dfrac{q^2}{p - q}$

    (vii) $x = \dfrac{y + 4}{y - 3}$ (viii) $\dfrac{pq}{p + q}$

13. $y = \dfrac{z + 2}{z - 3}; -1$

14. (i) $h = \dfrac{2A}{a + b}$ (ii) 14 cm

Exercise 21.6

1. (i) 16   (ii) 150   (iii) 114   (iv) 54
2. (i) 100°   (ii) 0°   (iii) −40°
    (iv) −10°   (v) −25°
3. (i) 29   (ii) 10   (iii) $\frac{10}{3}$
4. 10   **5.** (i) O; $m = \dfrac{y - c}{x}$ (ii) 3
6. (i) $P = 2(\ell + b)$ (ii) $P = 2y + 26$
7. 13; $b = \dfrac{6(T - C)}{a}; 13\frac{1}{5}$
8. (i) €21   (ii) 20 km
9. $T = 15 + 40a$
10. (i) €75   (ii) 354   (iii) 180
11. (i) €716   (ii) 180 km
12. (i) $N = 4\ell + 4$ (ii) 28   (iii) 7 m
13. (ii) $x = \sqrt{\dfrac{A}{2}}$ (iii) $\sqrt{10}$ cm
14. (i) 2900ℓ (ii) 8   (iii) 10
15. (i) $F = 4 + 1.5k + 2p$
    (ii) €39   (iii) 12 km

Test yourself 21

1. (a) (i) $4x^2$ (ii) $4y$ (iii) $4xy$
    (b) (i) $x = \dfrac{4y - 6}{3y - 2}$ (ii) $x^2 + 2x - 8$
    (c) $x = 6$
2. (a) 1
    (b) $b = \dfrac{c(7a - c)}{a}; -12$
    (c) (i) $P = 2(2x + y + z)$ (ii) 10
3. (a) $x^2 + x - 12$
    (b) (i) 10 hrs   (ii) 18 years old
    (c) $x = 2$
4. (a) $\frac{23}{10}$
    (b) (i) $x = \dfrac{b}{2(b - a)}$ (ii) $\dfrac{2a}{3c}$
    (c) $x = 18$
5. (a) $\dfrac{15x + 11}{12}$
    (b) (i) €650   (ii) 320
    (c) $a = \dfrac{4b + 3}{6}; 3$

6. (a) $\frac{2}{7}$
    (b) $x = 11$
    (c) (i) 32°F   (ii) 212°F
       (iii) 22.$\dot{2}$°C   (iv) 2.$\dot{2}$°C
7. (a) $p = \dfrac{6c}{2a - 3}; -3$
    (b) $2x^2 - 3x - 2$
    (c) $x = 5\frac{1}{4}$

Chapter 22: Trigonometry

Exercise 22.1

1. (i) 12 cm²   (ii) 12 cm²   (iii) 8 cm²
2. 32 cm²
3. (i) 6 cm   (ii) 33 cm²   (iii) 185 cm²
4. 13
5. (i) $\sqrt{13}$ cm   (ii) $2\sqrt{10}$ cm   (iii) $\sqrt{53}$ cm
    (iv) $2\sqrt{5}$ cm   (v) 15 cm   (vi) 12 cm
6. (i) 24.4 cm   (ii) 10.6 cm   (iii) 9.8 cm
7. 12.8 cm
8. 7, 4; 8.1
9. 3.5 m
10. 6.4 cm
11. (i) 3 cm   (ii) 5.8 cm
12. All sides are 7.1 units
13. $x = 5$ cm, $y = 12$ cm
14. $c = 10$ cm, $d = 24$ cm
15. 25 cm
16. each 12 cm²
17. 63.5 cm, 38.1 cm
18. $18^2 \neq 12^2 + 13^2$

Exercise 22.2

1. $\dfrac{3}{5}, \dfrac{4}{5}, \dfrac{3}{4}; \dfrac{5}{13}, \dfrac{12}{13}, \dfrac{5}{12}; \dfrac{\sqrt{3}}{2}, \dfrac{1}{2}, \sqrt{3}$
2. (i) Tangent   (ii) Cosine   (iii) Sine
3. (i) A   (ii) B   (iii) B
    (iv) Cos   (v) Cos   (vi) Tan
4. $x = 8$; (i) $\frac{8}{17}$ (ii) $\frac{15}{17}$ (iii) $\frac{8}{15}$
5. $a = 2$; (i) $\dfrac{3}{\sqrt{13}}$ (ii) $\dfrac{2}{\sqrt{13}}$ (iii) $\dfrac{3}{2}$
6. (i) Tan θ (ii) Sin θ (iii) Cos θ
7. $\frac{12}{13}, \frac{12}{5}$
8. (i) $\dfrac{1}{\sqrt{5}}$ (ii) $\dfrac{\sqrt{21}}{2}$
9. $\dfrac{1}{2}, \dfrac{\sqrt{3}}{2}$
10. (i) 1   (ii) 1

Exercise 22.3

1. (i) 28° 30′   (ii) 31° 24′   (iii) 62° 48′
    (iv) 74° 36′   (v) 16° 15′   (vi) 44° 45′
    (vii) 0° 30′   (viii) 27° 39′

2. (i) 24.5°   (ii) 46.6°   (iii) 72.7°
    (iv) 21.8°   (v) 65.4°   (vi) 13.5°
    (vii) 29.6°   (viii) 68.3°

3. (i) 40° 49′   (ii) 66° 8′   (iii) 83° 52′
    (iv) 16° 34′   (v) 6° 28′   (vi) 55° 37′

4. 51° 18′

5. (i) 0.7431   (ii) 0.2756   (iii) 0.2679
    (iv) 0.9511   (v) 0.8788

6. (i) 0.8805   (ii) 0.5976
    (iii) 3.7062   (iv) 0.3068

7. (i) 48°   (ii) 69°   (iii) 55°
    (iv) 78°   (v) 42°   (vi) 12°

8. (i) 36.9°   (ii) 41.1°   (iii) 75.4°   (iv) 74.2°

9. (i) 42°   (ii) 53°   (iii) 41°   (iv) 24°
    (v) 29°   (vi) 12°   (vii) 35°   (viii) 58°

10. A = 56.74°; Sin A = 0.84

11. 53° 24′

12. (i) Sin   (ii) Tan   (iii) Cos

13. A = 37°, B = 68°, C = 39°

14. $a = 22°$, $b = 65°$, $c = 30°$

15. A = 41.8°, B = 38.6°, C = 33.4°

16. (i) 30°   (ii) 66°   (iii) 27°

17. 22°

18. (i) No; Tan 75° = 3.7321
    (ii) Yes; Sin 30° = $\frac{1}{2}$, Sin 60° = 0.8660
    (iii) No; Cos 3° = 0.9986, Cos 83° = 0.1219

Exercise 22.4

1. (i) Cos   (ii) Tan   (iii) Sin
2. (i) 3.8   (ii) 10.0   (iii) 10.2
3. (i) 3.3   (ii) 16.7   (iii) 13.5
4. (i) 37°   (ii) 46°   (iii) 23°
5. (i) 67°   (ii) 24°   (iii) 37°
6. $x = 9.4$
7. (i) 12.0   (ii) 15.9   (iii) 18.8
8. $x = 15$, $y = 20$
9. $a = 17.8\,m$, $b = 53.5\,cm$, $c = 10.4\,cm$
10. (i) 13.9   (ii) 44°
11. 12.5 cm
12. (i) 8.2 m   (ii) 39°
13. (i) 4.2 cm   (ii) 25°

Exercise 22.5

1. 3.5 m
2. 21 m
3. 56°
4. (i) 124 km   (ii) 26°
5. 20 m
6. 4°
7. 47 m
8. (i) 5 m   (ii) 8.3 m   (iii) 10.1 m
9. 12 m
10. (i) 17 m   (ii) 65°   (iii) 25°

11. 61°
12. (i) 13.1 m   (ii) 9.9 m; 3.2 m
13. No; diagonal of desk = 2.8 m, 2.8 m > 2.75 m
14. (i) 14.2 cm   (ii) 53.1 cm
15. (i) 50.4 m   (ii) 47.0 m; 101.0 m
16. (i) 17.4 m   (ii) 68°   (iii) 24°
17. (i) 2 rolls   (ii) €116
18. (i) 4.0 m   (ii) 12.7 m

Exercise 22.6

1. $\frac{1}{2}$ **2.** 1

3. $\frac{1}{2}$ **4.** $\frac{1}{\sqrt{2}}$

5. $\frac{1}{4}$ **6.** $\frac{\sqrt{3}}{2}$

7. $\frac{\sqrt{3}}{2}$ **8.** $\frac{1}{2}$

9. $\frac{3}{4}$ **10.** $\frac{1}{3}$

12. $x = 3$, $y = 3\sqrt{3}$
13. $x = 3$, $y = 4$
14. $x = 4\sqrt{3}$, $y = 4$, $z = \frac{8}{\sqrt{3}}$
15. 60°
16. $400\sqrt{3}\ m^2$

Test Yourself 22

1. $x = 12$;   (i) $\frac{5}{12}$ (ii) $\frac{5}{13}$ (iii) $\frac{12}{13}$; 23°
2. 17.8 cm
3. (i) 13 cm²   (ii) 33 cm²   (iii) 26 cm²
4. (i) 8 cm   (ii) 22°
5. 15°
6. (i) 4.2 cm   (ii) 25°
7. (i) 28° 45′   (ii) 37.1°   (iii) $\frac{3}{2}$
8. (i) 100 cm   (ii) 27°
9. 15.8 cm
10. (i) 7 cm   (ii) 4 cm   (iii) 5 cm
11. 6°
12. (i) 72°, 18°   (ii) 0.32
13. (i) 150 m²   (ii) 12 m
14. (i) Radius of base of spire can be obtained
        from it.
    (ii) 125 m
15. (i) 101.6 cm   (ii) 50 cm, 88 cm
    (iii) The 2nd t.v. (542 cm² bigger)
16. $a = 2\sqrt{2}$, $b = \sqrt{6}$

Chapter 23: Graphing Functions

Exercise 23.1

1. (−1, −5), (0, −3), (1, −1), (2, 1), (3, 3), (4, 5)
3. (−1, −7), (0, −4), (3, 5)

6. (i) 4   (ii) 1   (iii) -3 (iv) -3 (v) 5

7. (i) (3, 4)

(ii) The point of intersection of the two lines

(iii) $x = 3$ (x-value)

(iv) Simultaneous equations   (v) $k = 3$

8. (3, 2)   **9.** (2, 0), (0, 4)

10. (2, 0), (0, 3)   **11.** (2, 0)

12. (i) All intersect at (0, 2)

(ii) All have the same constant number

(iii) All have different slopes

(iv) Coefficients of x are different

13. $(-2, 2), (-3, 0), (-4, -2)$

14.

t	0	1	2	3	4	5	6
T	-1	-1.5	-2	-2.5	-3	-3.5	-4

(iv) $-3.75°C$ (v) $-3.75°C$

15. (i)

t (mins)	0	1	2	3	4	5
d (metres)	0	40	80	120	160	200

t (mins)	6	7	8	9	10
d (metres)	240	280	320	360	400

(ii)

t (mins)	0	1	2	3	4	5
d (metres)	0	0	0	50	100	150

t (mins)	6	7	8	9	10
d (metres)	200	250	300	350	400

(v) 10 mins; 400 m

Exercise 23.2

1. $(-3, 5), (-2, 0), (-1, -3), (0, -4), (1, -3),$
(2, 0), (3, 5)

6. $(-\frac{1}{2}, 0), (3, 0), (0, -3)$

8. $(-1, 0), (3, 0)$

9. $(-1, 0), (1\frac{1}{2}, 0)$

10. (i) $(\frac{1}{2}, 0), (3, 0)$ (ii) $(0, -3)$

Exercise 23.3

1. (i) (1, 0), (3, 0)   (ii) -1

(iii) $-1, 5$ (iv) $(2, -1)$

2. (i) 3   (ii) 3   (iii) $(0, -1)$

(iv) $-1, 1$ (v) $-2, 2$

3. (i) $-1, 4$ (ii) $-2, 5$ (iii) 0, 3   (iv) -6

(v) $-5\frac{1}{4}$ (vi) $(1\frac{1}{2}, -6\frac{1}{4})$ (vii) $-6\frac{1}{4}$

4. (i) $10, -6$ (ii) $-1.4, 3.4$

(iii) $-2.5, 4.5$ (iv) $(1, -6)$

(v) -6 (vi) $-1.4 < x < 3.4$

5. (i) $x = -1, 3$ (ii) 0, 2

(iii) $1\frac{3}{4}$ (iv) 4

(v) (1, 4)   (vi) $-2 < x < 1$

(vii) $-1 < x < 3$ (viii) $x = 1$

6. (i) $-1, \frac{3}{2}$ (ii) $-1.9, 2.4$

(iii) $(0.25, -3.1)$ (iv) $-1 < x < 1\frac{1}{2}$

7. (i) $(-1, 1), (3, 9)$

(ii) $x = -1, 3$

(iii) x-values the same

(iv) The points where the curve and line
intersect

8. (i) $f(-2) = -4, g(3) = 6$

(ii) $x = -3, 2$ (iii) $-3.7, 2.7$ (iv) $x = -1, 3$

(v) $-1 \leqslant x \leqslant 3$ (vi) $-3 \leqslant x \leqslant 2$

9. (i) $x = 0, 3$ (ii) $x = -1, 4$

(iii) $x = -0.8, 3.8$ (iv) $x = -0.6, 3.6$

10. (i) $x = -1.3, 1.3$

(ii) $x = -2.9, 2.9; -2.9 < x < 2.9$

11. (i) $x = 0, 2$ (ii) $x = -1, 3$

(iii) $x = 0.4, 2.6$ (iv) $0 < x < 2$

(v) $x < 0.4$ and $x > 2.6$;

$x^2 - 2x - 2 = 0 \Rightarrow x^2 - 2x = 2$;

Draw the line $y = 2$ and find the x-values
of the points of intersection of this line
and the curve

12. (i) $x = -3.8, 0.8$

(ii) $x = -3.3, 0.3$

(iii) $-2.4, 0.4$

(iv) -5.25; The curve is below the line;
$-2.4 < x < 0.4$

13. (i) $x = -2$ (ii) One value

(iii) Graph touches the x-axis at one point only.

14. (i) Ⓐ corresponds to $g(x) = x^2 - 3x + 3$

Ⓑ corresponds to $f(x) = x^2 - 6x + 9$

(ii) $x = 2$

(iii) Curve touches the x-axis at one point
only (tangent)

Exercise 23.4

1. (i) 15   (ii) $x = 0, 4$

(iii) $x = 2$ (iv) 15

(v) 11.12 a.m. and 4.48 p.m.

(vi) 10 hours

2. (i) (0, 0), (1, 16), (2, 24), (3, 24), (4, 16), (5, 0)

(iii) (a) 25 m; 2.5 sec   (b) 0.7 sec, 4.3 sec

(c) 3 sec

3. $(-5, -6), (-4, 0), (-3, 4), (-2, 6), (-1, 6),$
(0, 4), (1, 0), (2, -6)$;

(i) $5.25°C$

(ii) 1 p.m.

(iii) 9.24 a.m. and 4.36 p.m.

(iv) 10 hours

4. (i) $13.75 \, m^2$ (ii) $16 \, m^2$; $x = 4$

(iii) $x = 2, 6$

5. (i) 45 m   (ii) 34 m

(iii) After 0.4 sec and 5.6 sec   (iv) 3 sec

6. (i) (0, 0), (1, 3), (2, 12), (3, 27)
  (ii) 18.7 m²
  (iii) 1.8 m
  (iv) Accurate versions are 19.6 m² and 1.78 cm
7. (i) $A = 20x - x^2$
  (iii) 2.25 and 17.75
  (iv) $6.8 < x < 13.2$
  (v) 100 m²; 10 m by 10 m

Exercise 23.5

1. (i) 1   (ii) 2   (iii) 2.8   (iv) 8   (v) 2.3
2. $(-2, \frac{1}{9}), (-1, \frac{1}{3}), (0, 1), (1, 3), (2, 9), (3, 27)$;
  (i) 5.2   (ii) 1.3
3. (i) 3   (ii) 12   (iii) $x = -1.6$
4.

x	−2	−1	0	1	2	
2ˣ	$\frac{1}{4}$	$\frac{1}{2}$	1	2	4	; 5.7
4.2ˣ	1	2	4	8	16	

5. (A) : $f(x) = 3.3^x$; (B) : $f(x) = 3^x$; (C) : $f(x) = 2^x$
6. (i) (0, 1)
7. (i) $k = 5$ (ii) $f(x) = 5.2^x$
8. 2.5

Test Yourself 23

1. (a) (i) 5   (ii) 7   (iii) 3
    (iv) −1   (v) 0
  (b) (i) −1.75   (ii) $x = 1, 3$
    (iii) −4   (iv) $x = 2$
  (c) (A) and $y = k - x$, (B) and $y = x^2 - k$,
    (C) and $y = k - x^2$
2. (a) (i) −5.5   (ii) $1\frac{1}{2}$
  (b) (i) $a = (-3, 0), b = (1, 0), c = (0, -3)$
    (ii) $-3 \leqslant x \leqslant 1$
    (iii) $k = 0, -2$
  (c) $(-3, \frac{1}{8}), (-2, \frac{1}{4}), (-1, \frac{1}{2}), (0, 1), (1, 2), (2, 4)$,
    (3, 8), (4, 16), (5, 32); (ii) $x = 2.6$
3. (a) (i) $x = -1\frac{1}{2}, 2$ (ii) −6.1
    (iii) 4   (iv) $-1.5 < x < 2$
  (b) $3x + 2y = 9; 2x - y = 13; x = 5, y = -3$
4. (a) (i) $x = 0, 2$
    (ii) $x = -1, 3; x = 1$,
  (b) A: $y = x^2 - 2$, B: $y = 2 - x^2$, C: $y = 2x$
  (c) (i) 36 m²   (ii) 2.2 m, 6.8 m
    (iii) 4.5 m by 9 m   (iv) 40.5 m²
5. (a) (i) $10t - c + 20 = 0$ (ii) €160
  (b)

x	0	0.5	1	1.5	2	2.5	3
f(x)	1	1.4	2	2.8	4	5.7	8
g(x)	−1	2.75	5	5.75	5	2.75	−1

    (i) 0.3, 2.2   (ii) 2.6

Chapter 24: Geometry 3: Transformations – Constructions

Exercise 24.1

1. (i) 5 units to the right
  (ii) 4 units to the right
  (iii) 1 unit up and 4 units right
  (iv) 1 unit right and 3 units up
  (v) 2 units right and 3 units up
  (vi) 1 unit left and 4 units up
2. (i) 5 units right and 3 units up
  (ii) 11 units right and 1 unit down
  (iii) 4 units right and 5 units up
  (iv) 7 units right and 6 units down
  (v) 4 units left and 5 units down
6. (i) B   (ii) [DC]   (iii) O   (iv) [AB]
7. (i) B   (ii) [BC]   (iii) △BCE   (iv) [BE]
8. (i) [EC]   (ii) E   (iii) △BEC
  (iv) D   (v) [AD]   (vi) △BEC
9. (i) A(2, 4), B(3, −2), C(−2, −3), D(−5, 1)
  (ii) A′(7, 6), B′(8, 0), C′(3, −1), D′(0, 3)

Exercise 24.2

3. (i) the point F (ii) [EF]   (iii) [DF]
  (iv) △DCF   (v) △EFD   (vi) [CF]
4. (i) and (iii)
5. M, O, D, A, Y
7. (i) B   (ii) A   (iii) [DA]   (iv) △COD
  (v) [CO]   (vi) △CBD (vii) [OA] (viii) CDAB
8. C
9. (i) D   (ii) A
10. (i) Axial symmetry in y-axis
  (ii) Axial symmetry in x-axis
  (iii) Central symmetry in origin
11. Central symmetry in C and axial symmetry in AB
12. D
13. (i) A′(4, 5), B′(1, 4), C′(5, 2)
  (ii) A″(−4, −5), B″(−1, −4), C″(−5, −2)
14. (i) 2   (ii) 2   (iii) 5   (iv) 0
15. (i), (ii), (iv)
16. (i) A.S. (ii) Tr.   (iii) A.S. (iv) A.S. (v) C.S.
17. A – C.S.   B – A.S.   C – Tr.   D – A.S.
18. (i) A.S. in y-axis
  (ii) Tr.; 3 units right and 3 units down
  (iii) A.S. in line $x + y = 0$
20. (i) △COB   (ii) △COD   (iii) △AOD
  (iv) △COF   (v) [EF]

Exercise 24.4

4. |AC| = 4.6 cm, |DE| = 3.1 cm, |XZ| = 7.7 cm
5. (i) |AC| = 3.1 cm   (ii) |AB| = 5.4 cm

6. $|AC| = 5.9\,cm$, $|DF| = 5.2\,cm$, $|XZ| = 9.2\,cm$
9. $|AC| = 10.8\,cm$
11. $8.3\,cm$

Test Yourself 24

1. (a) (i) 1   (ii) 1   (iii) 1   (iv) 1
   (c) (i) A.S. in y-axis
      (ii) A.S. in line $y = 2$
      (iii) Tr.; 3 units down
      (iv) A.S. in the line $x = 3$
      (v) C.S. in the point (1.5, 0.5)
      (vi) Tr.; 3 units to the right and 7 units
         down
2. (b) (i) 3   (ii) 1   (iii) 2
   (c) A′(−1, 4), B′(−3, 4), C′(−3, 1), D′(−1, 3)

3. (b) (i)
   (ii)
   (iii)
   (c) (i) C   (ii) [CB]   (iii) △COD
      (iv) [AB]   (v) No
4. (b) (i) Tr.   (ii) C.S.   (iii) A.S.